Student Solutions Manual, Study Guide, and Problems Book

for use with

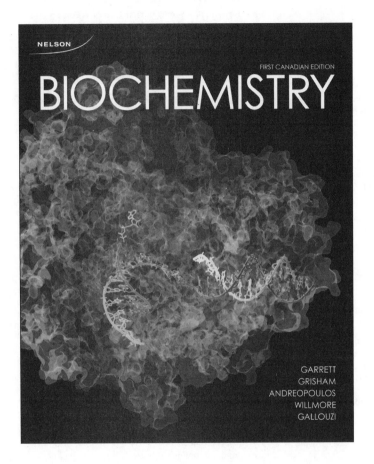

NELSON

FIRST CANADIAN EDITION

BIOCHEMISTRY

GARRETT
GRISHAM
ANDREOPOULOS
WILLMORE
GALLOUZI

Prepared by

DAVID K. JEMIOLO
VASSAR COLLEGE

STEVEN M. THEG
UNIVERSITY OF CALIFORNIA, DAVIS

STAVROULA ANDREOPOULOS
UNIVERSITY OF TORONTO

WILLIAM G. WILLMORE
CARLETON UNIVERSITY

IMED E. GALLOUZI
MCGILL UNIVERSITY

NELSON / EDUCATION

NELSON EDUCATION

Student Solutions Manual, Study Guide, and Problems Book
by David K. Jemiolo, Steven M. Theg, Stavroula Andreopoulos, William G. Willmore, and Imed E. Gallouzi

for use with Biochemistry, First Canadian Edition
by Reginal H. Garrett, Charles M. Grisham, Stavroula Andreopoulos, William G. Willmore, and Imed E. Gallouzi

Vice President, Editorial Higher Education:
Anne Williams

Publisher:
Paul Fam

Marketing Manager:
Leanne Newell

Developmental Editor:
Candace Morrison

Content Production Manager:
Jennifer Hare

Copy Editor:
Wendy Yano

Production Coordinator:
Ferial Suleman

Design Director:
Ken Phipps

Managing Designer:
Franca Amore

Cover Design:
Sasha Moroz

Cover Image:
David Bushnell, Kenneth Westover, and Roger Kornberg

Printer:
RR Donnelley

ISBN-13: 978-0-17-666242-4
ISBN-10: 0-17-666242-1

Table of Contents

• •

Part IV: **Nucleic Acids**

Part V: **Information Transfer**

Glossary

Chapter 1

The Facts of Life: Chemistry Is the Logic of Biological Phenomena

• •

Chapter Outline

- ❖ Properties of living systems
    - ⅄ Highly organized: Cells > organelles > macromolecular complexes > macromolecules (proteins, nucleic acids, polysaccharides)
    - ⅄ Structure/function correlation: Biological structures serve functional purposes
    - ⅄ Energy transduction: ATP and NADPH—energized molecules
    - ⅄ Steady state maintained by energy flow: Steady state not equilibrium
    - ⅄ Self-replication with high, yet not perfect, fidelity
- ❖ Biomolecules
    - ⅄ Elements: Hydrogen, oxygen, carbon, nitrogen (lightest elements of the periodic table capable of forming a variety of strong covalent bonds)
        - • Carbon: 4 bonds, nitrogen: 3 bonds, oxygen: 2 bonds, hydrogen: 1 bond
    - ⅄ Compounds: Carbon-based compounds—versatile
    - ⅄ Phosphorus- and sulfur-containing compounds play important roles
- ❖ Biomolecular hierarchy
    - ⅄ Simple compounds: H_2O, CO_2, NH_4^+, NO_3^-, N_2
    - ⅄ Metabolites: Used to synthesize building block molecules
    - ⅄ Building blocks: Amino acids, nucleotides, monosaccharides, fatty acids, glycerol
    - ⅄ Macromolecules: Proteins, nucleic acids, polysaccharides, lipids
    - ⅄ Supramolecular complexes: Ribosomes, chromosomes, cytoskeleton
- ❖ Membranes: Lipid bilayers with membrane proteins
    - ⅄ Define boundaries of cells and organelles
    - ⅄ Hydrophobic interactions maintain structures
- ❖ Organelles: Mitochondria, chloroplasts, nuclei, endoplasmic reticulum, Golgi, etc.
- ❖ Cells: Fundamental units of life
    - ⅄ Living state: Growth, metabolism, stimulus response, and replication
- ❖ Properties of biomolecules
    - ⅄ Directionality or structural polarity
        - • Proteins: N-terminus and C-terminus
        - • Nucleic acids: 5′- and 3′-ends
        - • Polysaccharides: Reducing and non-reducing ends
    - ⅄ Information content: Sequence of monomer building blocks and 3-dimensional architecture
- ❖ Three-dimensional architecture and intermolecular interactions (via complementary surfaces) of macromolecules are based on weak forces
    - ⅄ van der Waals interactions (London dispersion forces)
        - • Induced electric interactions that occur when atoms are close together
        - • Significant when many contacts form complementary surfaces
    - ⅄ Hydrogen bonding
        - • Donor and acceptor pair: Direction dependence
        - • Donor is hydrogen covalently bonded to electronegative O or N
        - • Acceptor is lone pair on O or N

- ⅄ Ionic interactions
  - ⋅ Stronger than H bonds
  - ⋅ Not directional
  - ⋅ Strength influenced by solvent properties
- ⅄ Hydrophobic interactions: Occur when non-polar groups are added to water
  - ⋅ Water molecules hydrogen bond
  - ⋅ Non-polar groups interfere with water H-bonding, and non-polar groups aggregate to minimize this
- ❖ Life restricted to narrow range of conditions (temperature, pH, salt concentration, etc.) because of dependence on weak forces
  - ⅄ Denaturation: Loss of structural order in a macromolecule
- ❖ Enzymes: Biological catalysts capable of being regulated
- ❖ Cell types
  - ⅄ Prokaryotes: Bacteria and archaea: Plasma membrane but no internal membrane-defined compartments
    - ⋅ Archaea include thermoacidophiles, halophiles, and methanogens
  - ⅄ Eukaryotes: Internal membrane-defined compartments: nuclei, endoplasmic reticulum, Golgi, mitochondria, chloroplasts, vacuoles, peroxisomes
  - ⅄ Viruses and bacteriophages: Incomplete genetic systems

Chapter Objectives

Understand the Basic Chemistry of H, O, N ,and C

H forms a single covalent bond. When bound to an electronegative element, like O or N, the electron pair forming the covalent bond is not equally shared, giving rise to a partial positive charge on the hydrogen (this is the basis of H bonds which will be covered in the next chapter). In extreme cases, the H can be lost as a free proton.

O forms two covalent bonds and has two lone pairs of electrons. It is an electronegative element and when bound to hydrogen it will cause H to be partially positively charged. O is highly reactive due to its high electronegativity.

N forms up to three covalent bonds and has a single lone pair of electrons. It is an electronegative element and will create a partial positive charge on a hydrogen bonded to it.

C forms four covalent bonds. With four single bonds, tetrahedral geometry is predominant. With one double bond, carbon shows trigonal planar geometry, with an additional pair of electrons participating in a pi bond.

Macromolecules and Subunits

Proteins are formed from amino acids composed of C, H, O, N, and in some instances S.

Nucleic acids are formed from nucleotides that are composed of phosphate, sugar, and nitrogenous base components (nucleosides lack phosphate).

Polysaccharides are made of carbohydrates or sugar molecules.

Lipids are a class of mostly non-polar, mostly hydrocarbon molecules.

Macromolecular Structures

Macromolecular structures are composed of complexes of macromolecules (i.e., proteins, nucleic acids, polysaccharides, and lipids). The ribosome, made up of protein and ribonucleic acid, is a prime example.

Organelles

Organelles are subcellular compartments defined by lipid bilayer membranes.

Cell Types

There are two fundamental cell types: eukaryotic, having organelles and a defined nuclear region; and prokaryotic, lacking organelles and a membrane-enclosed region of genetic material. The archaea and bacteria comprise the prokaryotes.

Problems and Solutions

1. *The nutritional requirements of* Escherichia coli *cells are far simpler than those of humans, yet the macromolecules found in bacteria are about as complex as those of animals. Because bacteria can make all their essential biomolecules while subsisting on a simpler diet, do you think bacteria may have more biosynthetic capacity and hence more metabolic complexity than animals? Organize your thoughts on this question, pro and con, into a rational argument.*

Answer: Although it is true that *Escherichia coli* are capable of producing all of their essential biomolecules (e.g., there is no minimum daily requirement for vitamins in the world of wild-type *E. coli*), they are rather simple, single-cell organisms capable of a limited set of responses. They are self-sufficient, yet they are incapable of interactions leading to levels of organization such as multicellular tissues. Multicellular organisms have the metabolic complexity to produce a number of specialized cell types and to coordinate interactions among them.

3. *Escherichia coli cells are about 2 μm (microns) long and 0.8 μm in diameter.*
    a.   How many E. coli cells laid end to end would fit across the diameter of a pinhead? (Assume a pinhead diameter of 0.5 mm.)
    b.   What is the volume of an E. coli cell? (Assume it is a cylinder, with the volume of a cylinder given by V = πr²h, where π = 3.14.)
    c.   What is the surface area of an E. coli cell? What is the surface-to-volume ratio of an E. coli cell?
    d.   Glucose, a major energy-yielding nutrient, is present in bacterial cells at a concentration of about 1 mM. What is the concentration of glucose, expressed as mg/mL? How many glucose molecules are contained in a typical E. coli cell? (Recall that Avogadro's number = 6.023 × 10²³.)
    e.   A number of regulatory proteins are present in E. coli at only 1 or 2 molecules per cell. If we assume that an E. coli contains just 1 molecule of a particular protein, what is the molar concentration of this protein in the cell? If the molecular weight of this protein is 40 kDa, what is its concentration, expressed as mg/mL?
    f.   An E. coli cell contains about 15 000 ribosomes, which carry out protein synthesis. Assuming ribosomes are spherical and have a diameter of 20 nm (nanometers), what fraction of the E. coli cell volume is occupied by ribosomes?
    g.   The E. coli chromosome is a single DNA molecule whose mass is about 3.0 × 10⁹ Da. This macromolecule is actually a circular array of nucleotide pairs. The average molecular weight of a nucleotide pair is 660 Mr and each pair imparts 0.34 nm to the length of the DNA molecule. What is the total length of the E. coli chromosome? How does this length compare with the overall dimensions of an E. coli cell? How many nucleotide pairs does this DNA contain? The average E. coli protein is a linear chain of 360 amino acids. If 3 nucleotide pairs in a gene encode 1 amino acid in a protein, how many different proteins can the E. coli chromosome encode? (The answer to this question is a reasonable approximation of the maximum number of different kinds of proteins that can be expected in bacteria.)

Answer: a.

$$\textit{E. coli} \text{ per pinhead} = \frac{\dfrac{0.5 \text{ mm}}{\text{dia.}}}{\dfrac{2 \ \mu m}{\textit{E. coli}}} = \frac{\dfrac{0.5 \times 10^{-3} m}{\text{dia.}}}{\dfrac{2 \times 10^{-6} m}{\textit{E. coli}}}$$

$$= 250 \ \textit{E. coli} \text{ per pinhead}$$

b.

$$V = \pi \times r^2 \times h$$

$$= 3.14 \times \left(\frac{0.8 \ \mu m}{2}\right)^2 \times 2 \ \mu m$$

$$= 3.14 \times \left(0.4 \times 10^{-6} m\right)^2 \times 2 \times 10^{-6} m$$

$$= 1 \times 10^{-18} m^3$$

But $1 \, \text{m}^3 = (100 \, \text{cm})^3 = 10^6 \text{cm}^3 = 10^6 \text{mL} = 10^3 \text{L}$

$V = 1 \times 10^{-18} \text{m}^3 = 1 \times 10^{-15} \text{L} = 1 \, \text{fL (femtolitre)}$

c.

Surface Area $= 2 \times \pi \times r^2 + \pi \times d \times h$

Surface Area $= 2 \times 3.14 \times (0.4 \times 10^{-6} \text{m})^2 + 3.14 \times (0.8 \times 10^{-6} \text{m}) \times (2 \times 10^{-6} \text{m})$

Surface Area $= 6.03 \times 10^{-12} \text{m}^2$

$\dfrac{\text{Surface Area}}{\text{Volume}} = \dfrac{6 \times 10^{-12} \text{m}^2}{1 \times 10^{-18} \text{m}^3} \text{(from b)}$

Surface Area per volume $= 6 \times 10^6 \text{m}^{-1}$

d.

$[\text{Glucose}] = 1 \, \text{mM} = 1 \times 10^{-3} \dfrac{\text{mol}}{\text{L}}$

$\text{Glucose} = \text{C}_6\text{H}_{12}\text{O}_6$

$M_r = 6 \times 12 + 12 \times 1.0 + 6 \times 16$

$M_r = 180$

$[\text{Glucose}] = 1 \times 10^{-3} \dfrac{\text{mol}}{\text{L}} \times 180 \dfrac{\text{g}}{\text{mol}}$

$[\text{Glucose}] = 0.18 \dfrac{\text{g}}{\text{L}} = 0.18 \dfrac{\text{mg}}{\text{mL}}$

moles of glucose $=$ concentration $\times$ volume

moles of glucose $= 1 \times 10^{-3} \dfrac{\text{mol}}{\text{L}} \times 1 \times 10^{-15} \text{L} \text{ (from b)}$

moles of glucose $= 1 \times 10^{-18}$

molecules $= 1 \times 10^{-18} \text{mol} \times 6.023 \times 10^{23} \dfrac{\text{molecules}}{\text{mol}}$

molecules $= 6 \times 10^5 \text{molecules}$

e.

$\dfrac{1 \text{ molecule}}{6.023 \times 10^{23} \dfrac{\text{molecules}}{\text{mol}}} = 1.66 \times 10^{-24} \text{mol}$

$\text{Molar Concentration} = \dfrac{\text{moles}}{\text{volume (in litres)}}$

$\text{Molar Concentration} = \dfrac{1.66 \times 10^{-24} \text{mol}}{1 \times 10^{-15} \text{L} \text{ (from b)}}$

$\text{Molar Concentration} = 1.66 \times 10^{-9} \text{M} = 1.7 \, \text{nM}$

$[\text{Protein}] = 1.66 \times 10^{-9} \dfrac{\text{mol}}{\text{L}} \times 40\,000 \dfrac{\text{g}}{\text{mol}}$

$[\text{Protein}] = 6.6 \times 10^{-5} \dfrac{\text{g}}{\text{L}} = 6.6 \times 10^{-5} \dfrac{\text{mg}}{\text{mL}} \text{ or } 66 \dfrac{\mu\text{g}}{\text{L}} \text{ or } 66 \dfrac{\text{ng}}{\text{mL}}$

f.

$\text{Volume of 1 ribosome} = \dfrac{4}{3} \times \pi \times r^3$

$\text{Volume of 1 ribosome} = \dfrac{4}{3} \times 3.14 \times \left(\dfrac{20 \times 10^{-9} \text{m}}{2} \right)^3$

$\text{Volume of 1 ribosome} = 4.2 \times 10^{-24} \text{m}^3$

$$\text{Volume of 15 000 ribosomes} = 15\,000 \times 4.2 \times 10^{-24}\,\text{m}^3 = 6.3 \times 10^{-20}\,\text{m}^3$$

$$\text{Fractional volume} = \frac{\text{Volume ribosomes}}{\text{Volume cell}}$$

$$\text{Fractional volume} = \frac{6.3 \times 10^{-20}\,\text{m}^3}{1 \times 10^{-18}\,\text{m}^3 \ (\text{from b})}$$

$$\text{Fractional volume} = 0.063 \text{ or } 6.3\%$$

g. The number of moles of base pairs in 3.0×10^9 Da dsDNA is given by

$$= \frac{3.0 \times 10^9 \dfrac{\text{g}}{\text{mol dsDNA}}}{660 \dfrac{\text{g}}{\text{mol bp}}}$$

$$= 4.55 \times 10^6 \frac{\text{mol bp}}{\text{mol dsDNA}}$$

$$\text{Length} = 4.55 \times 10^6 \frac{\text{mol bp}}{\text{mol dsDNA}} \times 0.34 \frac{\text{nm}}{\text{bp}}$$

$$\text{Length} = 4.55 \times 10^6 \times 0.34 \times 10^{-9}\,\text{m}$$

$$\text{Length} = 1.55 \times 10^{-3}\,\text{m} = 1.55 \text{ mm} = 1550\ \mu\text{m}$$

$$\text{Length } E.\,coli = 2\ \mu\text{m}$$

$$\frac{\text{Length DNA}}{\text{Length } E.\,coli} = \frac{1550\ \mu\text{m}}{2\ \mu\text{m}} = 775$$

To calculate the number of different proteins that would be encoded by the *E. coli* chromosome:

$$360 \frac{\text{aa}}{\text{protein}} \times 3 \frac{\text{bp}}{\text{aa}} = 1080 \frac{\text{bp}}{\text{protein}}$$

$$\text{\# different proteins} = \frac{4.55 \times 10^6\,\text{bp}}{1080 \dfrac{\text{bp}}{\text{protein}}} = 4213 \text{ proteins}$$

The exact number can be found at NCBI (http://www.ncbi.nlm.nih.gov/). The genomes of a number of strains of *E. coli* have been sequenced, but the first one was K-12 strain MG1655. At NCBI, search for MG1655 and view hits in the genome database. There should be 11 of them and NC_000913 should be one of them. Activate this link (or search for NC_000913 directly and then activate it). The returned page should indicate that this strain of *E. coli* has 4132 protein-coding genes.

5. *Assume that liver cells are cuboidal in shape, 20 μm on a side.*
   a. *How many liver cells laid end to end would fit across the diameter of a pinhead? (Assume a pinhead diameter of 0.5 mm.)*
   b. *What is the volume of a liver cell? (Assume it is a cube.)*
   c. *What is the surface area of a liver cell? What is the surface-to-volume ratio of a liver cell? How does this compare to the surface-to-volume ratio of an E. coli cell? (Compare this answer to that of problem 3c.) What problems must cells with low surface-to-volume ratios confront that do not occur in cells with high surface-to-volume ratios?*
   d. *A human liver cell contains 2 sets of 23 chromosomes, each set being roughly equivalent in information content. The total mass of DNA contained in these 46 enormous DNA molecules is 4×10^{12} Da. Because each nucleotide pair contributes 660 Da to the mass of DNA and 0.34 nm to the length of DNA, what is the total number of nucleotide pairs and the complete length of the DNA in a liver cell? How does this length compare with the overall dimensions of a liver cell? The maximal information in each set of liver cell chromosomes should be related to the number of nucleotide pairs in the chromosome set's DNA. This number can be obtained by dividing the total number of nucleotide pairs calculated above by 2. What is this value? If this information is expressed in proteins that average 400 amino acids in length and three nucleotide pairs encode one amino acid in a protein, how many different kinds of*

proteins might a liver cell be able to produce? (In reality, liver cells express at most about 30 000 different proteins. Thus, a large discrepancy exists between the theoretical information content of DNA in liver cells and the amount of information actually expressed.)

Answer: a.

$$\text{\# liver cells} = \frac{0.5\,\dfrac{mm}{pinhead}}{20\,\dfrac{\mu m}{cell}}$$

$$\text{\# liver cells} = \frac{0.5 \times 10^{-3}\,\dfrac{m}{pinhead}}{20 \times 10^{-6}\,\dfrac{m}{cell}}$$

$$\text{\# liver cells} = 25\,\frac{cells}{pinhead}$$

b.

$$\text{Volume of cubic liver cell} = \text{length}^3 = \left(20 \times 10^{-6} m\right)^3$$

$$\text{Volume of cubic liver cell} = 8 \times 10^{-15} m^3 \times \left(\frac{100\ cm}{m}\right)^3 \times \left(\frac{1\ L}{1000\ cm^3}\right)$$

$$\text{Volume of cubic liver cell} = 8 \times 10^{-12} L = 8\ pL$$

c.

$$\text{Surface Area} = 6 \times \left(20 \times 10^{-6} m\right) \times \left(20 \times 10^{-6} m\right) = 2.4 \times 10^{-9} m^2$$

$$\frac{\text{Surface Area}}{\text{Volume}} = \frac{2.4 \times 10^{-9} m^2}{8 \times 10^{-15} m^3 (\text{from b})}$$

$$\frac{\text{Surface Area}}{\text{Volume}} = 3.0 \times 10^5 m^{-1}$$

The surface-to-volume ratio of liver to that of *E. coli* is given by:

$$\frac{3.0 \times 10^5 m^{-1}}{6 \times 10^6 m^{-1}\ (\text{from 3c})} = 0.05\ (1/20^{th})$$

The volume of a cell sets or determines the cell's maximum metabolic activity, while the surface area defines the surface across which nutrients and metabolic waste products must pass to meet the metabolic needs of the cell. Cells with a low surface-to-volume ratio have a high metabolic capacity relative to the surface area for exchange.

d.

$$\text{\# base pairs} = \frac{4.0 \times 10^{12}\,Da}{660\,\dfrac{Da}{base\ pair}}$$

$$\text{\# base pairs} = 6.1 \times 10^9\ bp$$

$$\text{Length} = 0.34\,\frac{nm}{bp} \times 6.1 \times 10^9\ bp$$

$$\text{Length} = 2.06\ m$$

$$\text{Length relative to liver cell} = \frac{2.06\ m}{20\ \mu m} = \frac{2.06\ m}{20 \times 10^{-6}\ m}$$

$$\text{Length relative to liver cell} = 1.03 \times 10^5\ \text{or about } 100\,000 \text{ times greater!}$$

The maximal information is 3.0×10^9 bp.

$$\text{\# proteins} = 400\frac{\text{aa}}{\text{protein}} \times 3\frac{\text{bp}}{\text{aa}} = 1{,}200\frac{\text{bp}}{\text{protein}}$$

$$\text{\# proteins} = \frac{3.0 \times 10^9 \text{bp}}{1200\dfrac{\text{bp}}{\text{protein}}} = 2.5 \times 10^6 \text{proteins}$$

7. What structural features allow biological polymers to be informational macromolecules? Is it possible for polysaccharides to be informational macromolecules?

Answer: Biopolymers, like proteins and nucleic acids, are informational molecules because they are vectorial molecules, composed of a variety of building blocks. For example, proteins are linear chains of some 20 amino acids joined head-to-tail to produce a polymer with distinct ends. The information content is the sequence of amino acids along the polymer. Nucleic acids (DNA and RNA) are also informational molecules for the same reason. Here, the biopolymer is made up of 4 kinds of nucleotides. Monosaccharides can be linked to form polymers. When a polymer is formed from only one kind of monosaccharide—as for example in glycogen, starch, and cellulose—even though the molecule is vectorial (i.e., it has distinct ends), there is little information content. There are, however, a variety of monosaccharides and monosaccharide derivatives that are used to form polysaccharides. Furthermore, monosaccharides can be joined in a variety of ways to form branch structures. Branched polysaccharides composed of a number of different monosaccharides are rich in information.

9. What is the distance between the centres of 2 carbon atoms (their limit of approach) that are interacting through van der Waals forces? What is the distance between the centres of 2 carbon atoms joined in a covalent bond? (See Table 1.4.)

Answer: The limit of approach of two atoms is determined by the sum of their van der Waals radii, which are given in Table 1.4. For 2 carbon atoms, the limit of approach is (0.17 nm + 0.17 nm) 0.34 nm. The distance between the centres of 2 carbon atoms joined in a covalent bond is the sum of the covalent radii of the two carbons or (0.077 nm + 0.077 nm) 0.154 nm. Clearly, two carbons sharing electrons in a covalent bond are closer together than are two carbons interacting through van der Waals forces.

11. Describe what is meant by the phrase "cells are steady-state systems."

Answer: Life is characterized as a system through which both energy and matter flow. The consequence of energy flow in this case is order, the order of monomeric units in biopolymers, which in turn produce macromolecular structures that function together as a living cell.

13. Studies of existing cells to determine the minimum number of genes for a living cell have suggested that 206 genes are sufficient. If the ratio of protein-coding genes to non–protein-coding genes is the same in this minimal organism as the genes of Mycoplasma genitalium, how many proteins are represented in these 206 genes? How many base pairs would be required to form the genome of this minimal organism if the genes are the same size as M. genitalium genes?

Answer: For *M. genitalium* we determined in Problem 12 that 92.5% of the genes of this organism are protein-coding genes. Assuming the same percentage applies to a minimum set of genes, then 191 of the 206 genes are protein-coding genes.

$$\text{Protein-coding genes} = 0.925 \times 206 = 190.6 = 191$$

In Problem 12, we were told that 580 074 base pairs code for 523 genes. The genome size required to code for 206 genes is calculated as follows:

$$\frac{580\,074}{523} = \frac{x}{206}$$

$$x = 206 \times \frac{580\,074}{523} = 228\,480$$

Note: This calculation assumes that genes essentially do not overlap. A smaller genome size could be possible by allowing overlapping, but this would constrain the protein sequences.

15. *The endoplasmic reticulum (ER) is a site of protein synthesis. Proteins made by ribosomes associated with the ER may pass into the ER membrane or enter the lumen of the ER. Devise a pathway by which*
    a. a plasma membrane protein may reach the plasma membrane
    b. a secreted protein may be deposited outside the cell

Answer: Protein synthesis starts out on ribosomes located in the cytoplasm of cells. Proteins destined to be excreted or to become membrane proteins are synthesized with a signal sequence located near the N-terminus of the protein. (Protein synthesis begins at the N-terminus.) This signal sequence directs the ribosome to the endoplasmic reticulum where the ribosome docks with the reticular membrane. Endoplasmic reticulum studded with ribosomes is called rough endoplasmic reticulum. The signal-sequence-containing protein is synthesized by rough endoplasmic reticulum-bound ribosomes that synthesize the protein and simultaneously export it into the lumen of the endoplasmic reticulum. For a protein to be transported to the plasma membrane, it must be packaged into membrane vesicles in the endoplasmic reticulum, since the reticular membrane is separate from the plasma membrane. Vesicles from the endoplasmic reticulum containing membrane proteins do not, however, move directly to the plasma membrane. Rather, they are routed to the Golgi apparatus where a variety of post-translational modifications occur. Once proteins move through the Golgi, they are repackaged into vesicles that are directed to the plasma membrane. Secreted proteins follow the same pathway. Both membrane proteins and excreted proteins contain signal sequences that get them into the endoplasmic reticulum. Membrane proteins contain an additional domain or domains that are hydrophobic in nature and anchor the proteins into the reticular membrane.

Additional Problems

1. Silicon is located below carbon in the periodic chart. It is capable of forming a wide range of bonds similar to carbon, yet life is based on carbon chemistry. Why are biomolecules made of silicon unlikely?

2. Identify the following characters of the Greek alphabet: α, β, γ, δ, Δ, ε, ζ, θ, κ, λ, μ, ν, π, ρ, σ, Σ, τ, χ, ϕ, ψ, and ω.

3. Give a common example of each of the weak forces at work.

4. On a hot dry day, leafy plants may begin to wilt. Why?

Abbreviated Answers

1. Covalent silicon bonds are not quite as strong as carbon covalent bonds because the bonding electrons of silicon are shielded from the nucleus by an additional layer of electrons. In addition, silicon is over twice the weight of carbon. Also, silicon oxides (rocks, glass) are extremely stable and not as reactive as carbon.

2. These Greek letters are commonly used in biochemistry, though this set is not the complete Greek alphabet: alpha (α), beta (β), gamma (γ), delta (δ), capital delta (Δ), epsilon (ε), zeta (ζ), theta (θ), kappa (κ), lambda (λ), mu (μ), nu (ν), pi (π), rho (ρ), sigma (σ), capital sigma (Σ), tau (τ), chi (χ), phi (ϕ), psi (ψ), and omega (ω), the last letter of the Greek alphabet.

3. Ice is an example of a structure held together by hydrogen bonds. Sodium and chloride ions are joined by ionic bonds in table salt crystals. A stick of butter is a solid at room temperature because of van der Waals forces. The energetically unfavorable interactions between water and oil molecules cause the oil to coalesce.

4. The tonoplast loses water and begins to shrink, causing the plant cell membrane to exert less pressure on the cell wall.

Summary

The chapter begins with an outline of the fundamental properties of living systems: complexity and organization, biological structure and function, energy transduction, and self-replication. What are the underlying chemical principles responsible for these properties? The elemental composition of biomolecules is dominated by hydrogen, carbon, nitrogen, and oxygen. These are the lightest elements capable of forming strong covalent bonds. In particular, carbon plays a key role serving as the backbone element of all biomolecules. It can participate in as many as four covalent bonds arranged in tetrahedral geometry and can produce a variety of structures including linear, branched, and cyclic compounds.

The four elements are incorporated into biomolecules from precursor compounds: CO_2, NH_4^+, NO_3^-, and N_2. These precursors are used to construct more complex compounds such as amino acids, sugars, and nucleotides, which serve as building blocks for the biopolymers; and proteins, polysaccharides, and nucleic acids, as well as fatty acids and glycerol, which are the building blocks of lipids. These complex macromolecules are organized into supramolecular complexes such as membranes and ribosomes that are components of cells, the fundamental units of life.

Proteins, nucleic acids, and polysaccharides are biopolymers with structural polarity due to a head-to-tail arrangements of asymmetric building block molecules. In these biopolymers, the building blocks are held together by covalent bonds, but they assume an elaborate architecture due to weak, non-covalent forces such as van der Waals interactions, hydrogen bonds, ionic bonds, and hydrophobic interactions. The three-dimensional shape is important for biological function, especially for proteins. At extreme conditions such as high temperature, high pressure, high salt concentrations, extremes of pH, and so on, the weak forces may be disrupted, resulting in loss of both shape and function in a process known as denaturation. Thus, life is confined to a narrow range of conditions.

Life demands a flow of energy during which energy transductions occur in the organized, orderly, small, manageable steps of metabolism, each step catalyzed by enzymes.

The fundamental unit of life is the cell. There are two types: eukaryotic cells with a nucleus and prokaryotic cells without a nucleus. Prokaryotes are divided into two groups, eubacteria and archaea. All cells contain ribosomes, which are responsible for protein synthesis; however, prokaryotic cells contain little else in the way of subcellular structures. Eukaryotic cells, found in plants, animals, fungi, and single cell organisms (protista), contain an array of membrane-bound compartments or organelles, including a nucleus, mitochondria, chloroplasts, endoplasmic reticulum, Golgi apparatus, vacuoles, lysosomes, and perixosomes. Organelles are internal compartments in which particular metabolic processes are carried out.

Chapter 2

Water: The Medium of Life

• •

Chapter Outline

❖ Properties of water: High boiling point, high melting point, high heat of vaporization, high surface tension, high dielectric constant, maximum density as a liquid—all due to ability of water to hydrogen bond
❖ Water structure
    ⊥ Electronegative oxygen, two hydrogens: Non-linear arrangement: Dipole
    ⊥ Two lone pairs on oxygen: H-bond acceptors
    ⊥ Partially positively charged hydrogens: H-bond donors
❖ Ice
    ⊥ Lattice with each water interacting with 4 neighbouring waters
    ⊥ H-bonds: Directional, straight, and stable
❖ Liquid: H-bonds present but less than 4 and transient
❖ Solvent properties of water
    ⊥ High dielectric constant decreases strength of ionic interactions between other molecules
       • Force of ionic interaction , $F = e_1 e_2 / Dr^2$, inversely dependent on D
       • Salts dissolve in water
    ⊥ Interaction with polar solutes through H bonds
    ⊥ Hydrophobic interactions: Entropy-driven process minimizes solvation cage
❖ Colligative properties: Freezing point depression, boiling point elevation, lowering of vapour pressure, osmotic pressure effects; depend on solute particles per volume
❖ Ionization of water
    ⊥ Ions: hydrogen ion H^+ (protons), hydroxyl ion OH^-, hydronium ion H_3O^+ (protonated water)
    ⊥ Ion product: $K_w = [H_2O] \times K_{eq} = 55.5 \times K_{eq} = 10^{-14} = [H^+][OH^-]$
    ⊥ $pH = -\log_{10}[H^+]$, $pOH = -\log_{10}[OH^-]$, $pH + pOH = 14$
❖ Strong electrolytes: Completely dissociate: Salts, strong acids, strong bases
❖ Weak electrolytes: Do not fully dissociate: Hydrogen ion buffers
❖ Buffers
    ⊥ Henderson–Hasselbalch equation: $pH = pK_a + \log_{10}([A^-]/[HA])$
    ⊥ Biological buffers: Phosphoric acid ($pK_1 = 2.15$, $pK_2 = 7.2$, $pK_3 = 12.4$); histidine ($pK_a = 6.04$); bicarbonate ($pK_{overall} = 6.1$)
    ⊥ "Good" buffers: pK_a values in physiological pH range and not influenced by divalent cations

Chapter Objectives

Water
Its properties arise because of the ability of water molecules to form H bonds and to dissociate to H^+ and OH^-. Thus, water is a good solvent, has a high heat capacity, and hasa high dielectric constant.

Acid–Base Problems
For acid–base problems, the key points to remember are:

Henderson–Hasselbalch: $pH = pK_a + \log([A^-]/[HA])$

Conservation of acid and conjugate base: $[A^-] + [HA]$ = Total concentration of weak electrolyte added

Conservation of charge: $\sum [cations] = \sum [anions]$—i.e., the sum of the cations must equal the sum of the anions

In many cases, simplifications can be made to this equation. For example, [OH⁻] or [H⁺] may be small relative to other terms and ignored in the equation. For strong acids, it can be assumed that the concentration of the conjugate base is equal to the total concentration of the acid. For example, an x M solution of HCl is x M in Cl⁻. Likewise for x M NaOH, the [Na⁺] is x M. In polyprotic buffers (e.g., phosphate, citrate, etc.), the group with the pK_a closest to the pH under study will have to be analyzed using the Henderson–Hasselbalch equation. For groups with pK_a values 2 or more pH units away from the pH, they are either completely protonated or unprotonated.

The solution to a quadratic equation of the form, $y = ax^2 + bx + c$ is:

$$x = \frac{-b \pm \sqrt{b^2 - 4ac}}{2a}$$

Problems and Solutions

1. **Calculate the pH of the following.**
   a. 5×10^{-4} **M HCl**
   b. 7×10^{-5} **M NaOH**
   c. 2μ **M HCl**
   d. 3×10^{-2} **M KOH**
   e. **0.04 mM HCl**
   f. 6×10^{-9} **M HCl = 0.06×10^{-7} M HCl**

Answer: a.   HCl is a strong acid and fully dissociates into [H⁺] and [Cl⁻].

Thus, [H⁺] = [Cl⁻] = [HCl]$_{\text{total added}}$

$\text{pH} = -\log_{10}[\text{H}^+] = -\log_{10}[\text{HCl}_{\text{total}}]$

$= -\log_{10}(5 \times 10^{-4})$

$= 3.3$

b.   For strong bases like NaOH and KOH,

$\text{pH} = 14 + \log_{10}[\text{Base}]$

$= 14 + \log_{10}(7 \times 10^{-5})$

$= 9.85$

c.

$\text{pH} = -\log_{10}[\text{H}^+] = -\log_{10}[\text{HCl}_{\text{total}}]$

$= -\log_{10}(2 \times 10^{-6})$

$= 5.70$

d. $\text{pH} = 14 + \log_{10}(3 \times 10^{-2}) = 12.5$

e.

$\text{pH} = -\log_{10}[\text{H}^+] = -\log_{10}[\text{HCl}_{\text{total}}]$

$= -\log_{10}(0.04 \times 10^{-3})$

$= 4.4$

f.   Beware! Naively, one might fall into the trap of simply treating this like another strong acid problem and solving it like so:

$\text{pH} = -\log_{10}[\text{H}^+] = -\log_{10}[\text{HCl}_{\text{total}}]$

$= -\log_{10}(6 \times 10^{-9})$

$= 8.22$

However, something is odd. This answer suggests that addition of a small amount of a strong acid to water will give rise to a basic pH! What we have ignored is the fact that water itself will contribute H+ into solution, so we must consider the ionization of water as well. There are two approaches we can take in solving this problem. As a close approximation we can assume that:

$$[H^+] = 10^{-7} + [HCl] \text{ or,}$$
$$[H^+] = 10^{-7} + 6 \times 10^{-9} = 10^{-7} + 0.06 \times 10^{-7} = 1.06 \times 10^{-7}$$
$$pH = -\log_{10}(1.06 \times 10^{-7}) = 6.97$$

The exact solution uses the ion product of water.

$$[H^+][OH^-] = K_w = 10^{-14} \text{ (the ion product of water)} \qquad (1)$$

In solution HCl fully dissociates into H+ + Cl-. For any solution, the sum of negative and positive charges must be equal. Since we are dealing with monovalent ion, we can write:

$$[H^+] = [Cl^-] + [OH^-] \qquad (2)$$

Now because HCl is fully dissociated:

$$[Cl^-] = [HCl_{total}] = 6 \times 10^{-9} \qquad (3)$$

Substituting this into equation (2), solving equation (2) for [OH-] and substituting in equation (1), we have a quadratic equation in H+:

$$[H+]^2 - 6 \times 10^{-9}[H^+] - 10^{-14} = 0$$
whose general solution is given by
$$[H+] = \frac{-b \pm \sqrt{b^2 - 4ac}}{2a} = \frac{6 \times 10^{-9} \pm \sqrt{(6 \times 10^{-9})^2 - 4(-10^{-14})}}{2}$$

Before firing up the calculator, a little reflection suggests that the argument under the square root is dominated by 4×10^{-14} whose root is 2×10^{-7}. Furthermore, of the two solutions (i.e., ±), it must be the + solution (– given rises to a negative [H+]!). Therefore,

$$[H+] = \frac{6 \times 10^{-9} + 2 \times 10^{-7} + [OH^-]}{2}$$
$$\text{and } pH = -\log_{10}[H^+] = 6.99$$

3. *The pH of a 0.02 M solution of an acid was measured at 4.6.*
   a. *What is the [H+] in this solution?*
   b. *Calculate the acid dissociation constant K_a and pK_a for this acid.*

Answer: a. $[H^+] = 10^{-pH} = 10^{-4.6} = 2.5 \times 10^{-5} M = 25 \ \mu M$
b.

$$HA \rightleftharpoons H^+ + A-$$

$$K_a = \frac{[H^+][A^-]}{[HA]}$$

Assume that a small amount, x, of HA dissociates into equal molar amounts of H+ and A-. We then have:

$$HA \leftrightarrow H^+ + A^- \text{ or}$$
$$0.02 - x \leftrightarrow x + x$$

From (a), we know that $[H^+] = 25\,\mu M = x = A^-$

and $[HA] = 0.02 - 25 \times 10^{-6} \approx 0.02$

Thus, $K_a = \dfrac{(25 \times 10^{-6})^2}{0.02} = \dfrac{625 \times 10^{-12}}{0.02} = 3.13 \times 10^{-8}$ M

$pK_a = -\log_{10}(3.13 \times 10^{-8}) = 7.5$

5. Given 0.1 M solutions of acetic acid and sodium acetate, describe the preparation of 1 L of 0.1 M acetate buffer at a pH of 5.4.

Answer: From the Henderson–Hasselbalch equation, i.e.,

$$pH = pK_a + \log_{10} \frac{[A^-]}{[HA]}$$

$$\frac{[A^-]}{[HA]} = 10^{(pH - pK)} = 10^{(5.4 - 4.76)} = 10^{0.64} = 4.37 \qquad (1)$$

Further, we want

$$[HA] + [A^-] = 0.1 \text{ M} \qquad (2)$$

Solving equation (1) for $[A^-]$ and substituting into (2), we find:

$$[HA] + 4.37 \times [HA] = 5.37 \times [HA] = 0.1 \text{ M}$$
$$[HA] = 0.0186 \text{ M}$$

Substituting this value of $[HA]$ into (2), we find that $[A^-] = 0.0814$

Therefore, combine 186 mL 0.1 M acetic acid with 814 mL 0.1 M sodium acetate.

7. Given 0.1 M solutions of Na₃PO₄ and H₃PO₄, describe the preparation of 1 L of a phosphate buffer at a pH of 7.5. What are the molar concentrations of the ions in the final buffer solution, including Na⁺ and H⁺?

Answer: (See preceding two problems)

$$\frac{[HPO_4^{2-}]}{[H_2PO_4^-]} = 10^{(pH - pK_a)} = 10^{(7.5 - 7.2)} = 2.0 \text{ and,}$$

$$[HPO_4^{2-}] + [H_2PO_4^-] = 0.1 \text{ M so,}$$

$$[H_2PO_4^-] = 0.0333 \text{ M and } [HPO_4^{2-}] = 0.0667 \text{ M}$$

For charge neutrality

$$[H^+] + [Na^+] = 2 \times [HPO_4^{2-}] + [H_2PO_4^-] \text{ or}$$

$$[Na^+] \approx 2 \times [HPO_4^{2-}] + [H_2PO_4^-]$$

$$[Na^+] = 2 \times 0.0667 \text{ M} + 0.0333 \text{ M} = 0.1667 \text{ M}$$

Na⁺ comes from the Na₃PO₄ solution, where it is 0.3 M. (Note: The solution is 0.1 M in Na₃PO₄, which dissociates into 3 Na³⁺ and 1 PO₄³⁻.) To make the solution, we need to add enough Na₃PO₄ to result in 0.1667 M Na⁺. This is calculated as follows:

$$0.3 \text{ M} \times x = 0.1667 \text{ M} \times 1000 \text{ mL}$$
$$x = 555.7 \text{ mL}$$

Where x is the volume in ml of tribasic sodium phosphate. This will contribute 0.05557 M of phosphate to the solution. The final phosphate concentration must be 0.1 M, and so the remainder must come from phosphoric acid. Therefore, 444.3 mL of phosphoric acid must be added.

The final solution will be:

$$0.0667 \text{ M in } [\text{HPO}_4^{2-}]$$

$$0.0333 \text{ M in } [\text{H}_2\text{PO}_4^-]$$

$$0.1667 \text{ M in } [\text{Na}^+]$$

$$3.16 \times 10^{-8} \text{ M in } [\text{H}^+]$$

9. ***What are the approximate fractional concentrations of the following phosphate species at pH values of 0, 2, 4, 6, 8, 10, and 12?***
a. H₃PO₄   b. H₂PO₄⁻   c. HPO₄²⁻   d. PO₄³⁻

Answer: For phosphoric acid, the following equilibria apply:

$$\text{H}_3\text{PO}_4 \leftrightarrow \text{H}^+ + \text{H}_2\text{PO}_4^- \leftrightarrow \text{H}^+ + \text{HPO}_4^{2-} \leftrightarrow \text{H}^+ + \text{PO}_4^{3-}$$
$$\quad\quad\quad\quad 2.15 \quad\quad\quad\quad 7.20 \quad\quad\quad\quad 12.40$$

The Henderson–Hasselbalch equation may be used to calculate the ratio of any two species that differ by a proton. Thus,

$$\text{pH} = \text{p}K_a + \log_{10}\frac{[\text{A}^-]}{[\text{HA}]} \text{ or}$$

$$\frac{[\text{A}^-]}{[\text{HA}]} = 10^{(\text{pH} - \text{p}K_a)}$$

By applying this equation at a pH value and at the 3 pKa values, we can calculate the following ratios:

$$\frac{[\text{H}_2\text{PO}_4^-]}{[\text{H}_3\text{PO}_4]} = 10^{(\text{pH} - 2.15)}, \frac{[\text{HPO}_4^{2-}]}{[\text{H}_2\text{PO}_4^-]} = 10^{(\text{pH} - 7.20)}, \frac{[\text{PO}_4^{3-}]}{[\text{HPO}_4^{2-}]} = 10^{(\text{pH} - 12.40)}$$

or

$$\frac{[\text{H}_2\text{PO}_4^-]}{[\text{H}_3\text{PO}_4]} = x, \frac{[\text{HPO}_4^{2-}]}{[\text{H}_2\text{PO}_4^-]} = y, \frac{[\text{PO}_4^{3-}]}{[\text{HPO}_4^{2-}]} = z$$

The fraction of any one species, at a particular pH, is its concentration divided by the sum of the concentrations of all of the species. For example,

$$f_{\text{H}_3\text{PO}_4} = \frac{[\text{H}_3\text{PO}_4]}{[\text{H}_3\text{PO}_4] + [\text{H}_2\text{PO}_4^-] + [\text{HPO}_4^{2-}] + [\text{PO}_4^{3-}]}$$

This fraction can be written as a function of x, y, and z as follows:

$$f_{\text{H}_3\text{PO}_4} = \frac{[\text{H}_3\text{PO}_4]}{[\text{H}_3\text{PO}_4] + x[\text{H}_3\text{PO}_4] + x \times y[\text{H}_3\text{PO}_4] + x \times y \times z[\text{H}_3\text{PO}_4]}$$

or

$$f_{\text{H}_3\text{PO}_4} = \frac{1}{1 + x + x \times y + x \times y \times z}$$

Using this equation we can evaluate the fraction of the fully protonated species at each of the pH values given. For the other species, we can take a similar approach to find expressions for their fractional value as a function of x, y, and z.

$$f_{H_3PO_4} = \frac{1}{1 + x + (x \times y) + (x \times y \times z)}$$

$$f_{H_2PO_4^-} = \frac{1}{(1/x) + 1 + y + (y \times z)}$$

$$f_{HPO_4^{2-}} = \frac{1}{1/(x \times y) + 1/y + 1 + z}$$

$$f_{PO_4^{3-}} = \frac{1}{1/(x \times y \times z) + 1/(x \times y) + 1/z + 1}$$

The values of x, y, and z may be calculated by hand. A more efficient approach would be to use a spreadsheet to evaluate x, y, and z at the pH values given, and then to calculate the corresponding fractions at each of the pH values. The following two tables give this information (to three decimal points).

pH	x	y	z
0	0.007	0.000	0.000
2	0.708	0.000	0.000
4	70.795	0.001	0.000
6	7079.458	0.063	0.000
8	707945.784	6.310	0.000
10	70794578.438	630.957	0.004
12	7079457843.841	63095.734	0.398

pH	f_{H3P}	f_{H2P}	f_{HP}	f_P
0	0.993	0.007	0.000	0.000
2	0.585	0.415	0.000	0.000
4	0.014	0.985	0.001	0.000
6	0.000	0.941	0.059	0.000
8	0.000	0.137	0.863	0.000
10	0.000	0.002	0.994	0.004
12	0.000	0.000	0.715	0.285

Note: This is the exact solution. A good approximation is to evaluate the Henderson–Hasselbalch for species whose pK_a are nearest the pH under consideration. For example, for pH 0, 2, and 4, evaluation of the Henderson–Hasselbalch for $pK_a = 2.15$ would give answers close to those presented above.

11. a. *If 50 mL of 0.01 M HCl is added to 100 mL of 0.05 M phosphate buffer at pH 7.2, what is the resultant pH? What are the concentrations of H₂PO₄⁻ and HPO₄²⁻ in the final solution?*
b. *If 50 mL of 0.01 M NaOH is added to 100 mL of 0.05 M phosphate buffer at pH 7.2, what is the resultant pH? What are the concentrations of H₂PO₄⁻ and HPO₄²⁻ in this final solution?*

Answer: The relevant pK_a for phosphoric acid is 7.2 governing the following equilibrium:

$$H_2PO_4^- \leftrightarrow H^+ + HPO_4^{2-}$$

From the Henderson–Hasselbalch equation, we find:

$$pH = pK_a + \log_{10}\frac{[HPO_4^{2-}]}{[H_2PO_4^-]} \text{ or}$$

$$[HPO_4^{2-}] = [H_2PO_4^-] \times 10^{(pH - pK_a)} = [H_2PO_4^-] \times 10^{(7.20 - 7.20)} = [H_2PO_4^-]$$

And since $[HPO_4^{2-}] + [H_2PO_4^-] = 0.05$ M

$$[HPO_4^{2-}] = [H_2PO_4^-] = 0.025 \text{ M}$$

In 100 mL, we have $100 \text{ mL} \times \dfrac{1 \text{ L}}{1000 \text{ mL}} \times 0.025 \text{ M} = 0.0025 \text{ mol of each.}$

Now, addition of 50 mL of 0.1 M HCl accomplishes two things:
(1) It dilutes the solution; and
(2) It introduces protons that will convert HPO_4^{2-} to $H_2PO_4^{-}$.

The moles of protons is given by:

$$50 \text{ mL} \times \frac{1 \text{ L}}{1000 \text{ mL}} \times 0.01 \text{ M} = 0.0005 \text{ mol}$$

Thus, 0.0005 mol of HPO_4^{2-} will be converted to $H_2PO_4^{-}$ or

there will be $0.0025 - 0.0005$ mol HPO_4^{2-} and $0.0025 + 0.0005$ mol $H_2PO_4^{-}$

$$pH = pK_a + \log_{10}\frac{[HPO_4^{2-}]}{[H_2PO_4^{-}]} = 7.2 + \log_{10}\frac{0.0025 - 0.0005}{0.0025 + 0.0005} = 7.02$$

$$\text{and } [HPO_4^{2-}] = \frac{(0.0025 - 0.0005) \text{ mol}}{100 \text{ mL} + 50 \text{ mL}} \times \frac{1000 \text{ mL}}{1 \text{ L}} = 0.0133 \text{ M}$$

$$[H_2PO_4^{-}] = \frac{(0.0025 + 0.0005) \text{ mol}}{100 \text{mL} + 50 \text{ mL}} \times \frac{1000 \text{ mL}}{1 \text{ L}} = 0.0200 \text{ M}$$

Note: This amount of acid added to 100 mL of water gives pH = 2.5.

b.   For NaOH, the same equations apply with one important difference: HPO_4^{2-} is increased and $H_2PO_4^{-}$ is decreased. Thus,

$$pH = pK_a + \log_{10}\frac{[HPO_4^{2-}]}{[H_2PO_4^{-}]} = 7.2 + \log_{10}\frac{0.0025 + 0.0005}{0.0025 - 0.0005} = 7.38$$

$$\text{and } [H_2PO_4^{-}] = \frac{(0.0025 - 0.0005) \text{ mol}}{100 \text{ mL} + 50 \text{ mL}} \times \frac{1000 \text{ mL}}{1 \text{ L}} = 0.0133 \text{ M}$$

$$[HPO_4^{2-}] = \frac{(0.0025 + 0.0005) \text{ mol}}{100 \text{ mL} + 50 \text{ mL}} \times \frac{1000 \text{ mL}}{1 \text{ L}} = 0.0200 \text{ M}$$

Note: If added to water instead, this amount of NaOH would result in a solution with pH = 11.5.

13.   Draw the titration curve for anserine (Figure 2.16). The isoelectric point of anserine is the pH where the net charge on the molecule is zero; what is the isoelectric point for anserine? Given a 0.1 M solution of anserine at its isoelectric point and ready access to 0.1 M HCl, 0.1 M NaOH and distilled water, describe the preparation of 1 L of 0.04 M anserine buffered solution, pH 7.2.

Answer:

The structure of anserine is shown above. It has three ionizable groups: a carboxyl group pK_1 = 2.64, imidazole nitrogen pK_2 = 7.04, and amino group pK_3 = 9.49. Starting at acidic pH, all three groups will be protonated and thus the molecule will have a +2 charge. As base is added, the carboxyl group will be the first to deprotonate with a midpoint at 2.64. When fully deprotonated at about 4.64, anserine will have a +1 charge. As the pH approaches 7.0, the imidazole group will deprotonate, leaving anserine uncharged. Finally, as the pH passes 9.49, the amino group will deprotonate, and by about pH 11.5, anserine will have a −1 charge.

    The titration curve is shown below with the pK_a values labelled. The isoelectric point, pI, is the pH at which the molecule is uncharged. Clearly, this will happen at a pH at which the carboxyl group's −1 charge is balanced by positive charges from both the imidazole group and the amino group. The isoelectric point must be between the pK_a values of the imidazole and amino groups. Thus, the sum of the protonated imidazole group and the protonated amino group must equal to one equivalent of charge.

    Let I and IH^+ be the unprotonated and protonated imidazole groups respectively.

    Let A and AH^+ be the unprotonated and protonated amino groups.

$$[IH^+] + [AH^+] = \text{one equivalent}$$

That is, the sum of the positively charged species for the imidazole and the amino groups must sum to the one equivalent of negative charge from the carboxylate. (Remember, there is one of each group.) The concentrations of the imidazole species, protonated and unprotonated, must sum to one equivalent. The same is true for the amino species. Thus,

$$[I] + [IH^+] = [A] + [AH^+] \text{ and so}$$
$$[I] + \cancel{[IH^+]} = \cancel{[IH^+]} + [AH^+] \quad (1)$$
$$[A] + \cancel{[AH^+]} = [IH^+] + \cancel{[AH^+]} \quad (2)$$

From equations (1) and (2), we can see that:

$$[AH^+] = [I] \text{ or } [IH^+] = [A] \quad (3)$$

The Henderson–Hasselbalch equations for each are:

$$pH = pK_2 + \log\frac{[I]}{[IH^+]} = pK_3 + \log\frac{[A]}{[AH^+]}$$

Substituting (3) into these, we have:

$$pH = pK_2 + \log\frac{[AH^+]}{[IH^+]} \text{ and}$$

$$pH = pK_3 + \log\frac{[IH^+]}{[AH^+]}$$

Solving these two equations for the log terms, which are inversely related, and setting them equal:

$$pH - pK_2 = \log\frac{[AH^+]}{[IH^+]}$$

$$-pH + pK_3 = -\log\frac{[IH^+]}{[AH^+]} = \log\frac{[AH^+]}{[IH^+]}$$

Thus,

$$pH - pK_2 = -pH + pK_3$$

$$pH = \frac{pK_2 + pK_3}{2} = pI = \frac{7.04 + 9.49}{2}$$

$$pI = 8.27$$

In order to prepare 1 L of 0.04 M anserine, we need to use 400 mL (0.4 L) of 0.1 M anserine stock. (1 L × 0.04 M = 0.1 M × 0.4 L). Since the pH = 8.27, we will have to titrate to pH = 7.2 using 0.1 M HCl. At pH = 8.27, the amino group is nearly fully protonated, whereas the imidazole group is nearly unprotonated. Using the Henderson–Hasselbalch equation for the imidazole group, we can determine what the ratio of unprotonated to protonated form at pH 8.27 and 7.20.

$$pH = 7.04 + \log\frac{[I]}{[IH^+]}$$

At 7.2, $\dfrac{[I]}{[IH^+]} = 10^{(7.2-7.04)} = 1.445$

And since $[I] + [IH^+] = 0.04$

$$1.445 \times [IH^+] + [IH^+] = 0.04$$

$$[IH^+]_{7.2} = \frac{0.04}{2.445} = 0.0164$$

At 8.27, $\dfrac{[I]}{[IH^+]} = 10^{(8.27-7.04)} = 16.98$

And since $[I] + [IH^+] = 0.04$

$$16.98 \times [IH^+] + [IH^+] = 0.04$$

$$[IH^+]_{8.27} = \frac{0.04}{17.98} = 0.0022$$

$$[IH^+]_{7.2} - [IH^+]_{8.27} = 0.0164 - 0.0022 = 0.0142$$

Thus, we will need to add 142 mL of 0.1 M HCl to adjust the imidazole group. We will need additional HCl to titrate the amino group from pH 8.27 to 7.20.

$$pH = 9.49 + \log\frac{[N]}{[NH^+]}$$

At 7.2, $\dfrac{[N]}{[NH^+]} = 10^{(7.2-9.49)} = 0.00513$

And since $[N] + [NH^+] = 0.04$

$0.00513 \times [NH^+] + [NH^+] = 0.04$

$$[NH^+]_{7.2} = \frac{0.04}{1.00513} = 0.0398$$

At 8.27, $\dfrac{[N]}{[NH^+]} = 10^{(8.27-9.49)} = 0.06026$

And since $[N] + [NH^+] = 0.04$

$0.06026 \times [NH^+] + [NH^+] = 0.04$

$$[IH^+]_{8.27} = \frac{0.04}{1.06026} = 0.03773$$

$$[IH^+]_{7.2} - [IH^+]_{8.27} = 0.0398 - 0.03773 = 0.00207$$

Thus, we will need to add 21 mL of 0.1 M HCl to titrate the amino group. The total HCl needed will be 163 mL.

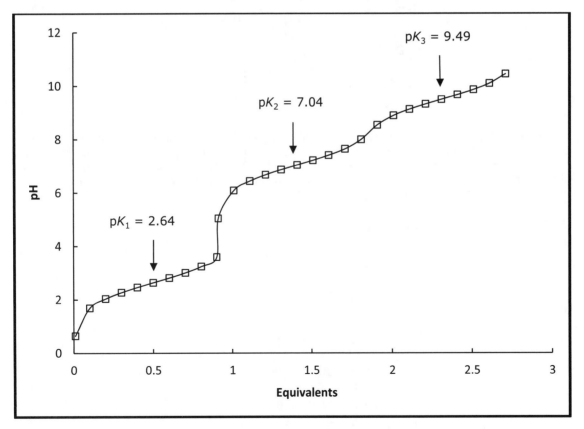

15. A 100 g amount of a solute was dissolved in 1000 g of water. The freezing point of this solution was measured accurately and determined to be –1.12°C. What is the molecular weight of the solute?

Answer: In the section dealing with colligative properties, we learn that 1 mol of an ideal solute dissolved in 1000 g of water (a 1.0 molal solution) depresses the freezing point by 1.86°C. We can set up a proportionality to calculate how many mol was added in this problem.

$$\frac{1.0 \text{ molal}}{-1.86°C} = \frac{x}{-1.12°C}$$

$$x = \frac{1.12}{1.86} \times 1.0 \text{ molal}$$

$$x = 0.60 \text{ molal}$$

The 0.6 molal solution was made by adding 100 g solute, which represents 0.6 mol. Therefore, the solute's molecular weight is:

$$\frac{100 \text{ g}}{0.6 \text{ mol}} = 167 \text{ Da}$$

17. Tris-hydroxymethyl aminomethane (Tris) is widely used for the preparation of buffers in biochemical research. Shown here is the structure of Tris in its protonated form:

Its acid dissociation constant, K_a, is 8.32 × 10⁻⁹. You have available at your lab bench a 0.1 M solution of Tris in its protonated form, 0.1 M solutions of HCl and NaOH, and ample distilled water. Describe the preparation of a 1 L solution of 0.02 M Tris buffer, pH 7.6.

Answer: Using the 0.1 M Tris solution, the amount needed to make 1 L of 0.02 M is determined as follows:

$$\frac{x \times 0.1 \text{ M}}{1 \text{ L}} = 0.02 \text{ M}$$

Where x is the volume of 0.1 M to be used.

Solving for x, we find:

$$x = \frac{0.02 \text{ M} \times 1 \text{ L}}{0.1 \text{ M}} = 0.2 \text{ L} = 0.2 \text{ L} \times \frac{1000 \text{ mL}}{\text{L}} = 200 \text{ mL}$$

Next, let's use the Henderson–Hasselbalch equation to calculate the ratio of Tris base to protonated Tris at pH = 7.6. Note: We are given the value for K_a, 8.32 × 10⁻⁹. The pK_a is calculated as follows:

$$pK_a = -\log\left(8.32 \times 10^{-9}\right) = 8.0799$$

Use the Henderson–Hasselbalch equation as follows:

$$pH = pK_a + \log\frac{[\text{Tris base}]}{[\text{Tris} \cdot \text{H}^+]}$$

$$7.6 = 8.0799 + \log\frac{[\text{Tris base}]}{[\text{Tris} \cdot \text{H}^+]}$$

$$\frac{[\text{Tris base}]}{[\text{Tris} \cdot \text{H}^+]} = 10^{(7.6-8.0799)} = 10^{-0.4799} = 0.331$$

But [Tris base] + [Tris·H⁺] = 0.02 M

Use the last two equations to solve for the concentration of each species:

$$[\text{Tris base}] = 0.331 \times [\text{Tris} \cdot \text{H}^+]$$

$$\text{But } 0.331 \times [\text{Tris} \times \text{H}^+] + [\text{Tris} \times \text{H}^+] = 0.02 \text{ M}$$

$$1.331 \times [\text{Tris} \times \text{H}^+] = 0.02 \text{ M}$$

$$[\text{Tris} \times \text{H}^+] = \frac{0.02 \text{ M}}{1.331} = 0.0150$$

and

$$[\text{Tris base}] = 0.02 \text{ M} - [\text{Tris} \times \text{H}^+] = 0.02 \text{ M} - 0.0150 = 0.005 \text{ M}$$

The protonated Tris solution was likely made using Tris.HCl, which is the chloride salt of Tris base. Thus, it contains equal amounts of chloride and Tris distributed between its protonated and unprotonated forms but mainly as the protonated form. The 200 mL represents 0.02 mol of protonated Tris. To adjust the pH to 7.6, we will need to lower the protonated Tris from 0.02 mol to 0.015 mol and so we will need to add NaOH in the amount of 0.005 mol. This corresponds to the following volume of 0.1 M NaOH:

$$x \times 0.1 \text{ M} = 0.005 \text{ mol}$$

$$x = 0.05 \text{ L} = 50 \text{ mL}$$

The final recipe is to use 200 mL of 0.1 M protonated Tris solution and add 50 mL of 0.1 M NaOH.

The final solution will actually be 0.02 M Tris buffer at pH = 7.6 but it will contain 5 mM NaCl produced when Tris HCl was adjusted with NaOH. A better way of preparing this solution is to use Tris base and then titrate with HCl to pH = 7.6.

19. Hydrochloric acid is a significant component of gastric juice. What is the concentration of chloride ion in gastric juice if pH = 1.2?

   a.   From the pK_a for lactic acid given in Table 2.4, calculate the concentration of lactate in blood plasma (pH = 7.4) if the concentration of lactic acid is 1.5 μM.

   b.   When a 0.1 M solution of a weak acid was titrated with base, the following results were obtained:

Equivalence of base added	pH observed
0.05	3.4
0.15	3.9
0.25	4.2
0.40	4.5
0.60	4.9
0.75	5.2
0.85	5.4
0.95	6.0

   Plot the results of this titration and determine the pK_a of the weak acid from your graph.

Answer: Strong acids like HCl fully dissociate in solution and so the pH, which is $-\log[\text{H}^+]$, is closely approximated by $-\log[\text{HCl}]$.

$$\text{HCl} \rightarrow \text{H}^+ + \text{Cl}^-$$

Thus, pH = $-\log[\text{HCl}]$ = 1.2
giving: $[\text{HCl}] = 10^{-1.2} = 0.0631$ or 63.1 mM

So the chloride concentration is 63.1 mM.

a.   From Table 2.4, the pK_a of lactic acid is 3.86. To determine the concentration of lactate at pH = 7.4, we need to use the Henderson–Hasselbalch equation.

$$pH = pK_a + \log\frac{[\text{lactate}]}{[\text{lactic acid}]}$$

$pH = 7.4$

$pK_a = 3.86$

$[\text{lactic acid}] = 1.5\ \mu M = 1.5 \times 10^{-6} M$

$[\text{lactate}] = [\text{lactic acid}] \times 10^{(7.4-3.86)} = 1.5 \times 10^{-6}\ M \times 10^{3.54}$

$[\text{lactate}] = 0.0052\ M = 5.2\ mM$

Note: The statement that the concentration of lactic acid is 1.5 μM was taken literally. It is possible that the concentration refers to the sum of lactate and its protonated, lactic acid form. In this case, the solution is as follows:

$$pH = pK_a + \log\frac{[\text{lactate}]}{[\text{lactic acid}]}$$

$pH = 7.4$

$pK_a = 3.86$

$[\text{lactic acid}] = 1.5\ \mu M = 1.5 \times 10^{-6} M = [\text{lactate}] + [\text{lactic acid}]$

$[\text{lactate}] = [\text{lactic acid}] \times 10^{(7.4-3.86)} = [\text{lactic acid}] \times 10^{3.54} = 3467 \times [\text{lactic acid}]$

$3467 \times [\text{lactic acid}] + [\text{lactic acid}] = 1.5 \times 10^{-6}\ M$

$[\text{lactic acid}] = \dfrac{1.5 \times 10^{-6} M}{3468} = 4.32 \times 10^{-10}\ M$, and

$[\text{lactate}] = 3467 \times [\text{lactic acid}] \approx 1.5 \times 10^{-6}\ M$

That is, the pH is so far from the pKa that essentially all the lactic acid is in the unprotonated lactate form.

b. In the chart shown below, the values for pH$_\text{calculated}$ were determined using the Henderson–Hasselbalch equation with a guess for pK_a shown. Values of [A$^-$] were assumed to be equal to the amount of base added while the values of [HA] were 1 − [A$^-$].

equivalence	pH	pH$_\text{calculated}$	pK_a	A$^-$	HA
0.05	3.4	3.42	4.7	0.05	0.95
0.15	3.9	3.95		0.15	0.85
0.25	4.2	4.22		0.25	0.75
0.4	4.5	4.52		0.4	0.6
0.6	4.9	4.88		0.6	0.4
0.75	5.2	5.18		0.75	0.25
0.85	5.4	5.45		0.85	0.15
0.95	6	5.98		0.95	0.05

In the graph shown below, pH is plotted against equivalence for the observed data (closed circles) and for the pH$_\text{calculated}$ (×). There is very close agreement between the two data sets indicating that the guess for 4.7 is close to the true value. We know we are dealing with an acid (something with pK_a lower that 7.0) because the initial pH is 3.42.

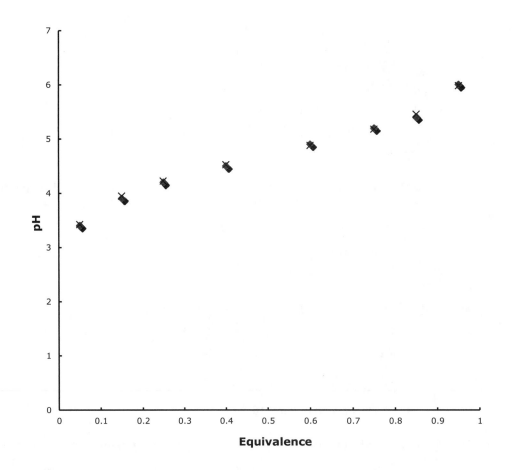

21. In light of the Human Biochemistry box on page 49, what would be the effect on blood pH if cellular metabolism produced a sudden burst of carbon dioxide?

Answer: The enzyme carbonic anhydrase rapidly hydrates carbon dioxide to form carbonic acid, which dissociates into a proton and bicarbonate as shown below.

Thus, production of carbon dioxide should lead to additional protons and hence a decrease in pH (acidosis). The body can compensate by increasing exchange of carbon dioxide in the lungs. In the lungs, since carbon dioxide is being eliminated the above equilibrium shifts to the left causing a decrease in proton concentration and an increase in pH.

Additional Problems

1. Tris [Tris(hydroxymethyl)aminomethane] is a commonly used buffer with a pK_a = 8.06. In making up a Tris solution, an appropriate amount of the free base is dissolved in water and the pH of the solution is adjusted, often with HCl. The M_r of Tris is 121.1.
    a. Describe the preparation of 1 L of 25 mM solution, pH = 8.4, using solid Tris base and 1 M HCl.
    b. Draw the structure of Tris in its protonated and unprotonated forms.

2. Many proteins are sensitive to divalent cations and often chelating agents are included in protein isolation solutions to bind divalent cations, lowering their concentration, and removing them from proteins. Two common agents used for this purpose are EDTA (Ethylenediaminetetraacetic acid) and EGTA [Ethyleneglycol-bis-(b-aminoethyl ether) N,N,N',N'-tetraacetic acid].
    a. Draw the structures of EDTA and EGTA.

b. These agents function by binding divalent cations. EDTA binds both Mg^{2+} and Ca^{2+} tightly while EGTA has a greater specificity for Ca^{2+}. (Both will bind a number of other divalent cations as well.) However, cation binding is pH-dependent. In making a solution of EDTA, it is often suggested that the pH of the solution be adjusted to around 8. The pK_a values of the four acetic acid groups on EDTA are 2.0, 2.67, 6.16, and 10.26. At pH = 8.0, what is the predominant ionic species of EDTA?

c. Divalent cations bind avidly to the fully ionized forms of both EDTA and EGTA. What fault do you find with using a solution of 10 mM Tris (pH = 7.0) and 25 mM EDTA to both buffer a protein solution and chelate divalent cations?

3. To make up 1 L of a 0.5 M solution of EDTA starting with the free acid, approximately how much 10 M NaOH will have to be added to adjust the pH to 7.0? Do you expect this solution to have a pH-buffering capacity? Explain.

4. The "Good" buffers were developed to provide buffers that would not interact strongly with divalent cations such as Mg^{2+} and Ca^{2+}. One such buffer is PIPES [Piperazine-N,N'-bis(2-ethanesulfonic acid)], pK_a = 6.8. You are asked to make 1 L of 25 mM solution of PIPES, pH = 7.0. In preparing the solution starting from the free acid, you notice that PIPES is not very soluble in water. You find that the solution is acidic (around 2), and so you begin to add NaOH. After addition of approximately 3.75 mL of 10 M NaOH, the solution clears. The pH is around 7. Explain.

5. a. On the same graph, sketch the titration curves of; acetic acid, pK_a = 4.76; ethylamine, pK_a = 10.63; and glycine, pK_a = 2.34 and 9.6.

b. The titrations of acetic acid, ethylamine, and glycine involve a single carboxyl group, a single amino group, and a carboxyl and amino group respectively. Can you suggest why the carboxyl group and the amino groups on glycine have lower pK_a values than the same groups on acetic acid and ethylamine?

Abbreviated Answers

1. a. Add 3.028 g Tris to approximately 900 mL of water. Carefully titrate the pH to 8.4 using approximately 7.8 mL of 1 M HCl. Finally, adjust the volume of the solution to 1 L.

(b)

2. (a)

EDTA

b. EDTA^{3-} (i.e., the singly-protonated species).

c.   Divalent cation binding to EDTA will result in release of a mole of proton per mole of cation bound to EDTA. The Tris functions as a proton buffer but it is one pH unit below its pK_a. Thus, it will not buffer the solution very effectively.

3.   To adjust the solution to pH = 7.0, sufficient NaOH must be added to fully titrate the two carboxyl groups with pK_a values = 2.0 and 2.67. This will require 100 mL of 10 M NaOH. Further, an additional 43.7 mL will be required to titrate the carboxyl group whose pK_a = 6.16. This is calculated using the Henderson–Hasselbalch equation. The total amount of NaOH is 143.7 mL. The solution will not be a good buffer at pH = 7.0 because the pH is 0.8 of a pH unit away from the nearest pK_a.

4.   To bring the pH of the solution to its pK_a normally requires approximately one-half of an equivalent of (in this case) base. The 3.75 mL of NaOH represents (3.75 mL × 10 M) 0.0375 equivalents of OH$^-$. One litre of 25 mM PIPES contains 0.025 moles of PIPES and 0.0375 equivalents of OH$^-$ corresponds to 1.5 equivalents of PIPES. Therefore, there must be two titratable groups on PIPES.

5.   The pK_a values of the carboxyl group and the amino group of glycine are shifted to lower pH values relative to the same groups on acetic acid and ethylamine. Clearly, the groups are influencing each other's pK_a values. The pK_a of the carboxyl group is lowered because it is influenced by the positively charged amino group. The unprotonated carboxyl group is negatively charged. This state is favoured by having a positively charged amino group nearby. Thus, the carboxyl group becomes a slightly stronger acid and will give up its proton at lower pH values. Similarly, the amino group becomes a slightly stronger acid because in its protonated state it is positively charged.

Summary

The most abundant molecule in living systems is H$_2$0. What physical properties make water such an important component of life? The two hydrogens in a water molecule make covalent bonds with a single O. However, there is something special about these covalent bonds. Oxygen is an electronegative element with a high affinity for electrons, surpassed only by F. (This high attraction for electrons is a consequence of a positively charged nucleus rather unshielded by electron clouds.) In covalent bonds with H, the electrons will be attracted to O, giving rise to charge separation or a dipole moment. The hydrogens become partially positively charged, whereas the oxygen becomes partially negatively charged. The four electron pairs in H$_2$0 form a distorted tetrahedron, with two lone pairs separated by an angle greater than 109° and the two shared electron pairs (shared between O and H) at 104.5°. The partially positively charged hydrogen can interact with lone-pair electrons to form hydrogen bonds. We will see that hydrogen bonds, although weak compared to covalent bonds, are important interactions in life.

   Water molecules can interact with each other to form hydrogen-bonded structures. Ice is a hydrogen-bonded structure, with each water molecule bonded to four other water molecules. In two of these bonds, the hydrogens interact with lone-pair electrons on two other water molecules. In these cases, water is serving as a hydrogen-bond donor. The two electron pairs make hydrogen bonds, participating as hydrogen-bond acceptors, with positively charged hydrogens on two other water molecules. The thermal properties of water are a consequence of hydrogen bonds. For example, the density of water decreases with decreasing temperature down to 4°C; as water molecules lose kinetic energy, they can approach each other more closely. As the temperature moves to the freezing point of water, more and more hydrogen bonds form, causing water molecules to move apart and density to decrease. Thus, ice floats. The environmental consequence is that ponds and lakes freeze from the surface, allowing life to continue in the liquid interior. The transition from solid to liquid to gas is accompanied by disruption of hydrogen bonds. A great many hydrogen bonds remain in liquid water, as evidenced by the difference in the heat of melting versus the heat of sublimation. Water has a high heat capacity (the ability to absorb heat without a large increase in temperature), because energy in the form of heat is used to break hydrogen bonds rather than increase temperature (increase kinetic energy). Finally, the rather large amount of energy required to vaporize water means that water can absorb energy with little increase in temperature.

   Water is a good solvent for ionic and polar substances because it forms hydrogen bonds with these substances. Salts dissolve and dissociate because the ionic components become hydrated with water molecules. The high dielectric constant of water is responsible for decreasing the attractive force between two ionic components of a salt. (The force between two charges, e_1 and e_2, is given by $F = e_1e_2/Dr^2$; it is inversely dependent on the dielectric constant.)

   The attraction between water molecules is strong and the tendency of water molecules to make these interactions is great. For example, at an air/water interface, interaction of water molecules on the surface is responsible for surface tension. But surface tension comes at a price. Water molecules at an interface are forced to make irregular hydrogen bonds, often with less than perfect geometry. In fact, this occurs at any interface, and when non-polar molecules are put into water, each molecule in effect represents an interface. To minimize the interface area, there is a tendency, driven by hydrogen bonding of H_2O, for non-polar substances to coalesce, to minimize their contact with water molecules. This tendency is termed hydrophobic interactions. We will see that biological membranes and proteins rely on hydrophobic interactions to maintain an ordered structure.

There are two other properties of water that are of extreme importance to biological systems: osmotic pressure and ionization of water. Osmotic pressure arises when two aqueous compartments are separated by a semipermeable membrane through which water can pass. If a solute is dissolved in one of the aqueous compartments (and the solute is not freely permeable to the membrane), water will move from the solute-free compartment into the compartment containing solute. The amount of pressure necessary to prevent this movement of water is the osmotic pressure. Osmotic pressure is a colligative property and as such its magnitude is directly proportional to concentration.

Water is capable of ionizing in solution to form hydrogen ions and hydroxyl ions. The pH is a measure of the hydrogen ion concentration; $pH = -\log[H^+]$. The pH scale in aqueous solution is set by the magnitude of the ion product. In aqueous solutions, $pH + pOH = 14$. Using this formula, the pH of solutions of strong acids or bases can be calculated. For weak acids and bases, the Henderson–Hasselbalch equation must be used: $pH = pK_a + \log([A^-]/[HA])$. Several of the problems illustrate the use of this equation.

Chapter 3

Thermodynamics of Biological Systems

• •

Chapter Outline

❖ Thermodynamic concepts
- ↳ Systems
  - • Isolated systems cannot exchange matter or energy with surroundings
  - • Closed systems exchange energy but not matter
  - • Open systems exchange both energy and matter
  - • First Law: $\Delta E = q + w$, where ΔE = change in internal energy (state function), q = heat absorbed, and w = work done on the system
    - • Work = generalized force × generalized distance
  - • $H = E + PV$, where H = enthalpy (energy transferred at P = constant); $\Delta H = q$ when work limited to $P\Delta V$
  - • $\Delta H^\circ = -Rd(\ln K_{eq})/d(1/T)$; van't Hoff plot $R\ln K_{eq}$ vs $1/T$ (R = gas constant = 8.314 J/mol·K
- ↳ Second Law: Disorder or randomness
  - • $S = k\ln W$, where k = Botzmann's constant = 1.38×10^{-23} J/K
  - • W = number of ways of arranging the components of a system at fixed internal energy
  - • $dS = dq/T$ for reversible process
  - • $\Delta S > 0$ for irreversible process, $\Delta S = 0$ for reversible process
- ↳ Third law: Entropy of a perfectly ordered, crystalline array at 0 K is exactly zero
  - • $S = \int_0^T C_p d \ln T$; C_p = heat capacity = dH/dT for constant P process
  - • Third law allows for calculation of S at any temperature provided C_p is known
- ↳ Gibbs free energy: $G = H - TS$
  - • $\Delta G = \Delta H - T\Delta S$ for constant T processes
  - • $\Delta G = \Delta G^\circ + RT\ln([P]/[R])$ and $\Delta G^\circ = -RT\ln([P]_{eq}/[R]_{eq})$
  - • When protons involved in process: $\Delta G^{\circ\prime} = \Delta G^\circ \pm RT\ln[H^+]$
    - • ("+" if reaction produces protons; "−" if protons consumed)

❖ Coupled processes: Enzymatic coupling of a thermodynamically unfavourable reaction with a thermodynamically favourable reaction to drive the unfavourable reaction. Thermodynamically favourable reaction is often hydrolysis of high-energy molecule.

❖ Energy transduction: high-energy phosphate in ATP and reduced cofactor NADPH
- ↳ Phototrophs use light energy to produce ATP and NADPH
- ↳ Chemotrophs use chemical energy to produce ATP and NADPH

❖ High-energy molecules
- ↳ Phosphoric anhydrides (ATP, ADP, GTP, UTP, etc.)
- ↳ Enol phosphates (phosphoenolpyruvate a.k.a. PEP)
- ↳ Phosphoric-carboxylic anhydrides (1,3-bisphosphoglycerate)
- ↳ Guanidino phosphates (creatine phosphate)

❖ Group transfer reactions
- ↳ Transfer of proton: $pK_a = \Delta G/2.303\ RT$
- ↳ Transfer of electron: $\Delta \mathscr{E}_o = -\Delta G/n\mathscr{F}$

❖ Why hydrolysis of high-energy bonds is favourable
- ↙ Destabilization of reactant due to electrostatic repulsion
- ↙ Product isomerization and resonance stabilization
- ↙ Entropy factors

❖ Thermodynamics of ATP hydrolysis influenced by pH, cation concentration, and reactant and product concentrations

Chapter Objectives

Laws of Thermodynamics

The first law of thermodynamics is simply a statement about the conservation of energy. The internal energy changes if work and/or heat are exchanged. In biological systems, we are usually dealing with constant-pressure processes and in this case the term enthalpy, $\boldsymbol{H}$, is used. Enthalpy is the heat exchanged at constant pressure. Since enthalpy is heat, it is readily measured using a calorimeter or from a plot of $R(\ln K_{eq})$ versus $1/T$, a van't Hoff plot. (To get ahead of the story, the point is that if ΔG and ΔH are known, ΔS can be calculated.)

The second law of thermodynamics introduces the term entropy, $\boldsymbol{S}$, which is a measure of disorder or randomness in a system. A spontaneous reaction is accompanied by an increase in disorder. For a reversible reaction, $dS_{reversible} = dq/T$. Also, $S = k\ln W$, where k = Boltzmann's constant, and W = the number of ways to arrange the components of a system without changing the internal energy.

Gibbs Free Energy

The change of Gibbs free energy for a reaction is the amount of energy available to do work at constant pressure and constant volume. This is an important concept and should be understood. For a general reaction of the type

$$A + B \rightleftarrows C + D$$
$$\Delta G = \Delta G° + \ln \frac{[C][D]}{[A][B]}$$

When a reaction is at equilibrium, clearly it can do no work (nor have work done on it) without change, so it must be true that $\Delta G = 0$ at equilibrium. Thus, $\Delta G° = -RT\ln K_{eq}$, and by measuring the equilibrium concentrations of reactants and products, $\Delta G°$ can be evaluated. Knowing the initial concentrations of reactants and products and $\Delta G°$ allows a calculation of ΔG. Why is this important? The sign on ΔG tell us in which direction the reaction will proceed. A negative ΔG indicates that the reaction has energy to do work and will be spontaneous in the direction written. A positive ΔG indicates work must be done on the reaction for it to proceed as written, otherwise it will run in reverse. The magnitude of ΔG is the amount of energy available to do work when the reaction goes to equilibrium. Finally, the relationship $\Delta G = \Delta H - T\Delta S$ can be used to evaluate ΔS, the change in disorder, if ΔG and ΔH are known.

High-Energy Compounds

ATP is the energy currency of cells and its hydrolysis is used to drive a large number of reactions. For ATP and other high-energy biomolecules, you should understand the properties that make them energy-rich compounds. These include destabilization due to electrostatic repulsion, stabilization of hydrolysis products by ionization and resonance, and entropy factors. Examples of high-energy compounds (from Table 3.3 in the textbook) include phosphoric acid anhydrides (e.g., ATP, ADP, GTP, UTP, CTP, and PPi), phosphoric-carboxylic anhydrides (acetyl phosphate and 1,3-bisphosphoglycerate), enol phosphates (PEP), and guanidinium phosphates (creatine and arginine phosphate). ATP is the cardinal high-energy compound. Hydrolysis of GTP is important in signal transduction and protein synthesis. UTP and CTP are used in polysaccharide and phospholipid synthesis, respectively. We will encounter 1,3-bisphosphoglycerate and PEP in glycolysis. These high-energy compounds, along with creatine and arginine phosphates, are used to replenish ATP from ADP. Other important high-energy compounds include coenzyme A derivatives such as acetyl-CoA and succinyl-CoA, important in the citric acid cycle. Aminoacylated-tRNAs, the substrates used by the ribosome for protein synthesis, are high-energy compounds.

Problems and Solutions

1. An enzymatic hydrolysis of fructose-1-P,

$$\text{Fructose-1-P} + H_2O \rightleftharpoons \text{fructose} + P_i$$

was allowed to proceed to equilibrium at 25°C. The original concentration of fructose-1-P was 0.2 M, but when the system had reached equilibrium the concentration of fructose-1-P was only 6.52×10^{-5} M. Calculate the equilibrium constant for this reaction and the standard free energy of hydrolysis of fructose-1-P.

Answer: For fructose-1-P + H_2O $\rightleftharpoons$ fructose + P_i, the equilibrium constant, K_{eq}, is given by

$$K_{eq} = \frac{[\text{fructose}]_{eq}[P]_{eq}}{[\text{fructose-1-P}]_{eq}}$$

At 25°C or 298 K (273 + 25), $[\text{fructose-1-P}]_{eq} = 6.52 \times 10^{-5}$ M. Initially, [fructose-1-P] = 0.2 M. The amount of the fructose produced is given by 0.2 M – 6.52×10^{-5} M.

Since an equal amount of $[P_i]$ is produced, K_{eq} may be written as follows:

$$K_{eq} = \frac{(0.2 \text{ M} - 6.52 \times 10^{-5})(0.2 \text{ M} - 6.52 \times 10^{-5})}{6.52 \times 10^{-5}}$$

$$K_{eq} = 613 \text{ M}$$

$$\Delta G° = -RT \ln K_{eq}$$

$$\Delta G° = -(8.314 \text{ J/mol} \cdot \text{K}) \times 298 \text{ K} \times \ln 613$$

$$\Delta G° = -15.9 \text{ kJ/mol}$$

3. The standard-state free energy of hydrolysis of acetyl phosphate is $\Delta G° = -42.3$ kJ/mol.

$$\text{Acetyl-P} + H_2O \rightarrow \text{acetate} + P_i$$

Calculate the free energy change for the acetyl phosphate hydrolysis in a solution of 2 mM acetate, 2 mM phosphate and 3 nM acetyl phosphate.

Answer: Since temperature is not specified in this problem, we are free to choose one. Both 20°C and 25°C are common choices, and 37°C makes sense if we are talking about reactions in warm-blooded mammals. The answer given in the back of the textbook was calculated using 20°C.

$$\Delta G = \Delta G° + RT \ln \frac{[\text{Product}]_{initial}}{[\text{Reactant}]_{initial}}$$

$$\Delta G = \Delta G° + 8.314 \text{ J/mol} \cdot \text{K} \times (273+20) \text{ K} \times \ln \frac{[\text{acetate}][P_i]}{[\text{acetyl-P}]}$$

$$\Delta G = -42\,300 \text{ J/mol} + 8.314 \text{ J/mol} \cdot \text{K} \times (273+20) \text{ K} \times \ln \frac{(2 \times 10^{-3})(2 \times 10^{-3})}{(3 \times 10^{-9})}$$

$$\Delta G = -24.8 \text{ kJ/mol}$$

5. ATP hydrolysis at pH 7.0 is accompanied by release of a hydrogen ion to the medium:

$$\text{ATP}^{4-} + H_2O \rightleftharpoons \text{ADP}^{3-} + \text{HPO}_4^{2-} + H^+$$

If the $\Delta G°'$ for this reaction is –30.5 kJ/mol, what is $\Delta G°$ (that is, the free energy change for the same reaction with all components, including H^+, at a standard state of 1 M)?

Answer: The reaction produces H^+, and we can use the following equation to calculate $\Delta G°$:

$\Delta G° = \Delta G°' - RT \ln [H^+]$, where $\Delta G°' = -30.5$ kJ/mol, $T = 298$ K, $R = 8.314$ J/mol·K and $[H^+] = 10^{-7}$. Thus,

$$\Delta G° = -30.5 \text{ kJ/mol} - 8.314 \times 10^{-3} \text{kJ/mol} \cdot \text{K} \times (273 + 25) \text{ K} \times \ln 10^{-7.0}$$

$$\Delta G° = -30.5 + 39.9 = 9.4 \text{ kJ/mol}$$

7.   Draw all possible resonance structures for creatine phosphate and discuss their possible effects on resonance stabilization of the molecule.

Answer:

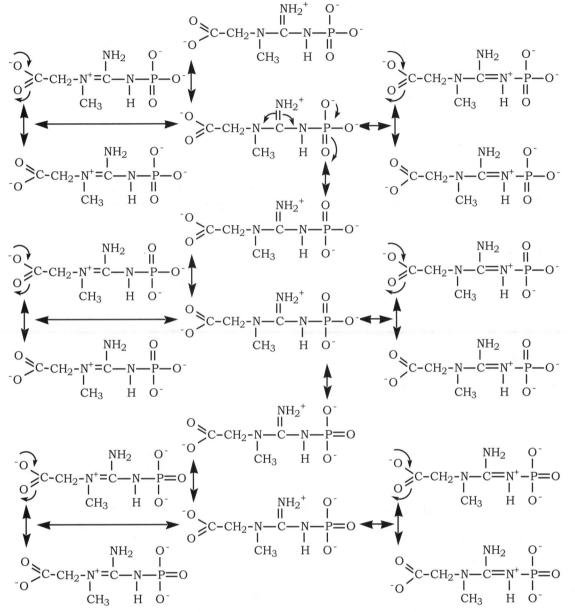

9.   Imagine that creatine phosphate, rather than ATP, is the universal energy-carrier molecule in the human body. Repeat the calculation presented in Section 3.6, calculating the weight of creatine phosphate that would need to be consumed each day by a typical adult human if creatine phosphate could not be recycled. If recycling of creatine phosphate were possible, and if the typical adult human body contained 20 grams of creatine phosphate, how many times would each creatine phosphate molecule need to be turned over or recycled each day? Repeat the calculation assuming that glycerol-3-phosphate is the universal energy carrier, and that the body contains 20 grams of glycerol-3-phosphate.

Answer: The calculation presented in Section 3.6 determined the number of moles of ATP that must be hydrolyzed under cellular conditions to provide 5860 kJ of energy. Under standard conditions, ATP hydrolysis yields 35.7 kJ/mol (see Table 3.3), whereas under cellular conditions, the value is approximately 50 kJ/mol. In order to repeat the calculation using creatine phosphate, we must estimate the free energy of hydrolysis under cellular conditions. Alternatively, we can assume that the same number of moles of creatine phosphate must be hydrolyzed as ATP. The energy of hydrolysis of creatine phosphate is larger (i.e., more negative) than that of ATP. So, hydrolysis of an equivalent molar amount of creatine phosphate will release considerably more energy. Let us try both solutions.

First, let us assume that an equivalent number of moles of creatine phosphate is hydrolyzed. (The reason for considering this is that metabolic energy is in effect quantized as high-energy bonds.) From Section 3.6 we see that 117 moles of ATP are required. An equal number of moles of creatine phosphate weighs:

$$117 \text{ mol} \times 180 \text{ g / mol} = 21\,060 \text{ g}$$

and the turnover of creatine phosphate is

$$\frac{21\,060 \text{ g}}{20 \text{ g}} = 1052 \text{ times}$$

To calculate the free energy of hydrolysis of creatine phosphate under cellular conditions, let us assume that in resting muscle, creatine phosphate is approximately 20 mM, the concentration of P_i is approximately 5 mM (see Problem 10), and approximately 10% of creatine phosphate or 2 mM is as creatine. Using these values and the standard free energy of hydrolysis of creatine phosphate (from Table 3.3), we calculate the energy of hydrolysis under cellular conditions as follows:

$$\Delta G = \Delta G° + RT\ln \frac{[\text{creatine}][P_i]}{[\text{creatine phosphate}]}$$

$$\Delta G = -43.3 \text{ kJ / mol} + 8.314 \times 10^{-3} \text{ kJ/mol} \cdot K \times (273 + 37) \text{ K} \times \ln\frac{(2 \times 10^{-3})(5 \times 10^{-3})}{20 \times 10^{-3}}$$

$$\Delta G = -62.9 \text{ kJ / mol}$$

The number of moles of creatine phosphate is given by

$$\frac{5860 \text{ kJ}}{62.9 \text{ kJ / mol}} = 93.2 \text{ mol}$$

The molecular weight of creatine phosphate is 180. Therefore, $93.2 \text{ mol} \times 180 \text{ g/mol} = 16\,780 \text{ g}$ is required.

The turnover of creating phosphate is $\dfrac{16\,780 \text{ g}}{20 \text{ g}} = 839 \text{ times}$.

If one uses −43.3 kJ/mol for the ΔG of hydrolysis of creatine phosphate, the number of moles required is 5860 kJ ÷ 43.3 kJ/mol = 135.3 mol. The M_r of creatine is 131.1 and so it would require 131.1 g/mol × 135.3 mol = 17 738 g.

The solution to the problem using glycerol-3-phosphate is slightly more complicated. From Table 3.3 we see that the standard free energy of hydrolysis of the compound is only −9.2 kJ/mol, considerably lower than the −35.7 kJ/mol listed for ATP hydrolysis. So, we cannot simply assume that an equivalent number of moles of glycerol-3-phosphate will substitute for ATP hydrolysis as we did for creatine phosphate above, because hydrolysis of an equivalent number of moles of glycerol-3-phosphate will not supply sufficient energy. To solve the problem, we must estimate the energy of hydrolysis of glycerol-3-phosphate under cellular conditions as we did for creatine phosphate hydrolysis above. Let us assume that $[P_i] = 5$ mM, and that the ratio of [glycerol]:[glycerol-3-phosphate] is 1:10. Under these conditions,

$$\frac{5860 \text{ kJ}}{9.2 \text{ kJ/mol}} = 637 \text{ mol or } 637 \text{ mol} \times 172.08 \text{ g/mol} = 109\,615 \text{ g}$$

The turnover of creating phosphate is $\dfrac{109\,615 \text{ g}}{20 \text{ g}} = 5480 \text{ times}$.

$$\Delta G = -9.2 \text{ kJ / mol} + 8.314 \times 10^{-3} \text{ kJ/mol} \cdot K \times (273 + 37) \text{ K} \times \ln\frac{5 \times 10^{-3}}{10}$$

$$\Delta G = -28.8 \text{ kJ / mol}$$

The number of moles of glycerol-3-phosphate is given by

$$\frac{5860 \text{ kJ}}{28.8 \text{ kJ / mol}} = 203 \text{ mol}$$

The molecular weight of glycerol-3-phosphate is 172.08.

Therefore, 203 mol × 172.08 g/mol = 35 013 g is required.

The turnover of glycerol-3-phosphate is $\dfrac{35\,013 \text{ g}}{20 \text{ g}} = 1751$ times.

11. Hexokinase catalyzes the phosphorylation of glucose from ATP, yielding glucose-6-P and ADP. Using the values of Table 3.3, calculate the standard-state free energy change and equilibrium constant for the hexokinase reaction.

Answer: Hexokinase catalyzes the following reaction: glucose + ATP ⇌ glucose-6-P + ADP

This reaction may be broken down into the following two reactions:

$$\text{glucose} + P_i \rightleftarrows \text{glucose-6-P} + H_2O$$

$$ATP + H_2O \rightleftarrows ADP + P_i$$

From Table 3.3, we find that $\Delta G^{\circ\prime} = -13.9$ kJ/mol for glucose-6-P hydrolysis. Thus, the reverse reaction, namely reaction (1), must have $\Delta G^{\circ\prime} = +13.9$ kJ/mol.

From Table 3.3, we also find that ATP hydrolysis has $\Delta G^{\circ\prime} = -30.5$ kJ/mol. The overall $\Delta G^{\circ\prime}$ for phosphoryl transfer from ATP to glucose is:

$$\Delta G^{\circ\prime} = +13.9 + (-30.5) = -16.6 \text{ kJ/mol, and}$$

$$K_{eq} = e^{-\frac{\Delta G^{\circ\prime}}{RT}} = e^{-\frac{(16.6 \times 10^3)}{8.314 \times 310}} = 626.9$$

13. Consider carbamoyl phosphate, a precursor in the biosynthesis of pyrimidines:

Based on the discussion of high-energy phosphates in this chapter, would you expect carbamoyl phosphate to possess a high free energy of hydrolysis? Provide a chemical rationale for your answer.

Answer: Is carbamoyl phosphate destabilized due to electrostatic repulsion? The carbonyl oxygen will develop a partial-negative charge causing charge-repulsion with the negatively charged phosphate. So, charge destabilization exists. Are the products stabilized by resonance or by ionization? Without regard to resonance states of the phosphate group, there are two possible resonance structures for carbamoyl phosphate:

$$H_2N-\underset{\overset{\parallel}{O}}{C}-O-PO_3^{2-} \longleftrightarrow {}^+H_2N=\underset{\overset{|}{O^-}}{C}-O-PO_3^{2-}$$

However, we expect that the carbonyl-carbon must pass through a positively charged intermediate and in doing so, affect phosphate resonance. Thus, the products are resonance stabilized. Finally, are there entropy factors? The products of hydrolysis are phosphate and carbamic acid. Carbamic acid is unstable and decomposes to CO_2 and NH_3 unless stabilized as a salt by interacting with a cation. With these considerations in mind, we expect carbamoyl phosphate to be unstable and therefore a high-energy compound. The free energy of hydrolysis of carbamoyl phosphate is −51.5 kJ/mol, whereas for acetyl phosphate it is only −43.3 kJ/mol.

15. Consider the data in Figures 3.3 and 3.4. Is the denaturation of chymotrypsinogen spontaneous at 58°C? And what is the temperature at which the native and denatured forms of chymotrypsinogen are in equilibrium?

Answer: Figure 3.3 is a plot of ΔG° versus temperature and from it we see that at 58°C, ΔG° is approximately −3 kJ/mol. Thus, we expect denaturation to be spontaneous at this temperature if we start with a solution of chymotrypsinogen in its native conformation. The data presented in Figure 3.4 do not address the question of spontaneity of the reaction at 58°C. The ΔS° is positive at this temperature, suggesting that disorder in the denatured state is greater than that in the native state. This is consistent with an unfolding process but not predictive of the process occurring.

To calculate the temperature at which the process is at equilibrium, we must find the temperature at which $K_{eq} = 1$ and $\Delta G° = 0$. We can use the data used to construct Figure 3.3 to make this calculation. From Figure 3.3, we see that a plot of $R\ln K_{eq}$ versus $1000/T$ is linear and with a slope of magnitude 533 kJ/mol. A linear plot implies the following:

$$R\ln K_{eq} = -533 \times \frac{1000}{T} + b$$

We can solve the equation for b, the x-intercept, and can evaluate b by using any one data point in Figure 3.3 that is in the linear portion of the plot. Once b is evaluated, we can substitute it into the above equation and find T at which $K_{eq} = 1.0$. Remembering that T is in degrees Kelvin, we find that the protein is in equilibrium at $T = 56.6°C$.

Questions for Self-Study

1. True or false:
   a. The internal energy of an isolated system is conserved. _____
   b. A closed system can exchange matter but not energy with the surroundings. _____
   c. An open system includes a system and its surroundings. _____
   d. An open system can exchange matter with another open system. _____
   e. The internal energy of an open system is always constant. _____

2. The first law of thermodynamics states that there are only two ways to change the internal energy of any system. What are they?

3. Enthalpy, H, is defined as $H = E + PV$ and $\Delta E = q + w$. Under what conditions is $\Delta H = q$?

4. Define the terms in the following expression: $S = k\ln W$.

5. Match the items in the two columns.
   a. $\Delta G = \Delta H - T\Delta S$ 1. Reaction spontaneous as written
   b. $\Delta G = \Delta G° + RT \ln ([P]/[R])$ 2. Used to determine standard Gibbs free energy change
   c. $\Delta G° = 0$ 3. Reaction unfavourable
   d. $\Delta G = 0$ 4. Used to calculate amount of free energy released when reaction proceeds to equilibrium
   e. $\Delta G > 0$ 5. Definition of change in Gibbs free energy
   f. $\Delta G < 0$ 6. System at equilibrium
   g. $\Delta G° = -RT \ln K_{eq}$ 7. $K_{eq} = 1$

6. The compounds shown below include ATP, pyrophosphate, phosphoenolpyruvate, creatine phosphate, and 1,3-bisphosphoglycerate. They are all examples of high-energy compounds. Identify each, locate the high-energy bond, and list the products of hydrolysis of this bond.

d. $^{2-}O_3P-O$
     $CH_2=\overset{|}{C}-C\overset{O^-}{\underset{O}{\diagup}}$

e. $^{2-}O_3P-\overset{H}{\underset{}{N}}-\overset{CH_3}{\underset{\underset{NH_2^+}{||}}{C}}-\overset{}{N}-CH_2-C\overset{O^-}{\underset{O}{\diagup}}$

7. What are the three chemical reasons for the large negative energy of hydrolysis of phosphoric acid anhydride linkage for compounds such at ATP, ADP, and pyrophosphate?

8. Creatine phosphate is an example of a guanidinium phosphate, a high-energy phosphate compound. This compound is abundant in muscle tissue. What is its function?

9. During protein synthesis amino acids are joined in amide linkage on the ribosome. The substrates for this reaction are not free amino acids but rather amino acids attached via their carboxyl groups to the 3′ hydroxyl group of tRNAs. What kind of bond is formed between the amino acid and the tRNA? Is this a high-energy bond? Given the fact that aminoacyl-tRNA formation is accompanied by hydrolysis of ATP to AMP and PP$_i$ and that PP$_i$ is subsequently hydrolyzed to 2 P$_i$, how many high-energy phosphates are consumed to produce an aminoacyl-tRNA?

10. Although the standard free energy of hydrolysis of ATP is around −30 kJ/mol the cellular free energy change is even more negative. What factors contribute to this?

Answers

1. a. T; b. F; c. F; d. T; e. F.

2. Energy flow in the form of heat or work.

3. In general, $\Delta H = \Delta E + P\Delta V + V\Delta P = q + w + P\Delta V + V\Delta P$. When the pressure of the system remains constant (i.e., $\Delta P = 0$) and work is limited to only mechanical work (i.e., $w = -P\Delta V$), then $\Delta H = q$.

4. S is the entropy, k is Boltzmann's constant, $\ln W$ is the natural logarithm of the number of ways, W, of arranging the components of a system.

5. a. 5; b. 4; c. 7; d. 6; e. 3; f. 1; g. 2.

6. a. pyrophosphate, hydrolysis products 2 P$_i$; b. 1,3-bisphosphoglycerate, hydrolysis products 3-phosphoglycerate and P$_i$; c. ATP, hydrolysis products either ADP and P$_i$ or AMP and pyrophosphate; d. phosphoenolpyruvate, hydrolysis products pyruvate and P$_i$; e. creatine phosphate, hydrolysis products creatine and P$_i$. The location of high-energy bonds is shown below.

7. Bond strain due to electrostatic repulsion, stabilization of products by ionization and resonance, and entropy factors.

8. Creatine phosphate is used to replenish supplies of ATP by transferring phosphate to ADP in a reaction catalyzed by creatine kinase.

9. Amino acid ester bonds in aminoacyl-tRNAs are high-energy bonds produced at the expense of two high-energy phosphate bonds.

10. The presence of divalent and monovalent cations and the maintenance of low levels of ADP and P_i and high levels of ATP are responsible for the large negative free energy change of ATP under cellular conditions.

Additional Problems

1. Show that $\Delta G° = -RT \ln K_{eq}$.

2. The term $\Delta G°$ may be evaluated by measuring ΔG for a reaction in which reactants and products start out at 1 M concentration. The ΔG measured in this case is the standard-state free energy and is equal to $\Delta G°$. Prove this.

3. If a particular reaction is allowed to reach equilibrium, is the equilibrium concentration of product ever dependent on the initial concentrations of reactant and product?

4. Confusion reigns supreme when work and energy expenditure are discussed. Define the term work. Are work and energy expenditure synonymous?

5. There are two statements about spontaneity of reactions: $\Delta S > 0$, and $\Delta G < 0$. Justify that these statements are in fact true descriptions of spontaneity.

6. DNA ligase catalyzes formation of a phosphodiester bond between a 5′-phosphate and a 3′-hydroxyl group on the ends of two DNAs to be joined. Many ligases use hydrolysis of ATP to drive phosphodiester bond synthesis; however, the *E. coli* ligase uses NAD^+ as a high-energy compound. Explain why NAD^+ is considered a high-energy compound. What type of reaction is required to release energy from NAD^+ and what are the products?

7. You find yourself in the laboratory, late at night, working on an important assay and you discover that the last of the ATP stock is used up. After frantically searching everywhere, you find a 10 mg bottle of 2′-deoxyadenosine 5′-triphosphate. Is this a high-energy compound? Will it substitute for ATP in your assay?

8. Stock solutions of ATP are usually adjusted to around neutral pH to stabilize them. Why?

9. Intense muscle activity depletes ATP and creatine phosphate stores and produces ADP, creatine, AMP, and P_i. ADP is produced by ATP hydrolysis catalyzed by myosin, a component of the contractile apparatus of muscle. Creatine is a product of creatine kinase activity, and AMP is produced by adenylate kinase from two ADPs. Given this information, explain how high-energy phosphate compounds in muscle are interconnected.

10. The standard free energy of hydrolysis of glucose-1-phosphate is −21 kJ/mol whereas it is only −13.9 kJ/mol for glucose-6-phosphate. Provide an explanation for this difference.

Abbreviated Answers

1. At equilibrium $\Delta G = 0$ and the concentration of reactants and products are at their equilibrium values. Using

$$\Delta G = \Delta G^{\circ\prime} + RT \ln \frac{[C][D]}{[A][B]} \text{ we see that}$$

$$\Delta G = 0 = \Delta G^{\circ} + RT \ln \frac{[C_{eq}][D_{eq}]}{[A_{eq}][B_{eq}]}$$

or solving for ΔG°, we find that:

$$\Delta G^{\circ} = -RT \ln \frac{[C_{eq}][D_{eq}]}{[A_{eq}][B_{eq}]} = -RT \ln K_{eq}$$

2. Using

$$\Delta G = \Delta G^{\circ\prime} + RT \ln \frac{[C][D]}{[A][B]} \text{ we see that}$$

$$\Delta G = \Delta G^{\circ} + RT \ln \frac{1M \times 1M}{1M \times 1M} = \Delta G^{\circ} + RT \ln 1$$

But $\ln 1 = 0$, and

$$\Delta G = \Delta G^{\circ}$$

3. The equilibrium constant is independent of the initial concentrations of reactants and products, but the equilibrium constant is the ratio of the product of the concentration of products to the product of the concentration of reactants. This ratio is independent of initial concentrations. Clearly, the absolute amount of product depends on the initial concentration of reactant.

4. Work is the application of a force through some distance, the consequence of which is a change in the energy of the object upon which the force is acting. Application of a force on an object at rest will cause the object to accelerate, and in the absence of friction, this will impart kinetic energy to the object. In the presence of friction, energy will be dissipated as heat raising the temperature of the object. However, one can have energy expenditure without doing work. As an example, holding an object at some position in a gravitational field requires a force equal and opposite to the force of gravity, and creation of this force requires expenditure of energy; yet, no work is done if the object does not move.

5. Entropy is a measure of disorder and for a reaction to be spontaneous $\Delta S > 0$ or since $S_f - S_i > 0$, $S_f > S_i$. A spontaneous reaction results in an increase in disorder. Gibbs free energy is the amount of energy available to do work at constant pressure and temperature. Using G as a criterion for spontaneity requires that $\Delta G < 0$ or since $G_f - G_i < 0$, $G_f < G_i$. The amount of energy available to do work decreases for a spontaneous reaction.

6. NAD⁺ contains a single high-energy phosphoric anhydride linkage between AMP and nicotinamide monophosphate nucleotide. Hydrolysis will release AMP and nicotinamide nucleoside monophosphate.

7. 2′-Deoxyadenosine 5′-triphosphate, or dATP, contains two high-energy phosphoric anhydride bonds. However, if the assays being performed are enzymatic assays (as opposed to some chemical assay), then it is out of the question to even think about substituting dATP for ATP. ATP is a ribonucleotide; dATP is a deoxyribonucleotide. dATP is used for synthesis of DNA and little else.

8. At first thought, it might seem reasonable to make the ATP solution slightly acidic. This will neutralize the negatively charged phosphates and should lead to stabilization of the phosphoric anhydride linkages. The problem with this idea is that the N-glycosidic linkage is acid labile. This bond is more stable in alkaline solution, but the anhydride bonds are readily cleaved by hydroxide attack.

9. The key here is to recognize that kinases are enzymes that transfer the γ-phosphate of ATP to a target molecule. Thus, creatine kinase phosphorylates creatine and adenylate kinase phosphorylates AMP. The following scheme outlines how ATP, ADP, AMP, creatine phosphate, creatine, and P_i are related.

$$\begin{array}{ccc}
\text{ATP + AMP} & \leftarrow & \text{ADP + ADP (adenylate kinase)} \\
\downarrow & & \uparrow \\
\text{ATP + H}_2\text{O} & \rightarrow & \text{ADP + P}_i \quad \text{(myosin)} \\
\nearrow & & \downarrow \\
\text{ATP + creatine} & \leftarrow & \text{ADP + creatine phosphate (creatine kinase)}
\end{array}$$

10. Phosphate is an electron-withdrawing group that is attached to quite different carbons in glucose-6-phosphate versus glucose-1-phosphate. In the latter, carbon-1 is already bonded to an electronegative oxygen in the pyranose form.

Summary

Thermodynamics—a collection of laws and principles describing the flows and interchanges of heat, energy, and matter—can provide important insights into metabolism and bioenergetics. Thermodynamics distinguishes between closed systems, which cannot exchange matter or energy with the surroundings; isolated systems, which may exchange heat, but not matter, with the surroundings; and open systems, which may exchange matter, energy, or both with the surroundings.

The first law of thermodynamics states that the total energy of an isolated system is conserved. E, the internal energy function, which is equal to the sum of heat absorbed and work done on the system, is a useful state function, which keeps track of energy transfers in such systems. In constant pressure processes, it is often more convenient to use the enthalpy function ($H = E + PV$) for analysis of heat and energy exchange. For biochemical processes, in which pressure is usually constant and volume changes are small, enthalpy (H) and internal energy (E) are often essentially equal. Enthalpy changes for biochemical processes can often be determined from a plot of $R(\ln K_{eq})$ versus $1/T$ (a van't Hoff plot).

Entropy is a measure of disorder or randomness in the system. The second law of thermodynamics states that systems tend to proceed from ordered (low entropy) states to disordered (high entropy) states. The entropy change for any reversible process is simply the heat transferred divided by the temperature at which the transfer occurs: $dS_{rev} = dq/T$.

The third law of thermodynamics states that the entropy of any crystalline, perfectly ordered substance must approach zero as the temperature approaches 0 K, and at 0 K, entropy is exactly zero. The concept of entropy thus invokes the notion of heat capacity—the amount of heat any substance can store as the temperature of that substance is raised by one degree K. Absolute entropies may be calculated for any substance if the heat capacity can be evaluated at temperatures from 0 K to the temperature of interest, but entropy changes are usually much more important in biochemical systems.

The free energy function is defined as $G = H - TS$. For any process at constant pressure and temperature (i.e., most biochemical processes), $\Delta G = \Delta H - T\Delta S$. If ΔG is negative, the process is exergonic and will proceed spontaneously in the forward direction. If ΔG is positive, the reaction or process is endergonic and will proceed spontaneously in the reverse direction. The sign and value of ΔG, however, do not allow one to determine how fast a process will proceed. It is convenient to define a standard state for processes of interest, so that the thermodynamic parameters of different processes may be compared. The standard state for reactions in solution is 1 M concentration for all reactants and products. The free energy change for a process A + B $\rightleftarrows$ C + D at concentrations other than standard state is given by:

$$\Delta G = \Delta G^{\circ} + RT \ln([C][D]/[A][B])$$

and the standard-state free energy change is related to the equilibrium constant for the reaction by $\Delta G^{\circ} = -RT \ln K_{eq}$. This states that the equilibrium established for a reaction in solution is a function of the standard-state free energy change for the process. In essence, ΔG° is another way of writing an equilibrium constant. Moreover, the entropy change for a process may be determined if the enthalpy change and free energy change calculated from knowledge of the equilibrium constant and its dependence on temperature are known.

The standard state convention of 1 M concentrations becomes awkward for reactions in which hydrogen ions are produced or consumed. Biochemists circumvent this problem by defining a modified standard state of 1 M concentration for all species except H^+, for which the standard state is 1×10^{-7} M or pH 7.

Thermodynamic parameters may provide insights about a process. As an example, consider heat capacity changes: Positive values indicate increase freedom of movement whereas negative values indicate less freedom of motion.

Many processes in living things must run against their thermodynamic potential, i.e., in the direction of positive ΔG. These processes are driven in the thermodynamically unfavourable direction via coupling with highly favourable processes. Coupled processes are vitally important in intermediary metabolism, oxidative phosphorylation, membrane transport, and many other processes essential to life.

There is a hierarchy of energetics among organisms: certain organisms capture solar energy directly, whereas others derive their energy from this group in subsequent chemical processes. Once captured in chemical form, energy can be released in controlled exergonic reactions to drive life processes. High-energy phosphate anhydrides and reduced coenzymes mediate the flow of energy from exergonic reactions to the energy-requiring processes of life. These molecules are transient forms of stored energy, rapidly carrying energy from point to point in the organism. One of the most important high-energy phosphates is ATP, which acts as an intermediate energy shuttle molecule. The free energy of hydrolysis of ATP (for hydrolysis to ADP and phosphate) is less than that of PEP, cyclic-AMP, 1,3-BPG, creatine phosphate, acetyl phosphate, and pyrophosphate, but is greater than that the lower energy phosphate esters, such as glycerol-3-phosphate and the sugar phosphates. Group transfer potential—the free energy change that occurs upon hydrolysis (i.e., transfer of a chemical group to water)—is a convenient parameter for quantitating the energetics of such processes. The phosphoryl group transfer potentials for high-energy phosphates range from −31.9 kJ/mol for UDP-glucose to −35.7 kJ/mol for ATP to −62.2 kJ/mol for PEP.

The large negative $\Delta G^{\circ\prime}$ values for the hydrolysis of phosphoric acid anhydrides (such as ATP, GTP, ADP, GDP, sugar nucleotides, and pyrophosphate) may be ascribed to 1) destabilization of the reactant due to bond strain caused by electrostatic repulsion; 2) stabilization of the products by ionization and resonance; and 3) increases in entropy upon product formation. Mixed anhydrides of phosphoric and carboxylic acids—known as acyl phosphates—are also energy-rich. Other classes of high-energy species include enol phosphates, such as PEP; guanidinium phosphates, such as creatine phosphate; cyclic nucleotides, such as 3′,5′-cyclic AMP; amino acid esters, such as aminoacyl-tRNA; and thiol esters, such as coenzyme A. Other biochemically important high-energy molecules include the pyridine nucleotides (NADH, NADPH), sugar nucleotides (UDP-glucose), and S-adenosyl methionine which is involved in the transfer of methyl groups in many metabolic processes.

Though the hydrolysis of ATP and other high-energy phosphates are often portrayed as simple processes, these reactions are far more complex in real biological systems. ATP, ADP, and similar molecules can exist in several different ionization states, and each of these individual species can bind divalent and monovalent metal ions, so that metal ion complexes must also be considered. For example, ATP has five dissociable protons. The adenine ring amino group exhibits a pK_a of 4.06, whereas the last proton to dissociate from the triphosphate chain possesses a pK_a of 6.95. Thus, at pH 7, ATP is a mixture of ATP^{4-} and $HATP^{3-}$. If equilibrium constants for the hydrolysis reactions are redefined in terms of total concentrations of the ionized species, then such equilibria can be considered quantitatively, and fractions of each ionic species in solution can be determined. The effects of metal ion binding equilibria on the hydrolysis equilibria can be quantitated in a similar fashion.

The free energy changes for hydrolysis of high-energy phosphates such as ATP are also functions of concentration. In the environment of the typical cell, where ATP, ADP, and phosphate are usually 5 mM or less, the free energy change for ATP hydrolysis is substantially larger in magnitude than the standard state value of −30.5 kJ/mol.

High-energy molecules such as ATP are rapidly recycled in most biological environments. The typical 70 kg human body contains only about 50 grams of ATP/ADP. Each of these ATP molecules must be recycled nearly 2000 times each day to meet the energy needs of the body.

Chapter 4

Amino Acids

• •

Chapter Outline

❖ Amino acids: Tetrahedral alpha (α) carbon with H, amino group, carboxyl group, and side chain
❖ Amino acids in proteins joined by peptide bonds
  ⅄ Amino group reacted with carboxyl group and removal of water
  ⅄ Peptide bonds join amino acid residues in polypeptides
❖ Classification
  ⅄ Non-polar: Ala, val, leu, ile, pro, met, phe, trp
  ⅄ Polar uncharged: Gly, ser, thr, tyr, asn, gln, cys
  ⅄ Acidic: Asp, glu
  ⅄ Basic: His, lys, arg
❖ Amino acids come in a variety of forms: There are far more than 20 amino acids
  ⅄ The 20 amino acids presented above are coded for in the genetic code
  ⅄ Selenocysteine and pyrrolysine are the 21st and 22nd amino acids to be coded for
  ⅄ Modified amino acids: Hydroxylysine, hydroxproline, thyroxin, methyl histidine, methyl arginine, methyl lysine, γ-carboxyglutamic acid, pyroglutamic acid, aminoadipic acid
❖ Small molecules derived from amino acids: GABA, histamine, serotonin, β-alanine, epinephrine, penicillamine, ornithine, citrulline, betaine, homocysteine, homoserine
❖ Ionic properties of amino acids
  ⅄ α-carboxyl group: pK_a values range from 2.0 to 2.4
  ⅄ α-amino group: pK_a values range from 9.0 to 9.8
  ⅄ Side chains
    • Acidic pK_a values for asp, glu
    • Basic pK_a values for his, arg, lys
❖ Amino acid chemistry: Edman reagent
  ⅄ Used to modify N-terminus and to sequence peptides
❖ Chirality: Asymmetric carbon has four different groups attached
  ⅄ Optically active compounds
    • Dextrorotatory (+), clockwise rotation
    • Levorotatory (−), counterclockwise rotation
  ⅄ Asymmetric carbon compounds
    • One asymmetric carbon: Mirror-image isomers or enantiomers
    • More than one asymmetric carbon: Enantiomers and diastereomers
  ⅄ D, L system: Typically naturally occurring amino acids: L-amino acids; related to L-glyceraldehyde
  ⅄ (R,S) System: Assign priorities to groups about the chiral carbon
    • SH > OH > NH_2 > COOH > CHO > CHOH > CH_3
      • First four above: Priority order is Mr of heaviest element
      • Last four: Priority is oxidation state of carbon
❖ Ultraviolet spectral properties of amino acids: Only phe, try, trp absorb UV light above 250 nm
❖ NMR signal from amino acids sensitive to magnetic environment
❖ Separation of amino acids
  ⅄ Ion exchange
    • Anion exchangers: Matrix is positively charged so anions bind
    • Cation exchangers: Matrix is negatively charged so cations bind
  ⅄ Gas chromatography and high-performance liquid chromatography (HPLC)

❖ Peptide bonds: Carboxyl group + amino group – water = peptide (amide) bond
- *Trans* arrangement (usually) of carbonyl oxygen and amide hydrogen

❖ Double-bond character
- Pi electron delocalization prevents free rotation about peptide bond
- Amide plane includes carbonyl, amide, and alpha carbons

❖ Peptide classification
- Up to 12 amino acid residues, dipeptide, tripeptide, tetrapeptide, etc.
  - Numerical prefix refers to number of amino acid residues not peptide bonds
- Oligopeptides: 12 to 20 residues
- Polypeptides: Several dozen residues
- Proteins: Polypeptides
  - Monomeric proteins have one chain
  - Multimeric proteins have more than one chain
    - Homomultimeric: Identical chains
    - Hetromultimeric: Different chains

Chapter Objectives

It is imperative to learn the structures and one-letter codes for the amino acids. Amino acids are key molecules, both as components of proteins and as intermediates to important biomolecules. The structures are shown in Figure 4.3 of the textbook. Figure 4.3 is presented on the following two pages.

Classification of Amino Acids

Here is an alternative classification scheme:
- Acidic amino acids and their amides: **aspartic acid, asparagine, glutamic acid, glutamine**
- Basic amino acids: **histidine, lysine, arginine**
- Aromatic amino acids: **phenylalanine, tyrosine, tryptophan**
- Sulfur-containing amino acids: **cysteine, methionine**
- Imido acid: **proline**
- Hydrophobic side chains: **glycine, alanine, valine, leucine, isoleucine**
- Hydroxylic amino acids: **serine, threonine, (tyrosine)**

To memorize the structures of the 20 amino acids, here are some aids:
- The side chain of **glycine** is **H**, that of **alanine** is a methyl group, CH_3.
- The side chain of **valine** is just the methyl side chain of alanine with two methyl groups substituting for two Hs. (In effect ,it is just dimethylalanine.)
- The side chain of **leucine** is just valine with a —CH_2— group between the valine side chain and the α-carbon (or leucine is alanine with the valine side chain attached).
- **Isoleucine** is an isomer of leucine with one of the methyl groups exchanged with an H on the carbon attached to the α-carbon.
- Several of the amino acids have alanine as a base.
- **Phenylalanine** has a phenyl group (i.e., benzene ring) attached to alanine.
- **Tyrosine** is hydroxylated phenylalanine.
- **Serine** has a hydroxyl group substituting for an H on the methyl group of alanine.
- **Cysteine** can be thought of as the sulfur variety of serine—i.e., with a sulfhydryl group in place of the hydroxyl group of serine.
- **Threonine**, a hydroxylic amino acid, can be thought of as methylated serine.

The acidic amino acids and their amides are quite easy to remember. **Aspartic acid** and **glutamic acid** have carboxylic acid groups attached to —CH_2— and (—CH_2—$)_2$, respectively. The amides of these amino acids, namely **asparagine** and **glutamine**, have nitrogen attached to the side chain carboxyl groups in amide linkage.

The basic amino acids all have six carbons, counting the carboxyl carbon and the α-carbon. **Lysine's** side chain is a linear chain of four —CH_2— groups with a terminal amino group. **Arginine** has a linear side chain of three —CH_2— groups to which a guanidinium group is attached. (The sixth carbon is the central C of the guanidinium group.) Guanidinium is like urea but with a nitrogen group replacing the carbonyl oxygen. **Histidine** has an imidazole ring attached to alanine. The ring contains two nitrogens and three carbons, a five-membered ring.

An easy way to remember the structure of **proline** is to know that it derives from glutamic acid. The carboxyl side chain forms a C–N bond to the amino group to form this imido acid. (In the process, the carbon is reduced so the side chain carboxyl oxygens do not show up in proline.)

Methionine is a sulfur-containing amino acid. Biologically, it is also used as a methyl group donor in the molecule S-adenosylmethionine (SAM). These two facts indicate that the side chain ends in a S—CH_3, which is attached to (—CH_2—)$_2$. The remaining amino acid is **tryptophan**. Its side chain is an indole ring attached to a —CH_2— group. In effect, it can be thought of as alanine with an indole ring. Substituted indole rings are widely used in biochemistry. The basic structure is a six-membered benzene ring fused to a five-membered ring containing a single N.

Nomenclature

The one-letter codes for the amino acids must be memorized. In journals, the one letter codes are used to show amino acid sequences. See the answer to Problem 2 for a discussion of how the one-letter codes are organized.

Chirality

The α-carbons of amino acids, excepting Gly, have four different groups attached to them, and hence they are chiral carbons. Two different arrangements of the four groups about the chiral carbon can be made, giving rise to two structural isomers. Structural isomers that are mirror images of each other are called enantiomers. When two or more chiral centres exist on a single molecule, 2^n structural isomers are possible, where n = the number of chiral centres. The various structural isomers include enantiomers (mirror-image-related isomers) and non-mirror-image-related isomers known as diastereomers.

The structural isomers can be distinguished from each other using the R and S prefixes assigned to each chiral centre of a molecule. The R and S prefixes are assigned according to a set of sequence rules. The four groups about a chiral centre are assigned priority numbers with the highest priority given to the atom with the highest atomic number: thus, S > O > N > C > H (for elements found in amino acids). When two or more groups have the same primary element, then elements attached to the primary element are considered. So for example, SH > OR > OH > NH_2 > COOH > CHO > CH_2OH > CH_3. Once priority assignments are made, the molecule is viewed with the group having the lowest priority away from the reader. Moving from highest to lowest priority, for the three remaining groups, clockwise movement indicates **R** and counterclockwise indicates **S** configuration.

UV-absorbing Properties

Only three amino acids—phenylalanine, tyrosine, and tryptophan—absorb light in the near UV range (i.e., 230 nm to 310 nm). These amino acids will dominate the UV absorption spectra of proteins. The wavelength maxima for tyrosine and tryptophan are around 280 nm. In addition, these two amino acids have extinction coefficients quite a bit larger than the extinction coefficient of phenylalanine, whose λ max = 260 nm. Thus, very many proteins have maximum absorbance around 280 nm. In contrast, nucleic acids absorb light with a maximum around 260 nm, due to the nucleotides. The extinction coefficients of the nucleotides are larger than those for the aromatic amino acids. In general, nucleic acid contamination of a protein sample will contribute to UV absorption at 260 nm. Often the 260/280 ratio is used as a criterion for purity.

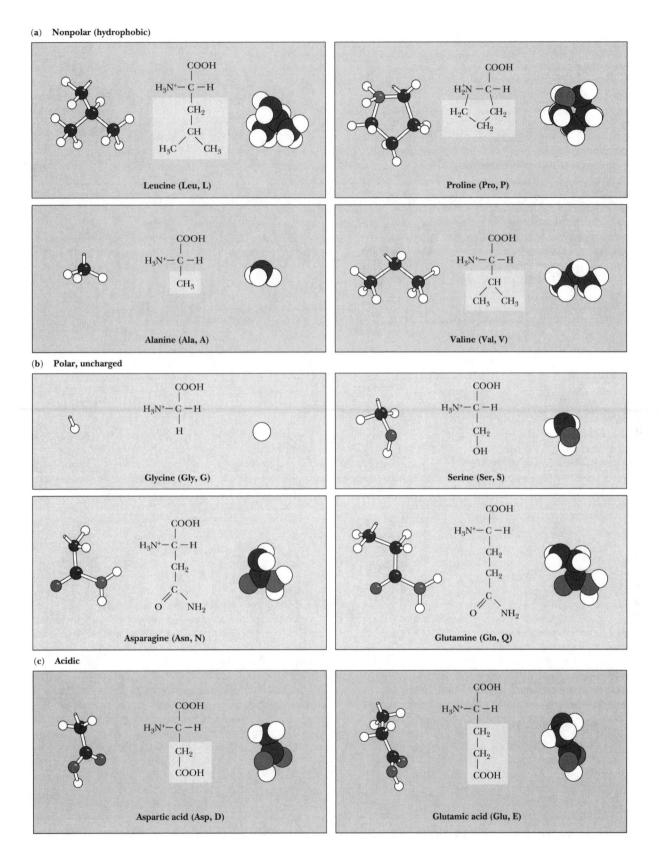

(a) Nonpolar (hydrophobic)

Leucine (Leu, L)

Proline (Pro, P)

Alanine (Ala, A)

Valine (Val, V)

(b) Polar, uncharged

Glycine (Gly, G)

Serine (Ser, S)

Asparagine (Asn, N)

Glutamine (Gln, Q)

(c) Acidic

Aspartic acid (Asp, D)

Glutamic acid (Glu, E)

Figure 4.3 The amino acids that are the building blocks of most proteins can be classified as (a) non-polar (hydrophobic), (b) polar, neutral, (c) acidic, or (d) basic. Also shown are the one-letter and three-letter codes used to denote amino acids. For each amino acid, the ball-and-stick (left) and space-filling (right) models show only the side chain.

Problems and Solutions

1. *Without consulting chapter figures, draw Fischer projection formulas for glycine, aspartate, leucine, isoleucine, methionine, and threonine.*

Answer:

3. *Write equations for the ionic dissociations of alanine, glutamate, histidine, lysine, and phenylalanine.*

Answer: Alanine dissociation:

Glutamate dissociation:

Histidine dissociation:

Lysine dissociation:

Phenylalanine dissociation:

5. *(Integrates with Chapter 2) Draw an appropriate titration curve for aspartic acid, labelling the axis and indicating the equivalence points and the pK$_a$ values.*

Answer: For a titration curve, the independent variable is the amount of acid or base used to titrate the amino acid. The dependent variable is pH.

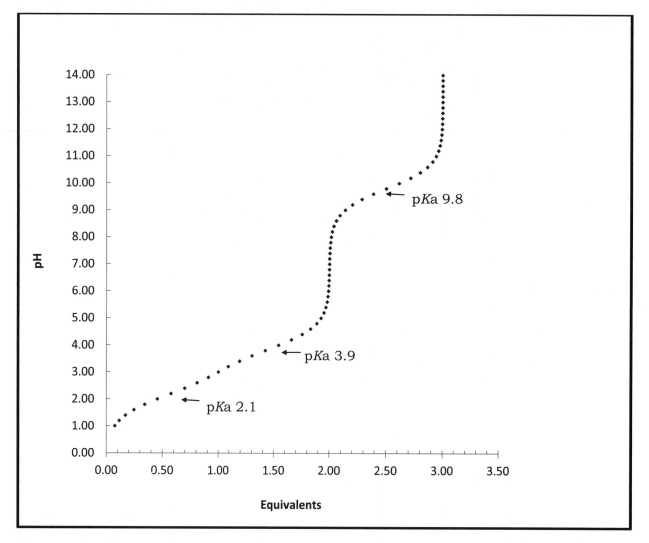

The equivalence point is a point on the titration curve reached after a molar equivalent of acid or base is added to the amino acid. For aspartic acid, there are actually three equivalence points at around 3.0, 6.2, and 12.2.

7.   (Integrates with Chapter 2) Calculate the pH at which the γ-carboxyl group of glutamic acid is two-thirds dissociated.

Answer: The pK_a of γ-carboxyl group of glutamic acid is 4.3.

Using the Henderson-Hasselbalch equation

$$pH = pK_{COOH} + \log\frac{[C_\gamma OO^-]}{[C_\gamma OOH]}$$

When the γ-carboxyl group is two-thirds dissociated:

$$\frac{[C_\gamma OO^-]}{[C_\gamma OO^-] + [C_\gamma OOH]} = \frac{2}{3} \text{ or } [C_\gamma OO^-] = \frac{2}{3}\left([C_\gamma OO^-] + [C_\gamma OOH]\right)$$

Thus, $[C_\gamma OOH] = \dfrac{1}{2}[C_\gamma OO^-]$

Upon substituting into the Henderson-Hasselbalch equation, we find:

$$pH = 4.3 + \log\frac{[C_\gamma OO^-]}{[C_\gamma OOH]} = 4.3 + \log\frac{[C_\gamma OO^-]}{\frac{1}{2}[C_\gamma OO^-]} = 4.3 + \log 2$$

$$pH = 4.6$$

9.   (Integrates with Chapter 2) Calculate the pH of a 0.3 M solution of (a) leucine hydrochloride, (b) sodium leucinate, and (c) isoelectric leucine.

Answer: a. The solution 0.3 M leucine HCl is composed of 0.3 M leucine and 0.3 M HCl. Thus, we expect it to have an acidic pH and only the α-carboxyl group of leucine is involved in proton equilibrium.
The pK_a of the α-carboxyl of leucine is 2.4. Thus:

$$pH = pK_a + \log\frac{[A^-]}{[HA]} = 2.4 + \log\frac{[COO^-]}{[COOH]} \quad (1)$$

and

$$[COO^-] + [COOH] = 0.3 \text{ M} \quad (2)$$

For charge neutrality:

$$[Cl^-] + [COO^-] = [H^+] + [NH_3^+]$$

If we recognize that $[Cl^-] = [NH_3^+]$ (because Cl^- and the amino acid are in equimolar amounts),

the charge neutrality equation may be simplified to $[COO^-] = [H^+]$

Combined with (1) and (2) we have:

$$pH = 2.4 + \log\frac{[H^+]}{0.3 - [H^+]}$$

If we make the assumption that $[H^+] << 0.3$,

$$pH = 2.4 + \log\frac{[H^+]}{0.3} = 2.4 + \log[H^+] - \log 0.3 = 2.4 - \log 0.3 + \log[H^+]$$

Recognizing that $\log[H^+] = -pH$ we see that

$$pH = 2.4 - \log 0.3 - pH \text{ or}$$

$$pH = \frac{2.4 - \log 0.3}{2} = 1.46$$

Note: If we did not make the simplification that $[H^+] < 0.3$ we would have had to solve a quadratic and would have found that pH = 1.49.

b.   Sodium leucinate: Here, we assume the solution is basic; therefore, only the α-amino group is involved. The mathematical solution is similar to that given for (a) with pK_a = 9.6.

$$pH = pK_a + \log \frac{[NH_2]}{[NH_3^+]} = 9.6 + \log \frac{[NH_2]}{[NH_3^+]} \quad (1)$$

and

$$[NH_2] + [NH_3^+] = 0.3 M \quad (2)$$

For charge neutrality: $[OH^-] + [COO^-] = [NH_3^+] + [Na^+]$

If we recognize that $[COO^-] = [Na^+]$ (because Na^+ and the amino acid are in equimolar amounts)

The charge neutrality equation may be simplified to $[OH^-] = [NH_3^+]$

Combined with (1) and (2), we have:

$$pH = 9.6 + \log \frac{0.3 - [OH^-]}{[OH^-]}$$

If we make the assumption that $[OH^-] << 0.3$

$$pH = 9.6 + \log \frac{0.3}{[OH^-]} = 9.6 + \log 0.3 - \log [OH^-]$$

Recognizing that $pOH \equiv -\log[OH^-]$ and that $pH + pOH = 14$, we have

$$pH = 9.6 + \log 0.3 + pOH = 9.3 + \log 0.3 + 14 - pH$$

or

$$pH = \frac{9.6 + 14 + \log 0.3}{2} = 11.5$$

c.   Isoelectric leucine: Isoelectric leucine is a leucine solution at a pH at which there is no net charge on the molecule. For this to occur, the carboxyl group must be unprotonated to the same extent as the amino group is protonated. This must occur at a pH halfway between the pK_a values of the two groups.

At the pI, $[COO^-] = [NH_3^+]$

Using the Henderson-Hasselbalch equations

$$pH = pK_{COOH} + \log \frac{[COO^-]}{[COOH]} \text{ and } pH = pK_{NH_3^+} + \log \frac{[NH_2]}{[NH_3^+]}$$

and recognizing that $[COOH] = [\text{Amino acid}]_{total} - [COO^-]$

and that $[NH_2] = [\text{Amino acid}]_{total} - [NH_3^+]$

upon substituting, solving for $[COO^-]$ and $[NH_3^+]$, and setting these terms equal at pH = pI, we find that

$$pI = \frac{pK_{COOH} + pK_{NH_3^+}}{2} \text{ or}$$

$$pI = \frac{2.4 + 9.6}{2} = 6.0$$

11.   How many moles of NaOH are required to adjust 0.75 L of a 0.2 M solution of Arg–Gly–Trp–Ala from pH 2.4 to 12.5? Calculate the pI of the tetrapeptide.

Answer:

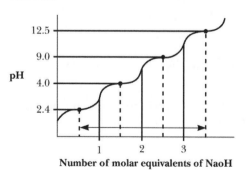

Number of molar equivalents of NaOH

You need 3 molar equivalents of NaOH. But 0.75 L of a 0.2 M solution is equal to 0.15 moles × 3 molar equivalents. Therefore, you need 0.45 moles of NaOH.

$$pI = (2 + 4 + 9 + 12.5)/4 = \text{approximately } 6.9$$

13. Describe the stereochemical aspects of the structure of cystine, the structure that is a disulfide-linked pair of cysteines.

Answer: Cystine (dicysteine) has two chiral carbons, the two α-carbons of the cysteine moieties. Since each chiral centre can exist in two forms, there are four stereoisomers of cystine. However, it is not possible to distinguish the difference between L-cysteine/D-cysteine and D-cysteine/L-cysteine dimers. So, three distinct isomers are formed.

| L-cysteine-
L-cysteine | L-cysteine-
D-cysteine | D-cysteine-
L-cysteine | D-cysteine-
D-cysteine |

The two middle structures are meso-cystine, and they can be identified as such because the top half and bottom half are mirror images. The two halves of L-cystine are composed of identical molecules. Remember in Fischer projections, bonds drawn horizontally are coming out of the plane of the paper whereas vertical bonds are into the plane. Fischer projections can only be rotated by 180° to retain their stereochemistry. Thus, the top half of L-cystine is L-cysteine. Taking L-cysteine and rotating it by 180° will give the bottom half of the structure and joining these gives L-cystine.

15. A previously unknown protein has been isolated in your laboratory. Others in your lab have determined that the protein sequence contains 172 amino acids. They have also determined that this protein has no tryptophan and no phenylalanine. You have been asked to determine the possible tyrosine content of this protein. You know from your study of this chapter that there is a relatively easy way to do this. You prepare a pure 50 μM solution of the protein, and you place it in a sample cell with a 1 cm path length. You measure the absorbance of this sample at 280 nm in a UV-visible spectrophotometer. The absorbance of the solution is 0.372. Are there tyrosines in this protein? How many? (Hint: You will need to use Beer's Law, which is described on page 89 of the textbook. You will also find it useful to know that the units of molar absorptivity are $M^{-1}cm^{-1}$.)

Answer: Beer's law relates the absorbance of a solution to the path length (l), solute concentration [C], and light-absorbing properties of the solute.
For a substance, the absorbance is defined as follows:

$$A_\lambda = -\log\frac{I}{I_0}$$

where I_0 is the intensity of incident light and I is the intensity of light after it passes through the substance. The ratio of I to I_0 is the transmission, T. The subscript λ specifies the wavelength of light and this is often the wavelength at which absorbance is maximum for the substance. Beer's law is:

$$A_\lambda = -\log\frac{I}{I_0} = \varepsilon \times [C] \times \ell$$

In our case, Beer's law is being applied to a solution of protein. The term [C] refers to the concentration of light-absorbing compound in solution. We are told that the protein lacks phenylalanine and tryptophan and so the only other amino acid that absorbs light at 280 nm is tyrosine*.

We are only interested in measuring the absorption of light due to the protein and not, for example, to the cuvette or solvent used to dissolve the protein. To accomplish this, the cuvette is first filled with solvent only and the instrument electronically zeroed. This, in effect, sets the transmitted light intensity for a cuvette filled with solvent-only equal to the incident light intensity. (The absorbance is zero when the transmission is one and this occurs when $I = I_o$.) The cuvette is then filled with the solution under consideration and the absorbance recorded. It is standard practice to use cuvettes with 1 cm path length. Thus, the magnitude of the absorbance measured is linearly dependent on the concentration, [C], and on the molar absorptivity, ε.

The absorbance is given as 0.371. Using Beer's Law, we can determine the concentration provided we know the molar absorptivity. The molar absorptivity of tyrosine is 1490 M^{-1}cm^{-1}.

$$A_{280nm} = 0.371 = \varepsilon \times [C] \times \ell$$

$$[C] = \frac{0.371}{1490 \text{ M}^{-1}\text{cm}^{-1} \times 1 \text{ cm}} = 2.49 \times 10^{-4} \text{M}$$

The molar concentration calculated above is the concentration of the chromophore, namely tyrosine, in the protein solution, which is at 50 μM. If we assume that there are n moles of tyrosine per mole of protein, then the molarity of tyrosine is simply $n \times 50$ μM. Equating these two and solving for n, we find the number of tyrosines in the protein.

$$2.49 \times 10^{-4} \text{M} = n \times 50 \times 10^{-6} \text{M}$$

$$n = \frac{2.49 \times 10^{-4} \text{M}}{50 \times 10^{-6} \text{M}} = 4.98 \approx 5$$

*The UV absorption spectra of proteins are determined by the aromatic amino acids and to a very small extent by cystine (essentially di-cysteine, two cysteines linked by a disulfide bond). Phenylalanine does not absorb at 280 nm, but tryptophan, tyrosine, and cystine do. (See "How to measure and predict the molar absorption coefficient of a protein" by Pace, CN, Vajdos F, Fee L, Grimsley G, and Gray T in *Proteins Science* (1995) 4:2411–23.) The protein being studied was likely treated with a reducing agent, such as dithiothreitol or β-mercaptoethanol, to break disulfide bonds—so there should be no contribution to UV absorbance by cystine at 280 nm. Another problem that can arise when measuring light-absorbing properties of proteins is that the absorptivity of the amino acids is influenced by the local environment in which the amino acid exists in the protein. Denaturing agents like 8 M urea or 6 M guanidinium HCl are often used in conjunction with a reducing agent to convert the protein into a so-called random coil whose UV-light absorbing properties more closely mimic those of its amino acid composition.

Questions for Self-Study

1. Fill in the blanks: A _____ bond is an amide bond between two _____ _____. The bond is formed by a reaction between the _____ _____ of one amino acid and the _____ _____ of a second amino acid with the elimination of the elements of _____. The result is a linear chain with an _____ end and a _____ end. The chain can be extended into a polymer with additional amino acids. The polymer formed is called either a _____ or a _____ depending on the number of amino acids joined. The amide bond can be broken by the addition of the elements of water across it in a _____ reaction.

2. List the four classes of amino acids.

3. Indicate which class of amino acids best represents the statements presented below:
   a. Their side chain may contain a hydroxyl group. _____
   b. Negatively charged at basic pH. _____
   c. Relatively poorly soluble in aqueous solution. _____
   d. Relatively soluble in aqueous solution. _____
   e. Positively charged at acidic pH. _____
   f. Side chains are capable of hydrogen bonding. _____
   g. Includes the amino acids arginine, histidine and lysine. _____
   h. Side chains contain predominantly hydrocarbons. _____
   i. Side chains are responsible for the hydrophobic cores of globular proteins. _____
   j. The amides of glutamic and aspartic acid belong to this group. _____

4. From the list of amino acids presented indicate which one best fits the description:
   a. The smallest amino acid (it also lacks a stereoisomer)
      alanine, glycine, phenylalanine, glutamine
   b. An aromatic amino acid
      glutamic acid, tyrosine, isoleucine, proline
   c. A sulfur-containing amino acid
      methionine, aspartic acid, arginine, leucine
   d. An amino acid capable of forming sulfur–sulfur bonds
      methionine, proline, cysteine, tryptophan
   e. A branched-chain amino acid
      methionine, leucine, aspartic acid, asparagine

5. Fill in the blanks. Most of the amino acids are chiral compounds because they have at least one carbon atom with _____ different groups attached. Thus, there are _____ ways of arranging the four groups about the carbon atom. For the case of an amino acid with a single asymmetric carbon, the isomers pairs that can be formed are called _____; they are non-superimposable, _____ images of each other. Using the D,L system of nomenclature, the commonly occurring amino acids are all _____ amino acids.

6. Which three amino acids absorb light in the ultraviolet region of the spectrum above 250 nm?

7. Of the following techniques, which are commonly used to separate amino acids?
   ion exchange, NMR, electroporation, HPLC, UV spectroscopy, Edman reaction

8. DTNB (Ellman's reagent), iodoacetate, and N-ethylmaleimide are three agents that are used to modify which amino acid? What is the reactive group on the amino acid with which all three agents react?

9. Although there are twenty common amino acids, there are hundreds of different amino acids found in nature, some of which derive from the common amino acids by simple chemical (biochemical) modification. Name one common modification of amino acids found in nature.

10. a. Of the 20 common amino acids, which amino acid has a pK_a around neutrality?
    b. What amino acid lacks an amino group?

Answers

1. peptide; amino acids; amino group; carboxyl group; water; N-terminal (or amino); C-terminal (or carboxyl); polypeptide; protein; hydrolysis.

2. Non-polar or hydrophobic; neutral polar; acidic; basic.

3. a. neutral polar; b. acidic; c. non-polar; d. neutral polar, acidic, and basic; e. basic; f. neutral polar, acidic, and basic; g. basic; h. non-polar; i. non-polar; j. neutral polar.

4. a. glycine; b. tyrosine; c. methionine; d. cysteine; e. leucine.

5. four; two; enantiomers (or mirror-image isomers); mirror; L.

6. Phenylalanine, tyrosine, and tryptophan.

7. Ion exchange, HPLC.

8. Cysteine; sulfhydryl group.

9. Hydroxylation, methylation, carboxylation, phosphorylation.

10. a. Histidine; b. proline.

Additional Problems

1. Sketch the titration curve of histidine.

2. In the protein hemoglobin, a number of salt bridges (ionic bonds) are broken when going from oxygenated to deoxygenated hemoglobin. One in particular involves an aspartic acid–histidine ionic interaction.
   a. At pH = 7.0, would you expect this salt bridge to form? Explain.
   b. Under certain conditions (low oxygen tension), the salt bridge does form. Explain how the influence of aspartic acid on histidine is similar to the influence of the α-carboxyl group on the pKa of the α-amino group (and vice versa).

3. How might the presence of calcium ions affect the apparent pK_a values of the side chains of aspartic acid and glutamic acid?

4. a. The ultraviolet spectra of proteins are largely determined by what three amino acids?
   b. In working with nucleic acids, it is often useful to measure the optical densities at 260 nm and 280 nm. Nucleic acids (DNA and RNA) absorb more strongly at 260 nm than 280 nm such that the ratio $A_{260} : A_{280}$ ranges from 1.6 to 2.0. What might happen to the $A_{260} : A_{280}$ ratio of a solution of nucleic acid contaminated with protein?
   c. Proteins typically have a $A_{260} : A_{280}$ ratio less than 1. Estimate the $A_{260} : A_{280}$ ratio of a protein whose amino acid composition includes two moles of Trp and one mole of Tyr per mole of protein. For appropriate extinction coefficients (molar absorptivity), use information given at http://omlc.ogi.edu/spectra/PhotochemCAD/html/index.html. Activate the link to the appropriate amino acids. Then under the absorption spectrum, activate the link to "Extinction Data."
   d. Certain proteins lack both Trp and Tyr yet still absorb ultraviolet light in the range of 240 nm to 270 nm. What amino acid is responsible for this? How would the $A_{260} : A_{280}$ ratio of a protein rich in this amino acid differ from a typical protein containing Trp and Tyr? Use the information at the URL given above to answer this.

5. Poetry comes in many forms. Can you write a short, two-line poem, using the single-letter abbreviations for the amino acids?

Abbreviated Answers

1. Histidine is the only amino acid with a pK_a around neutrality. The pK_a values of histidine are 1.8, 6.0, and 9.2. The titration curve will be similar to the one shown in the answer to Problem 5 but with an additional plateau around pH = 6.0.

2. a. The pK_a values of the side chains of aspartic acid and histidine are 3.9 and 6.0, respectively. At pH = 7.0, the side chain of aspartic acid is unprotonated and therefore negatively charged, whereas the side chain of histidine is also unprotonated and therefore uncharged. We might not expect this interaction to occur.
   b. The fact that the salt bridge forms indicates that the two amino acid side chains are close together in the three-dimensional structure of the protein. The proximity of the negatively charged aspartic acid must therefore raise the pK_a of the histidine side group.

3. Calcium (Ca^{2+}) may bind to carboxylate ions. Therefore, the presence of calcium may lower the apparent pK_a values of aspartic acid and glutamic acid.

4. a. Phe, Tyr, and Trp; b. $A_{260} : A_{280}$ ratio may be lower; c. The molar absorptivity for Trp at 280 nm and 260 nm are 5502 and 3765, respectively. The molar absorptivity for Tyr at 280 nm and 260 nm are approximately 1209 and 612, respectively. The $A_{260} : A_{280}$ ratio is given by:

$$\text{Ratio } A_{260} : A_{280} = \frac{(2 \times 3765) + 612}{(2 \times 5502) + 1209} = 0.67$$

d. Phe. The $A_{260} : A_{280}$ ratio would be much greater than 1.

$$\text{Ratio } A_{260} : A_{280} = \frac{144}{2} = 72$$

5.   Here is a start that is by no means original. "I think that I shall never see a ... "* Try composing one with the nucleoside one-letter code (A, T, G, and C), if you really want a challenge.

* The very next word of this poem by Joyce Kilmer is "poem." Before the discovery of pyrrolysine, we would have had to stop here because "o" was not used for an amino acid. With pyrrolysine and selenocysteine, the amino acid alphabet has been extended to 25 (20 amino acids, pyrrolysine, selenocysteine, b and z for asx and glx, respectively, and x for any amino acid) of the 26 letters in the English alphabet. The only letter to still unused is j. Here is the complete poem, "Trees" by Joyce Kilmer.

I think that I shall never see
A poem lovely as a tree.
A tree whose hungry mouth is prest
Against the sweet earth's flowing breast;

A tree that looks at God all day,
And lifts her leafy arms to pray;
A tree that may in summer wear
A nest of robins in her hair;

Upon whose bosom snow has lain;
Who intimately lives with rain.
Poems are made by fools like me,
But only God can make a tree.

Summary

Amino acids are the building blocks of proteins. There are 20 amino acids commonly found in proteins. The general structure of an amino acid is based on a central α-carbon, to which is attached a carboxyl group, a hydrogen, an amino group, and a variable side chain or R group. Amino acids can be classified according to the nature of their R groups into four classes. The non-polar, hydrophobic amino acids include **alanine**, **valine**, **leucine**, and **isoleucine**, in addition to **proline**, **methionine**, **phenylalanine**, and **tryptophan**. Polar, uncharged amino acids include **glycine**, **serine**, **threonine**, **tyrosine**, **asparagine**, **glutamine**, and **cysteine**. The acidic amino acids are **aspartic acid** and **glutamic acid**; the basic amino acids include **histidine**, **lysine**, and **arginine**. The amino acids are weak polyprotic acids. The carboxyl group is a rather strong carboxylic acid with pK_a around 2.0, whereas the amino group is a base with pK_a around 9.5. At neutral pH, the carboxyl group is unprotonated and negatively charged, whereas the amino group is protonated and positively charged. Considering only these two groups at pH = 7.0, amino acids are zwitterionic. Several of the side chains have titratable groups, including aspartic acid, glutamic acid, cysteine, tyrosine, arginine, histidine, and lysine.

In proteins, amino acids are joined by peptide (or amide) bonds. The carboxyl group of one amino acid is joined to the amino group of another amino acid, with elimination of the elements of water.

In addition to the 20 common amino acids, there are a large number of modified amino acids found in nature. Examples include hydroxylation of lysine and proline, methylation of lysine, carboxylation of glutamic acid, and phosphorylation of serine, threonine, and tyrosine. Metabolites derived from amino acids play key roles in cells. Knowing the structures of ornithine, citrulline, aspartic acid, and arginine will serve as a strong basis for understanding the urea cycle. Transamination of glutamic acid and aspartic acid produce α-ketoglutarate and oxaloacetate, respectively, two citric acid cycle intermediates. The same reaction with alanine produces pyruvate. A great many small molecules acting as neurotransmitters, hormones, antibiotics, and others are directly derived from amino acids.

The 20 common amino acids are coded for genetically, as are selenocysteine and pyrrolysine. The latter two amino acids are coded for by stop codons.

The α-carbons of all of the amino acids except glycine are chiral. Thus, amino acids can exist as stereoisomers. In nature, the L amino acids predominate. We will consider stereochemistry again when sugar structures are discussed.

The UV light–absorbing properties of unconjugated proteins are dominated by the aromatic amino acids, phenylalanine, tyrosine, and tryptophan. NMR can characterize amino acids and this technique is used to determine the three-dimensional structure of peptides and small proteins.

There are several methods for separating and analyzing amino acid mixtures. These included ion exchange chromatography, gas chromatography, and HPLC. It is often the case that the amino acids are derivatized on their amino end with a hydrophobic group and the modified amino acids separated by reverse phase chromatography.

The fundamental structure of a protein is a series of amide planes joining alpha carbons. The amide plane contains the peptide bond, a polar bond with partial double-bond character. Amino acid chains are composed of amino acid residues and are classified as peptides (12 residues), oligopeptides (up to a few dozen peptides) and polypeptides. Proteins are polypeptides with one or more peptide chains.

Chapter 5

Proteins: Their Primary Structure and Biological Functions

• •

Chapter Outline

❖ Protein architecture
  ⋏ Fibrous proteins
  ⋏ Globular proteins
  ⋏ Membrane proteins
❖ Protein structure
  ⋏ Primary structure: Sequence of amino acids
  ⋏ Secondary structure: Helices and sheets formed by interactions between peptide planes
  ⋏ Tertiary structure: 3-dimensional shape
  ⋏ Quaternary structure: How chains interact in multimeric protein
  ⋏ Protein conformation determined by primary structure and weak force interactions
  ⋏ Configuration: Actual arrangement of atoms held together by covalent bonds
❖ Protein purification
  ⋏ Size distinction: Size exclusion chromatography, ultracentrifugation, ultrafiltration
  ⋏ Solubility distinction: Ammonium sulfate (salts), organic solvent, pH (solubility minimum at isoelectric point)
  ⋏ Differential interactions: Ion exchange chromatography, hydrophobic interaction chromatography
❖ Amino acid composition
  ⋏ 6N HCl, 110°C, 24, 48, 72 h
    • Ser/Thr extrapolate to zero time, Val/Ile extrapolate to infinity
    • Trp destroyed, Asn/Gln converted to Asp/Glu
❖ Protein Sequencing
  ⋏ Separation of polypeptide chains: Reduction of disulfide bonds and denaturation
  ⋏ Inactivation of sulfhydryl groups: Performic acid oxidation or reduction with β-mercaptoethanol followed alkylation
  ⋏ Amino acid composition
  ⋏ N- and C-terminus identification
    • N-terminus chemistry: Edman degradation—phenylisothiocyanate to product PTH derivative of N-terminal amino acid
    • C-terminus: Carboxypeptidase C or Y cleaves any C-terminal amino acid, carboxypeptidase B cleaves only Arg or Lys, carboxypeptidase A does not cleave Arg, Lys, or Pro
  ⋏ Polypeptide chain fragmentation: Sets of short, overlapping peptides
    • Trypsin: Carbonyl side of Arg, Lys
    • Chymotrypsin: Carbonyl side of Phe, Tyr, Trp
    • Clostripain: Carbonyl side of Arg
    • Endopeptidase Lys-C: Carbonyl side of Lys
    • Staphyloccal protease: Carbonyl side of Asp, Glu
    • Cyanogen Bromide: Carbonyl side of Met
    • Hydroxylamine: Asn/Gly bond
    • Acid hydrolysis: Asp/Pro

- Sequence determination
  - Edman degradation
  - Mass spectrometry
- Sequence reconstruction: Match sequence of members of set of overlapping peptides
- Location of disulfide bonds: Analysis of fragments from non-reduced protein by diagonal electrophoresis (first dimension non-reducing; second dimension reducing)
- ❖ Mass spectrometry
  - Electrospray ionization
    - Often used in tandem to sequence peptides
      - Filter peptides with first mass spectrometer
      - Selected peptide fragmented and fragments analyzed by second mass spectrometer
  - Matrix-Assisted Laser Desorption Ionization-Time of Flight: MALDI-TOF
    - High sensitivity and accuracy used to determine mass of peptides
    - Peptide mass fingerprinting measures mass of proteolytic fragments of protein
      - Comparison to database allows for protein identification
- ❖ Amino acid sequence analysis
  - Homologous proteins
    - Proteins that perform the same function in different organisms
    - Proteins related evolutionarily and detected by sequence similarities
  - Homologous proteins can be orthologous or paralogous
    - Orthologous: Proteins in different species but with similar function and sequence; arose by gene duplication before speciation
    - Paralogous: Proteins is single species but with similar function and related function; arose by gene duplication after speciation
  - Computer programs to discover sequence similarities
    - BLAST (Basic Local Alignment Search Tool)
      - Align sequences, compare amino acids using scoring matrix, insert gaps to account for insertions/deletions (indels)
      - BLOSUM (Blocks Substitution Matrix) used to score observed substitutions
  - Phylogenetic studies: Comparison of identical protein from many species
    - Identifies invariant residues that are crucial to function
    - Used to construct phylogenetic trees to establish evolutionary relationships among proteins
- ❖ Tertiary structure analysis identifies proteins with similar structure yet different function
  - Amino acid analysis reveals many differences indicating distant relationship
- ❖ Merrifield solid phase synthesis: Chemical synthesis of polypeptides
- ❖ Protein complexity
  - Simple proteins: Composed of amino acids but no other chemical groups
    - Amino acid residues may be modified by post-translational modifications
    - RESID: Database of modifications (http://www.ebi.ac.uk/RESID/)
  - Conjugated proteins: Protein with prosthetic group: glyco- sugar, lipo- lipids, nucleo- nucleic acid, phospho- phosphorylated amino acid, metallo- metal atom, hemo- protoporphyrin, flavo- FMN or FAD
- ❖ Biological function of proteins
  - Enzymes: Biological catalysts
  - Regulatory proteins: Hormones, DNA binding proteins
  - Transport proteins: Hemoglobin, serum albumin
  - Storage proteins: Zein, ovalbumin, phaseolin, ferritin
  - Contractile and motile proteins: Actin, myosin, dynein, kinesin, tubulin
  - Structural proteins: α-keratins, collagen, elastin, β-keratin, proteoglycans
  - Scaffold or Adapter proteins: SH2, SH3, PH modules, PDZ-containing proteins
  - Protective proteins: Antibodies, blood clotting factors, antifreeze proteins, toxins
  - Exotic proteins: Monellin, glue protein

Chapter Objectives

Protein Structure

The four levels of protein structure are important to understand. The primary structure refers to the sequence of amino acids. The secondary structure refers to regular structures formed by hydrogen bond interactions between peptide bonds within a polypeptide. These include helices, sheet structures, and turns. The tertiary structure is the three-dimensional shape of the protein. Finally, the quaternary structure, reserved for multimeric proteins, describes how subunits are arranged.

Protein Sequencing

The basic strategy of protein sequencing is to first purify the protein and separate it into its component polypeptide chains. End-group analysis identifies the N- and C-terminal residues. The chains are cleaved to produce smaller, more manageable pieces whose amino acid sequence is determined using Edman degradation or mass spectrometry. Understand the basic idea behind Edman chemistry as applied to amino acid sequencing. It is often easier to sequence a protein by cloning its gene. However, knowing the sequence of even short oligopeptides from the protein gives information to search for the protein's gene.

In fragmenting a protein, remember: trypsin cuts after lysine and arginine; clostripain cuts after arginine; chymotrypsin cleaves after the aromatic amino acids, phenylalanine, tyrosine, and tryptophan; and cyanogen bromide cleaves after methionine.

Amino Acid Sequence Analysis

The primary structure of proteins may be analyzed to identify sequence similarities. These similarities reveal evolutionary relatedness among proteins and functional relatedness. Scoring matrices are used to identify related proteins. Invariant positions indicate functional importance of the particular position (and amino acid residue).

Biological Functions

Proteins are the most diverse category of biomolecules responsible for an array of biological functions. There are three classes of proteins: fibrous proteins, globular proteins, and membrane proteins. Protein functions include enzyme catalysis, regulation, transportation, storage, contractility and motility, structure, connectivity (scaffold), and as natural defence mechanisms.

Problems and Solutions

1. The element molybdenum (atomic weight 95.95) constitutes 0.08% of the weight of nitrate reductase. If the molecular weight of nitrate reductase is 240 000, what is its likely quaternary structure?

Answer: If molybdenum (95.95 g/mol) is 0.08% of the weight of nitrate reductase, and nitrate reductase contains at a minimum 1 atom of Mo per molecule, then

$$95.95 = 0.08\% \times M_r$$

$$M_r = \frac{95.95}{0.0008} = 119\ 937 \approx 120\ 000$$

Since the actual molecular weight is 240 000, the quaternary structure must be a dimer.

3. How many fragments will be generated from the following polypeptide if it is first treated with trypsin, followed by cyanogen bromide, and lastly by chymotrypsin?
MTSRAVLYFLKHINDRM

Answer: Seven fragments:

5. *Amino acid analysis of another heptapeptide gave*

     Asp   Glu   Leu   Lys   Met   Tyr   Trp   NH₄⁺

The following facts were observed:

a. **Trypsin had no effect.**

b. **The phenylthiohydantoin released by Edman degradation was**

c. **Brief chymotrypsin treatment yielded several products, including a dipeptide and a tetrapeptide. The amino acid composition of the tetrapeptide was Glx, Leu, Lys, and Met**

d. **Cyanogen bromide treatment yielded a tetrapeptide that had a net positive charge at pH 7 and a tripeptide that had a zero net charge at pH 7.**

What is the amino acid sequence of this heptapeptide?

Answer: Trypsin cleaves after Lys and Arg. Since amino acid analysis revealed the presence of lysine, it must be on the C-terminus. The PTH derivative amino acid is identified as tyrosine. So far we have:

Tyr _ _ _ _ _ Lys

From information in (d), we may place Met at positions 3 or 4, but from (c), we recognize that Met cannot be more than 3 residues from the N-terminal Lys. So, Met must be at position 4.

Tyr _ _ Met _ _ Lys

From (c), we may conclude that Glx and Leu are located between Met and Lys. For chymotrypsin to produce a tetrapeptide and a dipeptide, Trp must be at position 3. Asx (Asp or Asn) is at position 2. Thus,

Tyr Asx Trp Met (Glx and Leu) Lys

Analysis of cyanogen bromide cleavage products reveals that the tetrapeptide has a net positive charge at neutral pH. Since cleavage leaves the C-terminus as homoserine lactone (and not as a negatively charged carboxyl group), the tetrapeptide can be positively charged due to its N-terminal amino group if Asx is Asn. Asn-to-Asp conversion during acid hydrolysis would account for the ammonia. The Glx must be Glu and not Gln to account for a zero charge on the tripeptide at neutral pH. (Positive charge from the amino group of Met and the side chain of Lys, negative charge from the C-terminus of Lys and the side chain of Glu.)

From the information given, we cannot assign an order to Glu and Leu, thus two heptapeptides are consistent with the information:

Tyr Asn Trp Met Glu Leu Lys
Tyr Asn Trp Met Leu Glu Lys

7. *Analysis of the blood of a catatonic football fan revealed large concentrations of a psychotoxic octapeptide. Amino acid analysis of this octapeptide gave the following results:*

     2 Ala   1 Arg   1 Asp   1 Met   2 Tyr   1 Val   1 NH₄⁺

The following facts were observed:

a. *Partial acid hydrolysis of the octapeptide yielded a dipeptide of the structure*

b. *Chymotrypsin treatment of the octapeptide yielded 2 tetrapeptides, each containing an alanine residue.*

c. *Trypsin treatment of 1 of the tetrapeptides yielded 2 dipeptides.*

d. Cyanogen bromide treatment of another sample of the same tetrapeptide yielded a tripeptide and free Tyr.
e. End-group analysis of the other tetrapeptide gave Asp.
What is the amino acid sequence of this octapeptide?

Answer: The dipeptide produced by partial acid hydrolysis is Ala Val, AV.

Chymotrypsin cleaves at aromatics like Y. To produce two tetrapeptides from an octapeptide with two tyrosines, one must be the C-terminus and the other at position 4. Thus:

$$\_\,\_\,\_\;Y\;\_\,\_\,\_\;Y$$

Since trypsin cleaves, in this case, after R, from (c), we infer that R is at position 2 or 6:

$$\_\;R\;\_\;Y\;\_\,\_\,\_\;Y$$
$$\_\,\_\,\_\;Y\;\_\;R\;\_\;Y$$

That CNBr cleavage of the tetrapeptides produces free Y indicates the sequence MY adjacent to R. Thus,

$$\_\;R\;M\;Y\;\_\,\_\,\_\;Y$$
$$\_\,\_\,\_\;Y\;\_\;R\;M\;Y$$

End-group analysis of the second chymotrypsin tetrapeptide indicates Asp = D, but the presence of NH_4^+ suggests asparagine, N. (The end in question must be the N-terminus.) Thus:

$$\_\;R\;M\;Y\;N\;\_\,\_\;Y$$
$$N\;\_\,\_\;Y\;\_\;R\;M\;Y$$

We can now place AV (from (a)) into these sequences:

$$\_\;R\;M\;Y\;N\;A\;V\;Y$$
$$N\;A\;V\;Y\;\_\;R\;M\;Y$$

The only amino acid unaccounted for is an additional A, giving us:

$$A\;R\;M\;Y\;N\;A\;V\;Y$$
$$N\;A\;V\;Y\;A\;R\;M\;Y$$

9. *Amino acid analysis of an octapeptide gave the following results:*
   1 Ala   1 Arg   1 Asp   1 Gly   3 Ile   1 Val   1 NH4+
   The following facts were observed:
   a. Trypsin treatment yielded a pentapeptide and a tripeptide.
   b. Chemical reduction of the free a-COOH and subsequent acid hydrolysis yielded 2-aminopropanol.
   c. Partial acid hydrolysis of the tryptic pentapeptide yielded, among other products, two dipeptides, each of which contained C-terminal isoleucine. One of these dipeptides migrated as an anionic species upon electrophoresis at neutral pH.
   d. The tryptic tripeptide was degraded in an Edman sequenator, yielding first A, then B:

What is an amino acid sequence of the octapeptide? Four sequences are possible, but only one suits the authors. Why?

Answer: Trypsin digestion indicates R at position 3 or 5. Thus:

$$(1)\ \_\ \_\ R\ \_\ \_\ \_\ \_\ \_$$
$$(2)\ \_\ \_\ \_\ \_\ R\ \_\ \_\ \_$$

The product, 2-aminopropanol, must derive from reduction of a carboxyl terminal alanine. The structures of both are shown below:

$$H_2N\cdot CH-CH_2\cdot OH$$
$$|$$
$$CH_3$$
2-aminopropanol

$$\qquad\qquad O$$
$$\qquad\qquad \|$$
$$H_2N-CH-C-OH$$
$$|$$
$$CH_3$$
alanine

Our possibilities so far are:

$$(1)\ \_\ \_\ R\ \_\ \_\ \_\ \_\ A$$
$$(2)\ \_\ \_\ \_\ \_\ R\ \_\ \_\ A$$

From (d), we identify the PTH-derivatived amino acids as valine and isoleucine. So, the tryptic tripeptides must contain the sequence VI. For VI to be released by trypsin digestion it must precede R in (1) or it must follow R in (2):

$$(1)\ V\ I\ R\ \_\ \_\ \_\ \_\ A$$
$$(2)\ \_\ \_\ \_\ \_\ R\ V\ I\ A$$

Ammonium production and the finding that 1 Asp is present indicate that Asn (N) was in the original octapeptide. So, in the above two peptides we still need to account for G, N and two I's.

From (c), we know that _ I and _ I are located in the tryptic pentapeptide and these must be GI and NI. So, we know that GI and NI are in the remaining places in (1) and (2) but we do not know their order. Placing them into (1) and (2) produces four candidates:

$$(1a)\ V\ I\ R\ G\ I\ N\ I\ A$$
$$(1b)\ V\ I\ R\ N\ I\ G\ I\ A$$
$$(2a)\ G\ I\ N\ I\ R\ V\ I\ A$$
$$(2b)\ N\ I\ G\ I\ R\ V\ I\ A$$

GI is not charged at neutral pH but NI would be converted to DI by acid hydrolysis and DI is anionic at neutral pH.

Given the fact that both authors are at the University of Virginia, we could guess which they prefer!

11. Amino acid analysis of an oligopeptide containing 9 residues revealed the presence of the following amino acids:

$$\qquad\qquad Arg\quad Cys\quad Gly\quad Leu\quad Met\quad Pro\quad Tyr\quad Val$$

The following was found:
a. Carboxypeptidase A treatment yielded no free amino acid.
b. Edman analysis of the intact oligopeptide released

c. Neither trypsin nor chymotrypsin treatment of the nonapeptide released smaller fragments. However, combined trypsin and chymotrypsin treatment liberated free Arg.

d.   CNBr treatment of the 8-residue fragment left after combined trypsin and chymotrypsin action yielded a 6-residue fragment containing Cys, Gly, Pro, Tyr and Val; and a dipeptide.
e.   Treatment of the 6-residue fragment with β-mercaptoethanol yielded 2 tripeptides. Brief Edman analysis of the tripeptide mixture yielded only PTH-Cys. (The sequence of each tripeptide, as read from the N-terminal end, is alphabetical if the 1-letter designation for amino acids is used.)
What is the amino acid sequence of this nonapeptide?

Answer: The amino acid composition accounts for only eight amino acids, but since we are dealing with a nonapeptide, there must be two of one of the amino acids. If we focus on the information given in (e), we should conclude that there are two cysteines that are cross-linked as cystine in the original peptide. From (a), we infer that the C-terminus is R or P because carboxypeptidase A cuts at all C termini except P, R, and K. And this peptide contains both P and R. From (b), we see that the PHT-derivatized amino acid is leucine; thus, the N-terminus must be L. We know that trypsin cleaves after R and K and that the peptide contains one R, yet digestion with trypsin did not release smaller fragments. It could be that R is on the C-terminus, which is consistent with the carboxypeptidase A results. Alternatively, R could be internal such that it is between the two cysteines that are cross-linked. Chymotrypsin digestion also gives no smaller fragments. Since chymotrypsin cleaves after Y (W and F), one conclusion is that Y is on the C- terminus. But this would not be consistent with carboxypeptidase A treatment, so it must be internal and it must be between the two cysteines. Combined digestion with trypsin and chymotrypsin yields free R. For this to happen, Y must precede R; thus, the peptide must contain YR and it cannot be on the C-terminus (because it would have released R after chymotrypsin digestion alone). So, YR must be internal and it must be between the two cysteines.

$$\text{L \_ \_ \_ \_ \_ \_ \_ P with C – YR – C somewhere}$$

From (d), we realize that because M is not in the six-residue fragment it must be in the dipeptide. Of the amino acids, all but L is accounted for in the six-residue fragment and trypsin/chymotrypsin digestion released R. Thus, the dipeptide must be LM.
This gives us:

$$\text{L M \_ \_ \_ \_ \_ \_ P with C – YR – C somewhere}$$

From (e), we also learn that the two tripeptides have N-terminal C's and that they are joined by a disulfide bond:

$$\begin{array}{l} \text{C \_ \_} \\ \text{| lll} \\ \text{C \_ \_} \end{array}$$

We reasoned above that YR must have been somewhere between the two C's. But R is not in the six-residue fragment yet Y is. It must be that Y is on the N-terminus of one of the tripeptides. The six-residue fragment also contains P, which we established is on the C terminus. So we must have:

$$\begin{array}{l} \text{C \_ Y R} \\ \text{| llliiii} \\ \text{C \_ P \_} \end{array}$$

G and V are still unaccounted for and to fit into the above model in alphabetic order it must be:

$$\begin{array}{l} \text{C V Y R} \\ \text{| llliiii} \\ \text{C G P \_} \end{array}$$

The final sequence is:

$$\begin{array}{l} \text{S———S} \\ \text{| |} \\ \text{L M C V Y R C G P} \end{array}$$

13.   *Electrospray ionization mass spectrometry (ESI-MS) of the polypeptide chain of myoglobin yielded a series of m/z peaks (similar to those shown in Figure 5.24 for aerolysin K). Two successive peaks had m/z values of 1304.7 and 1413.2, respectively. Calculate the mass of the myoglobin polypeptide chain from these data.*

Answer: In electrospray mass spectrometry, the equation describing the observed m/z peaks is m/z = [M + n(mass of proton)]/n(charge of proton), where M = the mass of the protein and n = number of positive charges per protein molecule. The two successive peaks at 1304.7 and 1413.2 must differ by a single proton. Let the number of positive charges for the first peak be n. Since the second peak has a higher m/z value, it must have one fewer positive charge or n−1 positive charge. The mass, M, could be evaluated at either m/z value if we knew n. To determine n, we will first solve the equation for M as a function of m/z and n.

$$\left(\frac{m}{z}\right) = \frac{[M + n]}{n}$$

$$n\left(\frac{m}{z}\right) = [M + n]$$

$$M = (n)\left(\frac{m}{z} - 1\right)$$

We will now evaluate M at each of the m/z values.

$$M = (n_1)_1\left(\left(\frac{m}{z}\right)_1 - 1\right) \text{ and } M = (n_2)\left(\left(\frac{m}{z}\right)_2 - 1\right)$$

We will then set these equal with n_1 corresponding to m/z = 1304.7 and n_2 corresponding to m/z = 1413.2. The two peaks differ by a single positive charge, with n_1 having one more positive charge than n_2. Thus, $n_1 = 1 + n_2$.

$$(n_1)\left(\left(\frac{m}{z}\right)_1 - 1\right) = (n_2)\left(\left(\frac{m}{z}\right)_2 - 1\right)$$

$$(1 + n_2)(1304.7 - 1) = (n_2)(1413.2 - 1)$$

$$n_2 = \frac{(1304.7 - 1)}{(1413.2 - 1) - (1304.7 - 1)}$$

$$n_2 = 12$$

$$\text{But } M = (n_2)\left(\left(\frac{m}{z}\right)_2 - 1\right)$$

$$M = 12 \times (1413.2 - 1)$$

$$M = 16\,946$$

$$\text{Or } M = (n_1)\left(\left(\frac{m}{z}\right)_1 - 1\right)$$

$$M = 13 \times (1304.7 - 1)$$

$$M = 16\,948$$

Thus, M=16 947±1

15. A quantitative study of the interaction of a protein with its ligand yielded the following results:

Ligand concentration (mM)	1	2	3	4	5	6	9	12
v (moles of ligand bound per mole of protein)	0.28	0.45	0.56	0.60	0.71	0.75	0.79	0.83

Plot a graph of [L] versus v. Determine K_D, the dissociation constant for the interaction between the protein and its ligand, from the graph.

Answer: Plot v on the y-axis versus [L] on the x-axis and determine the location at which the v = 0.5. The data are plotted below as ×. A horizontal line was drawn at v = 0.5, and at the point it appears to intersect the data, a perpendicular line was drawn to the [L]-axis. On the plot, the open circles are values of v calculated using the equation shown below and 2.4 mM as a guess for K_D.

$$v = \frac{[L]}{K_D + [L]}$$

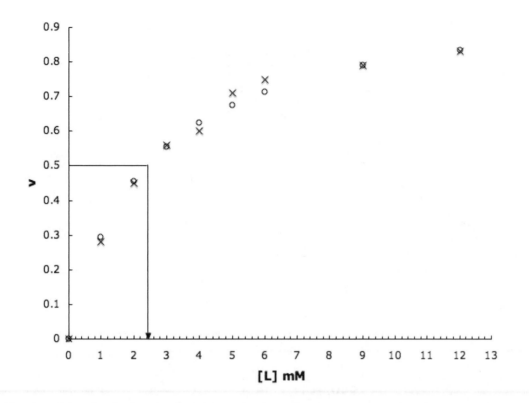

The data (×) and calculated points (○) are in close agreement, suggesting that our estimate of K_D is a good one. But this was accomplished "by eye," by actually making numerous guesses for K_D and then plotting them to see which value best fit the data. A more sophisticated approach is to transform the equation into a linear form.

$$v = \frac{[L]}{K_D + [L]}$$

$$(v)^{-1} = \left(\frac{[L]}{K_D + [L]} \right)^{-1}$$

$$\frac{1}{v} = \frac{K_D + [L]}{[L]}$$

$$\frac{1}{v} = K_D \times \frac{1}{[L]} + 1$$

A plot of $1/v$ versus $1/[L]$ should be linear with a slope equal to K_D. By transforming the data (from v to $1/v$ and [L] to $1/[L]$) and then plotting it, we can determine the "best fit line" by linear regression. This approach will determine a value of K_D that fits the data by minimizing the difference between data and calculated values.

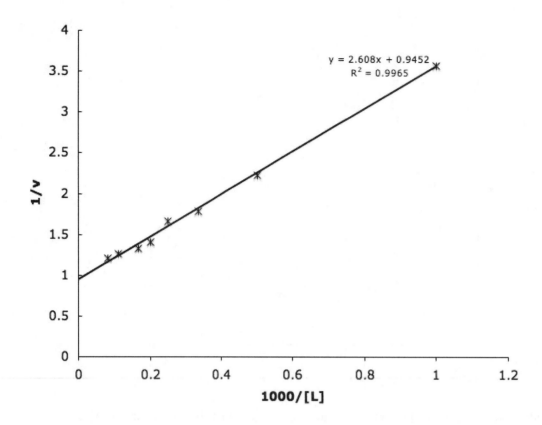

The equation of the "best fit" line is shown above, and from it we can see that the value for K_D is 2.61 mM. On the direct plot (v versus [L]), if you plot the open circles with data calculated using K_D = 2.61 mM, you will not see a dramatic difference from K_D = 2.4 mM. You will see, however, that the calculated values for K_D = 2.61 mM for low values of v fit the data better. In the $1/v$ versus $1/$[L] plot, these values are large in magnitude and quite spread out along the graph. Because of this they tend to dominate the best-fit linear regression.

Questions for Self-Study

1. Fill in the blanks. Proteins are linear chains of _____ _____ held together by covalent _____ bonds. Although these bonds are typically drawn as C–N single bonds, they in fact have partial double-bond characteristics because of delocalization of _____ _____. The result of this delocalization is to constrain four atoms in a single plane termed the _____ plane. The four atoms are _____, _____, _____, and _____. Thus, linear chains of amino acids can be considered as a string of _____ carbons joined together by amide or peptide planes.

2. Match the terms in the first column with terms in the second column.
   a. Dipeptide
   b. Protein
   c. Polypeptide
   d. Amino acid residue
   e. Peptide

   1. An amino acid minus the elements of water
   2. The bond joining amino acids in a protein
   3. Two amino acids joined in amide linkage
   4. Subunit of a multimeric protein
   5. A molecule composed of polypeptide chains

3. List the four levels of protein structure and give a brief definition of each.

4. Proteins represent an extremely diverse set of biomolecules. Match the functional class of proteins with their appropriate function.

	Class		Function
a.	Enzymes	1.	Source of amino acids for developing organisms
b.	Regulatory proteins	2.	Move glucose across the cell membrane
c.	Transport proteins	3.	Various venoms and toxins
d.	Storage proteins	4.	Structural components of motile cellular appendages
e.	Contractile proteins	5.	Biological catalysts
f.	Structural proteins	6.	Certain extracellular, fibrous elements
g.	Scaffold proteins	7.	Certain hormones
h.	Protective proteins	8.	Responsible for multiprotein complex formation

5. Trypsin, chymotrypsin, clostripain, staphylococcal proteins, and cyanogen bromide are agents used in amino acid sequence determination. What is their purpose?

6. Short polypeptides are subjected to Edman degradation for what purpose?

7. What is the difference between amino acid composition and amino acid sequence?

8. True or false:
   a. Proteins sharing a significant degree of sequence similarity are homologous. _____
   b. Proteins that perform the same function in different organisms are referred to as homologous. _____
   c. Invariant residues usually are a result of random mutations. _____
   d. Evolutionarily related proteins always have similar biological activities. _____

9. In solid-phase synthesis of peptides the amino group of the incoming amino acid is blocked. Why?

10. Give one reason why synthetic peptides may be useful tools.

Answers

1. Amino; acids; amide (or peptide); pi; electrons; amide (or peptide); the carbonyl carbon; the carbonyl oxygen; the amide nitrogen; amide hydrogen; alpha.

2. a. 3; b. 5; c. 4; d. 1; e. 2.

3. The primary structure is the sequence of amino acids of a protein. The secondary structure refers to regular structures such as helices and sheets that form as a result of hydrogen bonding interactions. The tertiary structure of a protein is its three dimensional shape. Finally, the quaternary structure is reserved for proteins composed of multiple subunits and describes how the subunits interact.

4. a. 5; b. 7; c. 2; d. 1; e. 4; f. 6; g. 8; h. 3.

5. These agents are used to cleave a polypeptide into short oligopeptides. Each oligopeptide is then sequenced. At least two different agents are used to separately cleave the polypeptide in order to produce overlapping oligopeptides.

6. Edman degradation is used to determine the amino acid sequence of an oligopeptide from the N-terminus to the C-terminus.

7. The amino acid sequence is the primary structure of a polypeptide and refers to the sequence of amino acids, N-terminus to C-terminus. The amino acid composition is the total number of each amino acid of each kind in a polypeptide.

8. a. T; b. T; c. F; d. F.

9. Blocking the amino group of the incoming amino acids prevents them from reacting with themselves either in solution or on the solid phase.

10. Antigenic peptides for antibody production; pharmacologically active peptides; structure-function studies; confirmation of structure of naturally occurring peptides.

Additional Problems

1. Protein purification schemes typically involve several techniques. For the techniques listed below provide a brief explanation for each and indicate at which relative point in a purification procedure the technique might be employed.
   a. Molecular sieve chromatography
   b. Ultracentrifugation
   c. Ammonium sulfate fractionation
   d. Affinity chromatography
   e. Polyacrylamide gel electrophoresis
   f. Reverse phase HPLC

2. How are protein purification procedures monitored?

3. What is the role of sulfur in protein structure?

4. The apparent molecular weight of globular proteins is often determined by SDS polyacrylamide gel electrophoresis. Explain.

5. The ultraviolet absorption spectra of proteins rarely looks like the sum of the absorption spectra of the component amino acids, but the situation improves when the protein is treated with high concentrations of urea or guanidinium hydrochloride. Explain.

6. Determining the amino acid sequence of even a small portion of a protein is extremely useful. Often this information can be used to identify the protein. Calculate the total number of different amino acid sequences for polypeptide chains of length 5, 10, and 15 amino acids.

Abbreviated Answers

1. a. Molecular sieve chromatography or molecular exclusion chromatography separates proteins based on size. A porous matrix is employed such as beads of dextrans, agarose, or polyacrylamide. A column of hydrated beads contains two aqueous volumes: the volume within the beads or the internal volume, and the volume outside of the beads, the external volume. The degree to which a protein can enter the internal volume is dependent on the protein's size. Large proteins cannot enter the internal volume at all, whereas smaller proteins may be partially or completely accessible to the internal volume. Separation of proteins of different sizes occurs because for every volume element added to the column, the proteins are displaced that volume element down the column. Large proteins can move only in the external volume, whereas smaller proteins move in the external and internal volumes. Molecular sieve chromatography is likely to be used at a later stage in protein purification. It may be performed under conditions favouring the native state of the protein, in which case the elution profile is dependent on the native molecular weight of the protein. Alternatively, denaturing conditions may be employed allowing individual polypeptide chains to be separated.

b. In ultracentrifugation, very high centrifugal forces are employed to separate proteins. Depending on the technique employed, proteins may be separated according to size and shape, or according to density. Very often one of the first steps employed in a purification scheme is to briefly centrifuge a cell lysate to separate cellular debris from soluble proteins. In differential ultracentrifugation, a sample is subjected to ultracentrifugation runs of increasing duration and/or force to separate large proteins from small proteins. Density gradients, either continuous or discontinuous, may be employed to fractionate proteins by size or by density. Centrifugation in general may be used at any stage in a purification scheme.

c. Ammonium sulfate fractionation operates on the principle that under certain ionic conditions, protein charge may be shielded by ionic interactions with solvent components, allowing proteins to aggregate and precipitate. Generally, it is used in early stages of protein purification. Variations of this basic technique include the use of other salts as precipitating agents or changing pH. Proteins are least soluble at their isoelectric point, the pH at which a protein's net charge is zero.

d. Affinity chromatography exploits the fact that proteins have complementary surfaces that exhibit incredible specificity. These surfaces might be a substrate-binding site, a cofactor-binding site, or a protein–protein interaction surface as examples. The principle is to attach a molecule that interacts specifically with a particular protein to an inert, insoluble matrix. A mixture containing the protein of interest is added to the affinity matrix under conditions favouring complementary interactions. The matrix is washed to remove unbound protein and then subjected to conditions that disrupt the complementary interactions. These conditions may be high salt, or high ionic strength, a change in pH, or high concentration of cofactor or substrate. In favourable cases, affinity chromatography may be a one-step purification scheme. Generally, affinity chromatography is employed at a later stage at which the protein of interest has been partially purified and therefore represents a high percentage of the total protein.

e.   Polyacrylamide gel electrophoresis separates proteins according to their charge to mass ratio and their size. The driving force is a voltage gradient. Charged proteins are forced to move through a porous matrix (typically of polyacrylamide). Separation occurs because the degree to which movement of a protein is impeded is proportional to the size of the protein. Under so-called native conditions, protein mixtures may be separated into component proteins retaining biological activity. In the presence of denaturing agents such as urea or SDS (see question 4), individual polypeptide chains may be separated. Gel electrophoresis is employed both preparatively and analytically (see question 2).

f.   HPLC refers to high performance (or high pressure) liquid chromatography. In general, the efficiency of chromatographic procedures depends on the number of interactions or discriminations made per volume or per distance. In high performance chromatography, a large number of interactions are made possible by using chromatography matrix material of very small size (resulting in an increase in the number of theoretical plates). The small size greatly increases resistance to flow and so chromatography must be carried out using high pressure. Reverse-phase HPLC is a particular application of HPLC that employs chromatography matrices with hydrophobic surfaces. Initial applications of chromatography employed cellulose, in the form of paper, as a stationary phase. Molecules are moved over this stationary phase in solutions containing organic solvents. Thus, the mobile phase favours hydrophobic compounds, whereas the stationary phase favours hydrophilic compounds (because cellulose contains numerous polar groups). In reverse phase, the stationary phase is hydrophobic, whereas the mobile phase, at least initially, is an aqueous solution. Proteins that adsorb to the column are removed by addition of increasing amounts of organic solvent (e.g., methanol) or by increasing the ionic strength.

2.   After each stage in a protein purification scheme, the total amount of protein is measured and the amount of the protein of interest is quantitated. Quantitation may include determining the biological activity of the protein by performing a specific assay. The specific activity is the activity normalized to total protein concentration. SDS polyacrylamide gel electrophoresis (SDS PAGE) is routinely employed to monitor purification. Using very thin slab gels, large numbers of samples can be examined in only a few hours. SDS PAGE allows a determination of the complexity of samples with respect to the number and kinds of polypeptides present.

3.   Of the two sulfur-containing amino acids, cysteine and methionine, the former is capable of an array of interactions that greatly influence protein structure. For example, cysteine (side chain -CH_2-SH) by virtue of its polar side chain may influence protein structure by making polar interactions with either the solvent or with other side chains. In addition, sulfur may coordinate iron atoms. Finally, sulfhydryl groups are capable of forming covalent bonds with each other. Two cysteines joined by a disulfide bond is referred to as cystine. Cystine formed by an oxidation reaction between two cysteines represents a covalent bond that is capable of bringing distant portions of a polypeptide chain together or of joining separate polypeptides.

4.   Globular proteins contain a core of hydrophobic amino acids that is largely responsible for their globular shape. This core is formed by hydrophobic interactions of amino acids distributed throughout the polypeptide chain. For typical globular proteins, the number of hydrophobic amino acids is a fixed percentage of the total number of amino acids. In solution, SDS forms micelles around each hydrophobic amino acid. This fact is exploited in SDS polyacrylamide gel electrophoresis to produce a protein/SDS complex with a charge dependent on the number of hydrophobic amino acids. The intrinsic charge of a protein contributes negligibly to the total charge of a protein/SDS complex. Because the total charge is proportional to the number of hydrophobic amino acids, and the number of hydrophobic amino acids is a fixed percentage of the total number of amino acids, the charge to mass ratio of protein/SDS complexes for globular proteins is constant. This means that protein/SDS complexes will migrate at a constant rate in an electric field, a rate completely independent of protein size. Separation of proteins is accomplished by forcing protein/SDS complexes through a polyacrylamide matrix. Here, migration is inversely dependent on size. By comparing the mobility of a protein of unknown size to the mobility of proteins of known size, an estimate of the molecular weight can be made.

5.   The amino acids phenylalanine, tryptophan, and tyrosine absorb ultraviolet light, and these amino acids are largely responsible for the UV-light absorption properties of most proteins. However, the

physical dimension of a protein may be comparable to the wavelength of ultraviolet light. In this case, the protein will exhibit light scattering. Urea and guanidinium HCl are both powerful denaturing agents that will disrupt protein/protein interactions and unfold proteins, thus minimizing light scattering. Also, there are effects due to polarity of the environment in which the aromatic ring is located.

6. The number of arrangements of 20 different amino acids taken n at a time is $(20)^n$.

Polypeptide Length	Number of Polypeptides
5	3.2×10^6
10	1.3×10^{13}
15	3.3×10^{19}

Summary

In describing protein structure, four levels are considered. The primary structure of a protein is the sequence of amino acids in each of the polypeptide chains of a protein. The secondary structure is a collection of regular structures that may be formed by H-bonding interactions with the groups of the peptide bond. The tertiary structure is the actual three-dimensional shape of the protein, which is the result of weak interactions involving interactions of amino acids with each other and with solvent and includes the location and orientation of secondary structure elements, amino acid side chains, and the backbone of the main chain. Finally, the quaternary structure, reserved for proteins composed of more than one polypeptide chain, describes how the polypeptides are arranged in the protein.

Protein characterization begins with purification of the protein. Protein purification is accomplished using a number of techniques including differential solubility, differential centrifugation, and gradient centrifugation; ion exchange, molecular sieve, or affinity column chromatography.

Next, the purified protein is separated into its individual polypeptide chains. This is accomplished by treating the protein with a reducing agent to disrupt interchain disulfide bonds and converting the resulting free sulfhydryls into forms that will not readily reform disulfides. This is accomplished with either performic acid or a combination of 2-mercaptoethanol and an alkylating agent (such as iodoacetate). To disrupt weak bonds, denaturing agents such as 8 M urea or 6 M guanidinium HCl are used.

The nature of the N-terminal and C-terminal amino acids of the polypeptide components is determined using techniques specific for each group. For example, phenylisothiocyanate is used during Edman degradation to convert N-terminal amino acids into PTH (phenylthiohydantoin) derivatives. C-terminal residues may be identified after enzymatic cleavage with carboxypeptidase A, B, C, or Y (A is blocked by Pro, Arg and Lys; B only cleaves at Arg or Lys; C and Y cleave at any amino acid).

The amino acid composition is determined by first hydrolyzing the polypeptide chains into amino acids using 6 N HCl at 110°C for 24, 48, and 72 h to insure that total hydrolysis has occurred. A time course is performed because some amino acids (e.g., Ser and Thr) are unstable under these conditions and slowly degrade, whereas others (e.g., hydrophobic amino acids) are only slowly released. The time course can be extrapolated to zero time to determine the initial level of unstable amino acids and to infinite time to predict when total hydrolysis will occur. The mixture of amino acids produced by acid hydrolysis is analyzed on an amino acid analyzer to determine the relative amount of each amino acid in the mixture. An amino acid analyzer separates and quantitates amino acids or amino acid derivatives. The separation may be based on the ionic properties of the amino acids (i.e., ion exchange chromatography), or it may be based on the degree of hydrophobicity of derivatized amino acids (i.e., reverse phase HPLC).

The primary structure or amino acid sequence is established by fragmenting polypeptides into short oligopeptides suitable for Edman degradation (see below). Fragmentation is accomplished by either 1) enzymatic cleavage at specific residues in the polypeptide using trypsin (hydrolyzes peptide bonds whose carbonyl group is donated by Arg or Lys), chymotrypsin (Phe, Tyr or Trp), clostripain (Arg), staphylococcal protease (Asp, Glu); or 2) using chemical means such as cyanogen bromide to cleave after Met.

The amino acid sequences of the short oligopeptides are established using Edman degradation. The basic idea is to subject an oligopeptide to multiple rounds of modification and cleavage. In Edman chemistry, the amino-terminal amino acid is modified using phenylisothiocyanate and specifically cleaved to release the derivatized N-terminal residue while producing a new terminus. The amino acid sequences of all of the oligopeptides produced by fragmentation using at least two different and overlapping fragmentation techniques are compared to establish how the individual fragments are represented in the protein. Mass spectrometry is also used to establish the sequence of short oligonucleotides. In tandem mass spectrometry, a protein fragmented by protease digestion is filtered using the first mass spectrometer into its components. Each component can then be directed into a collision chamber and then into a second mass spectrometer. The collision chamber fragments peptides at specific locations and comparison of mass differences between fragments reveals the amino acid residue lost by fragmentation. In peptide mass fingerprinting, proteins isolated, for example, by two-dimensional polyacrylamide gel electrophoresis (isoelectric focusing followed by SDS PAGE) are digested with a proteolytic enzyme like trypsin and the tryptic fragments analyzed by MALDI-TOF. The identity of the protein can be established by comparing the size of tryptic fragments to those predicted by analysis of proteins in a database.

Amino acid sequence information is useful in helping to determine the function of proteins. Proteins that have a high degree of sequence similarity often perform similar functions. Proteins whose genes evolve from a common ancestral gene are said to be homologous, and this homology is evidenced by high sequence similarity. Homologous proteins can be orthologous or paralogous. Orthologous proteins are proteins found in differ organisms. They arose by gene duplication before the two organisms diverged from each other. Paralogous proteins are homologous proteins found in the same organism and they arose from gene duplication within the species. BLAST programs are used to identify sequence similarities and these programs use scoring matrices to help identify distantly related proteins. BLOSUM substitution matrix derives from sequence information of related proteins and provides a numerical score for the likelihood of observing a particular amino acid substitution.

Chemical synthesis of peptides using solid-phase synthesis allows for production of peptides with a number of uses in the laboratory.

Proteins have a diversity of functions, and this diversity is possible because of the diversity in amino acid building blocks, the use of post-translational modifications of amino acids, and inclusion of non-protein constituents. As a crude classification, proteins are catalogued as fibrous, globular, or membrane. Fibrous proteins are elongated in shape; globular proteins are spherical in shape and water soluble; membrane proteins associate with biological membranes. Of the biopolymers, proteins are by far the most diverse group, serving a number of biological purposes. The vast majority of biological catalysts are enzymes, proteins capable of increasing the rate of specific reactions. Regulatory proteins modulate physiological responses of cells by binding to specific cell components. Transport proteins facilitate the movement of substances. Storage proteins provide a source of amino acids. Contractile and motile proteins are proteinaceous elements involved in force generation and motility in cells. Structural proteins provide mechanical support. Scaffold proteins recruit different proteins into multiprotein complexes. Protective proteins serve as a defence barrier. Many proteins have additional components including carbohydrates, lipids, nucleic acids and nucleotides, metal ions, and other more complicated organic molecules (coenzymes and prosthetic groups).

Chapter 6

Proteins: Secondary, Tertiary, and Quaternary Structure

• •

Chapter Outline

❖ Protein conformation: Three-dimensional shape
  ⅄ Weak forces act on amino acids to stabilize conformation: Hydrogen bonding, hydrophobic interactions, electrostatic interactions, van der Waals forces
    • H bonds: Peptide backbone and side chains H-bond wherever possible
    • Hydrophobic interactions: Non-polar residues aggregate to form protein core
    • Ionic interactions: Occur between charged amino acids typically on surface
    • Van der Waals: Weak but numerous and involve complementary surfaces
  ⅄ Amino acid sequence contains information to fold protein into conformation
❖ Secondary structure: Structural elements formed by peptide plane interactions
  ⅄ Peptide plane
    • Carbonyl oxygen: H-bond acceptor
    • Amide hydrogen: H-bond donor
  ⅄ ϕ and ψ angles: Describe orientation of peptide planes about alpha carbons
    • ϕ angle: Rotation about C_α—N bond
    • ψ angle: Rotation about C_α—$C_{carbonyl}$ bond
    • Ramachandran plot: Sterically reasonable values of these angles
  ⅄ Alpha-helix (Pauling and Corey)
    • Peptide carbonyl of ith residue H bonded to peptide H of $i+4^{th}$ residue
    • 3.6_{13}: 3.6 residues per turn, 13 atoms between carbonyl oxygen and amide hydrogen
    • 0.54 nm per turn (pitch), 0.15 nm per residue along helix (Z) axis
    • H bonds parallel to helix axis
    • Peptide planes point in same direction along helix
      • Helix has dipole moment
    • Proline, glycine helix breakers
  ⅄ Other helices
    • 3_{10}: 3 residues per turn 10 atoms between carbonyl oxygen and amide hydrogen
    • 2_7 ribbon
    • 4.4_{16} or π helix
  ⅄ Beta-pleated sheets
    • Polypeptide chain fully extended
    • Chains or strands joined by H bonds
    • Parallel sheets
    • Antiparallel sheets
  ⅄ Beta-turn
    • Carbonyl of ith residue H bonded to amide nitrogen of $i+3$
    • Peptide plane in *cis*
    • Gly or Pro common
❖ Tertiary structure principles: How atoms of polypeptide are arranged in space
  ⅄ Four principles
    • Secondary structures formed when possible
    • Secondary structures associate and pack to form layers

- Elements between secondary structures are short and direct
- Stability of final fold
  - Large number of intramolecular H bonds
  - Reduction in surface area
    - Two factors
      - Hydrophobic residues cluster in core
      - Polar backbone N—H and C==O H bond in helices and sheets
- ❖ Fibrous proteins: Proteins whose polypeptide chains are parallel to a single axis
  - ⅄ α-keratin: α-helical coiled coils
    - Subunit: 311–314 residue-long α-helix–rich region flanked by non-helical regions
    - Two-stranded coiled coils with helix repeat of 0.51 nm
    - 7-residue quasi repeat with 1st and 4th residues non-polar
    - Disulfide bonds: Rigid, inextensible, and insoluble structure
  - ⅄ Fibroin and β-keratin: Stacked β-sheets
    - Stacked antiparallel β-sheets
    - Gly-Ser or Gly-Ala repeats
    - Sheets stack Gly to Gly
  - ⅄ Collagen: A triple helix: Connective tissue protein in animals
    - Tropocollagen: Basic unit of three intertwined chains
    - Type I $\alpha1(I)_2\alpha2(I)$, Type II $\alpha1(II)_3$, Type III $\alpha1(III)_3$
    - Amino acid composition and amino acid sequence
      - One-third Gly and one-third Pro or Hyp
      - Modified amino acids: Hydroxyproline and hydroxylysine (vitamin C–dependent reaction)
      - Gly-Pro-Hyp repeat with G placed in centre of three-stranded coil
    - Collagen fibrils
      - Staggered arrays of 5 tropocollagen (300 nm)
      - 68 nm periodicity with 40 nm hole regions
        - 5×68 nm $= 300$ nm $+ 40$ nm
- ❖ Globular proteins
  - ⅄ Core composed of hydrophobic amino acids
  - ⅄ Peptide groups often H-bonded as helices or sheets
    - Surface helices amphiphilic
    - Internal helices or sheets are hydrophobic
    - Solvent exposed helices hydrophilic
  - ⅄ Packing of elements results in formation of small cavities imparting flexibility to structure
  - ⅄ Ordered regions with well-defined, non-repetitive structure
  - ⅄ Disordered, flexible regions
- ❖ Protein domains
  - ⅄ Proteins of around 250 amino acid residues have simple, compact globular shape
  - ⅄ Larger proteins made up of domains or modules
    - Domains often impart unique function
    - Domains often coded for on single exons
      - Protein domain: Fundamental unit of evolution
    - Proteins classified on basis of domains
      - SCOP (http://scop.mrc-lmb.cam.ac.uk/scop)
      - CATH (http://www.cathdb.info)
        - Hierarchy based on structural elements, arrangements, function, sequence
- ❖ Loss of 3-D structure by disruption of weak forces: denaturation
  - ⅄ Sharp temperature dependence indicates two-state transition
  - ⅄ Temperature, pH, organic solvents, detergents, urea: denaturing agents
  - ⅄ Three-dimensional structure determined by amino acid sequence
  - ⅄ Anfinsen: RNase A denaturation/renaturation with urea and reducing agent

❖ Molecular motion: Proteins are dynamic structures
  ⅄ Atomic fluctuations: Movement over small distances
  ⅄ Collective motions: Movement of groups of atoms
  ⅄ Conformational changes: Movement of large domains
❖ Chain folding
  ⅄ Structural stability
  ⅄ Right-handed structures
    • Right-handed twists in sheets
    • Right-handed cross-overs joining secondary structural elements
  ⅄ β-strand connections
    • Antiparallel strands connected by hairpins
    • Parallel strands connected by cross-overs forming βαβ loop
  ⅄ Hydrophobic amino acids sequestered in interior: Layers
    • Two layers of backbone form a single hydrophobic core
    • Three layers of backbone form two hydrophobic cores
    • Four-layered and five-layered structures
❖ Globular protein classification based on secondary structure
  ⅄ Antiparallel α-helix
  ⅄ Parallel or mixed β-sheet
  ⅄ Antiparallel β-sheet
  ⅄ Metal- and disulfide-rich
❖ Molecular chaperones: Protein complexes that catalyze process of protein folding
  ⅄ Intrinsically unstructured proteins
    • Do not possess uniform structural properties
    • Capable of binding multiple ligands
    • Form large intermolecular interfaces
❖ Protein design: Domains: Regions 40–100 amino acids long that form stable tertiary structures
❖ Quaternary structure
  ⅄ Subunits typically fold into independent globular structures
  ⅄ Subunits interactions
    • Isologous interactions: Identical faces of identical subunits
    • Heterologous interactions: Interacting surfaces not identical
  ⅄ Symmetry
    • Cyclic symmetry: Single rotational axis
    • Dihedral symmetry: 2-fold axis perpendicular to n-fold axis
  ⅄ Subunit association forces
    • Hydrophobic interactions between faces
    • Disulfide bond stabilized
  ⅄ Polymers: Open quaternary structures
❖ Structural and functional advantages to quaternary associations
  ⅄ Protein stabilized by reduction in surface-to-volume ratio
  ⅄ Genetic economy: Encode self-assembling subunits rather than single complex protein
  ⅄ Catalytic sites brought together
❖ Cooperativity: Influence on catalytic sites by neighbouring sites

Chapter Objectives

The key to understanding protein structure is to understand the weak forces responsible for maintaining a protein in the folded state: hydrogen bonds, hydrophobic interactions, electrostatic interactions, and van der Waals forces. It will be helpful to review the structures of the amino acids and to recall the kinds of weak interactions each amino acid side chain is capable of making.

Peptide Bond
Know the characteristics of the peptide bond: the fact that it is planar because of π-bonding and resonance stabilization and the fact that it has a hydrogen-bond donor and an acceptor.

Secondary Structure

Protein secondary structures are regular structures formed by hydrogen bonds between amide planes. Understand the structure of the α-helix. The key is to understand how hydrogen bonding occurs in the α-helix. The carbonyl group of the ith residue is H-bonded to the peptide hydrogen of the $i + 4$th residue. Other, less common helices are found in nature (2_7 ribbon, 3_{10} helix, and π-helix) that form when hydrogen bonds occur between residues closer or further along the polypeptide chain. Sheet structures form between fully extended peptide chains. Beta-turns are tight turns stabilized by a hydrogen bond and requiring *cis* orientation of amide planes. The α-helix and β-sheet are shown in Figure 6.6 and Figure 6.10.

Tertiary Structure

The tertiary structure of a protein is its three-dimensional structure. Fibrous proteins have secondary structure elements arranged parallel to a single axis. Examples include α-keratin and collagen. Be familiar with the structures of these two proteins. Globular proteins are by far the most abundant class of proteins. As additional protein structures are solved by X-ray crystallography and nuclear magnetic resonance, a greater understanding of the rules governing protein folding and structure stabilization will unfold. Currently a majority of globular proteins are classified into four broad groups: antiparallel α-helix, parallel or mixed β-sheet, antiparallel β-sheet, and the small metal- and disulfide-rich proteins.

Quaternary Structure

Quaternary structure is reserved for proteins composed of multiple subunits. The subunits represent distinct structural domains that interact in specific ways to form the native protein.

Protein Denaturation

The three-dimensional shape of a functional protein is called the native conformation. A conformational change to a state or states lacking activity is known as denaturation. Protein denaturation may occur when the weak forces, responsible for the native conformation, are disrupted. Denaturing agents or conditions include heat, high concentrations of urea, guanidine HCl, high salt concentrations, low ionic strength solutions, SDS, organic solvents, or extremes in pH.

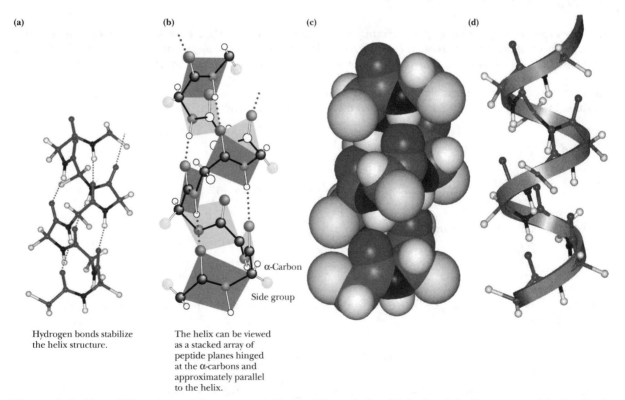

(a) Hydrogen bonds stabilize the helix structure.

(b) The helix can be viewed as a stacked array of peptide planes hinged at the α-carbons and approximately parallel to the helix.

α-Carbon

Side group

Figure 6.6 Four different graphic representations of the α-helix. (a) As it originally appeared in Pauling's 1960 *The Nature of the Chemical Bond.* (b) Showing the arrangement of peptide planes in the helix. (c) A space-filling computer graphic presentation. (d) A "ribbon structure" with an inlaid stick figure, showing how the ribbon indicates the path of the polypeptide backbone. (*Irving Geis*)

Figure 6.11 The arrangement of hydrogen bonds in (a) parallel and (b) antiparallel β-pleated sheet.

Problems and Solutions

1.   The central rod domain of a keratin protein is approximately 312 residues in length. What is the length (in Å) of the keratin rod domain? If this same peptide segment were a true α-helix, how long would it be? If the same segment were a β-sheet, what would its length be?

Answer: α-keratin has extensively distorted α-helical secondary structure. The helix repeats every 3.6 residues but has a pitch of 0.51 nm (compared to 0.54 nm for a true α-helix).

$$\frac{312 \text{ residues}}{3.6 \dfrac{\text{residues}}{\text{turn}}} = 86.7 \text{ turns}$$

$$86.7 \text{ turns} \times 0.51 \frac{\text{nm}}{\text{turn}} = 44.2 \text{ nm} = 442 \text{ Å}$$

For an α-helix of the same number of residues:

$$86.7 \text{ turns} \times 0.54 \frac{\text{nm}}{\text{turn}} = 46.8 \text{ nm} = 468 \text{ Å}$$

For pleated sheets, the distance between residues is 0.347 nm for antiparallel sheets and 0.325 nm for parallel sheets. Thus:

$$312 \text{ residues antiparallel sheet} \times 0.347 \frac{\text{nm}}{\text{residue}} = 108.3 \text{ nm} = 1083 \text{ Å}$$

$$312 \text{ residues parallel sheet} \times 0.325 \frac{\text{nm}}{\text{residue}} = 101.4 \text{ nm} = 1014 \text{ Å}$$

3.   Discuss the potential contributions to hydrophobic and van der Waals interactions and ionic and hydrogen bonds for the side chains of Asp, Leu, Tyr, and His in a protein.

Answer: Aspartic acid has a relatively small side chain composed of a —CH$_2$— group and a carboxyl group. The presence of the ionizable carboxyl group indicates that aspartic acid can participate in ionic bonds. In addition, lone-pair electrons on the oxygen of the carboxyl group can participate in H bonds, as can the hydrogen when the carboxyl group is protonated. Hydrophobic interactions and van der Waals interactions are negligible.

The leucine side chain is an alkane and as such will not participate in hydrogen bonds or ionic bonds. The side chain is hydrophobic and relatively bulky, indicating that it will participate in hydrophobic interactions and is capable of participating in numerous van der Waals interactions.

Tyrosine has a phenolic group attached to the α carbon by a methylene bridge (i.e., —CH$_2$—). The phenolic group is weakly ionizing with a pK_a of 10. Thus, only under special conditions or environments would it be expected to participate in ionic bonds. The hydroxyl group can both donate and accept H bonds. When protonated, tyrosine is capable of hydrophobic interactions, and, because it is a bulky amino acid, it is expected to participate in numerous van der Waals interactions.

The imidazole side chain of histidine has an ionizable nitrogen and, when protonated, allows histidine to participate in ionic bonds. In addition, hydrogen-bond donor and acceptor groups support participation in hydrogen bonds. Thus, the ability to form both hydrogen bonds and ionic bonds precludes hydrophobic bonding. The large side chain is expected to participate in van der Waals interaction.

5. For flavodoxin (pdb ID = 5NLL), identify the right-handed crossovers and the left-handed crossovers in the parallel β-sheet.

Answer: Visit the protein data bank at http://www.rcsb.org/pdb/home/home.do and download 5NLL. There are a number of options for viewing this protein's structure and these are found under the image. Launch one of the programs or download the pdb file for 5NLL. (MBT Protein Workshop, Rasmol, and Swiss-PDB viewer are all reasonable programs to use. The latter two are stand-alone programs you must download.) View the molecule as a ribbon and locate the N-terminus and C-terminus.

For a right-handed cross-over, moving in the N-terminal to C-terminal direction, the crossover moves in a clockwise direction. The reverse is true for a left-handed crossover, namely, movement from N-terminus to C-terminus is accompanied by counterclockwise rotation.

Various programs have options for colouring secondary structure elements and this is a useful option to identify sheets and helices. Using this option, we find that flavodoxin has 5 regions of α-helix and 5 regions involved in sheet formation. The core of the protein is formed by a 5-stranded, curved parallel β-sheet that has two α-helices inside and three α-helices outside (a three-layered protein) the curved parallel sheet.

Moving from the N-terminus, we encounter the first secondary structure: the second strand of the parallel β-sheet followed by an α-helix, which is inside the curved parallel sheet, and then the outside strand of the parallel β-sheet. A short helix, which runs on the outside curve of the sheet, connects the outside strand of the sheet to its third strand. Another helix again on the outside of the sheet connects to the fourth strand of the sheet. The fifth strand is also connected by a helix running on the outside. Finally, the C-terminus is part of the last helix that is on the inside of the sheet. A diagram of the connectivity of the parallel β-sheet strands is shown below.

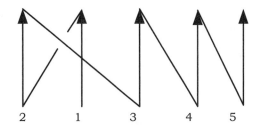

The crossovers from strand 2 to 3, 3 to 4, and 4 to 5 are easy to identify as right-handed. For example, the connection from strand 2 to strand 3 moves in a clockwise direction. The connection between 1 and 2 is also right-handed. To see this, flip the diagram vertically.

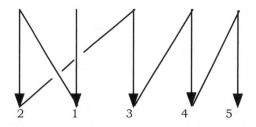

Now, rotate by 180° so that strand 2 is to the right of strand 1.

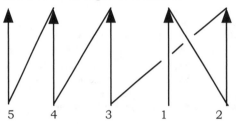

Focus on moving from strand 1 to 2. The connection is clockwise and thus right-handed. All the crossovers in flavodoxin are right-handed.

7.   A new protein of unknown structure has been purified. Gel filtration chromatography reveals that the native protein has a molecular weight of 240 000. Chromatography in the presence of 6 M guanidine hydrochloride yields only a peak for a protein of M_r 60 000. Chromatography in the presence of 6 M guanidine hydrochloride and 10 mM β-mercaptoethanol yields peaks for proteins of M_r 34 000 and 26 000. Explain what can be determined about the structure of this protein from these data.

Answer: Guanidine hydrochloride is a powerful denaturing agent that disrupts tertiary and quaternary structure by disrupting hydrogen bonds. In the presence of 6 M guanidine-HCl, only a 60 kD species is observed, indicating that the native protein may in fact be a tetramer of four 60 kD subunits. Upon denaturation in the presence of β-mercaptoethanol (a disulfide-reducing agent), two protein peaks are observed, one at 34 kD and one at 26 kD. This indicates that the 60 kD subunit is a heterodimer of two chains, 34 kD and 26 kD, held together by a disulfide bond.

9.   The hemagglutinin protein in influenza virus contains a remarkably long α-helix, with 53 residues.
    a.   How long is this α-helix (in nm)?
    b.   How many turns does this helix have?
    c.   Each residue in an α-helix is involved in two H bonds. How many H bonds are present in this helix?

Answer: The α-helix repeats every 0.54 nm (3.6 amino acid residues) and the distance along the helical axis between residues is 0.15 nm. An α-helix of 53 residues is:

$$\frac{53 \text{ residues}}{3.6 \dfrac{\text{residues}}{\text{turn}}} \times 0.54 \frac{\text{nm}}{\text{turn}} = 7.95 \text{ nm, or}$$

$$53 \text{ residues} \times 0.15 \frac{\text{nm}}{\text{residue}} = 7.95 \text{ nm}$$

The number of turns is:

$$\frac{53 \text{ residues}}{3.6 \dfrac{\text{residues}}{\text{turn}}} = 14.7 \text{ turns}$$

To calculate the number of H bonds, the ith residue is H-bonded to the $(i + 4)^{\text{th}}$ residue to form a helix. For a 53-residue helix, the carbonyl groups of the first 49 residues are involved in H bonding ($i + 4 = 53$; $\therefore i = 49$).

The amide H for the four residues on the N-terminal side are not hydrogen-bonded nor are the carbonyl groups of the last 4 residues, on the C-terminal side. Thus, 49 hydrogen bonds are made.

11. Explain how Anfinsen confirmed that the information driving the formation of 3D structure is found in the primary sequence.

Answer: Denatured ribonuclease (in the presence of urea and beta-marcatoethanol) possessed no enzymatic activity. Subsequent removal of the bate-mercaptoethanol (but not urea) leads to some of the ribonuclease activity being restored. This was attributed to the formation of random (albeit not correct) disulfide bridges upon renaturation. However, when both the beta-mercaptoethanol and urea were removed simultaneously, the protein could refold into its native conformation and form the correct disufide bridges. Enzymatic activity was also restored. Thus, information needed for protein folding resides within the primary sequence of ribonuclease which dictates non-covalent interactions are necessary for the correct structure to form first, followed by correct disulfide bridge formation.

13. Poly-L-glutamate adopts an α-helical structure at low pH but becomes a random coil above pH 5. Explain this behaviour.

Answer: The side chain of glutamic acid contains a carboxylic acid group with a pK_a of 4.25. At pH 5.0 glutamic acid's side chain is largely ionized with a 1− charge. Thus, polyglutamic acid at this pH has negative charges, which will repel each other. At pH 2.0, the side chain is protonated and thus uncharged, making it possible for the peptide chain to form an α-helix, which brings amino acids closer together than in random coil.

15. Consider the following peptide sequences:
   EANQIDEMLYNVQSLTTLEDTVPW
   LGVHLDITVPLSWTWTLYVKL
   QQNWGGLVVILTLVWFLM
   CNMKHGDSQCDERTYP
   YTREQSDGHIPKMNCDS
   AGPFGPDGPTIGPK
Which of the preceding sequences would be likely to be found in each of the following:
   a.   a parallel β-sheet
   b.   an antiparallel β-sheet
   c.   a tropocollagen molecule
   d.   the helical portions of a protein found in your hair?

Answer: To help identify β-sheets, we can look at distributions of hydrophobic amino acids, which are typically distributed on one side of an antiparallel sheet and both sides of a parallel sheet. To help, we will display hydrophobic amino acids in bold. (The font is changed to Courier, a non-proportional font, to allow for alignment of the sequence with the residue numbers.)

```
123456789012345678901234
EANQIDEMLYNVQSLTTLEDTVPW
LGVHLDITVPLSWTWTLYVKL
QQNWGGLVVILTLVWFLM
CNMKHGDSQCDERTYP
YTREQSDGHIPKMNCDS
AGPFGPDGPTIGPK
```

The second sequence has hydrophobic amino acids at nearly every other residue. If this sequence were in β-sheet structure, it would have a hydrophobic surface and a hydrophilic surface. Thus, sequence two is likely to be an antiparallel sheet.

The first and third sequences also contain significant numbers of hydrophobic amino acids. For the third sequence, if it were in β-sheet structure, it would have hydrophobic amino acids on both sides of the sheet consistent with a parallel sheet.

The first sequence also has nearly an equal distribution of hydrophobic amino acids at odd-numbered and even-numbered positions, which would be expected to support parallel sheet formation. However, the first sequence seems to have hydrophobic amino acids distributed evenly throughout its length. If fact, starting at the alanine in position 2, one sees hydrophobic amino acids at positions 5 (an I) and 8 (an M), which is reminiscent of the primary structure of α-keratins with quasi-repeating segments, seven-residues long and containing hydrophobic amino acids at positions 1, 4 and 7. If arranged in an α-helix, this would put hydrophobic amino acids on one face of the helix. Thus, the first sequence is a good candidate for the helical portions of a protein found in hair.

Of the remaining sequences, the best fit for a tropocollagen sequence is the sixth sequence. Tropocollagen is a triple helix of a special type formed by intertwining three chains together. The chains have a three-residue repeat, Gly-x-y, with x and y often being proline (and or hydroxyproline).

Programs designed to identify parallel and antiparallel sheets have been developed and several may be found at SwissProt (http://us.expasy.org/sprot/) under Proteomics tools (http://us.expasy.org/tools/). Under "Primary Structure Analysis," the link to ProtScale gives several useful programs to analyze primary protein structure. The figure below was constructed by analyzing each of the sequences using "beta-sheet/Chou & Fasman". There are also programs listed that will analyze parallel and antiparallel sheets. Sequences are entered into the text box. The programs calculate the probability of a particular structure using a scoring matrix, which gives the likelihood of finding a particular amino acid in a structure. Average scores are calculated over a window of amino acids. Before activating the program, change the window size to the smallest allowable. Because several of the sequences are quite small, it may help to add glycines to each end of the sequences.

Data for the figure was generated using ten G's on each end of each of the sequences. After the program was activated, the results were reported both graphically and numerically by activating the link at the bottom of the results page. The numerical results were pasted into a Microsoft Word document as unformatted text using "Paste Special". The data were converted from text to table and the values were then transferred to Microsoft Excel.

Sequences 1, 2, and 3 all score high, relative to 4, 5, and 6 in the Chou and Fasman analysis in addition to antiparallel and parallel sheet programs. Sequence 3 scores highest as a parallel sheet.

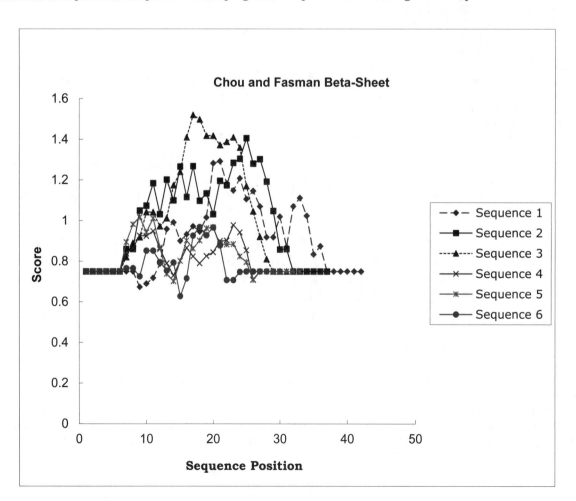

Questions for Self-Study

1. List the weak interactions responsible for maintaining protein conformation.

2. For the structures shown, below indicate by D, A, D&A, or B if the structure contains only a hydrogen-bond donor, only a hydrogen-bond acceptor, a donor and separately an acceptor, or a group that functions both as donor or acceptor.

3. Fill in the blanks. The α-helix is an example of a _____ structural element. It is a helical structure formed by _____ _____ between groups in peptide bonds. In particular, the _____ _____ of the ith residue of an α-helix is bonded to the _____ _____ of the $(i + 4)$th residue. The result is a helical structure that repeats every _____ residues. The _____ of the helix, or distance along the z-axis per turn, is 0.54 nm. This arrangement orients the amide planes _____ to the helix axis and the side chains _____ to the helix axis.

4. Proteins composed predominantly of β-pleated sheets may be expected to form structures that are flexible yet inextensible. Please explain.

5. What two amino acids are most suited to beta-turns?

6. What post-translational modification is necessary to produce collagen, and what water-soluble vitamin is this modification dependent on?

7. Give two examples of fibrous proteins.

8. What are the four globular protein groups found in nature?

9. The agents listed below are all expected to affect protein tertiary structure. For each, give a brief explanation of how they affect protein structure.
    a. urea
    b. SDS
    c. high temperature
    d. β-mercaptoethanol
    e. distilled water
    f. organic solvents

10. What are the advantages to quaternary associations?

Answers

1. Hydrogen bonds, hydrophobic interactions, electrostatic interactions, van der Waals interactions.

2. a. A; b. D; c. B; d. D&A; e. A

3. secondary; hydrogen bonding; carbonyl oxygen; amide nitrogen; 3.6; pitch; parallel; perpendicular

4. The polypeptide chain in a β-pleated sheet is already fully extended; however, the chains are free to bend.

5. Proline and glycine.

6. Hydroxylation; vitamin C.

7. α-keratin, silk fibroin proteins, collagen.

8. Antiparallel α-helix; parallel or mixed β-sheet; antiparallel β-sheet; small metal- and disulfide-rich proteins.

9. a. Urea will disrupt hydrogen bonds; b. SDS is a detergent that will disrupt the hydrophobic cores of proteins; c. β-mercaptoethanol will reduce disulfide bonds; d. High temperature will disrupt weak forces; e. Distilled water will perturb ionic interactions; f. Organic solvents will interact with hydrophobic amino acid side chains.

10. Genetic economy and efficiency; structural stability due to reduction of surface-to-volume ratio; formation of catalytic centers; cooperativity.

Additional Problems

1. For the following conditions or agents, explain how they may denature proteins: heat, urea, guanidine HCl, distilled water, SDS, liquid phenol.

2. An often-cited example of protein denaturation is the change accompanying the heating of egg-whites. Clearly, this process is irreversible yet the classic experiments of Anfinsen on RNase A showed that denaturation is reversible. Rectify these two seemingly conflicting facts.

3. In the movie *Papillon*, a criminal, played by the late Steve McQueen, is imprisoned on a remote tropical island for many years. Needless to say, conditions in prison are not idyllic; the prisoners are served only enough gruel to keep them alive. In one scene, the main character reaches into his mouth and pulls out a tooth. What disease might the prisoner have suffered from?

4. Gelatin desserts are prepared by adding hot water to a dry powder. This popular dessert is made from collagen from pig skins. Given your understanding of the structure of collagen explain the gel-like consistency of gelatin.

5. Myoglobin was the first globular protein whose structure was solved by X-ray crystallography. The protein contains a hydrophobic core formed by the sides of several α-helices. For human myoglobin, the sequence of helix E is given below. For this helix, label the hydrophobic residues likely to contribute to the hydrophobic core.
   E Helix Sequence: S E D L K K H G A T V L T A L G G I L

Abbreviated Answers

1. Gentle heating will disrupt hydrogen bonds. The structures of urea and guanidine HCl are shown below:

$$\begin{array}{cc} \overset{\displaystyle O}{\underset{\displaystyle \parallel}{}} & \overset{\displaystyle NH_2^+ \; Cl^-}{\underset{\displaystyle \parallel}{}} \\ H_2N-C-NH_2 & H_2N-C-NH_2 \\ \text{Urea} & \text{Guanidinium HCl} \end{array}$$

Urea and guanidine HCl are both very soluble in water and may be used to form highly concentrated solutions. These agents denature proteins by disrupting hydrogen bonds. The low ionic strength and high dielectric constant of distilled water cause changes in ionic bonds that may lead to protein denaturation. SDS is an ionic detergent that disrupts hydrophobic interactions. In solution, SDS forms micelle structures by association of their hydrocarbon tails. Micelles will form around hydrophobic amino acid side chains, disrupting the normal hydrophobic interactions these side chains make. Liquid phenol will disrupt hydrophobic interactions.

2. Egg whites contain about 10% by weight of ovalbumin and, while it is true the heat of a hot frying pan is sufficient to denature the protein, the real problem comes subsequently. The denatured protein readily aggregates in this highly concentrated protein solution and the aggregation is for all intents and

purposes irreversible. Anfinsen's experiments were done at much lower protein concentrations (and with a considerably smaller protein).

3. The disease was probably scurvy caused by a deficiency of vitamin C. Cross-linking of collagen fibres is catalyzed by prolyl hydroxylase in a vitamin C–dependent reaction. A deficiency of vitamin C results in incomplete cross-linking leading to defective collagen fibres. Collagen fibres are found in connective tissues, which are thus weakened in scurvy.

4. Collagen fibres hydrate and interact to form a tangled mass of crisscrossed fibres.

5. The residues in helix E are plotted in a helical wheel plot to identify the location of amino acids on the helix surface. To construct a helical wheel plot, a projection of the residues in a helix is made along the helical axis (z-axis) onto the x–y plane. In an α-helix, the helix repeats every 3.6 residues. Thus, each residues is 100° apart. The helical wheel plot is shown below with hydrophobic amino acids highlighted.

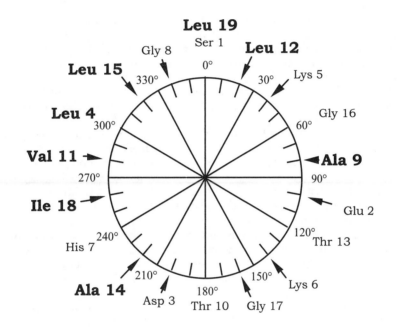

The plot clearly shows that hydrophobic amino acids (in boldface) are concentrated along one side of the helix. This is the side of the helix that faces the hydrophobic core.

Summary

Proteins are composed of linear chains of amino acids held together by peptide bonds. The sequence of amino acids is the primary structure of the protein. It contains all the information necessary to fold up the chains into a functional protein. This folding involves weak forces such as hydrogen bonds, electrostatic interactions, hydrophobic interactions, and van der Waals interactions. The peptide bond itself is capable of participating in hydrogen bonds with both hydrogen-bond donor and acceptor groups. For example, the carbonyl group has two pairs of lone-pair electrons capable of accepting hydrogen bonds. Also, the electronegative nitrogen induces a partial positive charge on its attached hydrogen, allowing the hydrogen to function as a hydrogen-bond donor. Hydrogen bonding between peptide bond groups is the basis of protein secondary structure elements, namely, helices, pleated sheets, and turns.

The side chains of the amino acids are capable of many interactions including H bonds, ionic bonds, hydrophobic interactions, and van der Waals interactions. These interactions and secondary structural elements are responsible for the tertiary structure of proteins, their actual three-dimensional shape.

Secondary structure elements include helices, pleated sheets, and β-turns. Stable helices are a result of hydrogen-bond formation between donor and acceptor groups in peptide bonds. The α-helix is a right-handed helix (in moving from the N-terminus to the C-terminus, rotation is clockwise) formed by the carbonyl oxygen of the ith residue hydrogen bonded to the amide hydrogen of the $(i + 4)^{th}$ residue. The helix makes one turn every 0.54 nm and has 3.6 amino acid residues per turn. Amino acids are spaced 0.15 nm along the helix axis. The hydrogen bonds are parallel to the helical axis, with the peptide-bond planes and the amino acid side chains perpendicular. The α-helix is also referred to as a 3.6_{13} helix; it has 3.6 residues per turn with the hydrogen-bonded groups separated by 13 atoms. Other helical structures are known that involve formation of hydrogen bonds between the carbonyl of the ith amino acid and the amide nitrogen at $i + 2$, (2_7 ribbon), $i + 3$, (3_{10}), and $i + 5$, (4.4_{16} or π helix). When the polypeptide chain is in an extended state, β-pleated sheets may form by hydrogen bonding between parallel chains (parallel β-pleated sheets) or antiparallel chains (β-pleated sheets). The disposition of α-carbons in these structures forms a pleated pattern.

The peptide chain is often required to make sharp turns (as, for example, when antiparallel β-pleated sheets are formed) and the β-turn is often used to accomplish this. In this secondary structure element, a sharp turn is stabilized by hydrogen bonding between the carbonyl of a peptide bond with the amide hydrogen 2 residues away. In a polypeptide chain, peptide bonds are usually *trans* but in the β-turn a *cis* arrangement is required. Proline and glycine are often found in β-turns because they can assume the *cis* configuration.

Some proteins are dominated by secondary structure. In α-keratin, found in hair, wool, claws, fingernails, and horns of animals, two-stranded coiled coils composed of distorted α-helices predominate. Connective tissue, including tendons, cartilage, bones, teeth, skin, and blood vessels, contains collagen, whose structure is dominated by a triple helix. The collagen helix has 3.3 residues per turn, a fact reflected in its amino acid sequence. The primary structure is dominated by repeats of Gly-Pro-Hyp. Glycines are located on the helix interior, making contact with each other to form the three-stranded structure. In contrast to these helical proteins, the fibroin protein of silk fibres is composed of stacked antiparallel β-sheets.

The largest class of proteins is that of the globular proteins. Here, helices, sheets, and turns are used to form a globular structure held together by weak forces. Hydrophobic interactions play a major role in globular protein structure; the core is often formed by hydrophobic amino acid side chains. Structural motifs consisting of secondary structure elements are often components contributing to protein structure, as for example β-sheet arrays with right-handed twists and $\beta\alpha\beta$-loops. The globular proteins can be classified based on the type and arrangement of secondary structure. In antiparallel helix proteins, the core structure is a bundle composed of antiparallel α-helices. Parallel or mixed β-sheet proteins have an extended sheet of β-structure. The sheet may be internal, in which case hydrophobic amino acids are distributed on both sides of the sheet. Alternatively, the sheet may be arranged in a barrel shape. Antiparallel β-sheet proteins have two sheets, each composed of antiparallel β-sheets. Finally, metal-rich proteins and disulfide-rich proteins rely on either metal binding sites or numerous disulfide bonds to maintain a stable globular structure.

Some proteins appear to be composed of more than one structural domain and each of the domains serves a particular role in protein function. Often, a distinct structural domain is a protein module dedicated to a particular function.

Proteins are dynamic, delicate structures that function in a narrow range of conditions such as pH, ionic strength, and temperature. This is because tertiary structure is stabilized by weak forces. When these weak forces are perturbed, the protein assumes a nonfunctional conformation in a process known as denaturation. Denaturation can be accomplished by an elevation of temperature over a narrow range, giving rise to a sharp transition. In addition to temperature, chemicals like acids, bases, organic solvents, detergents. and urea and guanidine hydrochloride are potent denaturing agents.

The experiments of Anfinsen and White showed that the information to fold a peptide chain into a protein is contained in the primary structure. Working with ribonuclease, a small protein capable of hydrolyzing phosphodiester bonds in RNA, they showed that enzymatic activity is dependent on the native conformation of the protein. The protein contains numerous disulfide bridges that stabilize the native state. By reducing these bonds and treating the protein with a denaturing agent, activity is lost. However, the activity is regained if the denaturant is first removed, allowing the chain to fold into its native conformation before disulfide bonds are allowed to reform.

Quaternary structure is reserved for oligomeric proteins, proteins composed of distinct subunits. When the subunits are identical, the protein is a homomultimer; when the subunits are different, the protein is a heteromultimer. In multimeric proteins, the subunits typically fold into independent structures and make isologous (same surface) or heterologous (different surface) interactions with other subunits in the protein. The driving forces for these interactions are hydrophobic in nature and disulfide bonds may stabilize the interactions. Quaternary associations have functional advantages including stability due to a reduction is surface-to-volume ratio, genetic economy, formation of active protomeric enzymes by bringing catalytic sites, located on separate sites on the monomer, together in the polymer and, finally, cooperativity of ligand binding sites and catalytic sites.

Chapter 7

Carbohydrates and the Glycoconjugates of Cell Surfaces

• •

Chapter Outline

❖ Carbohydrates $(CH_2O)_n$, $n \geq 3$
❖ Nomenclature
   ↙ Monosaccharides (simple sugars)
   ↙ Olio and polysaccharides: Polymers of simple sugars
❖ Classification
   ↙ Aldose (aldehyde) and ketose (ketone)
   ↙ Triose, tetrose, pentose, hexose, etc.
❖ Stereochemistry
   ↙ Aldose $n \geq 3$, ketose $n \geq 4$ have asymmetric carbons (chiral centres)
   ↙ D- and L-configuration: Refer to configuration of highest numbered asymmetric carbon
   ↙ D- and L-forms: Mirror images: Enantiomers
   ↙ With >1 asymmetric carbon: Diastereomers: Configurations that differ at 1 or more chiral carbons but not mirror-image molecules
   ↙ Epimers: Two molecules that differ in configuration about 1 asymmetric carbon
❖ Ring structures
   ↙ Pyranoses: Six-membered, oxygen-containing ring
   ↙ Furanose: Five-membered, oxygen-containing ring
   ↙ Anomeric carbon: Ketone or aldehyde carbon that becomes chiral upon ring formation
   ↙ Anomers: α, β differ in configuration about anomeric carbon
      • α-configuration: In Fisher projection, OH of anomeric carbon on same side as OH of highest numbered asymmetric carbon
      • β-configuration: In Fisher projection, OH of anomeric carbon on opposite side as OH of highest numbered asymmetric carbon
   ↙ Haworth projections: Three-dimensional representation: Groups to right in Fisher projection draw down in Haworth projection
   ↙ Conformations
      • Chair and boat conformations due to ring pucker
      • Axial and equatorial orientation of groups attached to ring
❖ Sugar derivatives
   ↙ Acids: Oxidation of free anomeric carbon to carboxylate
      • Aldonic acid (gluconic acid from glucose)
   ↙ Acids: At C-6: Uronic acid (glucuronic acid from glucose)
   ↙ Alcohols: Alditols: Carbonyl reduced to alcohol
   ↙ Deoxysugars: H replaces OH group
   ↙ Phosphate esters (ATP and GTP)
   ↙ Amino sugars: Amino group in place of OH: Glucosamine
      • Muramic acid and neuraminic acid: Glucosamine with acids linked to C-1 or to C-3
   ↙ Glycosides: Anomeric carbon reacted with alcoholic function
❖ Sugars with free anomeric carbon are reducing sugars
   ↙ End of sugar polymer with free anomeric carbon: Reducing end
   ↙ Opposite end: Non-reducing end

- ❖ Oligosaccharides
  - ⅄ Disaccharides
    - • Maltose: Diglucose
    - • Lactose: Galactose and glucose
    - • Sucrose: Fructose and glucose: Non-reducing sugar
- ❖ Storage polysaccharides
  - ⅄ Starch: α-Amylose and amylopectin
    - • α-Amylose: Linear chains of $\alpha(1{\to}4)$D-glucose
    - • Amylopectin: Linear chains of $\alpha(1{\to}4)$D-glucose with $\alpha(1{\to}6)$D-glucose branches every 12 to 30 residues
    - • Plant digestion of starch: Starch phosphorylase: Phosphorolytic cleavage producing glucose-1-phosphate
    - • Animal digestion of starch
      - • α-Amylase: Animals: Hydrolysis of internal $\alpha(1{\to}4)$ glycosidic linkage
  - ⅄ Glycogen: $\alpha(1{\to}4)$ D-glucose chains with $\alpha(1{\to}6)$ D-glucose branches every 8 to 12 residues
  - ⅄ Dextrans: Bacteria: $\alpha(1{\to}6)$ D-glucose polymers
- ❖ Structural polymers
  - ⅄ Cellulose: Plant cell wall: Linear polymer of $\beta(1{\to}4)$ D-glucose
  - ⅄ Chitin: Exoskeleton and fungi cell wall: $\beta(1{\to}4)$ N-acetyl-D-glucosamine
  - ⅄ Agar: Two components: Agarose and agaropectin
    - • Agarose: Alternating D-galactose and 3,6-anhydro-L-galactose chains with 6-methyl-D-galactose side chains
    - • Agaropectin: Agarose with negatively charged sulfate or carboxylate groups
  - ⅄ Glycosaminoglycans: Polymers with disaccharide repeat: Negatively charged
    - • Heparin: Sulfated glucuronic acid/disulfated glucosamine: Highly charged
    - • Hyaluronate, condroitin-4 or -6 sulfate, dermatan sulfate, keratan sulfate
- ❖ Peptidoglycan of bacterial cell walls
  - ⅄ Gram-negative bacterial cell wall
    - • NAG-NAM repeats crosslinked with tetrapeptide
    - • Cell wall sandwiched between inner and outer lipid bilayers
    - • Outer lipid bilayer: Lipopolysaccharides: Antigenic
  - ⅄ Gram-positive bacterial cell walls
    - • NAM-NAG repeats crosslinked with tetrapeptide and pentaglycine
    - • No outer cell wall
    - • Teichoic acid: Ribitol phosphate or glycerol phosphate polymers
- ❖ Glycoproteins
  - ⅄ Functions: Structural, enzymatic, receptors, transport, immunoglobins
  - ⅄ Linkage
    - • O-linked
      - • Amino acids are serine, threonine or hydroxylysine
      - • Sugars: *N*-Acetylgalactosamine
      - • Cell surface glycoproteins: Two motifs
        - ○ Glycosylated extracellular domain: Adopts extended conformation
        - ○ Glycosylated extracellular stem: Separates extracellular globular domain from membrane surface
      - • Antifreeze glycoproteins: $[\text{A-A-T}]_n$-A-A
        - ○ n from 5 to 50
        - ○ T has O-linked disaccharide
    - • N-linked
      - • Amino acid is asparagine
      - • Sugars: Two *N*-Acetylglucosamines linked to branched mannose triad
      - • Variety of functions: Protein stabilization, protect against proteolysis, help folding
        - ○ Blood protein age sensed by liver receptor sensitive to charge on protein oligosaccharides

- ❖ Proteoglycans: Glycoproteins
  - ⅄ Sugar: Glycosaminoglycans: O-linked to Ser of (Ser-Gly) repeats
  - ⅄ Function: Interact with a variety of proteins via glycosaminoglycan
    - • BBXB and BBBXB (B = basic amino acid) are binding sites on proteins that bind to glycosaminoglycan
  - ⅄ Syndecan: Transmembrane proteoglycan
    - • Binds to actin cytoskeleton intracellularly
    - • Binds to fibronectin extracellularly
  - ⅄ Growth-modulating proteoglycans
    - • Heparin internalization inhibits cell proliferation
    - • Heparin binds fibroblast growth factor and protects it from degradation
    - • Proteoglycan synthesis and secretion stimulated by transforming growth factor β
    - • Some proteoglycan core proteins have domains that may bind to growth factor receptors
  - ⅄ Cartilage flexibility and resilience
    - • Matrix: Hyaluronic acid filaments studded with proteoglycan
    - • Polyanionic complex coordinates water that is squeezed out and reabsorbed
- ❖ Carbohydrate code
  - ⅄ Glycoconjugates: Information-rich protein–sugar interactions
    - • Sugar polymers provide information
      - • Information organized by enzymes (glycosyltransferases, glycosidases)
    - • Sugar-binding proteins like lectins translate code
      - • Proteins bind with specificity and high affinity
    - • Interactions mediate a host of cell activities: migration, cell interactions, immune response, blood clotting
      - • Selectins involved in movement of leukocytes along endothelial cells
      - • Galectins regulate cell adhesion, growth, inflammation, immunity, and metastasis
      - • C-reactive protein: A pentraxin that limits tissue damage by binding to damaged membranes

Chapter Objectives

It is important to know basic carbohydrate nomenclature, stereochemistry, and chemistry. Monosaccharides, with the general formula $(CH_2O)_n$, are either aldoses or ketoses. The more important monosaccharides range from $n = 3$ to $n = 7$. Because carbohydrates contain a number of chiral centres (carbons with four different groups attached), L- and D-isomers can be formed. Figures 7.2 and 7.3 show D-aldoses and D-ketoses having from three to six carbons.

Cyclic carbohydrates are produced by an intramolecular reaction between an aldehyde or ketone group and a hydroxyl group. In this reaction, the carbonyl carbon of the aldehyde or ketose is converted to a chiral carbon, the anomeric carbon. As a consequence, two structural isomers, α or β anomers, can be formed. Stable five- and six-membered rings, furanose and pyranose, are very common. Sugars with free anomeric carbons are reducing sugars. Oligosaccharides and polysaccharides are composed of monosaccharides held together by glycosidic bonds. If a linear polymer contains a free anomeric carbon at one end, that end is called the reducing end and the other end, the non-reducing end.

The following carbohydrates should be known:

trioses:	glyceraldehyde and dihydroxyacetone
pentoses:	ribose, ribulose, and deoxyribose
hexoses:	fructose, galactose, glucose, and mannose
heptoses:	sedulose
disaccharides:	lactose, maltose, and sucrose
polysaccharides:	amylose, amylopectin, glycogen, cellulose, and chitin

Important modified sugars include sugar acids, sugar phosphate esters, deoxy sugars, and amino sugars. Many of these modifications are found in the sugar moieties of important biological compounds. Monosaccharides do not display as wide a range of chemical characteristics as, for example, the amino acids. Nonetheless, polysaccharides are a diverse group of biomolecules because of the ability to join monosaccharides at a number of different positions to form branch polymers and the availability of numerous modified monosaccharides for polymer construction.

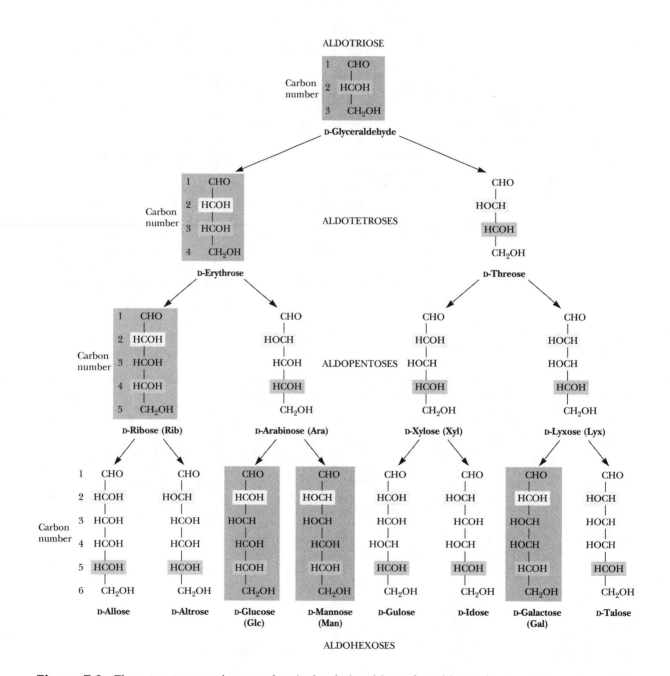

Figure 7.2 The structure and stereochemical relationships of D-aldoses having 3–6 carbons. The configuration in each case is determined by the highest numbered asymmetric carbon.

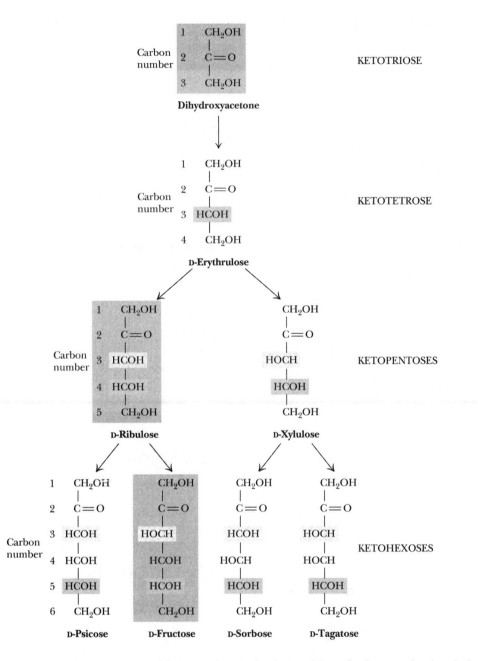

Figure 7.3 The structure and stereochemical relationships of D-ketoses having 3–6 carbons. The configuration in each case is determined by the highest numbered asymmetric carbon.

Problems and Solutions

1. Draw Haworth structures for the two possible isomers of D-altrose (Figure 7.2) and D-psicose (Figure 7.3).

Answer: To draw Haworth projections:
1.   Rotate the Fisher projection by 90° as shown below.
2.   Groups that are to the right in Fisher projection are down in Haworth projection.
3.   To form the ring, the hydroxyl at C4 must be reoriented. This reorientation brings C6 above the plane of the ring.

4. For C1, the orientation of H and OH depends on which side of the carbonyl plane the OH attacks, β is up, and α is down.

α-D-altrose

β-D-altrose

For psicose, a ketose orientation about C2 depends on which side of the ketone group the hydroxyl of C5 attacks.

α-D-psicose

β-D-psicose

3. (Integrates with Chapters 5 and 6) Human hemoglobin can react with sugars in the blood (usually glucose) to form covalent adducts. The α-amino groups of N-terminal valine in the Hb β-subunits react with the C-1 (aldehyde) carbons of monosaccharides to form aldimine adducts, which rearrange to form very stable ketoamine products. Quantitation of this "glycated hemoglobin" is important clinically, especially for diabetic individuals. Suggest at least three methods by which glycated Hb could be separated from normal Hb and quantitated.

Answer: Modification of the N-terminus of a polypeptide will change the ionic properties and separation of modified and unmodified proteins may be accomplished by ion exchange. The two forms may also be separated using isoelectric focusing because they have different pI's. Addition of a glucosyl moiety will change the protein's molecular weight; however, this small difference may be difficult to detect unless the protein is cleaved into smaller polypeptides or even individual amino acids. Mass spectrometry may also be used to detect and quantitate this modification.

5. Draw Fischer projection structures for L-sorbose (D-sorbose is shown in Figure 7.3).

Answer: L-sorbose

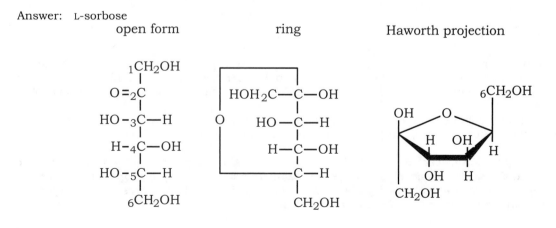

7. Use the information in the Critical Developments in Biochemistry box titled "Rules for Description of Chiral Centres in the (R,S) System" (Chapter 4) to name D-galactose using (R,S) nomenclature. Do the same for L-altrose.

Answer: D-galactose and L-altrose are shown below. In both cases, carbons 2, 3, 4, and 5 are all chiral centres. Starting at carbon 5 for galactose, we prioritize each of the groups as follows: OH-1, C4-2, C6-3, and H-4. (The difference in priority between C4 and C6 was determined by recognizing that both carbons have H and OH bonded to them but C6 has an additional H whereas C4 is bonded to C3 making C4 higher priority over C6.) To arrange the molecule such that the group with lowest priority is behind C5, recognize that H and OH are out of the plane and thus C6 and C4 are into the plane. Rotating the molecule such that H is placed behind C5 will flip the OH to the left and C4 and C6 to the right as shown below.

Moving from highest to lowest priority is clockwise and thus *R*. So, C5 is D-galactose is *R*.

Assignment of priorities around C4 is OH-1, C3-2, C5-3, and H-4. (C3 and C5 both have H and OH and single bonds to C2 and C6. So, to determine priority we have to see which of C2 and C6 is of higher priority.) Picture C4 having bonds to OH and H coming out of the page. The bonds to C3 and C5 must be into the page. Rotating the molecule such that H is behind C4 swings OH to the right and C3 and C5 to the left. Moving from OH to C3 to C5 is counterclockwise or *S*.

Assignment of priorities around C3 is OH-1, C2-2, C4-3, and H-4. Picture bonds from C3 to OH and H as being out of the page. This puts bonds to C2 and C3 into the page. Rotating H such that it is behind C3 swings OH to the right and C2 and C4 to the left. Moving from OH to C2 to C4 is counterclockwise or *S*.

Priorities around C2 are OH-1, CHO-2, C3-3, and H-4. Picturing bonds to H and OH as out of the plane puts bonds to CHO and C3 into the plane. Rotation of H behind C2 swings OH to the left and CHO and C3 to the right. Moving from highest to lowest priority moves clockwise or *R*.

Thus, D-galactose is 2*R*, 3*S*, 4*S*, 5*R*.

D-galactose   L-altrose

An easy way to visualize the molecule is to download its PDB file, which can be found at the RCSC Protein databank can be found at http://www.rcsb.org/pdb/home/home.do. The PDB file for any protein can be searched by typing its name in the "Search" box. You can view the PDB file using either RasMol or Swiss PdbViewer.

For L-altrose, we would go through a similar exercise. The priorities about each of the carbons would be identical to those described for the carbons of galactose. L-altrose is 2*R*, 3*S*, 4*S*, 5*S*.

9. (Integrates with Chapters 5, 6, and 10) Consider the sequence of glycophorin (see Figure 10.10), and imagine subjecting glycophorin and also a sample of glycophorin treated to remove all sugars, to treatment with trypsin and chymotrypsin. Would the presence of sugars in the native glycophorin make any difference in the results?

Answer: Glycophorin A is an intrinsic membrane protein that spans the erythrocyte (red blood cell) membrane using a single alpha-helical segment. The C-terminal end of the protein is intracellular and completely unmodified, whereas the N-terminal end is extracellular and is heavily glycosylated. In particular, there are numerous O-linked an N-linked glycosylations in the N-terminal domain of this protein. Trypsin cleaves peptide bonds whose carbonyl groups are from the amino acids lysine and arginine. Chymotrypsin cleaves peptide bonds involving the bulky, hydrophobic amino acids like phenylalanine, tyrosine, and tryptophan. Although the glycosylation modifications in glycophorin involve serines, threonines, and asparagines, the presence of bulky sugar groups will interfere with digestion by these enzymes. In addition, peptides containing sugar moieties will differ in molecular weight from peptides without modifications.

11. Write a reasonable chemical mechanism for the starch phosphorylase reaction (Figure 7.22).

Answer: Starch phosphorylase cleaves glucose units from starch by phosphorlysis using phosphate to release glucose as glucose-1-phosphate. All phosphorylases have pyridoxal phosphate as a cofactor and it is thought that the phosphate group of this cofactor plays a role in catalysis. The phosphate group of pyridoxal phosphate may function alternatively as an acid and then a base to promote the cleavage of the glycosidic bond by the substrate phosphate.

13. Treatment with chondroitin and glucosamine is offered as one popular remedy for arthritis pain. Suggest an argument for the efficacy of this treatment, and then comment on its validity , based on what you know of polysaccharide chemistry.

Answer: Chondroitin is a glycosaminoglycan consisting of linear chains of D-glucuronate and N-acetyl-D-galactosamine-4(or 6)-sulfate. Glucuronate is a sugar acid derived from glucose by oxidation of C-6 to a carboxylic acid function. At neutral pH this group has a 1− charge. Sulfated sugars are also negatively charged. Thus, condroitin sulfate is highly negatively charged. One question to ask is how effectively is condroitin sulfate absorbed by the body and how well is it transported to joints. Glucosamine is used in synthesis of cartilage matrix proteoglycan. In addition to being a component of hyaluronate and keratan sulfate, it is converted into galactosamine, which is found in chondroitin. It is possible that dietary supplements of chondroitin and/or glucosamine help to maintain levels of glycosaminoglycans. Dietary supplements, however, and not subject to regulations covering drugs and pharmaceuticals.

15. Give the systematic name for stachyose.

Answer: β-D-fructofuranosyl-O-α-D-galactopyranosyl-(1→6)-O-α-D-galactopyranosyl-(1→6)-O-α-D-glucopyranoside.

17. Biochemist Joseph Owades revolutionized the production of beer in the United States by developing a simple treatment with an enzyme that converted regular beer into "light beer," which was marketed aggressively as a beverage that "tastes great," even though it is "less filling." What was the enzyme-catalyzed reaction that Owades used to modify the fermentation process so cleverly, and how is regular beer different from light beer?

Answer: The alcohol in beer is produced by fermentation of carbohydrates by yeast. The carbohydrates derive from starch in barley grain, which includes amylose and amylopectin. Yeast cannot, however, ferment either of these polysaccharides, so to make starch sugars available for yeast fermentation, barley grains are induced to sprout. Soaking barley grains in water induces production of alpha- and beta-amylase, two enzymes that digest starch into simpler carbohydrates that would be used by the barley endosperm to begin plant growth. Alpha-amylase is an endohydrolase that cleaves α-(1→4) linkage randomly in starch. Beta-amylase digests α-(1→4) linkage starting at the non-reducing ends of polysaccharides. Combined action of alpha- and beta-amylase converts starch into a complex mixture that includes glucose and maltose (di-glucose), both of which are fermentable by yeast, and numerous oligosaccharides. The oligosaccharides are produced in part because digestion of starch by amlyase enzymes is interrupted to prevent utilization of sugar by the endosperm. Additionally, neither enzyme can hydrolyze α-(1→6) linkage, and so the oligosaccharides are branched.

A typical "regular" beer contains approximately 100 Calories from alcohol and around 50 Calories from carbohydrate in a 12 oz serving. Light beers are around 100 Calories per serving. While some "light beers" have slightly lower alcohol content (by around 1%), the big difference between regular beers and "light" beers is the carbohydrate content. Lower carbohydrate content is achieved by treating the ferment with a variety of enzymes including alpha- and beta-amylase and a debranching enzyme, an α-(1→6) glucosidase that will hydrolyze α-(1→6) branches. The consequence of this is to convert more of the carbohydrates into a form that is fermentable by yeast. Yeast fermentation results in a brew that has a higher alcohol content than normal beer, but this is diluted to a value typically below that of regular beer.

The first light beer was produced in 1967 by Rheingold Brewery and marketed as Gablinger's Diet Beer. The ad campaign for Gablinger's beer was a flop apparently because it highlighted the consequence of excessive caloric intake due to beer drinking. Owades gave the light beer formulation to Meister Brau of Chicago. This company sold a "lite" beer for a few years before the company was bought by Miller. Miller brewed their own light beer but sold it as Miller Lite. Their "taste great, less filling" ad campaign was a success that made Miller Lite the first successful low-calorie beer.

19.   *Kudzu is a vine that grows prolifically in the southern and southeastern United States. A native of Japan, China, and India, kudzu was brought to the United States in 1876 at the Centennial Exposition in Philadelphia. During the Great Depression of the 1930s, the Soil Conservation Service promoted kudzu for erosion control, and farmers were paid to plant it. Today, however, kudzu is a universal nuisance, spreading rapidly, and covering and destroying trees in large numbers. Already covering 7–10 million acres in the United States, kudzu grows at the rate of a foot per day. Assume that the kudzu vine consists almost entirely of cellulose fibres, and assume that the fibres lie parallel to the vine axis. Calculate the rate of the cellulose synthase reaction that adds glucose units to the growing cellulose molecules. Use the structures in your text to make a reasonable estimate of the unit length of a cellulose molecule (from one glucose monomer to the next).*

Answer: Cellulose is a polymer of β-D-glucose linked (1→4). The glucose chain is extended with alternating glucose residues flipped 180°. Thus, the repeat unit is a di-glucose termed cellobiose. The length from the oxygen on carbon 1 of glucose to the oxygen on carbon 4 of the same glucose is approximately 0.55 nm, making the length of cellobiose approximately 1.1 nm. The repeat distance measured by X-ray diffraction is approximately 1.03 nm, and we will use this distance in our calculation below.

The velocity of growth is one foot per day. Converting this to ft per min we have:

$$\frac{1\ \text{ft}}{\text{day}} \times \frac{1\ \text{day}}{24\ \text{hr}} \times \frac{1\ \text{hr}}{60\ \text{min}} = 6.94 \times 10^{-4}\ \frac{\text{ft}}{\text{min}}$$

And, conversion to nm per min we have:

$$6.94 \times 10^{-4}\ \frac{\text{ft}}{\text{min}} \times \frac{12\ \text{in}}{\text{ft}} \times \frac{2.54\ \text{cm}}{\text{in}} \times \frac{1 \times 10^{7}\ \text{nm}}{1\ \text{cm}} = 2.12 \times 10^{5}\ \frac{\text{nm}}{\text{min}}$$

For an enzyme, velocity is typically given in units of micromole per min:

$$2.12 \times 10^{5}\ \frac{\text{nm}}{\text{min}} \times \frac{2\ \text{molecules glucose}}{1.03\ \text{nm}} \times \frac{\text{mol}}{6.022 \times 10^{23}\ \text{molecules}} \times \frac{1 \times 10^{6}\ \text{micromol}}{1\ \text{mol}} = 7.03 \times 10^{-12}\ \frac{\mu\text{mol}}{\text{min}}$$

21.   *What properties of hyaluronate, chondroitin sulfate, and keratan sulfate make them ideal components of cartilage?*

Answer: The structures of hyaluronate, chondroitin sulfate, and keratan sulfate are shown below. It is clear that these glycosaminoglycans are rich in anionic groups (carboxylate or sulfate) in addition to hydroxyl groups and amide bonds all of which interact strongly with water. These compounds will be heavily hydrated and form a cushion in joints.

Hyaluronate

Chondroitin sulfate

Keratan sulfate

Questions for Self-Study

1. For the compounds shown below, identify the following: aldose, ketose, chiral centre, potential pyranose, potential furanose, anomeric carbon, enantiomers, epimers, diastereomers.

2. For each of following disaccharides what are their monosaccharide components? Which are reducing sugars?
   a. lactose
   b. sucrose
   c. maltose

3. Starch (S), glycogen (G), and dextrans (D) are storage polysaccharides found in plants, animals, and yeast and bacteria. Which applies the best to each of the following statements?
   a. contains α-amylose
   b. many $\alpha(1{\to}6)$ branches
   c. is used to produce Sephadex, a chromatographic material
   d. is cleaved by phosphorylation
   e. may have $1{\to}2$, $1{\to}3$, or $1{\to}4$ branch points depending on species

4. Amylose and cellulose are both plant polysaccharides composed of glucose in $1{\to}4$ linkage. However, amylose is a storage polysaccharide that is readily digested by animals, whereas cellulose is a

structural polysaccharide that is not digested by animals. What difference in the two polymers accounts for this?

5. Another structural polysaccharide, found in cell walls of fungi and the exoskeletons of crustaceans, insects, and spiders, is chitin. Chitin is similar to cellulose in that the repeat units are held together by $\beta(1{\rightarrow}4)$ linkage. However, the repeat units are different for the two polymers. What are they?

Answers

1. aldose: b. or d.
    ketose: a. or c.
    chiral centre: carbons 3, 4, 5 of a. and c. and carbons 2, 3, 4, 5 of b and d.
    potential pyranose: b. or d.
    potential furanose: a. or c.
    anomeric carbon: carbon 2 of a. and c., carbon 1 of b. and d.
    enantiomers: a. and c.
    epimers: b. and d.
    diastereomers: b. and d.

2. For lactose: galactose and glucose; for sucrose: glucose and fructose; for maltose: glucose and glucose. Lactose and maltose are reducing sugars.

3. a. S; b. G; c. D; d. S or G; e. D

4. Amylose is α-(1$\rightarrow$4)-linked D-glucose, whereas cellulose is β-(1$\rightarrow$4)-linked D-glucose. Animals have enzymes that cleave amylose linkage but not cellulose linkage.

5. Cellulose is a polymer of D-glucose; chitin is a polymer of N-acetyl-D-glucosamine.

Additional Problems

1. Protocols for ethanol precipitation of small quantities of DNA often include the addition of glycogen to act as a carrier. Typically, the ethanol precipitation is carried out by adding two volumes of 95% ethanol to a solution of salty DNA at 4°C. Explain why glycogen will precipitate under these conditions. What properties of the two polymers, DNA and glycogen, make them behave in a similar manner under these conditions?

2. In one orientation, newsprint can be torn to produce a smooth, straight tear; however, in a perpendicular orientation, the tear line is jagged. Given the fact that newsprint is made from cellulose, explain this behaviour.

3. The specific rotations of two freshly prepared solutions of α-D-glucose and β-D-glucose, each at 1 g/mL, were measured and found to be +112.2° and +18.7° respectively. After some time, the specific rotations were remeasured and they were both found to be +52.7°. Why?

4. a. Honey bees collect nectar, a dilute solution of approximately 10% sucrose, and convert it into honey, a concentrated solution of about 40% each of glucose and fructose. They accomplish this conversion by mixing the nectar with a salivary enzyme, then busily aerating and fanning the solution to drive off water. Given the specific rotations, $[\alpha]_D^{20}$, of sucrose (+66.5°), glucose (+52.7°), and fructose (−92°), calculate the rotation that accompanies honey production.
    b. The enzyme is known as invertase. Why?

5. a. Pectins are highly branched polysaccharides that are an important component of plant cell walls. The predominant fibres in plant cell walls are cellulose microfibrils composed of cellulose molecules in parallel arrays. In the plant cell wall, the cellulose microfibrils are embedded in a network that is composed of, among other things, pectin. Pectin is highly soluble and readily extracted from plant tissue with hot water, whereas cellulose is not. Given this information, pectin is responsible for what property of plant cell walls ?

b.   Pectins are used to make jams and jellies. Typically, an acidic fruit is boiled with sugar and pectin and the mixture allowed to cool. With luck, a jam or jelly of the proper consistency is produced. The principal monosaccharide in pectin is galacturonic acid. Why is the combination of acid, sucrose, and pectin important for gellation?

Abbreviated Answers

1.   Glycogen is a polymer of glucose that is soluble in aqueous solution because of the presence of numerous hydroxyl groups capable of hydrogen bonding with water. It is insoluble in alcohol because this uncharged polymer readily aggregates. DNA is a sugar/phosphate polymer that is also quite soluble in aqueous solution. To precipitate DNA with ethanol, a counter ion must be present in order to form a DNA salt. In the absence of a counter ion, DNA is negatively charged and will not readily precipitate from dilute solutions with ethanol.

2.   In newsprint, cellulose fibres are somewhat aligned along one axis of the print. This axis can be determined by ripping the paper in two orientations. A rip along the axis in which the cellulose fibres are aligned will produce a smooth tear, whereas a rip perpendicular to this axis will produce a jagged tear.

3.   Initially, the two solutions start out with only one D-glucose anomer, but with time they both equilibrate to a mixture of the two anomeric forms. The addition of alkali will speed up this conversion. Can you calculate the concentration of α-D-glucose and β-D-glucose in the mixture? See the answer to Question 6 from the textbook for an example of how to solve the problem.

4.   a.   Assuming a 1 dm path length, the rotation of a 10% solution of sucrose (10 g/100 mL) is given by

$$\text{rotation (degrees)} = [\alpha]_{D}^{20} \times 1\ \text{dm} \times 0.1\ \text{g/mol}$$
$$= +65.5° \times 1 \times 0.1 = +6.65°$$

Similarly, the rotation of a mixture of 40% glucose and 40% fructose is given by

$$\text{rotation (degrees)} = +52.7° \times 1 \times 0.4 + (-92) \times 1 \times 0.4 = -15.7°$$

b.   The conversion of sucrose to a mixture of glucose and fructose is accompanied by inversion of rotation (the sign changes from positive to negative). A mixture of equal parts glucose and fructose is called invert sugar. Invert sugar is made by bees during honey production. Cane sugar is converted to invert sugar by catalysis using invertase in dilute HCl.

5.   a.   Anyone who has eaten overcooked green vegetables should know that pectins are responsible for the rigidity of plant cell walls. As vegetables are cooked, pectins are slowly leached out of the plant cell walls and, as a result, the material becomes tender.

b.   Because galacturonic acid is a sugar acid, pectin is a charged molecule at neutral pH. Pectin will form a gel-like mass when the acidic groups on galacturonic acid residues are neutralized at slightly acidic pH. Gel formation is also dependent on the presence of sucrose, which apparently forms hydrogen bonds with neutralized pectin.

Summary

Carbohydrates are the most abundant class of organic molecules found in nature. As their name implies, they are hydrates of carbon, with the formula $(CH_2O)_n$. The versatile nature of carbohydrates arises from their chemical features, including 1) the existence of one or more asymmetric centres, 2) the ability to adopt linear or ring structures, 3) the formation of polymer structures through glycosidic bonds, and 4) the ability to form multiple hydrogen bonds.

Carbohydrates include monosaccharides, oligosaccharides, and polysaccharides. Monosaccharides include aldoses and ketoses, and may also be named for the number of carbons they contain (i.e., trioses, tetroses, etc.). Aldoses with at least three carbons and ketoses with at least four carbons contain chiral centres—carbon atoms with four different groups. Monosaccharides are usually named using the Fischer nomenclature convention, which designates the chiral centre farthest from the carbonyl carbon as either D- or L-configuration. The D-forms of monosaccharides predominate in nature, but L-forms are found in specialized roles. D- and L- forms of monosaccharides are mirror images of each other and are designated as enantiomers.

Monosaccharides spontaneously cyclize, forming cyclic hemiacetals with an additional chiral centre, and these cyclic furanose and pyranose forms are the preferred structure for monosaccharides in solution. The α- and β-anomers of cyclic monosaccharides may undergo interconversion with intermediate formation of the linear aldehyde or ketone in a process called mutarotation. Pyranose forms are usually favoured over furanose forms for aldohexose sugars, and furanose forms are usually more stable for ketohexoses. Furanose and pyranose rings are puckered, not planar, and the most stable conformations place as many bulky groups as possible in equatorial orientations. β-D-glucose, which can adopt a conformation with all its bulky groups in equatorial positions, is the most widely occurring organic group in nature and the central hexose in carbohydrate metabolism. Derivatives of monosaccharides include sugar acids such as gluconic acid, sugar alcohols such as sorbitol (used in sugarless gums), deoxy sugars such as rhamnose (a component of the toxin ouabain), sugar esters such as ATP and GTP, amino sugars such as muramic and neuraminic acids, and acetals, ketals, and glycosides.

Oligosaccharides, the simplest of which are the disaccharides, consist of monosaccharides linked by glycosidic bonds. Oligosaccharides possessing a free, unsubstituted anomeric carbon are referred to as reducing sugars. Sucrose is not a reducing sugar, but maltose and lactose are. Lactose is the principal carbohydrate in milk, but some individuals do not produce the lactase that breaks lactose down to galactose and glucose and cannot tolerate lactose in their diet. Maltose is di-glucose with $\alpha(1{\rightarrow}4)$ linkage and cellobiose is di-glucose with $\beta(1{\rightarrow}4)$ linkage.

Polysaccharides function as storage materials, as structural components of organisms, as protective substances, and as mediators of cellular recognition and communication. Starch and glycogen are the principal storage polysaccharides in plants and animals, respectively. Both are $\alpha(1{\rightarrow}4)$-linked chains of glucose units. α-amylose is a linear starch molecule and amylopectin is a highly branched structure. Glycogen is more highly branched than amylopectin. Dextrans are $\alpha(1{\rightarrow}6)$-linked glucose polymers produced by yeast and bacteria and are components of dental plaques. Structural polysaccharides of note include cellulose, a $\beta(1{\rightarrow}4)$-linked glucose polymer which is the most abundant carbohydrate polymer in nature. The β-linkage makes cellulose difficult to digest for most animals, but bacteria living symbiotically in the digestive tracts of termites, shipworms, and ruminant animals secrete cellulases which effect the breakdown of cellulose. Chitin, a $\beta(1{\rightarrow}4)$-linked N-acetyl-D-glucosamine polymer, is the principal skeletal material in crustaceans, insects, and spiders and is also present in the cell walls of fungi. It can occur in sheets composed of parallel or antiparallel chains or in structures with mixed parallel and antiparallel sheets. Other structural polysaccharides include the alginates of marine brown algae; agar found in marine red algae; glycosaminglycans, such as heparin, hyaluronates, chondroitins, keratin sulfate, and dermatan sulfate; peptidoglycan and lipopolysaccharide in bacterial cell walls; and glycoproteins and proteoglycans.

Bacterial cell walls are made of the peptidoglycan called murin. The backbone of this structure is a polymer of N-acetylglucosamine linked $\beta(1{\rightarrow}4)$ to N-acetylmuramic acid. This polysaccharide is substituted with a tetrapeptide that is attached to the lactic acid moiety of NAM by its N-terminus and crosslinked to the C-terminus of another tetrapeptide via a side chain lysine. Gram-negative bacteria have this structure sandwiched between two plasma membranes, the outer one modified by lipopolysaccharides that are antigenic determinants called O antigens. Gram-positive cell walls have pentaglycine bridges between the side chain lysine and the C-terminus of another peptide. Additionally, polymers of ribitol phosphate or glycerol phosphate are covalently attached to murin. Animal cells have an array of polysaccharides on their cell surface in the form of glycoproteins. Proteoglycans are found in the extracellular matrix. Glycoprotein have either O-linked or N-linked saccharides. O-linkage occurs on hydroxyl groups on serine, threonine, or hydroxylysine, and the carbohydrate is typically N-acetylgalactosamine. O-Linked membrane glycoproteins have two structural motifs. In one, glycosylation occurs through out the entire extracellular domain of the protein, causing it to adopt an extended conformation. In the second, a globular domain is held distal to the membrane surface by a glycosylated domain that adopts an extended conformation. O-linked glycoproteins are used by Antarctic and Artic fish as antifreeze. N-linkage occurs on asparagines with a dimer of N-acetylglucosamine linked to a branched mannose triad, often with additional sugars attached to mannose. N-glycosylation is known to support a number of functions including stabilization of protein conformation, protection from proteolysis, and membrane trafficking to intracellular organelles. In blood proteins, degradation of oligosaccharides on N-linked glycoproteins is used as a measure of protein age and functionality. Asialoglycoprotein receptors in the liver bind to proteins not fully glycosylated. The receptor-protein complex is internalized by endocytosis and degraded.

Proteoglycans are glycoproteins with glycosamionglycans O-linked to serine residues in Ser-Gly repeats. Proteoglycans are either soluble components of the extracellular matrix or integral transmembrane proteins. In general, proteoglycans, via their glycosaminoglycan groups, bind to specific proteins containing BBXB and BBBXXB (B is basic) sequences. Several proteoglycans are involved in modulation of cell growth.

The complexity of living systems is a consequence in part of an organism's proteome, the proteins expressed by an organism's genome. This complexity also depends on a diverse array of polysaccharides that arise from a number of modified monosaccharides joined in a variety of ways to produced complex linear and branched structures. Cells present themselves to the environment coated with carbohydrate, and this coating is used in an array of cell functions including signalling, recognition, growth, and regulation of cell differentiation. For example, selectins are adhesion proteins found on the cell surface of leukocytes and on endothelial cells that line the walls of blood vessels. Movement of leukocytes along the vascular wall is achieved by selectin-carbohydrate interactions. Galectins are carbohydrate-binding proteins involved in cell adhesion, growth regulation, inflammation, immunity, and metastasis.

Chapter 8

Lipids

• •

Chapter Outline

❖ Lipids: Compounds composed largely of reduced carbons and exhibiting low water solubility. Lipids may be completely hydrophobic or, if they contain polar groups, amphipathic.
❖ Fatty acids: Carboxyl head group and hydrocarbon tail
  ⅄ Typically even number of carbons (14 to 24)
  ⅄ Saturated fatty acids lack carbon–carbon double bonds
  ⅄ Unsaturated fatty acids contain one or more double bonds in *cis* configuration
    • Monosaturated: Single carbon–carbon double bond
    • Polyunsaturated: *cis* double bonds separated by methylene carbon (—CH₂—)
  ⅄ Nomenclature:
    • Systematic: e.g., octadecanoic acid: 18 carbons long
    • Common names: Stearic acid
    • Short-hand notation:
      • 18:0—18 carbons long with no double bonds
      • 18:1$^{\Delta 9}$—18 carbons long with one double bond starting at carbon 9
  ⅄ Essential fatty acids: Linoleic and γ-linolenic acid: Plant fatty acids required in diets of animals: used to synthesize arachidonic acid—precursor to eicosanoids (prostaglandins)
❖ Triacylglycerols (triacylglycerides): Fats and oils
  ⅄ Glycerol esterified with three fatty acids
  ⅄ Saponification: Alkali hydrolysis of triacylglycerols:
    • Products: Glycerol and free fatty acids (salt of free fatty acids—soap)
❖ Glycerophospholipids: A class of phospholipids
  ⅄ 1,2-diacylglycerol with phosphate ester at carbon 3
  ⅄ Stereospecific numbering system: Number glycerol carbons based on (*R,S*) system: C1 is carbon that would lead to (*S*) configuration if its priority were increased
  ⅄ Phosphatidic acid: *sn*-glycerol-3-phospate with fatty acids esterified to C-1 and C-2
    • Phosphatidic acid precursor of glycerophospholipids
    • C-1 fatty acid typically saturated
    • C-2 fatty aid typically unsaturated
  ⅄ Glycerophospholipids: Polar group esterified to phosphate of phosphatidic acid
    • Ethanolamine: Phosphatidylethanolamine
    • Choline: Phosphatidylcholine
    • Glycerol: Phosphatidylglycerol
    • Serine: Phosphatidylserine
    • Inositol: Phosphatidylinositol
    • Diphosphatidyl glycerol (cardiolipin)
  ⅄ Ether glycerophospholipids
    • Ether linkage at carbon 1
    • Alkyl group esterified to carbon 2
  ⅄ Plasmalogens: Ether glycerophospholipids with *cis-α,β*-unsaturated alkyl group at C-1
❖ Sphingolipids: Backbone of sphingosine: 18-carbon amino alcohol with C–C *trans* double bond
  ⅄ Ceramide: sphingosine with fatty acid in amide linkage
  ⅄ Sphingomyelins: Alcohol esterified to phosphoceramide

- Choline
- Ethanolamine
⅄ Glycosphingolipids: Ceramide with sugars in β-glycosidic linkage
- Cerebroside: Sugar is glucose or galactose
- Sulfatide: Sugar is galactose with sulfate esterified at carbon 3 of galactose
- Gangliosides: Ceramide with three or more sugars including sialic acid
❖ Waxes: Esters of long-chain alcohol and long-chain fatty acid
❖ Terpenes: Class of lipids formed from 2-methyl-1,3-butadiene (isoprene)
⅄ Monoterpene: Two isoprene units: 10 carbons
⅄ Sesquiterpenes: Three isoprene units: 15 carbons
⅄ Diterpenes: Four isoprenes: two monoterpenes: 20 carbons
⅄ Triterpenes: Six isoprenes: 30 carbons: Cholesterol precursors squalene and lanosterol
⅄ Tetraterpenes: Eight isoprenes: 40 carbons: Carotenoids
⅄ Polyprenols: Long-chain polyisoprenoid alcohols
❖ Steroids
⅄ Cholesterol
- Bile salts: Cholic acid and deoxycholic acid
- Steroid hormones
  - Androgens: Testosterone
  - Estrogens: Estradiol
  - Progestins: Progesterone
  - Glucocorticoids: Cortisol
  - Mineralocorticoids
❖ Lipid metabolites are biological signal molecules
⅄ Phospholipases hydrolyze ester bonds
- Phospholipase A_1 and A_2 release fatty acid from C-1 or C-2
- Phospholipase C and D release phosphorylated head group or unphosphorylated
⅄ Inositol phospholipids hydrolyzed by phospholipase C
- Diacylglycerol: Activates protein kinase C
- Inositol trisphosphate: Regulates cellular calcium levels
⅄ Acachidonic acid released by phospholipase A_2
- Used to synthesize eicosanoids: Local hormones
⅄ Sphingosine-1-phosphate
- Allergic reactions, heart rate, cell movement and migration

Chapter Objectives

Lipids are amphipathic molecules with both polar and non-polar groups. Understand why this is the case for both simple lipids (like cholesterol) and complex lipids (like phospholipids).

Fatty acids are important components of membrane lipids and triacylglycerols (fats and oils). Fatty acids are most commonly composed of an even number of carbons. Saturated fatty acids have only carbon–carbon single bonds (their carbons are saturated with respect to hydrogens), whereas unsaturated fatty acids have one or more (polyunsaturated) carbon–carbon double bonds in *cis* configuration. When more than one double bond is present, the bonds are not conjugated but rather separated by a —CH2— group.

Complex lipids include triacylglycerols, glycerophospholipids, and sphingolipids. They are classified as complex because they contain at least one fatty acid group. For example, triacylglycerols have a glycerol backbone to which three fatty acids are esterified. Glycerophospholipids again have a glycerol backbone but with only two fatty acids (in ester linkage to carbons 1 and 2) and, attached to the third carbon of glycerol, a phosphate group to which a polar alcohol is linked (like ethanolamine, choline, serine, or inositol). Sphingolipids are composed of sphingosine, a fatty acid, and a polar head group (like phosphocholine or one or more sugar moieties).

The carbons of simple lipids (terpenes or cholesterol and its derivatives) all derive from isoprene. Know the general structure of isoprene and cholesterol and appreciate the fact that important biomolecules such as steroid hormones and bile salts are derivatives of cholesterol.

Problems and Solutions

1. Draw the structures of (a) all the possible triacylglycerols that can be formed from glycerol from stearic and arachidonic acid and (b) all the phosphatidylserine isomers that can be formed from palmitic and linolenic acids.

Answer: Triacylglycerols have a glycerol backbone to which three fatty acids are esterified. With non-identical fatty acids at carbons 1 and 3, carbon 2 is chiral. Two stereoisomers are possible, but biological triacylglycerols have the L-configuration. Stearic acid is an 18-carbon saturated fatty acid. Arachidonic acid is a 20-carbon fatty acid with four *cis* double bonds at carbons 5, 8, 11, and 14.

b. Palmitic acid is 16:0; linolenic acid is 18:3$^{(\Delta 9,12,15)}$. The backbone structure of phosphatidylserine is 3-phosphoglycerol with L-serine in phosphate ester linkage. Fatty acids are esterified at carbons 1 and 2. There is a preference for unsaturated fatty acids at carbon 2. The alpha carbon of serine is chiral; L- and D- serine are possible; however, the L isomer occurs in phosphatidylserine. The central carbon in the glycerol backbone of phosphatidylserine is prochiral and only one isomer is used, the one based on *sn*-glycerol-3-phosphate.

Note: Phosphatidylserine with unsaturated lipids at position 1 are very rare. Unsaturated fatty acids are usually found at position 2.

3. *From your memory of the structures, name*
   a. *the glycerophospholipids that carry a net positive charge.*
   b. *the glycerophospholipids that carry a net negative charge.*
   c. *the glycerophospholipids that have zero net charge.*

Answer: a. Since all the glycerophospholipids derive from phosphatidic acid, in order to form a positively charged lipid, the head group must carry a positive charge. This is true for ethanolamine and choline and for serine at low pH. However, keeping in mind that the phosphodiester bond is negatively charged, phosphatidylethanolamine, phosphatidylcholine, and phosphatidylserine will be positively charged only at low pH.

b. Negatively charged glycerophospholipids include phosphatidic acid, phosphatidylglycerol, phosphatidylinositol, phosphatidylserine, and diphosphatidylglycerol (cardiolipin). Because glycerol and inositol are uncharged, lipids with these head groups will have −1 charge at all but acidic pH values. The charge on phosphatidic acid will range from 0 to −1 to −2 depending on pH. When phosphotidylserine is negatively charged (at all but acidic values of pH) it ranges from −1 to −2 at basic pH when serine's amino group is not protonated. Cardiolipin typically carries −2 charge.

c. Phosphatidylethanolamine and phosphatidylcholine are the only uncharged glycerophospholipids at neutral pH.

5. *In the United States, James G. Watt, Secretary of the Interior (1981–1983) in Ronald Reagan's first term, provoked substantial controversy by stating publicly that trees cause significant amounts of air pollution. Based on your reading of this chapter, evaluate Watt's remarks.*

Answer: During the 1980 presidential campaign, James Watt stated that trees cause more air pollution than do automobiles. Trees in fact do emit large quantities of hydrocarbons, principally in the form of isoprenes. These volatile hydrocarbons may react with ozone to form compounds similar to those found in smog. (Trees, however, play a key role in removing pollutants from air.) (The press had a field day with Watt's comment, which evoked numerous light-hearted reactions. For example, at Claremont College a tree was draped with a banner that read: "Chop me down before I kill again." [*The Washington Post* Oct. 15, 1980])

7. *As you read Section 8.8, you might have noticed that phospholipase A$_2$, the enzyme found in rattlesnake venom, is also the enzyme that produces essential and beneficial lipid signals in most organisms. Explain the differing actions of phospholipase A$_2$ in these processes.*

Answer: Phospholipase A$_2$ (EC 3.1.1.4) hydrolyzes glycerophospholipids at carbon 2, releasing free fatty acids and monoacylglycerol (lysophosphopholipid). When the fatty acid at position 2 is arachidonic acid, this compound can serve as substrate for prostaglandin synthesis. Prostaglandins have a range of physiological activities including response to inflammation and pain. Lysophospholipids are also lipid-signaling molecules that act through G-protein–coupled receptors and regulate cellular functions such as migration and chemotaxis, calcium ion homeostasis, and cell proliferation and survival.

Rattlesnake venom catalyzes the same reaction, producing lysophospholipid and fatty acids. It is likely that these products, acting as detergents, contribute to cell membrane damage initiated by phospholipase activity. Further, there is evidence that venom phospholipase A$_2$ can exhibit specificity in toxicity by binding to specific membrane target proteins. Target proteins on muscle cells, for example, localize phospholipase activity to muscle.

9. *Refer to Figure 8.13 and draw each of the structures shown and try to identify the isoprene units in each of the molecules. (Note that there may be more than one correct answer for some of these molecules, unless you have the time and facilities to carry out ^{14}C labeling studies with suitable organisms.)*

MONOTERPENES

Geranyl dpyrophosphate

Limonene
path 1

Citronellal
path 1

Menthol
path 1

α–Pinene
path 1, 2

Camphene
path 3

SESQUITERPENES

Farnesyl pyrophosphate

Bisabolene

Eudesmol

DITERPENES

Phytol

All-trans-retinal

Gibberellic acid

TRITERPENES

Squalene   Lanosterol

TETRAPENES

Lycopene

11. *If you are still at the grocery store working on Problems 8, stop by the cookie shelves and choose your three favourite cookies from the shelves. Estimate how many calories of fat, and how many other calories from other sources, are contained in 100 g of each of these cookies. Survey the ingredients listed on each package, and describe the contents of the package in terms of (a) saturated fat, (b) cholesterol, and (c) trans fatty acids. (Note that food makers are required to list ingredients in order of decreasing amounts in each package.)*

Answer: I looked up nutritional information on four popular cookies and easily found most of the information asked for in this question. Information about *trans* fatty acid content has been required on nutritional labels since 1 January 2006 in the United States (21 CFR 101). After a lengthy process, the U.S. Food and Drug Administration decided to require this information on a separate line in the nutritional data immediately under the line for saturated fatty acids. Prior to this, consumers had no idea about the levels of *trans* fats in foods. Products containing "hydrogenated" or "partially hydrogenated" vegetable oils contain *trans* fatty acids and this information is typically found in the ingredients section of nutritional labels. You will see, however, that hydrogenated vegetable oils are often listed as an ingredient despite levels of *trans* fats listed as 0 (zero). This happens because of the serving size and significant figures. A level of *trans* fats of 0.49 gram is 0 when recorded to one significant figure. It is interesting to note that there is not a standard serving size. I purposefully avoided listing the brand name of the cookies. The data are presented in two charts. The chart below has information taken directly from the nutritional information label.

Cookie	Serving size (g)	Calories per serving (listed)	Total fat per serving (g)	Total saturated fat (g)	Trans fat (grams)	Cholesterol per serving (mg)	Total carbohydrate (g)	Percent of calories from fat	Percent calories from carbs$	Dietary fibre (g)	Protein (g)	Calculated Total Calories#
Three-layered	34	160	7.0	2.0	0	0	25	37.5	62.5	1.0	2.0	171
Chocolate chip	33	160	8.0	2.5	0*	0	22	43.8	55.0	1.0	2.0	168
Vanilla wafers	30	140	6.0	2.0	0	0	21	35.7	60.0	1.0	1.0	142
Fruit-based	31	110	2.0	0.0	0*	0	22	18.2	80.0	1.0	1.0	110

$ Total calories from fat are listed on the nutritional facts panel.
# Calculated using 9 Calories per gram for fat, 4 for carbohydrate, and 4 for protein.
* The ingredients listed some form of hydrogenated vegetable oil.

The data in the first chart were used to calculate various values presented below.

Cookie	Calories per gram	Calories per 100 grams	Total fat per 100 grams	Total saturated fat per 100 grams	Cholesterol per 100 grams	Total carbohydrates per 100 grams	Percent of calories as fat*	Percent of calories as carbohydrate
Three-layered	4.7	470.6	20.6	5.9	0	73.5	39.4	62.5
Chocolate chip	4.8	484.8	24.2	7.6	0	66.7	45.0	55.0
Vanilla wafers	4.7	466.7	20.0	6.7	0	70.0	38.6	60.0
Fruit-based	3.5	354.8	6.5	0.0	0	71.0	16.4	80.0

* Calculated using 9 Calories per gram for fat.

Clearly, there are differences. You may notice that the total Calories does not equal to the sum of the Calories from fat and carbohydrate. In some cases, the data presented by the cookie makers are not consistent, and they (the cookie makers) attribute this to rounding errors! The zeros under cholesterol should not be taken as fact because they were based on a serving size less than 100 grams and likely rounded to 1 significant figure. Finally, as a gentle reminder nutritional Calories (note the capital C) are actually kilocalories.

13. Describe in your own words the functions of androgens, glucocorticoids, and mineralocorticoids.

Answer: Androgens, glucocorticoids and mineralocorticoids are all steroid hormones derived from cholesterol. Androgens are responsible for development of sexual characteristics of males and for sperm production. In addition, androgens control libido and aggressiveness. The principal androgen is testosterone, which is produced by interstitial cells of the testis. Glucocorticoids and mineralocorticoids are steroid hormones produced by the adrenal cortex. Glucocorticoids regulate metabolism, specifically of carbohydrate, protein, and lipid. The major glucocorticoid is cortisol. It stimulates gluconeogenesis and amino acid uptake by the liver and kidney. In adipocytes (fat cells), it inhibits glucose uptake and stimulates lipolysis. Glucocorticoids also have anti-inflammatory properties. Mineralocorticoids regulate extracellular fluid volume by modulating potassium uptake in the kidney. The principal mineralocorticoid is aldosterone.

15. Our ancestors kept clean with homemade soap (page 232), often called "lye soap." Go to http://www.wikihow.com/Make-Your-Own-Soap and read the procedure for making lye soap from vegetable oils and lye (sodium hydroxide). What chemical process occurs in the making of lye soap? Draw reactions to explain. How does this soap work as a cleaner?

Answer: Lye is first dissolved in water and cooled to around 37°C. Next, coconut oil and vegetable shortening are heated to liquefy them and then olive oil is added. This mixture is then brought to 37°C and slowly added to the lye solution.

Lye is sodium hydroxide, which is very soluble and will dissociate into Na^+ and OH^-, making a solution with very high pH. The various oils are triacylglycerols and the reaction that ensues is saponification: base-catalyzed hydrolysis of an ester. The reaction is shown below:

This reaction occurs at all three carbons on the glycerol backbone, producing glycerol and three fatty acids that are unprotonated and thus negatively charged. These carboxylates bind sodium to form a salt of a fatty acid that aggregates as soap.

Soaps clean by forming fatty acid micelles that present a hydrophobic interior in which water-insoluble materials can dissolve. These substances are then, in effect, made water-soluble by being coated with negative charge from the carboxyl groups on the fatty acids.

The mixture of lipids used for this homemade soap deserves comment. Vegetable shortening is hydrogenated vegetable oil typically made by passing hydrogen gas through oil containing a nickel catalyst. This process saturates some of the double bonds found in vegetable oils that make them liquid at room temperature. Hydrogenation, however, also produces some *trans* fatty acids. Removal of unsaturated fatty acids allows hydrocarbon chains to interact more effectively via van der Waals forces to produce a solid at room temperature. Coconut oil is actually a solid at room temperature because it contains long-chained fatty acids in its triacylglycerols. The use of coconut oil and vegetable oil will make the soap form firm cakes because of the favourable van der Waals interactions long-chained fatty acids and *trans* fatty acids can make. By varying the proportions of triacylglycerol sources, one can vary the hardness of the soap cakes.

This is not to be confused with hard soap and soft soap. Hard soap is a consequence of saponification using sodium hydroxide. Soft soaps are made using potassium hydroxide. Sodium salts of fatty acids tend to be less soluble than potassium salts, and in general the solubility tends to increase with group I elements. Salts of fatty acids and group II elements, in particular magnesium and calcium, are insoluble. Water with high concentrations of divalent cations is termed "hard water." Soaps work poorly in hard water and leave a "ring around the bathtub" as calcium and magnesium salts of fatty acids precipitate out of solution. Water-softening agents are agents like citrate or polyphosphates that chelate divalent cations, preventing them from interacting with soap molecules.

17. *The cholesterol-lowering benefit of stanol-ester margarine is only achieved after months of consumption of stanol esters (see graph, page 247). Suggest why this might be so. Suppose dietary sources represent approximately 25% of total serum cholesterol. Based on the data in the graph, how effective are stanol esters at preventing uptake of dietary cholesterol?*

Answer: The cholesterol-lowering activity of stanol esters is complex and involves both the secretion of cholesterol in bile and lowering the uptake of cholesterol in the small intestine. Blocking uptake of cholesterol occurs in the small intestine where stanol esters incorporate in micelles formed in the gut from bile salts, phospholipids, free sterols—including cholesterol and phytosterols—and fatty acids. Stanol-esters are more soluble than cholesterol in micelles and so they reduce the levels of cholesterol. Micelles are then taken up by the intestine and repackaged as chylomicrons. Stanol, a phytosterol, is actively excreted back into the lumen of the intestine by sterolin, an integral membrane protein that functions as a heterodimer of ABCG5 and ABCG8 to actively pump phytosterols out of the intestine. Sterolin is also active in the liver where it secretes phytosterols and cholesterol into bile.

If the cholesterol-lowering effect of phytosterols is only due to blockage of uptake, then one might expect an immediate lowering of cholesterol levels. That it takes months to achieve lower cholesterol levels may be an indication that gene expression is at work. Higher dietary stanol would lead to higher uptake of stanol that is actively removed from the body by the liver. The liver might be responding to higher stanol levels by expression of ABCG5 and ABCG8, which in turn actively pumps phytosterols and cholesterol into bile secretions.

The graph on page 247 shows approximately a 14% decrease in cholesterol levels over time (240 mg/dL to 210 mg/dL). If the 240 gm/dl level is being maintained by dietary cholesterol, which represents 25% of total cholesterol, then (25% of 240) 60 mg/dL is due to diet alone. Stanol ester lowers cholesterol by around 30 mg/dl. Thus, stanol-ester treatment appears to be blocking 50% of cholesterol uptake. This assumes that endogenous cholesterol production remains constant. There is evidence that cholesterol production does in fact increase, so stanol esters are likely blocking considerably more than 50% of dietary cholesterol.

19. If most plant-derived food products contain plant sterols and stanols, would it be as effective (for cholesterol-lowering purposes) to simply incorporate plant fats in one's diet as to use a sterol- or stanol-fortified spread like Benecol? Consult a suitable reference (for example, http://lpi.oregonstate.edu/infocenter/phytochemicals/sterols/#sources at the Linus Pauling Institute) to compose your answer.

Answer: According to the Micronutrient Information Center, a single serving (14 g or 1 tablespoon) of Benecol spread has 850 mg of stanol esters (500 mg free stanols). Normal daily dietary intakes of phytosterol range from 150 to 450 mg and only around 10% is stanol. Thus, one or two servings of Benecol provide far more stanol than a typical diet. While dietary phytosterols likely play a role in lowering cholesterol levels, there are not many studies showing this. Studies on diets supplemented with phytosterols show that the effective intake levels range from 1.5 to 3 grams per day. Saturated fatty acids have an effect on cholesterol levels, and plant triacylglycerols tend to have less saturated fatty acids, so increasing one's intake of plant-derived food products would have an indirect effect on cholesterol independent of phytosterols.

Questions for Self-Study

1. Fill in the blanks. _____ _____ are important biomolecules composed of a long hydrocarbon chain or tail and a carboxyl group. When all of the carbon–carbon bonds are single bonds, the compound is said to be _____. This term also indicates that the carbons in the tail are associated with a maximum number of _____ atoms. Compounds of this type with one carbon–carbon double bond are _____, whereas those with multiple carbon–carbon double bonds are _____. Usually there are an _____ number of carbons atoms. These compounds are components of fats and oils in which they are joined to a _____ backbone in _____ linkage. The hydrolysis of fats or oils with alkali is called _____.

2. True or false:
   a. 2-methyl-1,3-butadiene is also known as isoprene. _____
   b. Cholesterol is a phospholipid. _____
   c. The androgens are a class of terpene-based lipids involved in absorption of dietary lipids in the intestine. _____
   d. Vitamins A, E, and K are highly water-soluble vitamins. _____
   e. Cholesterol is a hydrocarbon composed of three six-membered rings and one five-membered ring in addition to a hydrocarbon tail. _____

3. Identify the following from the structures shown below: phosphatidic acid, phosphatidylcholine, phosphatidylserine, phosphatidylinositol, ceramide, phosphatidylethanolamine.

4. Based on your knowledge of lipid and carbohydrate biochemistry, identify components of the following compound and state how this compound is chemically similar in structure to triacylglycerols? How does it differ biochemically?

5. Very often grocery stores sell produce with a waxy coating applied to their outside (cucumbers and turnips are often treated this way). What is the general structure of a wax? For what purpose is the layer of wax applied? Would something like a fatty acid or a triacylglycerol not be a good substitute?

Answers

1. Fatty; acids; saturated; hydrogen; monounsaturated; polyunsaturated; even; glycerol; ester; saponification.

2. a. T; b. F; c. F; d. F; e. T.

3. phosphatidic acid: d.; phosphatidylcholine: a.; phosphatidylserine: c.; phosphatidylinositol: e.; ceramide: f.; phosphatidylethanolamine: b.

4. You should readily identify the two rings as substituted sugars. The six-membered ring is glucose and the five-membered ring is fructose. The disaccharide they form is sucrose. Each of the hydroxyl groups of sucrose has a fatty acid attached by ester bonds. The compound is sucrose polyester, more commonly known as olestra (Trade name: Olean). Olestra is currently being used as a fat substitute because it has properties identical to fats and oils but is not digested.

   Triacylglycerols contain fatty acids esterified to glycerol, a three-carbon alcohol. Both triacylglycerol and olestra are amphiphilic molecules with uncharged, weakly polar head groups and hydrocarbon tails.

5. Waxes are composed of a long-chain alcohol and a long-chain fatty acid joined in ester linkage. Waxes are often used to make surfaces water-impermeable thus a waxy coating will prevent water loss and prolong shelf life.

   A layer of triacylglycerol might accomplish the same results; however, typical fats and oils have lower melting temperatures and would not be expected to form as stable a layer as wax.

Additional Problems

1. More stable mayonnaise can be produced by pre-treating egg yolk with phospholipase A_2. Suggest a rationale for this.
2. In regions with mineral-rich water supplies (hard water), it is often difficult to work up a rich lather using hand soaps. Why?

3. At a romantic candlelight dinner, the conversation turns to properties of waxes and what exactly happens when a candle burns. Contribute to the conversation.

4. a. Margarine is made from vegetable oil by a process called hydrogenation in which the oil is reacted with hydrogen gas in the presence of a small amount of nickel that functions as a catalyst. Hydrogenation saturates double bonds. Explain why hydrogenated vegetable oil is a solid.
   b. Margarines may be purchased in stick form or in small tubs. What is the important chemical difference between these two kinds of margarines?

5. Venom from honey bees (*Apis mellifera*) contains a phospholipase and several other components including a small amount of a polypeptide that acts as a detergent. Can you suggest a function for the polypeptide in terms of phospholipase activity?

6. Oil–water emulsions like mayonnaise and Hollandaise sauce contain, in addition to egg yolk and a lipid source (like oil or butter), sodium chloride and an acid source (vinegar or lemon juice). Salt and acid are added for flavour, but they also contribute to emulsion formation. They do this by interacting with egg yolk proteins. What might these agents be doing to yolk proteins to help with emulsion formation?

Abbreviated Answers

1. Phospholipase A_2 cleaves phospholipids to produce a free fatty acid and lysophospholipid, both of which are good emulsifying agents.

2. Mineral-rich water contains, among other things, high levels of divalent cations. Divalent cations will interact with and precipitate fatty acids. Water softeners are agents that chelate the offending divalent cations. Water can also be softened by ion exchange with resins that bind divalent cations.

3. Waxes are esters of long-chain alcohols and fatty acids. For example, in beeswax, straight-chain alcohols 24 to 36 carbons in length are esterified to long, straight-chain fatty acids up to 36 carbons in length. The melting temperature of beeswax is around 63°C. When a candle burns, the lit wick produces heat that melts the wax. The liquid wax is drawn up the wick to be consumed in the flame. A good candle will produce very little dripping wax because the wax is all consumed in the flame.

Wax is a rich source of oxidizable hydrocarbons and serves the same purpose as oil does in a lamp, or gasoline does in an internal combustion engine. However, waxes and oils do not explode because they have very low vapour pressures.

4. Margarines are typically made from vegetable oils such as corn oil and soybean oil. They are oils, liquids at room temperature, because their composition includes greater than 50% unsaturated fatty acids. Hydrogenation is the addition of hydrogen to double bonds, producing a saturated hydrocarbon. For a given chain length, saturated hydrocarbons have a higher melting temperature than do unsaturated hydrocarbons. Thus, saturation of the double bonds in the fatty acids in corn and soy oil reduces the level of unsaturated fatty acids and as a consequence, the melting temperature is increased.

The difference between tub-margarine and stick-margarine is the degree of saturation. Tub-margarine is distributed in a container because it is softer than stick-margarine due to a lower degree of hydrogenation.

5. The phospholipase of bee venom requires free lipids as substrates, and the purpose of the detergent-like polypeptide may be to dissolve some of the victim's membrane to provide substrates. Once the reaction starts, the products, free fatty acids and lysolecithin, are both detergent-like molecules that will aid in dissolving membranes.

6. The ion components of salts might be interacting with the charged amino acid side chains of yolk proteins to neutralize charge. This might lessen repulsive forces among proteins. In addition, low pH produced by vinegar or lemon juice will alter the charge on yolk proteins.

Summary

Lipids are a large and diverse class of cellular compounds defined by their insolubility in water and solubility in organic solvents. Lipids serve several biological functions. As highly reduced forms of carbon, lipids yield large amounts of energy in the oxidative reactions of metabolism. As hydrophobic molecules, lipids allow membranes to act as effective barriers to polar molecules. The unique bilayer structure of membranes derives mainly from the amphipathic nature of membrane lipids. Certain lipids also play roles as cell-surface components involved in immunity, cell recognition, and species specificity. Other lipids act as intracellular messengers and triggers, which regulate a variety of processes.

Most fatty acids found in nature have an even number of carbon atoms. Fatty acids may either be saturated or unsaturated, and double bonds are normally of the *cis* configuration. "Essential" fatty acids, including linoleic and linolenic acids, are not synthesized by mammals, but are required for growth and life. Triacylglycerols consist of a glycerol molecule with three fatty acids esterified. Triacylglycerols in animals are found primarily in adipose tissue, and serve as a major metabolic reserve for the organism.

Glycerophospholipids, a major class of lipids, are composed of an *sn*-glycerol-3-phosphate with fatty acids esterified at the 1- and 2- positions. Many different "head groups" can be esterified to the phosphate, including choline, ethanolamine, serine, glycerol, and inositol. Ether glycerophospholipids are glycerol-based lipids but with a fatty alcohol in ether linkage at carbon 1. Sphingolipids are lipids formed from sphingosine, a long-chain fatty alcohol, to which another fatty acid is attached in amide linkage to form a ceramide. Sphingomyelin is a phosphate-containing sphingolipid. Glycosphingolipids consist of a ceramide backbone with one or more sugars. Cerebroside is a glycosphingolipid containing either glucose or galactose. Gangliosides have three or more sugars esterified, one of which must be a sialic acid. Glycosphingolipids are present in only small amounts, but serve numerous important cell functions. Terpenes are a class of lipids derived from isoprene units. The steroids, including cholesterol, are an important class of terpene-based lipids. Other steroids in animals, including the androgens and estrogens (male and female hormones, respectively) and the bile acids (used in digestion) are derived from cholesterol.

Waxes are esters of long-chain fatty acids and long-chain alcohols. Because of their low water solubility and ability to aggregate, waxes are used to form water-impermeable surfaces.

In addition to being components of biological membranes, certain lipids serve as substrates to produce chemica- signalling molecules. For example, action of phospholipase A2 on a phosphatidic acid containing arachidonic acid leads to production of free arachidonic acid, which is the precursor of the eicosanoids, and lysophosphatidic acid, an extracellular-signalling molecule. Digestion of **phosphatidylinositol** by phospholipase C releases diacylglycerol, an activator of protein kinase C, and **inositol phosphate**, which regulates cellular calcium levels.

Chapter 9

Lipid Biosynthesis

• •

Chapter Outline

❖ Fatty acid biosynthesis
  ⅄ Biosynthesis localized in cytosol: Fatty acid degradation in mitochondria
  ⅄ Intermediates held on acyl carrier protein (ACP): Phosphopantetheine group attached to serine (CoA in degradation)
  ⅄ Fatty acid synthase: Multi-enzyme complex
  ⅄ Carbons derived from acetyl units
    • Acetyl CoA to malonyl CoA by carboxylation
    • Acetyl unit added to fatty acid with decarboxylation of malonyl CoA
  ⅄ Carbonyl carbons of acetyl units reduced using NADPH
❖ Source of acetyl units
  ⅄ Amino acids, glucose
  ⅄ Acetyl CoA used to produce citrate
  ⅄ Citrate exported to cytosol: ATP-citrate lyase forms acetyl-CoA and oxaloacetate
❖ Source of NADPH
  ⅄ Oxaloacetate utilization
    • Oxaloacetate (from citrate) to malate: NADH-dependent reaction
    • Malate to pyruvate: Malic enzyme: NADPH produced
  ⅄ Pentose phosphate pathway
❖ Malonyl-CoA production: Acetyl-CoA carboxylase
  ⅄ Biotin-dependent enzyme
  ⅄ ATP drives carboxylation
  ⅄ Enzyme regulation
    • Filamentous polymeric form active
      • Citrate favours active polymer
      • Palmitoyl-CoA favours inactive protomer
      • Citrate/palmitoyl-CoA effects depend on protein phosphorylation
        ○ Unphosphorylated protein binds citrate with high affinity: Activation
        ○ Phosphorylated protein binds palmitoyl with high affinity: Inactivation
❖ Acetyl transacetylase: Acetylates acyl carrier protein (ACP): Destined to become methyl end of fatty acid
❖ Malonyl transacetylase: Malonylates ACP
❖ β-ketoacyl-ACP synthase (acyl-malonyl-ACP–condensing enzyme): Accepts acetyl group: Transfers acyl group to malonyl-ACP
  ⅄ Malonyl carboxyl group released: Decarboxylation drives synthesis
  ⅄ Malonyl-ACP converted to acetoacetyl-ACP
❖ β-ketoacyl-ACP reductase
  ⅄ Carbonyl carbon reduced to alcohol
  ⅄ NADPH provides electrons
❖ β-hydroxyacyl-ACP dehydratase: Elements of water removed: Double bond created
❖ 2,3-*trans*-enoyl-ACP reductase
  ⅄ Double bond reduced
  ⅄ NADPH provides electrons

- ❖ Megasynthase complexes
  - ⅄ Bacterial fatty acid synthesis catalyzed by discrete enzymes
  - ⅄ Fungi and higher eukaryotes fatty acid synthesis organized into multiprotein complexes
    - • Mammalian enzyme: Homodimer with each monomer containing domains for multiple enzymatic activities involved in fatty acid synthesis
    - • Fungal enzyme: Multiple subunits with each having one or more domains with enzymatic activity
- ❖ Subsequent cycles produce C-16: Palmitoyl-CoA
- ❖ Additional modifications
  - ⅄ Elongation
    - • Mitochondrial-based system uses reversal of β-oxidation
    - • Endoplasmic reticulum–based system uses malonyl-CoA
  - ⅄ Monounsaturation: One double bond
    - • Bacteria: Oxygen-independent pathway: Chemistry performed on carbonyl carbon
    - • Eukaryotes: Oxygen-dependent pathway
  - ⅄ Polyunsaturation
    - • Plants can add double bonds between C-9 and methyl end
    - • Animals
      - • Add double bonds between C-9 and carboxyl end
      - • Require essential fatty acids to have double bonds closer to methyl end
- ❖ Regulation
  - ⅄ Malonyl-CoA inhibition of carnitine-acyl transferase: Blocks fatty acid uptake
  - ⅄ Citrate/palmitoyl regulation of acetyl-CoA carboxylase
- ❖ Complex lipids
  - ⅄ Glycerolipids: Glycerol backbone
    - • Glycerophospholipids
    - • Triacylglycerols
  - ⅄ Sphingolipids: Sphingosine backbone
  - ⅄ Phospholipids
    - • Sphingolipids
    - • Glycerophospholipids
- ❖ Glycerolipid biosynthesis
  - ⅄ Phosphatidic acid is precursor
    - • Glycerokinase produces glycerol-3-phosphate
    - • Glycerol-3-phosphate acyltransferase acylates C-1 with saturated fatty acid: Monoacylglycerol phosphate
    - • Eukaryotes can produce monoacylglycerol phosphate using DHAP
    - • Acyldihydroxyacetone phosphate reduced by NAPDH to monoacylglycerol phosphate
    - • Acyltransferase acylates C-2: Phosphatidic acid
  - ⅄ Phosphatidic acid used to synthesize two precursors of complex lipids
    - • Diacylglycerol: Precursor of
      - • Triacylglycerol: Diacylglycerol acyltransferase
      - • Phosphatidylethanolamine, phosphatidylcholine
        - o Ethanolamine phosphorylated
        - o CTP and phosphoethanolamine produce CDP-ethanolamine
        - o Transferase moves phosphoethanolamine onto diacylglycerol
        - o (Dietary choline: As per ethanolamine)
        - o (Phosphatidylethanolamine to phosphatidylcholine by methylation)
      - • Phosphatidylserine: Serine for ethanolamine exchange
    - • CDP-diacylglycerol
      - • Phosphatidate cytidylyltransferase produces CDP-diacylglycerol
      - • CDP-diacylglycerol used to produce:
        - o Phosphaphatidyl inositol
        - o Phosphaphatidyl glycerol
        - o Cardiolipin

- Plasmalogens: α,β-unsaturated ether-linked chain at C-1
  - DHAP acylated
  - Acyl group exchanged for alcohol
  - Keto group on DHAP reduced to alcohol and acylated
  - Head group attached
  - Desaturase produces double bonds
- Sphingolipid biosynthesis
  - Serine and palmitoyl-CoA condensed with decarboxylation to produce 3-ketosphinganine
  - Reduction forms sphingamine
  - Sphingamine acylated to form N-acyl sphingamine
  - Desaturase produces ceramide
    - Cerebrosides: Galactose or glucose added
    - Gangliosides: Sugar polymers: Sugars derive from UDP-monosaccharides
- Eicosanoids: Derived from 20-C fatty acids: Arachidonate is precursor
  - Local hormones: Prostaglandins, thromboxanes, leukotrienes, hydroxyeicosanoic acids
  - Prostaglandins
    - Cyclopentanoic acid formed from arachidonate by prostaglandin endoperoxidase synthase (cyclooxygenase [COX])
    - Aspirin inhibits enzyme
- Cholesterol
  - Membrane component
  - Precursor of important biomolecules
    - Bile salts
    - Steroid hormones
    - Vitamin D
- Cholesterol biosynthesis: In liver
  - Mevalonate biosynthesis
    - Thiolase condenses two acetyl-CoA to produce acetoacetyl-CoA
    - HMG-CoA synthase produces HMG-CoA
    - HMG-CoA reductase produces mevalonate
      - Rate-limiting step
      - Regulation
        - Inactivated by cAMP-dependent protein kinase
        - Short half-life of enzyme when cholesterol levels high
        - Gene expression regulated
      - Pharmacological target for blood cholesterol regulation
  - Isopentenyl pyrophosphate and dimethylallyl pyrophosphate from mevalonate
  - Squalene to lanosterol to cholesterol
- Lipid transport
  - Fatty acids complexed to serum albumin
  - Phospholipids, triacylglycerol, cholesterol transported as lipoprotein complexes
    - Lipoprotein complex types: HDL, LDL, IDL, VLDL, chylomicrons
      - Chylomicrons formed in intestine
      - HDL, VLDL assembled in liver
        - Core of triacylglycerol
        - Single layer of phospholipid
        - Proteins and cholesterol inserted
        - VLDL to IDL to LDL to liver for uptake and degradation
        - HDL: Assembled without cholesterol but picks up cholesterol during circulation
- Bile salts
  - Glycocholic acid
  - Taurocholic acid

> ❖ Steroid hormones
> > ⅄ Cholesterol to pregnenolone
> > ⅄ Pregnenolone to progesterone
> > > • Hormone
> > > • Sex hormone precursor
> > > > ● Androgens
> > > > ● Estrogens
> > > • Corticosteroids precursor
> > > > ● Glucocorticoids
> > > > ● Mineralocorticoids

Chapter Objectives

Fatty Acid Biosynthesis

The steps of fatty acid biosynthesis (Figure 9.7) are similar in chemistry to the reverse of β-oxidation. Two-carbon acetyl units are used to build a fatty acid chain. The carbonyl carbon is reduced to a methylene carbon in three steps: reduction to an alcoholic carbon, dehydration to a carbon–carbon double bond intermediate, and reduction of the double bond. The two reduction steps utilize NADPH as a reductant. Two-carbon acetyl units are moved out of the mitochondria as citrate and activated by carboxylation to malonyl-CoA. We have already seen similar carboxylation reactions and should remember that biotin is involved when carbons are added at the oxidation level of a carboxyl group. The enzyme, acetyl-CoA carboxylase, is regulated by polymerization/depolymerization with the filamentous polymeric state being active. You should understand the regulatory effects of citrate (favours polymer formation), palmitoyl-CoA (depolymerizes), and covalent phosphorylation (blocks citrate binding) on acetyl-CoA carboxylase activity. In β-oxidation, we saw that the phosphopantetheine group of coenzyme A functioned as a molecular chauffeur for two-carbon acetyl units. In synthesis, phosphopantetheine, attached to the acyl carrier protein, functions as a molecular carrier by guiding the growth of fatty acid chains.

In plants and bacteria, the steps of fatty acid biosynthesis are catalyzed by individual proteins, whereas in animals, a large multifunctional protein is involved. Synthesis starts with formation of acetyl-ACP and malonyl-ACP by specific transferases. The carboxyl group of malonyl-ACP departs, leaving a carbanion that attacks the acetyl group of acetyl-ACP to produce a four-carbon β-ketoacyl intermediate, which is subsequently reduced by an NADPH-dependent reductase, dehydrated, and reduced a second time by another NADPH-dependent reductase. To continue the cycle, malonyl-ACP is reformed, decarboxylates, and attacks the acyl-ACP. The original acetyl group is the methyl-end of the fatty acid, whereas the malonyl groups are added at the carboxyl end. NADPH is supplied by the pentose phosphate pathway and by malic enzyme, which converts the oxaloacetate skeleton, used to transport acetyl groups out of the mitochondria as citrate, into pyruvate and CO_2 with $NADP^+$ reduction.

Additional elongation and introduction of double bonds can occur after synthesis of a C_{16} fatty acid. Elongation can occur in the endoplasmic reticulum, where malonyl-CoA is utilized, or in the mitochondria where acetyl-CoA is used. Introduction of double bonds occurs via oxygen-independent mechanisms in bacteria and oxygen-dependent mechanisms in eukaryotes. Be familiar with the reaction catalyzed by stearoyl-CoA desaturase, involving stearoyl-CoA and oxygen as substrates and oleoyl-CoA and water as products.

Complex Lipids

The glycerolipids, including glycerophospholipids and triacylglycerols, are synthesized from glycerol, fatty acids, and head groups. Synthesis starts with the formation of phosphatidic acid from glycerol-3-phosphate and fatty acyl-CoA. C-1 is esterified usually with a saturated fatty acid. Phosphatidic acid may be converted to diacylglycerol and then to triacylglycerol. Alternately, diacylglycerol can be used to synthesize phosphatidylethanolamine and phosphatidylcholine with CDP-derivatized head groups serving as substrates. Phosphatidylserine is produced by exchange of the ethanol head group from PE with serine. Phosphatidylinositol, phosphatidylglycerol, and cardiolipin (two diacylglycerols linked together by glycerol) are synthesized using CDP-diacylglycerol as an intermediate. Plasmalogens are synthesized from acylated DHAP. The acyl group is exchanged for a long-chain alcohol followed by reduction of the keto carbon of DHAP, acyl group transfer from acyl-CoA to C-2, head group transfer from CDP-ethanolamine and formation of a *cis* double bond between C-1 and C-2 of the long-chain alcohol.

The sphingolipids all derive from ceramide, whose synthesis starts with bond formation between palmitic acid and the α-carbon of serine (with loss of the serine carboxyl carbon as bicarbonate). After a few steps, a second fatty acid is attached to serine in amide linkage. Subsequent sugar additions lead to cerebrosides and gangliosides.

Prostaglandins

The prostaglandins are produced from arachidonic acid released by phospholipase A_2 action on phospholipids. Production of these local hormones is blocked by aspirin and non-steroid anti-inflammatory agents such as ibuprofen and phenylbutazone.

Cholesterol

Cholesterol derives from HMG-CoA, a product we already encountered in ketone body formation. You might recall that ketone bodies are produced from acetyl-CoA units. HMG-CoA is a six-carbon CoA derivative produced from three acetyl units. The rate-limiting step in cholesterol synthesis is formation of $3R$-mevalonate from HMG-CoA by HMG-CoA reductase, which catalyzes two NADPH-dependent reductions. This enzyme is carefully regulated by 1) phosphorylation leading to inactivation, 2) degradation, and 3) gene expression. Mevalonate, a six-carbon intermediate, is converted to isopentenyl pyrophosphate, which is used to synthesize cholesterol. Cholesterol is the precursor of bile salts and the steroid hormones. You should understand how lipoproteins are responsible for movement of cholesterol and other lipids in the body.

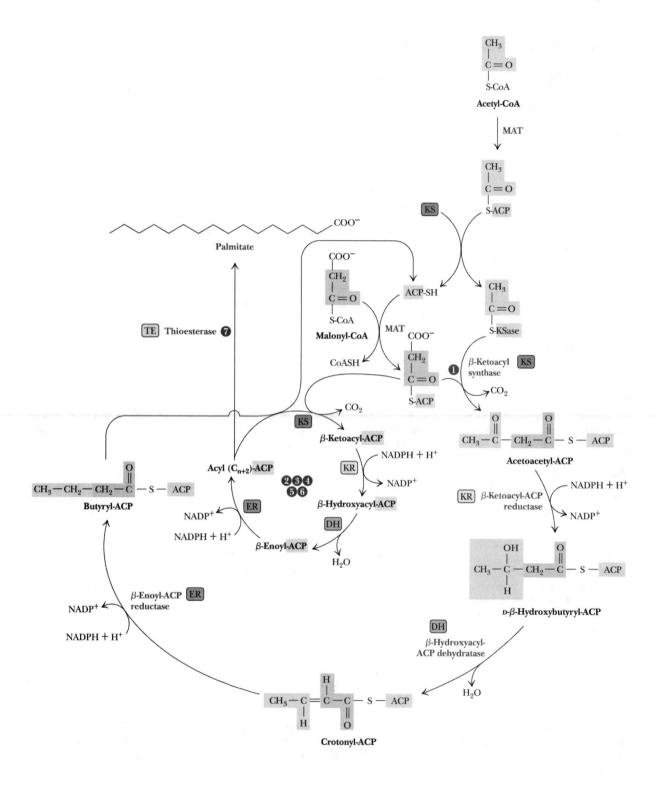

Figure 9.7 The pathway of palmitate synthesis from acetyl-CoA and malonyl-CoA. Acetyl and malonyl building blocks are introduced as acyl carrier protein conjugates. Decarboxylation drives the β-ketoacyl-ACP synthase and results in the addition of two-carbon units to the growing chain. Concentrations of free fatty acids are extremely low in most cells, and newly synthesized fatty acids exist primarily as acyl-CoA esters.

Problems and Solutions

1. *Carefully count and account for each of the atoms and charges in the equations for the synthesis of palmitoyl-CoA, the synthesis of malonyl-CoA, and the overall reaction for the synthesis of palmitoyl-CoA from acetyl-CoA.*

Answer: Malonyl-CoA is synthesized as follows:

$$Acetyl\text{-}CoA + HCO_3^- + ATP^{4-} \rightarrow malonyl\text{-}CoA^- + ADP^{3-} + P_i^{2-} + H^+$$

The carbons in the acetyl group of acetyl-CoA derive from glucose via glycolysis or from the side chains of various amino acids. The bicarbonate anion is produced from CO_2 and H_2O by carbonic anhydrase: $CO_2 + H_2O \rightarrow H_2CO_3 \rightarrow H^+ + HCO_3^-$. Generation of ADP and P_i from ATP is a hydrolysis reaction; however, water does not show up in the equation because incorporation of bicarbonate carbon into malonyl-CoA is accompanied by release of water.

   Synthesis of palmitoyl-CoA is described as follows:

$$Acetyl\text{-}CoA + 7\ malonyl\text{-}CoA^- + 14\ NADPH + 7\ H^+ + 7\ ATP^{4-} \rightarrow$$
$$palmitoyl\text{-}CoA + 7\ HCO_3^- + 14\ NADP^+ + 7\ ADP^{3-} + 7\ P_i^{2-} + 7\ CoASH$$

For bicarbonate to show up on the right-hand side of the equation, the carbon dioxide released by reacting malonyl-CoA and acetyl-CoA must be hydrated and subsequently ionized. So, each bicarbonate is accompanied by production of protons. This is the reason why only half as many protons as NADPH are found in the reaction. Carbons 15 and 16 derive from acetyl-CoA directly; the remaining carbons in palmitoyl-CoA derive from acetyl-CoA by way of malonyl-CoA.

3. *Based on the information presented in the text and in Figures 9.4 and 9.5, suggest a model for the regulation of acetyl-CoA carboxylase. Consider the possible roles of subunit interaction, phosphorylation, and conformational changes in your model.*

Answer: Acetyl-CoA carboxylase catalyzes the formation of malonyl-CoA, the committed step in synthesis of fatty acids. This enzyme is a polymeric protein composed of protomers, or subunits, of 230 kD. In the polymeric form, the enzyme is active, whereas in the protomeric form, the enzyme is inactive. Polymerization is regulated by citrate and palmitoyl-CoA such that citrate, a metabolic signal for excess acetyl units, favours the polymeric and, therefore, active form of the enzyme, whereas palmitoyl-CoA shifts the equilibrium to the inactive form. The activity of acetyl-CoA carboxylase is also under hormonal regulation. Glucagon and epinephrine stimulate cyclic AMP-dependent protein kinase that will phosphorylate a large number of sites on the enzyme. The phosphorylated form of the enzyme binds citrate poorly and citrate binding occurs only at high citrate levels. Citrate is a tricarboxylic acid with three negative charges, and its binding site on the enzyme is likely to be composed of positively charged residues. Phosphorylation introduces negative charges, which may be responsible for the decrease in citrate binding.

   In the phosphorylated form, low levels of palmitoyl-CoA will inhibit the enzyme. Thus, the enzyme is sensitive to palmitoyl-CoA binding and to depolymerization in the phosphorylated form. If we assume that the palmitoyl-CoA binding site is located at a subunit–subunit interface, and that phosphorylated, and hence negatively charged, subunits interact with lower affinity than do unphosphorylated subunits, we see that it is easier for palmitoyl-CoA to bind to the enzyme.

5. *Carefully study the reaction mechanism for the stearoyl-CoA desaturase in Figure 9.14, and account for all of the electrons flowing through the reactions shown. Also account for all of the hydrogen and oxygen atoms involved in this reaction, and convince yourself that the stoichiometry is correct as shown.*

Answer: Stearoyl-CoA desaturase catalyzes the following reaction:

$$Stearoyl\text{-}CoA + NADH + H^+ + O_2 \rightarrow oleoyl\text{-}CoA + 2\ H_2O$$

This reaction involves a four-electron reduction of molecular oxygen to produce two water molecules. Two of the electrons come from the desaturation reaction directly, in which desaturase removes two electrons and two protons from stearoyl-CoA to produce the carbon–carbon double bond in oleoyl-CoA. The other two electrons and protons derive from NADH + H⁺. Two electrons from NADH are used by another enzyme, NADH-cytochrome b_5 reductase, to reduce FAD to $FADH_2$. Electrons are then passed one at a time to cytochrome b_5, which passes electrons to the desaturase to reduce oxygen to water. So, two electrons and two protons come from palmitoyl-CoA and two electrons come from NADH, with two protons being supplied by the surrounding solution.

7. *Write a balanced, stoichiometric reaction for the synthesis of cholesterol from acetyl-CoA.*

Answer: The immediate precursors of cholesterol are isopentenyl pyrophosphate and dimethylallyl pyrophosphate, both of which derive from hydroxymethylglutaryl-CoA (HMG-CoA). HMG-CoA is synthesized from acetyl-CoA by the following route:

The reaction is:

$$3 \text{ Acetyl-CoA} \rightarrow \text{HMG-CoA} + 2 \text{ CoA-SH}$$

HMG-CoA is anabolized into isopentenyl pyrophosphate and dimethylallyl pyrophosphate, both of which are used to synthesize squalene, which is converted by way of lanosterol into cholesterol. (The next question asks us to trace carbons from mevalonate to cholesterol, so it is worthwhile now to look at these reactions in detail).

Synthesis of isopentenyl pyrophosphate from HMG-CoA is as follows:

isopentenyl pyrophosphate   dimethylallyl pyrophosphate

Overall, the reaction is:

$$\text{HMG-CoA} + 2 \text{ NAPDH} + 3 \text{ ATP} \rightarrow \text{isopentenyl pyrophosphate (or dimethylallyl}$$
$$\text{pyrophosphate)} + \text{CoA-SH} + 2 \text{ NADP}^+ + 3 \text{ ADP} + P_i + CO_2$$

Production of squalene using isopentenyl pyrophosphate and dimethylallyl pyrophosphate proceeds as follows. Two farnesyl pyrophosphates are produced from two dimethylallyl pyrophosphates and four isopentenyl pyrophosphates. The farnesyl pyrophosphates are reacted to produce squalene as follows:

2 farnesyl pyrophosphates

squalene

Squalene is converted to lanosterol in two steps catalyzed by squalene epoxidase and squalene oxidocyclase:

$$\text{Squalene} + 0.5 \, O_2 + \text{NADPH} \rightarrow \text{lanosterol}$$

The overall equation for acetyl-CoA to lanosterol is:

$$18 \, \text{Acetyl-CoA} + 13 \, \text{NADPH} + 13 \, H^+ + 18 \, \text{ATP} + 0.5 \, O_2 \rightarrow$$
$$\text{Lanosterol} + 18 \, \text{CoA-SH} + 13 \, \text{NADP}^+ + 18 \, \text{ADP} + 6 \, P_i + 6 \, PP_i + 6 \, CO_2$$

The pathway from lanosterol to cholesterol involves the oxidation and loss of three carbons.

9. Suggest a structural or functional role for the O-linked saccharide domain in the LDL receptor (Figure 9.40).

Answer: LDL receptors are synthesized on the rough endoplasmic reticulum and move through the smooth endoplasmic reticulum and Golgi apparatus before being incorporated into the plasma membrane. On the plasma membrane, LDL receptors bind LDL, aggregate into patches, and are internalized into coated vesicles that fuse with lysosomes where LDL is degraded. The O-linked saccharide domain functions to extend the receptor domain away from the cell surface, above the glycocalyx coat. This allows the receptor to bind circulating lipoproteins.

11. Determine the number of ATP equivalents needed to form palmitic acid from acetyl-CoA. (Assume for this calculation that each NADPH is worth 3.5 ATPs.)

Answer: Palmitate is synthesized with the following stoichiometry:

$$8 \, \text{Acetyl-CoA} + 7 \, \text{ATP} + 14 \, \text{NADPH} \rightarrow \text{palmitate} + 7 \, \text{ADP} + 14 \, \text{NADP}^+ + 8 \, \text{CoA-SH} + 6 \, H_2O + 7 \, P_i$$

The 14 NADPHs are equivalent to (14 × 3.5 =) 49 ATPs. Combining these with the 7 ATPs used to synthesize malonyl-CoA gives a total of 56 ATPs consumed.

13.   *Why is the involvement of FAD important in the conversion of stearic acid to oleic acid?*

Answer: In eukaryotes, unsaturation reactions are catalyzed by stearoyl-CoA desaturase. This enzyme functions along with cytochrome b_5 reductase and cytochrome b_5 to pass electrons, one at a time to desaturase. Desaturase reduces O_2, a 4-electron reduction for which two electrons come from the fatty acid that is desaturated and two ultimately from NADH. The two electrons from NADH pass through cytochrome b_5 reductase, an FAD-containing enzyme, which must pass electrons one at a time to cytochrome b_5. NAD cannot participate in one-electron transfers whereas FAD can. $FADH_2$ can lose one electron or two.

15.   *Write a suitable reaction mechanism for the β-ketoacyl-ACP synthase, showing how the involvement of malonyl-CoA drives this reaction forward.*

Answer: β-ketoacyl ACP synthase links an acetyl group from malonyl-ACP onto an acyl-group (acetyl- in the first round) during fatty acid synthesis. Malonyl-CoA, in effect, is an activated acetyl group produced at the expense of hydrolysis of ATP by acetyl-CoA carboxylase. The mechanism of action involves decarboxylation of malonyl-CoA to produce a carbanion on the beta carbon, which attacks the carbonyl carbon of acyl-ACP, producing β-ketoacyl ACP. This mechanism is shown below.

17.   *In the LDL receptor structure shown in Figure 9.41c, the β-propeller interaction with domains R4 and R5 is partly stabilized by salt bridges between acidic residues on R4 and R5 that also coordinate Ca^{2+} ions. Use a molecular modelling program or consult the literature to identify at least two such interactions. Two suitable references are Beglova, N., and Blacklow, S. C., 2005. Trends in Biochemical Sciences 30:309–316; and Rudenko, G., Henry, L., et al., 2002. Science 298:2353–2358.*

Answer: From the two references we learn that the LDL receptor is a multi-domain, single-pass transmembrane protein. The N-terminus is extracellular whereas the C-terminus is intracellular. The N-terminus is composed of seven type-A LDL receptor (LA) modules that are responsible for ligand binding. Each LA module contains three disulfide bonds that stabilize two loops. One of the loops contains conserved acid residues that form a calcium-binding site. Calcium binding and the disulfide bonds stabilize the structure. Following the LA modules the protein contains two epidermal growth factor-like (EFG) domains, six YWTD repeats, and another EFG domain. This region (the three EFG domains and the 6 YWTD repeats—organized into a β-propeller) is important for ligand release. A region with numerous O-linked glycosylation sites follows the ligand release domain and precedes the transmembrane domain, which is followed by a 50-residue C-terminal region located within the cytoplasm. The O-linked sugar domain is responsible for keeping the other extracellular domains away from the membrane surface.

The LDL receptor adopts two conformations, an open conformation at neutral pH and a closed or compact conformation at acidic pH (pH < 6.0). In the closed conformation the ligand release domain interacts with two of the LA domains. Specifically LA4 and 5 interact with the β-propeller structure.

In the open structure, the LA domains have a cluster of acidic residues organized by calcium coordination of residues in the loops within the LA domains. These acidic clusters are thought to be responsible for ligand binding. The protein component of LDL has a series of basic residues that is required for LDL binding to the receptor, which likely occurs through electrostatic interactions.

In the closed conformation, LA4 and 5 interact with the β-propeller via electrostatic interactions. Three histidine residues participate in these interactions and are thought to be the pH-sensitive switches. Histidines 562 and 586 are located on the propeller domain. A third histidine, His190, is situated on the tip of one of the loops of LA5. Histidine's pK_a is around 6, and so we expect a dramatic change in histidine's charge in going from neutral pH to pH < 6. There are a number of observations supporting the involvement of these histidines in ligand release. In certain cases of familial hypercholesterolemia, mutations are found at either histidine 190 or 562. LDL receptors with these mutations appear to bind LDL normally but show a decrease in LDL-release activity. Site-directed mutagenesis of all three histidines produces a receptor that does not release LDL.

Thus, LDL binds to its receptor through electrostatic interactions between the protein component of LDL and the LA domains on the receptor. When the LDL receptor is internalized in endosomes and the endosomes made acidic, the ligand release region of the LDL receptor becomes positively charged and associates tightly with LA4 and LA5, two domains critical for LDL binding to the receptor. This releases LDL from LA4 and LA5.

Questions for Self-Study

1. How are acetate units moved from the mitochondria to the cytosol? What other role does the acetate carrier play in regulation of metabolism?

2. Although acetate units are incorporated into fatty acids during synthesis, they derive from three-carbon compounds attached to coenzyme A. What is this three-carbon coenzyme A derivative? What enzyme is responsible for its formation? How many high-energy phosphate bonds are cleaved to drive its synthesis?

3. Describe how, in animals, the activity of acetyl-CoA carboxylase is regulated by citrate and palmitoyl-CoA and how this regulation is sensitive to covalent modification of the enzyme.

4. Match an enzyme with an activity.
    a. Acetyltransferase
    b. Dehydrase
    c. Malonyltransferase
    d. Enoyl reductase
    e. β-ketoacyl reductase
    f. β-ketoacyl synthase

    1. Keto carbon converted to alcoholic carbon
    2. Attaches malonyl group to fatty acid synthase
    3. Attaches acetyl group to acyl carrier protein
    4. Carbon–carbon double bond reduced
    5. Condensation of acetyl group and malonyl group
    6. Enoyl intermediate formed

5. From the following list of compounds, identify those that are cholesterol derivatives and appropriately identify each cholesterol derivative as a hormone (H), bile salt (B), or vitamin (V).
    a. Prostaglandin D_2
    b. Glycocholic acid
    c. Squalene
    d. Testosterone
    e. Arachidonic acid
    f. Cortisol
    g. Cholecalciferol
    h. Progesterone
    i. Thromboxanes
    j. Taurocholic acid
    k. Aldosterone

6. What is the rate-limiting step in cholesterol biosynthesis?

7. Match a lipoprotein complex with a function.
    a. Chylomicrons
    b. Very-low-density lipoproteins
    c. Low-density lipoproteins
    d. High-density lipoproteins

    1. Formed from very low density lipoproteins
    2. Formed in the intestine
    3. Slowly accumulate cholesterol
    4. Carry lipid from the liver

8. In eukaryotes, glycerolipids are all derived from phosphatidic acid. Draw the structure of phosphatidic acid and outline its biosynthesis from dihydroxyacetone phosphate and from glycerol-3-phosphate.

9. What is the role of cytidine in lipid biosynthesis?

10. Fill in the blanks. The prostaglandins are _____ that function locally and at very low concentrations. They are synthesized from _____ _____, a 20-carbon polyunsaturated fatty acid. Mammals can produce this fatty acid from _____ _____ ($18:2^{\Delta 9,12}$) but must acquire this polyunsaturated fatty acid from their diet.

Answers

1. Acetate units on acetyl-CoA are used to produce citrate in the mitochondria. Citrate is exported to the cytosol where it is converted to acetyl-CoA and oxaloacetate. Citrate inhibits phosphofructokinase and thus serves as a regulator of glycolysis. It also stimulates fatty acid synthesis.

2. Malonyl-CoA is produced by acetyl-CoA carboxylase at the expense of one high-energy phosphate bond.

3. Acetyl-CoA carboxylase is active in a polymeric state. The equilibrium between active polymer and inactive protomers is affected by citrate and palmitoyl-CoA. Citrate is an allosteric activator of the enzyme and shifts the equilibrium to the polymer. Palmitoyl-CoA shifts the equilibrium to the inactive, protomeric state. The enzyme is phosphorylated by a number of kinases and the phosphorylated state has a low affinity for citrate and a high affinity for palmitate.

4. a. 3; b. 6; c. 2; d. 4; e. 1; f. 5.

5. b. B; d. H; f. H; g. V; h. H; j. B; k. H.

6. The production $3R$-mevalonate from HMG-CoA catalyzed by HMG-CoA reductase.

7. a. 2; b. 4; c. 1; d. 3.

8. Dihydroxyacetone phosphate is converted to 1-acyldihydroxyacetone-phosphate by an acyltransferase reaction and reduced to 1-acylglycerol-3-phosphate by a reductase. This compound can also be synthesized from glycerol-3-phosphate by acyltransferase. Transfer of a second acyl group to C-2 produces phosphatidic acid whose structure is shown below.

$$
\begin{array}{c}
\quad\quad O \\
\quad\quad \parallel \\
R_1-C-O-CH_2 \\
\quad\quad O \quad\quad | \\
\quad\quad \parallel \quad\quad | \\
R_2-C-O-C-H \quad\quad O \\
\quad\quad\quad\quad CH_2-O-C-O^- \\
\quad\quad\quad\quad\quad\quad\quad | \\
\quad\quad\quad\quad\quad\quad\quad O^-
\end{array}
$$

9. The head groups of phosphatidylethanolamine and phosphatidylcholine derive from cytidine diphosphate derivatives. CDP-diacylglycerol is a precursor of phosphatidylinositol, phosphatidylglycerol, and cardiolipin.

10. Hormones; arachidonic acid; linoleic acid.

Additional Problems

1. What are the sources of carbons for fatty acid biosynthesis? What is the role of the citrate-malate-pyruvate shuttle in making carbon compounds available for fatty acid biosynthesis?

2. Movement of citrate out of the mitochondria coordinates glycolysis and fatty acid biosynthesis. Explain.

3. Name the three water-soluble vitamins that are crucial to fatty acid synthesis and briefly describe the roles they play in this process.

4. Why do mammals require certain essential fatty acids in their diet?

5. Outline the synthesis of glycerophospholipid.

6. Lovastatin lowers serum cholesterol by interfering with HMG-CoA reductase, the enzyme that catalyzes the rate-limiting step in cholesterol synthesis. The drug is administered as an inactive lactone that is activated by hydrolysis to mevinolinic acid, a competitive inhibitor of HMG-CoA reductase. Can you recall another lactone hydrolysis reaction encountered in an earlier chapter?

7. What is the role of high-density lipoproteins in regulation of cholesterol levels in the blood?

8. Synthesis of the steroid hormones from cholesterol starts with the reaction catalyzed by desmolase shown below. Why is this a critical reaction for formation of steroid hormones?

Cholesterol

Isocaproic aldehyde

Pregnenolone

Abbreviated Answers

1. The immediate source of carbons is acetyl-CoAs, which are produced from carbohydrates, amino acids, and lipids. Acetyl-CoA is produced in the mitochondria, but fatty acid biosynthesis occurs in the cytosol. To move acetyl units out of the mitochondria, they are condensed onto oxaloacetate to form citrate, in a citric acid cycle reaction. Citrate is then transported out of the mitochondria to the cytosol, where ATP-citrate lyase catabolizes citrate to acetyl-CoA and oxaloacetate. This cytosolic acetyl-CoA is used to synthesize fatty acids. So, the citrate-malate-pyruvate shuttle is responsible for moving two-carbon units from the mitochondria to the cytosol. However, it has another purpose: it supplies some of the NADPH needed for fatty acid synthesis. Cytosolic oxaloacetate is reduced to malate and then oxidatively decarboxylated to CO_2 and pyruvate by malic enzyme, in an NADP+-dependent reaction. The NADPH thus formed is consumed during the reduction steps of fatty acid biosynthesis.

2. When covering glycolysis, we note that phosphofructokinase activity is inhibited by citrate. In this chapter, we saw how citrate is used to move two-carbon units from the mitochondria to the cytosol for fatty acid biosynthesis. An increase in the concentration of citrate is a signal that the citric acid cycle is backing up, either because energy stores are satisfactory or because there is an abundance of acetyl

units. In either case, there is not reason to continue glycolysis. Movement of citrate out of the mitochondria shifts acetyl units from degradation via the citric acid to storage via cytosolic fatty acid synthesis and serves to turn down glycolysis at phosphofructokinase.

3. Biotin is a component of acetyl-CoA carboxylase. Nicotinamide is found in NADPH. Phosphopantetheine is covalently attached to acyl carrier protein. Biotin functions as an intermediate carrier of activated carboxyl groups in malonyl-CoA biosynthesis by acetyl-CoA carboxylase. NADPH is required at two reduction steps in each round of chain elongation in fatty acid biosynthesis. Phosphopantotheine serves as a carrier of the growing fatty acid. This group is covalently attached to a serine residue in acyl carrier protein and serves to carry acetyl groups, malonyl groups, and acyl groups during various stages of fatty acid biosynthesis.

4. Mammals cannot introduce a double bond beyond C-9 in a given fatty acid. The prostaglandins are synthesized from linoleic acid, $\Delta^{9,12}$-octadecadienoic acid, which cannot be produced by mammals and is therefore an essential fatty acid.

5. The components of glycerophospholipids are glycerol, phosphate, fatty acids, and an alcoholic head group. Synthesis starts with either glycerol (via reduction of glyceraldehyde) or DHAP being converted to glycerol-3-phosphate by glycerokinase or glycerol-3-phosphate dehydrogenase, respectively. Glycerol-3-phosphate is converted to 1-acylglycerol-3-P and then to phosphatidic acid (1,2-diacylglycerol-3-P) by two acyltransferase reactions. Phosphatidic acid serves as the precursor for triacylglycerol and the glycerophospholipids phosphatidylethanolamine (PE), phosphatidylcholine (PC), phosphatidylserine (PS), phosphatidylinositol (PI), phosphatidylglycerol (PG), and cardiolipin (diphosphatidylglycerol). Phosphatidic acid is converted to diacylglycerol, which is converted to PE or PC by transferases using CDP-derivatized ethanolamine or choline. Alternatively, phosphatidic acid can be converted to its CDP derivative, CDP-diacylglycerol, which is metabolized to PI or PG. PS is produced from PE using serine to displace ethanolamine.

6. In the pentose phosphate pathway, conversion of 6-phosphogluconolactone to 6-phosphogluconate involves hydrolysis of a lactone.

7. HDL is assembled in the endoplasmic reticulum of liver cells and secreted into the blood. Newly synthesized HDL contains very little cholesterol, but with time, it accumulates cholesterol as both free cholesterol and as cholesterol esters. HDL then returns to the liver where cholesterol is either stored or converted to bile salts and excreted.

8. The steroid hormones are transported in the blood to target tissues and must therefore be slightly more soluble than cholesterol. The reaction catalyzed by desmolase removes the hydrocarbon tail of cholesterol, making the product more soluble.

Summary

The biosynthesis of lipid molecules proceeds via mechanisms and pathways, which are different from those of their degradation. In the synthesis of fatty acids, for example, 1) intermediates are linked covalently to the —SH groups of acyl carrier proteins instead of coenzyme A, 2) synthesis occurs in the cytosol instead of the mitochondria, 3) the nicotinamide coenzyme used is NADPH instead of NADH, and 4) in eukaryotes, the enzymes of fatty acid synthesis are associated in one large polypeptide chain instead of being separate enzymes. Fatty acids are synthesized by the addition of two-carbon acetate units, which have been activated by the formation of malonyl-CoA, decarboxylation of which drives the reaction forward. Once the growing fatty acid chain reaches 16 carbons in length, it dissociates from the fatty acid synthase and is subject to the introduction of unsaturations or additional elongation. Acetyl-CoA needed for fatty acid synthesis is provided in the cytosol by citrate that is transported across the mitochondrial membrane and converted to acetyl-CoA and oxaloacetate by ATP-citrate lyase. Formation of malonyl-CoA by acetyl-CoA carboxylase (ACC), a biotin-dependent enzyme, commits acetate units to fatty acid synthesis. In animals, ACC is a multifunctional protein, which forms long, filamentous polymers. It is allosterically activated (and polymerized) by citrate and inhibited (and depolymerized) by palmitoyl-CoA. Affinities for both these regulators are decreased by phosphorylation of the enzyme at up to 8 to 10 separate sites. The fatty acid synthesis reactions involve formation of O-acetyl and O-malonyl enzyme intermediates, followed by transfer of the acetyl group to the —SH of an acyl carrier protein (ACP) and then to the β-ketoacyl-ACP synthase. Transfer of the malonyl group to the ACP is followed by decarboxylation of the malonyl group and condensation of the remaining two-carbon unit with the carbonyl carbon of the acetate group on the synthase. This is followed by reduction of the β-carbonyl to an alcohol, dehydration to yield a *trans-α,β* double bond and reduction to yield a saturated bond. Introduction of unsaturations in the nascent chain occurs by O_2-dependent and O_2-independent pathways and may be followed by further chain elongation. Several mechanisms are utilized to introduce multiple unsaturations in a fatty acid chain. Regulation of fatty acid synthesis is related to regulation of fatty acid breakdown and the activity of the TCA cycle, because of the importance of acetyl-CoA in all these processes. Malonyl-CoA inhibits carnitine transport, blocking fatty acid oxidation. Citrate activates ACC and palmitoyl-CoA inhibits, both in chain-length–dependent fashion. The enzymes of fatty acid synthesis are also under hormonal control.

Glycerolipid synthesis is built around the synthesis of phosphatidic acid from glycerol-3-phosphate or dihydroxyacetone phosphate. Specific acyltransferases add acyl chains to these glycerol derivatives. Other glycerolipids, such as phosphatidylcholine (PC) and phosphatidylethanolamine (PE) are synthesized from phosphatidic acid via CDP-diacylglycerol and diacylglycerol. Base exchange converts phosphatidylethanolamine to phosphatidylserine. Other phospholipids, such as phosphatidylinositol, phosphatidylglycerol and cardiolipin are synthesized from CDP-diacylglycerol. Dihydroxyacetone phosphate is a precursor to the plasmalogens. Platelet activating factor (PAF), an ether lipid, dilates blood vessels, reduces blood pressure, and aggregates platelets. Sphingolipids are produced via condensation of serine and palmitoyl-CoA by 3-ketosphinganine synthase and reduction of the ketone product to form sphingamine. Acylation followed by desaturation yields ceramide, the precursor to other sphingolipids and cerebrosides.

Eicosanoids, derived from arachidonic acid by oxidation and cyclization, are ubiquitous local hormones. They include the prostaglandins, thromboxanes, leukotrienes, and other hydroxyeicosanoic acids. A variety of stimuli, including histamine, epinephrine, bradykinin, proteases, and other agents associated with tissue injury and inflammation, can stimulate the release of eicosanoids, which have short half-lives and are rapidly degraded. Aspirin acetylates endoperoxide synthase on its cyclooxygenase subunit, irreversibly inhibiting the synthesis of prostaglandins.

Cholesterol biosynthesis begins with mevalonic acid, which is formed from acetyl-CoA by thiolase, HMG-CoA synthase, and HMG-CoA reductase. The HMG-CoA reductase reaction is the rate-limiting step in cholesterol biosynthesis. Inhibition of this enzyme by lovastatin blocks cholesterol biosynthesis and can significantly lower serum cholesterol. Mevalonate is converted to squalene via isopentenyl pyrophosphate and dimethylallyl pyrophosphate, which join to yield farnesyl pyrophosphate and then squalene. Squalene is cyclized in two steps and converted to lanosterol. The conversion of lanosterol to cholesterol requires another 20 steps.

Lipids circulate in the body in lipoprotein complexes, including high-density lipoproteins, low-density lipoproteins, very-low-density lipoproteins, and chylomicrons. Lipoproteins consist of a core of mobile triacylglycerols and cholesterol esters, surrounded by a single layer of phospholipid, into which is inserted a mixture of cholesterol and proteins. Lipoproteins are bound to lipoprotein receptors at target sites and progressively degraded in circulation by lipoprotein lipases. Defects of lipoprotein metabolism can lead to elevated serum cholesterol.

Steroids such as the bile acids and steroid hormones are synthesized from cholesterol via key intermediates such as pregnenolone and progesterone. The male hormone testosterone is a precursor to the female hormones, including estradiol. Steroid hormones modulate transcription of DNA to RNA in the cell nucleus. The corticosteroids, including glucocorticoids and mineralocorticoids, synthesized by the adrenal glands, are important physiological regulators.

Chapter 10

Membranes and Membrane Transport

• •

Chapter Outline

❖ Membrane functions
  ⅄ Boundary for cell and organelle
  ⅄ Surface on which reactions can occur
  ⅄ Regulation of material flux through membrane proteins
  ⅄ Signal transduction interface
  ⅄ Specialized properties: Photosynthesis, electron transport, electrical activity
❖ Membrane components
  ⅄ Lipids: Amphipathic molecules arranged as bilayers with polar groups out and non-polar groups in
  ⅄ Proteins: Surface associated or embedded in bilayer
❖ Plasma membrane
  ⅄ Delimits cell
  ⅄ Excludes and retains certain ions and molecules
  ⅄ Major role in energy transduction
  ⅄ Cell locomotion
  ⅄ Reproduction
  ⅄ Signal transduction
  ⅄ Interactions with other cells or extracellular matrix
❖ Lipid interactions
  ⅄ Monolayers: Formation of single-molecule-thick layer at air–water interface with polar groups in contact with water
  ⅄ Micelles: Lipid spheres with polar groups out and hydrophobic tails in the centre: Critical micelle concentration is the concentration of amphiphilic compound at which micelles form
  ⅄ Lipid bilayer: Two lipid monolayers with hydrophobic surfaces face to face
  ⅄ Liposomes: Vesicles formed by lipid bilayers
❖ Fluid Mosaic Model
  ⅄ Singer and Nicholson, 1972
  ⅄ Phospholipid bilayer forming fluid matrix
  ⅄ Three classes of membrane proteins
    • Peripheral (extrinsic) proteins
    • Integral (intrinsic) proteins
    • Lipid-anchored proteins
❖ Membrane proteins
  ⅄ Peripheral membrane proteins (extrinsic): Surface proteins held by variety of weak forces like ionic bonds, hydrogen bonds, and hydrophobic interactions
  ⅄ Integral membrane proteins (intrinsic): Two classes
    • Single transmembrane segment proteins: Hydrophobic alpha helix that spans the lipid bilayer: Glycophorin: 19-amino acid–long alpha helix that spans the membrane with extracellular domain decorated with oligosaccharides that are ABO and MN blood group antigens
    • Multi-transmembrane segment proteins: Essentially globular proteins embedded in membrane
      • Bacteriorhodopsin: Seven alpha-helical segments embedded in bilayer: Segments organized into a channel

- Porins: Beta-sheet motifs
- Wza: α-helices used to form β-helical barrel
- Hydropathy plot: Tool to identify membrane protein topology
    - Calculate average hydrophobicity over window of amino acids
    - Move window by one residue and recalculate average hydrophobicity and repeat
        - Single-segment proteins: Hydrophobic helix
        - Multi-segmented protein: Multiple hydrophobic helices
- Proline in transmembrane α-helix
    - Proline common in interior of membrane α-helix
    - Proline distorts α-helix by introduction of kink
- Amino acid location preferences in transmembrane helix
    - Hydrophobic amino acids interior
    - Charged residues at lipid–water interface
        - Positive inside rule: Lys and Arg often found on cytoplasmic face
- Lipid-anchored membrane proteins: Four types
    - Amide-linked myristoylated proteins
        - Myristic acid (14:0 fatty acid)
        - Amide linkage to amino group of N-terminal glycine
    - Thioester-linked: Fatty acid attached to cysteine as thioester or Ser or Thr as ester
    - Thioether-linked prenylated proteins
        - Prenyl: Long-chain isoprene polymers: Farnesyl or geranylgeranyl
        - Attachment as thioether to C-terminal cysteine of CAAX (A= Aliphatic)
        - AXX cleaved after phrenyl addition
    - Amide-linked glycosyl phosphotidylinositol (GPI) anchors
        - Lipid: Oligosaccharide-modified phosphoinositol
        - Linkage: Carboxy terminus attached via phosphoethanolamine to mannose residue of oligosaccharide
- Membrane asymmetry
    - Lateral asymmetry arises from clustering of membrane components within the plane
        - Lipid clustering: Phase separation induced by divalent cations and influenced by lipid type
        - Protein clustering: Self-associating membrane proteins e.g., bacteriorhodopsin
    - Transverse asymmetry
        - Lipids: Lipid asymmetry due to two processes
            - Asymmetric synthesis
            - Energy-dependent transport: Flippases and floppases
        - Proteins: Asymmetric molecules
        - Carbohydrates: Glycoproteins and glycolipids on outer surface
- Membrane mobility
    - Lipids
        - Rapid lateral movement
        - Slow transverse movement
            - Flippases: ATP-dependent movement of phosphatidyl serine from outer to inner surface of membrane
            - Floppases: ATP-dependent movement from inner to outer surface of membrane
            - Scramblases: Ca^{2+}-dependent randomize of lipids: Degrades transverse asymmetry
        - Lipid bilayer states
            - Gel phase: Solid-ordered state: S_o: Lipid chains extended and packed
            - Liquid crystalline phase: Liquid-disordered state: L_d: Acyl bond rotation and bending
                - Membrane thickness decreases and surface area increases
            - Gel-to-liquid phase transition: Phase transition
                - Characterize by melting temperature, T_m

- Liquid-ordered state: L_o: Acyl chain order like S_o and translational disorder of L_d
  - Microdomains: Membrane rafts: Regions in L_o phase
- Protein-dependent modifications of membrane properties
  - Hop diffusion: Membrane–skeleton fences restrict lateral diffusion to regions
  - Membrane curvature
    - Lipid composition
    - Membrane proteins
    - Scaffolding proteins and amphipathic α-helices: Bind to membrane surface
    - Caveolae: Flask-shaped indentions in plasma membrane
      - Caveolins: Integral membrane proteins: Palmitoyl lipid anchored
  - Vesicle formation and membrane fusion
    - SNAREs: Integral membrane proteins with single transmembrane domain and SNARE domain
      - Q_a-SNARE and Q_{bc}-SNARE: Plasma membrane protein
      - R-SNARE: Vesicle membrane
        - SNAREs interact to form complex stabilized by protein complexin
        - Ca^{2+} binding to synaptotagmin displaces complexin and promotes membrane fusion
- ❖ Membrane transport: Three types
  - Passive diffusion
    - Entropically driven process: Molecules move down a concentration gradient
      - $\Delta G = RT\ln([C_2]/[C_1])$ for uncharged molecule
      - $\Delta G = RT\ln([C_2]/[C_1]) + Z\mathscr{F}\Delta\psi$ for charged molecules
      - R = 8.3145 J/K·mol, T = K, Z = charge, $\mathscr{F}$ = 96485 J/V·mol, $\Delta\psi$ = electrical potential
    - Rate depends on concentration gradient and lipid solubility
  - Facilitated diffusion
    - Entropically driven process as in passive diffusion
    - Involves integral membrane protein
      - Rate depends on concentration but is saturatable
      - Specificity and affinity due to protein–transported molecule interaction
    - Membrane channel proteins
      - Channels: Single channels to multiple channels
        - Aqueous cavity or funnels lead to selectivity filter
        - Selectivity filters
          - Often bind multiple transported species
          - Gated
    - Examples:
      - Potassium channels
        - Selectivity filter that distinguishes K^+ from Na^+
          - TVGYG in KcsA K^+ channel protein
          - Sequence modified in other ion-specific channel proteins
        - Gates: Ligand-gated or voltage-gated
      - Pentameric Mg^{2+} channel (CorA)
        - Transmembrane pore of 5 α-helices
        - Cytosolic domain functions as basic sphincter
  - Active transport: Energy-driven process
    - Primary active transport: Energy sources
      - ATP hydrolysis (most common)
      - Light energy
      - Redox chains
    - Secondary active transport (Energy is ion gradient formed by some other process)
    - Electrogenic transport: Active transport of ions and net charge both occur

- ❖ Na$^+$,K$^+$-ATPase (sodium pump)
    - ⅄ 120 kD α-subunit; 35 kD β-subunit, 6.5 kD, γ-subunit
    - ⅄ 3 Na$^+$ out, 2 K$^+$ in per ATP hydrolyzed: Electrogenic
    - ⅄ Ouabain: Cardiac glycoside that inhibits sodium pump
- ❖ Calcium ATPase
    - ⅄ 2 Ca^{2+} out of cytoplasm per ATP hydrolyzed
    - ⅄ Restores/maintains low cytoplasmic calcium
- ❖ H$^+$,K$^+$-ATPase
    - ⅄ 1 H$^+$ out, 1 K$^+$ in per ATP hydrolyzed
    - ⅄ Gastric enzyme: ΔpH largest gradient known
- ❖ Vacuolar ATPases: Pump H$^+$ in number of vacuoles and cells
- ❖ ABC Transporters: ATPase that drives import or export
    - ⅄ Multidrug resistance efflux pump: Export cellular wastes and toxins
    - ⅄ Cancer cells activate these and become drug resistant
- ❖ Light-energy driven pumps
    - ⅄ Bacteriorhodopsin
        - • Light-driven H$^+$ pump
    - ⅄ Halorhodopsin
        - • Light-driven Cl$^-$ pump
- ❖ Secondary active transport systems
    - ⅄ Na$^+$ or H$^+$ coupled movement of amino acids or sugars
    - ⅄ Symport: Ion and substance move in same direction
    - ⅄ Antiport: Ion and substance move in opposite directions

Chapter Objectives

Lipids associate to form two- and three-dimensional structures. Understand the forces responsible for this behaviour, including hydrophobic interactions and van der Waals forces. Know why monolayers of lipids form at an air–water interface, and what a micelle is and how it forms. Lipids are also capable of forming bilayers, an important structural component of biological membranes.

Biological membranes are composed of various lipids arranged in a bilayer and, embedded in the bilayer, integral (or intrinsic) proteins. The fluid mosaic model of membranes suggests that both lipids and proteins are free to move within a bilayer. The two surfaces of bilayers of biological membranes are asymmetric with respect to protein, lipid, and carbohydrate composition.

Membrane-phase transitions occur when membrane components, in particular lipids, interact in a manner causing loss of fluidity. The temperature of this transition, a transition from solid to liquid, is known as the melting temperature (T_m). What are the effects of degree of saturation, of chain length, of cholesterol on T_m?

Two types of membrane proteins are peripheral and integral proteins. Peripheral proteins interact through electrostatic bonds and hydrogen bonds with the surfaces of bilayers. Integral proteins are strongly associated with the bilayer. There are three kinds of protein motifs responsible for anchoring integral proteins to membranes. Certain integral proteins have a single transmembrane segment, in the form of an α-helix composed of hydrophobic amino acid residues, anchoring the protein to the lipid bilayer. Another structural motif found is the 7-helix, transmembrane segment used by integral proteins involved in transport and signalling activities. Some proteins use β-sheets to form β-barrels. Certain proteins have covalently linked lipid molecules that serve as anchors. You should understand the four kinds of anchors.

Passive Diffusion

Passive diffusion proceeds down a concentration gradient. The driving force is a change in free energy given by $\Delta G = RT\ln([C_2]/[C_1])$ where $[C_2] < [C_1]$ and the substance moves from side 1 to side 2. For a charged species, the driving force is an electrochemical potential given by $\Delta G = RT\ln([C_2]/[C_1]) + Z\mathcal{F}\Delta\psi$ where Z is the charge, $\mathcal{F}$ is Faraday's constant, and $\Delta\psi$ is the membrane potential.

Facilitated Diffusion

Facilitated diffusion is reminiscent of enzyme kinetics because it is a carrier-mediated process and as such depends on an interaction between a carrier and a transported molecule. The flux is still dependent on a difference in concentration, and it occurs from high concentration to low concentration, but the dependence is no longer linear. The flux shows saturation at high concentrations and is critically dependent on stereochemistry of the compound. The glucose transporter and the anion transporter (both in erythrocytes) are examples of facilitated diffusion.

Active Transport

Unlike passive and facilitated diffusion, active transport can move a substance against a concentration gradient. However, the overall ΔG of the reaction must be favourable, and this is achieved by coupling transport to some other energy-yielding process like ATP hydrolysis, capture of light energy, and coupling to other gradients. The sodium pump, or Na^+,K^+-ATPase, is a well-characterized active transporter for movement of 3 Na^+ out of the cell and 2 K^+ into the cell coupled to hydrolysis of ATP. The enzyme is an intrinsic membrane protein that exists in two conformational states that differ in ion- and ATP-binding properties. Understand how transient phosphorylation leads to conformational changes and movement of ions. The cardiac glycosides are important inhibitors of the sodium pump. Understand the consequences of sodium pump inhibition to calcium ion levels in heart muscle. Finally, because of the difference in charge transported (a difference of one positive charge), the sodium pump is electrogenic, leading to formation of a membrane potential. The calcium transporter of sarcoplasmic reticulum is also an ATP-dependent transporter, but of calcium. It has a similar mechanism of action to the sodium pump, shuffling between two conformational states with ATP hydrolysis driving calcium uptake. This transporter is a key player in relaxation of muscle and is also electrogenic. The H^+,K^+-ATPase moves protons out of the cell and potassium back into the cell with ATP hydrolysis. This non-electrogenic pump is capable of producing extremely high concentration gradients of protons.

Light energy-driven active transport systems include bacteriorhodopsin, a H^+-pump, and halorhodopsin, a Cl^--pump. There are many important examples of transport systems driven by ion gradients. Proton gradients, produced by electron-transport driven proton pumping or by proton-ATPases, sodium gradients, produced by the sodium pump, and other cation and anion gradients are used to move a range of molecules, including sugars and amino acids. You should know the terms symport and antiport.

Problems and Solutions

1. In Problem 1(b) in Chapter 8 (page 249) you were asked to draw all the phosphatidylserine isomers that can be formed from palmitic and linoleic acids. Which of these PS isomers are not likely to be found in biological membranes?

Answer: Phosphatidylserine with unsaturated lipids at position 1 are very rare. Unsaturated fatty acids are usually found at position 2. Glycerophospholipids with two unsaturated chains, or with a saturated chain at C-1 and an unsaturated chain at C-2, are commonly found in biomembranes.

3. Sucrose gradients for separation of membrane proteins must be able to separate proteins and protein–lipid complexes having a wide range of densities, typically 1.00 to 1.35 g/mL.
   a. Consult reference books (such as the CRC Handbook of Biochemistry) and plot the density of sucrose solutions versus percent sucrose by weight (g sucrose per 100 g solution), and versus percent by volume (g sucrose per 100 mL solution). Why is one plot linear and the other plot curved?
   b. What would be a suitable range of sucrose concentrations for separation of three membrane-derived protein–lipid complexes with densities of 1.03, 1.07, and 1.08 g/mL?

Answer: The density, at 20° C (ρ, g/mL), of sucrose solutions and their percent by volume (g per 100 mL) are shown in the first two columns. The third column shows the corresponding percent by weight for values shown in the second column.

ρ (g/mL)	% Sucrose (g per 100 mL)	% Sucrose (g per 100 g)*
0.9988	0	0.00
1.0380	10	9.63
1.0806	20	18.51
1.1268	30	26.62
1.1766	40	34.00
1.2299	50	40.65
1.2867	60	46.63
1.3470	70	51.97

*The values in this column are calculated as follows. First, the weight of a weight per volume solution is calculated. For example, a 10% weight per volume solution of sucrose has a density of 1.0380 g/mL. Therefore, 100 mL of this solution has a weight of:

$$100 \text{ mL} \times 1.038 \frac{\text{g}}{\text{mL}} = 103.8 \text{ g}$$

The percent weight is determined by calculating the amount of sucrose required to make 100 g of solution.

$$\frac{10 \text{ g}}{103.8 \text{ g}} = \frac{x}{100 \text{ g}}$$

$x = 9.63$ g sucrose in 100 mL.

Why is there a difference in the two plots?

For the 10% solution (g per 100 mL), 100 mL of this solution weighs:

$100 \text{ mL} \times 1.0380 \frac{\text{g}}{\text{mL}} = 103.8$ g of which 10 g was sucrose and

103.8 g – 10 g = 93.8 g was water.

The volume of 93.8 g of water is $\dfrac{93.8 \text{ g}}{0.9988 \frac{\text{g}}{\text{mL}}} = 93.91$ mL.

Thus, the 100 mL volume of 10% sucrose is composed of 93.91 mL water and

100 mL – 93.91 mL = 6.09 mL of sucrose.

Therefore, the 10 g of sucrose occupied 6.09 mL corresponding to a density of

$\dfrac{10 \text{ g}}{6.09 \text{ mL}} = 1.64 \dfrac{\text{g}}{\text{mL}}$

To prepare a 10 g per 100 g solution, 90 g of water is mixed with 10 g sucrose.

The final volume is $\dfrac{90 \text{ g}}{0.9988 \frac{\text{g}}{\text{mL}}} + \dfrac{10 \text{ g}}{1.64 \frac{\text{g}}{\text{mL}}} = 96.21$ mL

The solution's density is $\dfrac{100 \text{ g}}{96.21 \text{ mL}} = 1.0394 \dfrac{\text{g}}{\text{mL}}$

Thus, the 10% (g per 100 g) solution's density ($1.0394 \frac{\text{g}}{\text{mL}}$) is greater than

the 10% (g per 100 mL) solution's density ($1.64 \frac{\text{g}}{\text{mL}}$).

5. Protein lateral motion is much slower than that of lipids because proteins are larger than lipids. Also, some membrane proteins can diffuse freely through the membrane, whereas others are bound or anchored to other protein structures in the membrane. The diffusion constant for the membrane protein fibronectin is approximately 0.7×10 cm^{-12} cm^2/sec, whereas that for rhodopsin is about 3×10^{-9} cm^2/sec.

　　a. Calculate the distance traversed by each of these proteins in 10 msec.

　　b. What could you surmise about the interactions of these proteins with other membrane components?

Answer:

$$\text{For fibronectin, } D = 0.7 \times 10^{-12} \frac{\text{cm}^2}{\text{sec}}$$

$$\text{For rhodopsin, } D = 3.0 \times 10^{-9} \frac{\text{cm}^2}{\text{sec}}$$

$$t = 10 \text{ msec} = 10 \times 10^{-3} \text{ sec}$$

$$r = \sqrt{4 \times D \times t}$$

$$\text{For fibronectin } r = \sqrt{4 \times (0.7 \times 10^{-12} \frac{\text{cm}^2}{\text{sec}}) \times (10 \times 10^{-3} \text{ sec})} = 1.67 \times 10^{-7} \text{cm}$$

$$\text{For fibronectin } r = 1.67 \times 10^{-7} \text{cm} \times \frac{1 \text{ m}}{100 \text{ cm}} = 1.67 \times 10^{-9} \text{m} = 1.67 \text{ nm}$$

$$\text{For rhodopsin } r = \sqrt{4 \times (3.0 \times 10^{-9} \frac{\text{cm}^2}{\text{sec}}) \times (10 \times 10^{-3} \text{ sec})} = 1.10 \times 10^{-5} \text{cm}$$

$$\text{For rhodopsin } r = 1.10 \times 10^{-5} \text{cm} \times \frac{1 \text{ m}}{100 \text{ cm}} = 1.10 \times 10^{-7} \text{m} = 110 \times 10^{-9} \text{m} = 110 \text{ nm}$$

b. The diffusion coefficient is inversely dependent on size, and unless we know the size of each protein we can surmise very little. The M_r of rhodopsin and fibronectin are 40 000 and 460 000 respectively. For spherical particles, D is roughly proportioned to $[M_r]^{-1/3}$. We might expect the ratio of diffusion coefficients (rhodopsin : fibronectin) to be

$$\frac{(40\ 000)^{-\frac{1}{3}}}{(460\ 000)^{-\frac{1}{3}}} = 2.3$$

The measured ratio is 4286! Clearly the size difference does not explain this large difference in diffusion coefficients. Fibronectin is a peripheral membrane protein that anchors membrane proteins to the cytoskeleton. Its movement is severely restricted.

7. Calculate the free energy difference at 25°C due to a galactose gradient across a membrane, if the concentration on side 1 is 2 mM and the concentration on side 2 is 10 mM.

Answer:

$$\Delta G = RT \ln \frac{[C_2]}{[C_1]},$$

where $[C_1]$ and $[C_2]$ are the concentrations of C on opposites of the membrane.

$$\Delta G = 8.314 \times 10^{-3} \frac{\text{kJ}}{\text{K} \cdot \text{mol}} \times 298 \text{ K} \times \ln \frac{10 \text{ mM}}{2 \text{ mM}}$$

$$\Delta G = 4.0 \frac{\text{kJ}}{\text{mol}}$$

9. Transport of histidine across a cell membrane was measured at several histidine concentrations:

[Histidine], µM	Transport, µmol/min
2.5	42.5
7	119
16	272
31	527
72	1220

Does this transport operate by passive diffusion or by facilitated diffusion?

Answer: A characteristic of transport by passive diffusion is that the rate of transport is linearly dependent on concentration, and so a plot of transport rate versus concentration will be linear. For facilitated diffusion, the transported molecule interacts with a carrier protein in the membrane. The rate of transport will be dependent on concentration, but the dependence is not linear. Rather, the dependence is reminiscent of Michaelis–Menten enzyme kinetics in that it shows saturation. A plot of rate versus concentration is presented below. The data show a linear relationship, indicating that transport is by passive diffusion. However, a facilitated transport system with a high K_m relative to the concentrations of histidine tested here will also be approximately linear. The concentrations tested here are high relative to physiologically reasonable concentrations of histidine, and if facilitated diffusion is at work it may not be of physiological importance. One way to confirm that the transport is passive is to retest transport using D-histidine. Using a different stereoisomer of histidine will have no affect on passive diffusion. Facilitated diffusion will show a specificity for one of the stereoisomers.

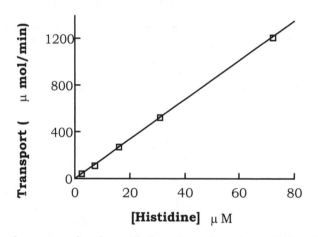

11. In this chapter, we have examined coupled transport systems that rely on ATP hydrolysis, on primary gradients of Na⁺ or H⁺, and on phosphotransferase systems. Suppose you have just discovered an unusual strain of bacteria that transports rhamnose across its plasma membrane. Suggest experiments that would test whether it was linked to any of these other transport systems.

Answer: If uptake is sensitive to ion gradients, ionophores may be used to destroy the gradients. Uncouplers like dicumarol or dinitrophenol can be used to degrade proton gradients. Ouabain can be used to inhibit the sodium pump. Dependence on ATP hydrolysis may be determined by using non-hydrolyzable ATP analogs. PEP-dependent mechanisms similar to PTS in *E. coli* are sensitive to fluoride.

13. Which of the following peptides would be the most likely to acquire a prenyl anchor?
   a. RIGHTCALL
   b. PICKME
   c. ICANTICANT
   d. AINTMEPICKA
   e. none of the above

Answer: Prenylations typically occur on cysteines in sequences CAAX where the A's are aliphatic amino acids and X is any residue. The only peptide to fit this description is (a)" This peptide has a cysteine followed by alanine and two leucines on its C-terminus.

15. Proline residues are almost never found in short α-helices; nearly all transmembrane α-helices that contain proline are long ones (about 20 residues). Suggest a reason for this observation.

Answer: Proline is a helix breaker when located deeper than 3 residues from the N-terminus of an α-helix. You might recall that proline is in fact an imido acid, not an amino acid. Proline's nitrogen is connected to both its α-carbon and its δ-carbon to form a ring, and so the nitrogen has only one hydrogen covalently bonded to it. When proline's nitrogen participates in a peptide bond, it loses its only hydrogen and so the peptide bond lacks a hydrogen-bond donor. Any amino acid located within the first three residues of the N-terminus of an α-helix does not have its amino hydrogen participating in hydrogen bonds because H-bonding in an α-helix is between the carbonyl group of the ith residue and the amino group of the $i + 4^{th}$ residue. Put conversely: the amino group of the ith residue and the carbonyl group of the $i - 4^{th}$ residue. So proline is okay in the first three positions of an α-helix but not any deeper. The stability of a helix depends on hydrogen bonds, and long helices can accommodate the disruption in the hydrogen bond that results from an internal proline.

17. Compare the porin proteins, which have transmembrane pores constructed from β-barrels, with the Wza protein, which has a transmembrane pore constructed from a ring of α-helices. How many amino acids are required to form the β-barrel of a porin? How many would be required to form the same-sized pore from α-helices?

Answer: The problem is to span a biological membrane with a protein composed of β-pleated sheets or α-helices. In the section discussing the thickness of biological membranes, we were informed that dipalmitoyl phosphtidylcholine bilayers measure approximately 37 Å from phosphorus to phosphorus with a 26 Å hydrophobic layer. Porin proteins form transmembrane pores composed of 16- to 18-stranded antiparallel β-barrels. For antiparallel β-pleated sheets, the distance between residues is 3.47 Å. If a single strand of polypeptide in antiparallel pleated sheet were arranged perpendicular to a membrane, it would have to be between 8 and 11 residues long to span 26 Å to 37 Å of membrane.

$$\text{Number of residues} = \frac{26 \text{ Å or } 37 \text{ Å}}{3.47 \dfrac{\text{Å}}{\text{residue}}} = 8 \text{ to } 11 \text{ residues}$$

To make an 18-stranded β-barrel, requires

$$8 \text{ or } 11 \ \frac{\text{residues}}{\text{strand}} \times 18 \text{ strands} = 144 \text{ to } 198 \text{ residues}$$

To make a pore using α-helices arranged perpendicular to the membrane surface to form a barrel would require α-helices approximately 17 to 25 residues long using 1.5 Å per residue as Δz.

$$\text{Number of residues} = \frac{26 \text{ Å or } 37 \text{ Å}}{1.5 \dfrac{\text{Å}}{\text{residue}}} = 17 \text{ to } 25 \text{ residues}$$

In the Wza protein, a barrel is formed by association of 8 α-helices and this would require

$$17 \text{ or } 25 \ \frac{\text{residues}}{\text{strand}} \times 8 \text{ strands} = 136 \text{ to } 200 \text{ residues}$$

These calculations, however, are based on incorrect models. For the porins and for the Wza protein the secondary structure elements are not perpendicular to the membrane but tilted. For porins, strands are tilted from 30° to 60°. In OmpF, an *E. coli* porin protein with 16 strands, strands range from 7 residues to 18 residues (see 2OMF) with 16 as the most frequent length. A barrel of 16 strands each 16 residues long contains 256 residues. For OmpF (2OMF) there are 206 residues in β-sheets out of a total of 340 residues. For the Wza protein, the C-terminus that forms the pore is organized into a 28-residue irregular helix. So, Wza invests (28 × 8 =) 224 residues to form its pore.

To answer this question, I used Swisspdb viewer and studied 2OMF (porin) and 2J58 (Wza) both found at the RSCB Protein Data Bank (http://www.rcsb.org/pdb/home/home.do). In Swisspdb viewer, the protein's sequence is displayed in a separate "control panel" that shows the sequence and indicates in which polypeptide chain any residue is located in addition to the residue's involvement in α-helix or β-sheet. It is an easy task to identify, for example, the C-terminal helical residues in Wza that contribute to the pore. These residues in the helix can be viewed alone and the length of the helix measured or the number or residues in the helix determined.

19. What are the energetic consequences of snorkelling for a charged amino acid? Consider the lysine residue shown in Figure 10.16. If the lysine side chain was reoriented to extend into the centre of the membrane, how far from the centre would the positive charge of the lysine be? The total height of the peak for the lysine plot in Figure 10.15 is about 4kT, where k is Boltzmann's constant. If the lysine side chain in Figure 10.16 was reoriented to face the membrane centre, how much would its energy increase? How does this value compare with the classical value for the average translational kinetic energy of a molecule in an ideal gas (3/2 kT)?

Answer: To answer this question, one needs to know the distance from the alpha carbon to the side chain amino group of a lysine. To get an estimate of this distance, I used Swisspdb viewer. I restricted viewing to single lysines (in the porin 2OMF) and simply measured the distance between the alpha carbon and side chain amino group nitrogen. The longest distance I found was 6.33 Å. (Variation occurs because of different orientations about the dihedral angles in the side chain.) The thickness of the membrane shown in Figure 10.16 is 30 Å or 15 Å from surface to centre. If the alpha carbon is located such that lysine's amino nitrogen is just on the surface of the membrane in its snorkelling position, then the alpha carbon is 15 Å – 6.3 Å = 8.7 Å from the centre of the membrane. If lysine's side chain now reorients toward the centre of the membrane, it would be 8.7 Å – 6.3 Å = 2.4 Å from the centre of the membrane.

Lysine's total movement is 6.3 Å × 2 = 12.6 Å. From Figure 10.15a, the energy required to move 15 Å (to the centre of a membrane) is 4 kT. Thus:

$$\frac{4\ kT}{15\ \text{Å}} = \frac{x}{12.6\ \text{Å}}$$

Solving for x, we find $x = 3.36\ kT$. The ratio of this energy to 3/2 kT is

$$\text{Ratio of energies} = \frac{3.36\ kT}{\frac{3}{2}kT} = 2.24$$

21. Extending the discussion from Problem 20, how would a hydrophobic environment affect the dissociation behaviour of the side chains of lysine and arginine residues in a protein? Why?

Answer: Lysine and arginine have high pK_a values for their side chains, 10.5 and 12.5 respectively (see Table 4.1), and when protonated they are positively charged. In a hydrophobic environment, the unprotonated and hence uncharged forms are more stable, and to achieve this, the pK_a values have to be lowered.

(In dealing with the carboxyl group of an aspartic acid in Problem 20, the pKa is raised to make aspartic acid a weaker acid because its acidic form is protonated and uncharged. In the case of lysine and arginine, the acidic form is protonated and charged and so the pK_a values need to be shifted to favour deprotonation at lower pH to achieve the uncharged conjugate base form.)

23. Singer and Nicolson's fluid mosaic model of membrane structure presumed all of the following statements to be true EXCEPT:
   a. The phospholipids bilayer is a fluid matrix.
   b. Proteins can be anchored to the membrane by covalently linked lipid chains.
   c. Proteins can move laterally across the membrane.
   d. Membrane should be about 5 nm thick.
   e. Transverse motion of lipid molecules can occur occasionally.

Answer: When Singer and Nicolson proposed the fluid mosaic model membrane proteins anchored by covalently linked lipids had not been discovered. Thus, (b) is the exception. Lipid-anchored proteins would, however, fit nicely into the model.

Questions for Self-Study

1. Match the items in the two columns.
   a. Singer and Nicolson
   b. Extrinsic protein
   c. Integral protein
   d. Liposome
   e. Micelle
   f. Flippase
   g. Transition temperature

   1. Peripheral protein
   2. Lipid bilayer structure
   3. Lipid transfer from outside to inside
   4. Phase change
   5. Intrinsic protein
   6. Lipid monolayer structure
   7. Fluid mosaic model

2. Explain why, for proteins with a single transmembrane segment, the segment is a hydrophobic helix. Why a helix? Why hydrophobic residues?

3. Give three examples of lipid-anchoring motifs.

4. Explain the term critical micelle concentration.

5. For each of the statements below, state if each applies to one or more of the following: passive diffusion (P), facilitated diffusion (F), and active transport (A).
   a. Can only move down a concentration gradient. _____
   b. Is expected to transport L-amino acid and D-amino acid at the same rate. _____
   c. Can be saturated. _____
   d. Can occur in both directions across a biological membrane. _____
   e. Can be used to concentrate substances. _____
   f. Movement is coupled to exergonic process. _____
   g. Rate is linearly proportional to concentration difference. _____
   h. Movement across biological membrane dependent on lipid solubility. _____
   i. Sodium pump. _____

6. Match the active transport system with an appropriate function.
   a. Na^+,K^+-ATPase
   b. Ca^{2+}-ATPase
   c. H^+,K^+-ATPase
   d. Vacuolar ATPase
   e. MDR ATPase

   1. Acidifies membrane bound compartments
   2. Transports a host of cytotoxic drugs
   3. Resets levels of important second message after stimulation
   4. Electrogenic pump inhibited by cardiac glycosides
   5. Responsible for production of the largest concentration gradient known in eukaryotic cells

7. What is a symport? Antiport? How can they be used to move a substance against its concentration gradient?

8. Bacteriorhodopsin and halorhodopsin are active transport proteins for the movement of protons and chloride ions, respectively. What energy source do they use to support ion pumping?

Answers

1. a. 7; b. 1; c. 5; d. 2; e. 6; f. 3; g. 4.

2. The hydrogen bonding groups in the peptide bond are all involved in hydrogen bonds in a helix. Hydrophobic residues can interact with the hydrophobic interior of membranes through hydrophobic interactions.

3. Amide-linked myristoyl anchors, thioester-linked fatty acyl anchors, thioether-linked prenyl anchors, and amide-linked glycosyl phosphatidylinositol anchors.

4. The critical micelle concentration is that concentration of lipid at which micelle formation is supported. Concentrations of lipid below the critical micelle concentration do not form micelles. Lipid solutions whose concentration is greater than the critical micelle concentration contain micelles in equilibrium with free lipid molecules. The concentration of the free lipid is equal to the critical micelle concentration.

5. a. P and F; b. P; c. F and A; d. P and F; e. A; f. A; g. P; h. P; i. A.

6. a. 4; b. 3; c. 5; d. 1; e. 2.

7. A symport is a transport system that couples movement of two substances in the same direction. An antiport couples the movement of two substances in opposite directions. They can be used to move substances against a concentration gradient if transport of the coupled substance is down a concentration gradient. In this case, the energy of the concentration gradient of the co-transported substance is used to drive uptake.

8. Light.

Additional Problems

1. The transport properties of two potassium ionophores were being studied in synthetic lipid bilayers with a phase transition temperature of 50°C. Ionophore X transports potassium at a rate proportional to temperature from 20°C to 70°C. In contrast, ionophore Y transports potassium very well above 60°C; however, from 60°C to 40°C the rate of transport falls off precipitously to very low values below 40°C. Based on this information, can you suggest modes of action for these two ionophores?

2. For integral membrane proteins, α-helices play an important role in anchoring the protein to the membrane. Explain why a helix is a thermodynamically stable structural element to embed in a membrane.

3. How might you expect helical wheel plots of α-helical segments from the following proteins to differ: (a) a typical globular protein, (b) an integral membrane protein with a single transmembrane segment, and (c) an integral membrane protein with several α-helices forming a channel through which a water-soluble compound is transported?

4. Explain how soaps and detergents help to remove water-insoluble substances.

5. Explain how lipid membrane asymmetry might arise in a natural membrane through action of a flippase that does not couple lipid movement to another thermodynamically favourable process (like ATP hydrolysis).

6. Compare the expected rate of passive diffusion across a cell membrane for the following list of compounds: glyceraldehyde, glyceraldehyde-3-phosphate, erythrose, ribulose, ribose-5-phosphate, D-glucose, L-glucose.

7. Activity of the sodium pump results in the net movement of a positive charge across the membrane. How does this lead to a change in the electrical potential of the membrane?

8. Would you expect proton pumps to be capable of creating large proton gradients if the pumps operated by an electrogenic mechanism? Explain.

9. Construct a helical wheel plot of melittin, whose amino acid sequence is: Gly-Ile-Gly-Ala-Val-Leu-Lys-Val-Leu-Thr-Thr-Gly-Leu-Pro-Ala-Leu-Ile-Ser-Trp-Ile-Lys-Arg-Lys-Arg-Gln-Gln-Gly. Assume that this peptide forms an α-helix and comment on the structure.

Abbreviated Answers

1.   Ionophore X may be a channel-forming ionophore, perhaps like the antibiotic gramicidin. Channel-forming ionophores span the membrane forming a channel through which an ion can diffuse across the membrane. Ionophore Y may be a carrier-ionophore. Carrier-ionophores form a complex with the ion to be transported. This complex diffuses across the membrane and dissociates, releasing the ion on the opposite side of the membrane. Valinomycin is an example of a potassium ionophore of this type.

2.   The hydrophobic interior of membranes excludes polar compounds. The peptide bond is a polar bond with both hydrogen-bond donor and acceptor groups that would normally be excluded from membranes. However, in a helical conformation, the donors and acceptors are involved in intrachain hydrogen bonds, making a helix a stable conformation even in a hydrophobic environment.

3.   In globular proteins containing α-helices, the helices often contribute to the hydrophobic core of the protein with hydrophobic amino acid residues located along one face of the helix. Integral membrane proteins, with a single stretch of α-helix responsible for anchoring the protein into the membrane, have a helix composed of hydrophobic amino acids. For integral proteins anchored by several helices, the helices are often amphipathic with both a hydrophobic surface and a hydrophilic surface. The hydrophobic surfaces contact the fatty acid side chains of the membrane lipid component, whereas the hydrophilic surfaces face inward and may form a pore though which hydrophilic substances diffuse.

4.   Soaps and detergents form micelles in solution. The interior of the micelles is a hydrophobic environment into which non-polar molecules may dissolve.

5.   Energy must be expended to produce an asymmetric distribution of lipids. In the case of a flippase that simply equilibrates lipids in response to a concentration gradient of free lipids, lipid asymmetry might arise if lipids preferentially interact with a membrane protein.

6.   For passive diffusion, the flux across the membrane is linearly dependent on the permeability coefficient given by $P = (KD)/x$, where K is the partition coefficient, D the diffusion coefficient, and x the membrane thickness. All of the compounds are water soluble and are expected to have relatively low partition coefficients, decreasing in value in going from glyceraldehyde to glucose. The presence of phosphate groups on two of the compounds will decrease diffusion relative to the unphosphorylated compounds because of an increase in size (leading to a decrease in D) and a decrease in K. A difference in diffusion rates is not expected between the glucose isomers because diffusion does not involve molecular recognition.

7.   There are two ways of looking at this. The net movement of a positive charge gives rise to an imbalance of charge across the membrane, resulting in an electrical potential. Alternatively, the movement of charge across the membrane represents a current. Current flowing across the resistance of the membrane will produce a voltage change.

8.   For a non-electrogenic proton pump, the captured energy input would be in the form of a proton chemical gradient. For an electrogenic proton pump, the same energy input would be captured in a smaller proton chemical gradient, with the rest of the energy present in an electric potential across the membrane. Accordingly, for the same energy input the proton gradient would be higher with the non-electrogenic pump.

9.   The helical wheel plot of melittin in an α-helical conformation is shown below. One face of the helix is lined with hydrophobic amino acids, and a cluster of basic amino acids is found at the C-terminus. A proline residue is positioned approximately in the middle of the helix.

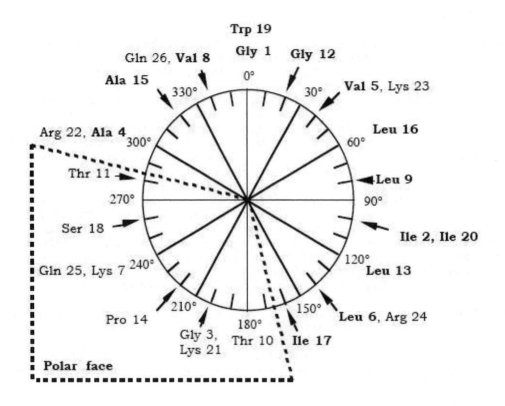

Summary

Lipids form a variety of structures spontaneously in solution, including monolayers, micelles, and bilayer structures. Lipid bilayers have a polar surface, composed of charged or neutral lipid head groups, and a non-polar interior, composed of hydrophobic lipid chains. The fluid mosaic model of membrane structure, proposed by Singer and Nicholson, pictures the lipid bilayer as a fluid, dynamic matrix, with lipids and proteins able to undergo free, rapid, lateral motion. A variety of experiments has now confirmed the essential features of the fluid mosaic model.

The fatty acid chains in membrane lipids are oriented roughly perpendicular to the bilayer plane, and this ordering is more pronounced near the bilayer surface. As one proceeds into the bilayer interior, the ordering of the lipid chains decreases, so that the interior is a highly fluid environment. Transverse motion of lipids and proteins is very slow. Different lipid classes show different distributions between the inner and outer monolayers of the membrane bilayer. This lipid asymmetry is a consequence of ATP-dependent flippases that move lipids from the outer leaflet to the inner leaflet of the plasma membrane. Floppases work similarly but in the opposite direction. Finally, scramblases degrade transverse asymmetries by bidirectional movement of lipids in a calcium-dependent process. Proteins are asymmetrically distributed between the two faces of the bilayer, allowing a variety of vectorial (i.e., directionally dependent) functions including transport processes. Lateral asymmetries also exist in membranes, with proteins and lipids able to arrange themselves in clusters or aggregates important to cell function. Lipids in membranes exhibit dramatic, cooperative changes of state at characteristic temperatures. Such phase transitions between the solid, gel-like state at lower temperatures and the fluid, liquid-crystalline state at higher temperatures are sensitive to the lipid composition and to the presence of proteins, and may be important in a host of biological functions.

Membrane proteins are of three fundamental types. Peripheral proteins form ionic interactions or hydrogen bonds with the surface of the lipid bilayer. Integral proteins intercalate into the lipid bilayer and are strongly associated with the membrane. The lipid-anchored proteins attach to membranes via covalently linked lipid moieties. Peripheral proteins can be extracted with high salt, EDTA, or urea, while integral proteins can only be removed with organic solvents or detergents. Detergents are amphipathic molecules, with both polar and non-polar moieties, and function by intercalating into the membrane and solubilizing lipids and proteins. At the critical micelle concentration (CMC), detergents spontaneously form micelles and become much more effective solubilizing agents.

Integral membrane proteins take on a variety of conformations in membranes. Proteins such as glycophorin of the erythrocyte membrane have a single hydrophobic α-helix extending across the bilayer, with hydrophilic segments extending on either side of the lipid bilayer. Other proteins, such as bacteriorhodopsin of the purple patches of *Halobacterium halobium*, traverse the bilayer several times, with six or more hydrophobic alpha helices spanning the bilayer. These latter proteins are often involved in membrane transport activities and other processes that require a substantial portion of the peptide to be imbedded in the membrane.

Four different types of lipid-anchoring motifs for membrane proteins have been found to date, including amide-linked myristic acid anchors, thioester-linked fatty acyl anchors, thioether-linked prenyl anchors, and amide-linked glycosyl-phosphatidylinositol anchors. In amide-linked myristic acid (14:0) proteins, the fatty acid is attached in amide linkage to the α-amino group of N-terminal glycine. In thioester- and thioether-linked proteins, lipids are attached to cysteine residues. Ether-linked lipids are long-chain polyisoprenoids. In GPI (glycosylphosphatidylinositol) anchors, the C-terminus of the target protein is linked via phosphoethanolamine to a mannose residue on an oligosaccharide attached to phosphatidylinositol.

Transport processes are important to all life forms. The acquisition of nutrients, the elimination of waste materials, and the generation of concentration gradients vital to nerve impulse transmission and the normal function of brain, heart, kidneys, and other organs all depend on membrane transport systems. All transport processes are mediated by transport proteins, which may function either as channels or carriers. The three classes of transport are passive diffusion, facilitated diffusion, and active transport. In passive diffusion, the transported species moves across the membrane in the thermodynamically favoured direction without the assistance of a specific transport system. Analogous to Brownian motion, passive diffusion is in essence an entropic process. The rate of flow of an uncharged molecule depends upon concentration and the permeability coefficient of the molecule. For charged species, the charge of the molecule and the electrical potential difference also affect transport. In facilitated diffusion, the transported species moves according to its thermodynamic potential, but with the help of a specific transport system. Facilitated diffusion systems display saturation behaviour. The glucose transporter and the anion transporter of erythrocytes are both facilitated diffusion systems.

Active transport systems use energy input to drive a transported species against its thermodynamic potential. The most common energy input is ATP hydrolysis, but light energy and the energy stored in ion gradients may also be used. All active transport systems are energy-coupling devices. Na^+,K^+-ATPase, which transport Na^+ ions out of cells and transports K^+ ions into the cells, is an active transport system. Na^+,K^+-ATPase consists of a 120 kD α-subunit and a 35 kD β-subunit. The enzyme mechanism involves an aspartyl phosphate intermediate. Na^+,K^+-ATPase is strongly and specifically inhibited by cardiac glycosides such as ouabain. Calcium transport across the sarcoplasmic reticulum membrane is mediated by Ca^{2+}-ATPase, an enzyme that is homologous to Na^+,K^+-ATPase. The gastric H^+,K^+-ATPase likewise transports protons across the membrane of stomach mucosal cells, generating the high concentrations of acid in the stomach that are essential to digestion of food. The H^+,K^+-ATPase is homologous to Na^+,K^+-ATPase and Ca^{2+}-ATPase. Proton pumps in osteoclasts enable these cells to degrade the mineral matrix of bone during the remodeling and reconstruction of bone tissue. ATPases also transport peptides and drugs. Another transport protein known as the multi-drug resistance (MDR) ATPase actively transports a wide spectrum of drugs out of human cells. This transport system is induced by the chronic administration of drugs (in cancer chemotherapy, for example).

Bacteriorhodopsin (bR) is a light-driven proton transport system from *Halobacterium halobium*. The characteristic purple colour of this transport protein arises from a molecule of retinal covalently bound in a Schiff base linkage with the ε-amino group of Lys-216 on the protein. bR is a 26 kD transmembrane protein that packs so densely in the membrane that it naturally forms a two-dimensional crystal. The structure consists of seven transmembrane helical protein segments, with the retinal moiety lying parallel to the membrane plane, about 10 Å below the extracellular surface of the membrane. The mechanism of proton transport involves conversion of the retinal chromophore from the all-*trans* configuration to the 13-*cis* configuration upon light absorption. An analogous transport protein, halorhodopsin, mediates light-driven anion transport across the *H. halobium* membrane.

Secondary active transport systems use the ion and proton gradients established by primary active transport systems to transport amino acids, sugars, and other species in certain cells. Most of these operate as symport systems, with the ion or proton and the transported amino acid or sugar moving in the same direction. The lactose permease of *E. coli* is a lactose/H^+ symport system, which actively transports lactose into *E. coli* cells, deriving energy from the proton-motive force across the bacterial membrane.

In addition to the specific systems described above, several rather non-specific systems also carry out transport processes. For example, Gram-negative bacteria enable the transport of small molecule nutrients and certain other molecules through the outer membrane via porins, which form large, non-specific pores in the outer membrane. Certain porins are specific, such as *LamB* and *Tsx* of *E. coli* and porins P and D1 of *P. aeruginosa*, which possess specific binding sites for maltose and related oligosaccharides, nucleosides, anions, and glucose, respectively.

Chapter 11

The Reception and Transmission of Extracellular Information

• •

Chapter Outline

❖ Hormones: Three types
  ⅄ Steroid hormones: Cholesterol derivatives
    • Regulate metabolism, salt and water balance, inflammatory process, sexual function
    • Two modes of action
      • Pass through cell membrane and localize on receptors on DNA
      • Bind to cell membrane to regulate ion channels
  ⅄ Amino acid derivatives
    • Epinephrine and norepinephrine
      • Regulate smooth muscle contraction, cardiac rate, lipolysis, glycogenolysis
    • Thyroid hormone
      • Stimulates metabolism
  ⅄ Peptide hormones
    • Secreted hormones initially synthesized with signal sequence
    • Synthesized as preprohormones
    • Cleavage of preprohormone may produce several peptide hormones
❖ Signal transduction systems: Features
  ⅄ Receptor proteins
  ⅄ Protein interaction domains used to form signalsomes
  ⅄ Messages include covalent modifications and small molecule second messengers
  ⅄ Signalling pathways of proteins
❖ Transmembrane signal–processing hormone receptors: Three families
  ⅄ G-protein–coupled receptors
    • Extracellular hormone-binding domain
    • Seven-transmembrane segments
    • Intracellular G-protein–binding site
  ⅄ Single-transmembrane segment
    • Extracellular ligand recognition site
    • Intracellular catalytic domain: Either of two types
      • Tyrosine kinase
      • Guanylyl cyclase
  ⅄ Oligomeric ion channels: Multiple subunit proteins
    • Ligand-gated channels: Ligands are neurotransmitters
❖ Receptor tyrosine kinases (RTK) and receptor guanylyl cyclase (RGC)
  ⅄ Extracellular ligand binding, transmembrane helix, intracellular catalytic domains
    • EFG receptor: RTK that dimerizes when it binds EFG
    • Insulin receptor: RTK that dimerizes when it binds insulin
    • Natriuretic hormone receptors: RGC: Dimers that activate with ligand binding
    • pp60$^{v\text{-}src}$: Non-receptor tyrosine kinase involved in transforming cells
    • Soluble guanylyl cyclases: Activated by NO
❖ Signal transduction events
  ⅄ G-protein–coupled receptors activate G protein

- Hormone binding to receptor induces GTP for GDP exchange on G-protein heterotrimer
- G_α(GTP) dissociates from trimer
- GTPase activity of G_α hydrolyzes GTP: Adenylyl cyclase stimulation stops
- G_α(GDP) reassociates with $G_{\beta\gamma}$ to reform trimer
- Two kinds of G_α
    - Stimulatory
    - Inhibitory
- ❖ Cyclic AMP: A second messenger
    - Adenylyl cyclase produces cAMP from ATP
    - Phosphodiesterase hydrolyzes cAMP to AMP
    - cAMP activates protein kinase A
- ❖ Phospholipase activation produces second messengers
    - Hydrolysis of phosphatidylinositol produces two products
        - DAG (diacylglycerol)
            - Remains in membrane: Activates protein kinase C
        - Inositol phosphate (IP) or IP_2 (which is converted to IP_3)
            - IP_3: Water soluble stimulates intracellular calcium release
                - Catabolized by phosphatases into inositol-1,4-bisphosphate, I-4-P, and myo-inositol
                - Metabolized by kinases into inositol-1,2,4,5-tetraphosphate
    - Activation of phospholipase C
        - Phospholipase C-β, C-γ, C-δ calcium stimulated
        - Phospholipase C-β also stimulated by G protein
        - Phospholipase C-γ also stimulated by receptor tyrosine kinase
    - Hydrolysis of phosphatidylcholine produce diacylglycerol or phosphatidic acid
    - Hydrolysis of sphingomyelin produces ceramide: Stimulates ceramide-activated protein kinase
- ❖ Calcium as second messenger
    - Two sources
        - Extracellular: Entry via plasma membrane channels in response to cAMP
        - Intracellular: Endoplasmic reticulum and calciosomes release calcium in response to IP_3
            - Calcium released from ER opens plasma membrane channels and together with DAG stimulates protein kinase C
            - Calcium oscillations often induced by excitation of phosphoinositide pathway
    - Calcium-binding proteins: Three groups
        - Calcium-modulated proteins: Calmodulin, parvalbumin, troponin-C: Contain EF hands
            - Calcium binding allows protein to bind to target
            - Target is basic amphiphilic alpha (Baa) helix
        - Annexin proteins: Peripheral membrane proteins
        - Protein kinase C
            - Soluble protein inactive
            - Target-bound protein active
                - DAG binding to soluble protein opens substrate-binding domain
                    - Phorbol esters mimic DAG binding
                - Calcium binding activates kinase
- ❖ Nervous system cells
    - Neurons: Transmit nerve impulses
        - Axons: Cell processes that transmit impulse away from cell body
            - Synaptic terminal: Specialized ends of axon
        - Dendrite: Receives input
    - Glial cells: Protect and support neurons
- ❖ Electrical signals: Change in electrical potential: Potential generated by ion gradients
    - Nernst equation: Membrane potential based on unequal distribution of single ion
    - Goldman equation: Membrane potential based on unequal distribution of several ions
    - Action potential
        - Activated by depolarization

- • Voltage-gated sodium channels open allow Na^+ in
- • Sodium causes depolarization until channels close
- • Potassium channels open to allow K^+ out
- • Potassium causes repolarization (hyperpolarization)
- ❖ Synapses: Junctions
  - ⅄ Electrical synapse: Small gaps: Pass depolarization electrically
  - ⅄ Chemical synapse: Axon releases neurotransmitter into synaptic cleft
    - • Acetylcholine
      - • Cholinergic synapse receptors
        - o Nicotinic receptors: Ligand-gated cation channel
        - o Muscarinic receptors: Interact with G proteins
          - ▪ 7-TMS proteins: Stimulation causes
            - • Inhibition of adenylyl cyclase
            - • Stimulation of phospholipase C
            - • Potassium channel opening
      - • Amino acid neurotransmitters
        - o Glu, Asp: Excitatory
        - o GABA, Gly: Inhibitory
      - • Catecholamines: Epinephrine, norepinephrine, dopamine, L-dopa
      - • Peptides: Endorphins, enkephalins
      - • Gaseous neurotransmitters

Chapter Objectives

Hormones

There are three major classes of hormones: steroid hormones, which are derived from cholesterol, amino acid–derived hormones, and peptide hormones. The steroid hormones either interact with surface receptors or bind to intracellular proteins. Amino acid–derived hormones and peptide hormones bind to surface receptors and lead to stimulation of a signal transduction pathway, in turn leading to second messenger production. There are three families of membrane receptors. The 7-transmembrane segment (7-TMS) receptors have seven helical segments that span the membrane, an intracellular recognition site for G proteins, and an extracellular domain for hormone binding. The single-transmembrane segment catalytic receptors have a single-transmembrane segment, an extracellular domain containing the hormone-binding site, and an internal domain with catalytic activity, either tyrosine kinase or guanylyl cyclase. The third family is the oligomeric ion channels. These are ligand-gated ion channels that open in response to neurotransmitters.

Second Messages

cAMP is produced by adenylyl cyclase and degraded by phosphodiesterase. cGMP is produced by guanylyl cyclase. Ca^{2+} is released from internal stores or moves across the membrane via a calcium channel from the extracellular environment. Inositol trisphosphate, diacylglycerol, and phosphatidic acid are released by metabolism of membrane components. Nitric oxide is produced by action of NO synthase.

G Proteins

G proteins function to transduce a cell surface signal into an internal signal. Hormone binding to a hormone-receptor protein on the cell surface results in release of G protein. The G proteins are heterotrimers with the α-subunit functioning as the messenger between hormone binding to the receptor and production of an intracellular signal. This subunit is a guanine nucleotide–binding protein. GTP bound to the G_α leads to release of a G_α(GTP) complex that activates adenylyl cyclases. G_α has intrinsic GTPase activity and hydrolysis of GTP leads to inactivation of G_α. There are many G proteins, exhibiting a range of activities from stimulatory to inhibitory. ADP-ribosylation by cholera toxin inhibits the $G_{s\alpha}$ GTPase activity, locking it into the active messenger state. ADP-ribosylation of $G_{i\alpha}$ inhibits GDP–GTP exchange, thus preventing its inhibition of adenylyl cyclase.

Membrane-Derived Second Messages

Specific phospholipases function to produce a host of second messages, including inositol trisphosphate (IP$_3$); diacylglycerol; free arachidonic acid, which serves as the precursor of eicosanoids; and ceramide. IP$_3$ stimulates release of calcium from internal stores and calcium in concert with diacylglycerol stimulates protein kinase C.

Calcium

The importance of calcium as a second messenger is covered in muscle contraction, where troponin C functions as the key calcium-binding protein. Calcium can be released from internal stores by IP$_3$ or from the plasma membrane by other signals. Calcium binds to calcium-modulated proteins, including calmodulin, parvalbumin, and troponin C or to annexin proteins. The first three proteins all have virtually identical calcium-binding domains, an EF hand, consisting of a two helices separated by a calcium binding loop. Calmodulin can bind to a number of other proteins and modulate their activity in a calcium-dependent manner.

Tyrosine Kinases

The first tyrosine kinase to be discovered was an oncogene carried by Rous sarcoma virus. The gene product, pp60$^{\text{v-src}}$, is capable of phosphorylating a number of cellular target proteins. This activity is responsible for transformation. Epidermal growth factor, insulin, and platelet-derived growth factor all function by binding to surface receptor proteins that have tyrosine kinase activity dependent on hormone binding.

Peptide Hormones, NO, and Steroids

The peptide hormones, a diverse group of hormones, derive from a primary translation product by post-translational–processing events including proteolytic cleavage of a hydrophobic N-terminal signal peptide, proteolytic cleavage internally, and post-translational covalent modifications. NO is a small, gaseous hormone produced from arginine. It functions as a hormone by stimulating guanylyl cyclase. The steroid hormones bind to internal receptor proteins that function as transcriptional activators, leading to synthesis of new proteins.

Neurons

Understand the basic anatomy of a neuron and the role of dendrites, axons, nodes of Ranvier, and synaptic knobs. Sensory neurons are the input gateways to the nervous system; interneurons are the connections between neurons; and motor neurons pass information to muscle cells. All cells have an electrical potential across their membrane. You should understand the Nernst equation and the Goldman equation. The sequence of events responsible for an action potential includes opening and closing of voltage-sensitive sodium channels followed by opening and closing of potassium channels. Action potentials are uniform in size and thus their number and frequency are important in carrying information. The ability to affect specific channels by various agents has led to our understanding of channel functioning. Tetrodotoxin and saxitoxin lock sodium channels in a closed conformation; veratridine and batrachotoxin lock channels in an open conformation. Potassium channels are blocked by 4-aminopyridine, tetraethylammonium ion, dendrotoxins, mast cell degranulation peptide, and charybdotoxin. The anatomy of synaptic clefts should be understood. Be familiar with these terms: presynaptic cell, postsynaptic cell, synaptic cleft, and synaptic vesicle. Migration and fusion of synaptic vesicles is a calcium-mediated event. Voltage-gated calcium channels open in response to the arrival of an action potential, allowing calcium to enter the presynaptic cell followed by synaptic membrane fusion and release of neurotransmitter into the synaptic cleft. Neurotransmitter receptors on the postsynaptic cell are often voltage-gated ion channels. Acetylcholine is the neurotransmitter of cholinergic synapses. There are muscarinic receptors and nicotinic receptors for acetylcholine. Nicotinic receptors are ligand-gated ion channels. Antagonists of nicotinic receptors include tubocurarine, cobratoxin and α-bungarotoxin. Muscarinic receptors cause the opening of potassium channels in a G-protein–mediated process. Agents active against muscarinic receptors include atropine and of course muscarine. Succinylcholine and decamethonium are acetylcholine analogs that over-stimulate receptors. DIFP, malathion, parathion, sarin, and tabun all inhibit acetylcholinesterase. Other important neurotransmitters include the amino acids glutamate, aspartate, and glycine; γ-aminobutyric acid; the catecholamines, epinephrine, norepinephrine, dopamine, and L-dopa; and various peptide neurotransmitters.

Problems and Solutions

1. Compare and contrast the features and physiological advantages of each of the major classes of hormones, including the steroid hormones, polypeptide hormones, and the amino acid–derived hormones.

Answer: The steroid hormones have two modes of action. They can bind to surface receptors, leading to regulation of ion channels. Alternately, steroid hormones can diffuse into the cell and interact with specific internal receptor proteins, leading to stimulation of transcription and gene expression. The time course and duration of stimulation is quite different for these two modes of action. Ion channel stimulation is a rapid though brief response. Alteration in gene expression is slower but long-lasting. The polypeptide hormones function by receptor binding at the cell surface, resulting in production or release of a second messenger. Production of the peptide hormones requires gene expression and several post-translational modifications, including proteolytic cleavages and covalent modifications. Peptide hormones are the most diverse group of hormones and as a result can participate in a wide variety of specific hormone-receptor interactions. The amino acid–derived hormones include two groups. The catecholamine hormones, including epinephrine and norepinephrine, are derived from the amino acid tyrosine and function by surface receptor binding and second-message production. The second group of amino acid–derived hormones includes the thyroid hormones thyroxine and triiodothyronine, which bind to intracellular receptors that in turn regulate gene expression.

3. Nitric oxide may be merely the first of a new class of gaseous second messenger/neurotransmitter molecules. Based on your knowledge of the molecular action of nitric oxide, suggest another gaseous molecule that might act as a second messenger and propose a molecular function for it.

Answer: Nitric oxide is synthesized from arginine by NO synthase. This gaseous compound is capable of rapidly diffusing across cell membranes. The target of NO is the heme prosthetic group of soluble guanylyl cyclase. NO binding results in an increase in enzyme activity leading to increased concentrations of cGMP. In studying hemoglobin (Chapter 14), we discover that carbon monoxide has a high affinity for heme groups. Carbon monoxide is produced during heme catabolism when one of the methylene carbons of heme is converted to CO, while the remainder of the heme group is converted to bilirubin. The enzyme that produces CO from heme is heme oxygenase.

NO is known to activate guanylyl cyclase, which leads to production of cGMP. cGMP is involved in a number of physiological responses including gating of ion channels in phototransduction, activation of myosin phosphatase to relax smooth muscle, and roles in platelet inhibition and cell growth and differentiation. CO also activates guanylyl cyclase, but it is much less effective than is NO. CO, however, is a comparatively stable molecule relative to NO. There is evidence that NO synthase activity depends on normal oxygen concentrations, and so in anaerobic conditions, NO production may decline. In contrast, heme oxygenase remains active at low oxygen levels. NO and CO signalling may be acting through the same pathways but at different levels of oxygen tension.

5. Monoclonal antibodies that recognize phosphotyrosine are commercially available. How could such an antibody be used in studies of cell signalling pathways and mechanisms?

Answer: The ability to measure changes of phosphotyrosine levels in response to a hormonal signal is necessary to establish a role for tyrosine kinases in a particular signalling pathway. It is an easy task to use the radioactive isotope of phosphorous, ^{32}P, to establish that a protein is phosphorylated, but it is difficult to distinguish between phosphotyrosine, phosphoserine, and phosphothreonine. The protein would have to be converted to amino acids, but this presents a problem because phosphotyrosine is not particularly stable. Further, phosphoproteins are not abundant and therefore difficult to isolate. Monoclonal antibodies against protein phosphotyrosine would allow rapid quantitation of phosphotyrosine levels, and using Western blots, identification of phosphotyrosine-containing proteins.

7. Synaptic vesicles are approximately 40 nm in outside diameter, and each vesicle contains about 10 000 acetylcholine molecules. Calculate the concentration of acetylcholine in a synaptic vesicle.

Answer: A synaptic vesicle with a 40 nm outside diameter has an inside diameter of approximately 36 nm. The volume occupied by one synaptic vesicle is given by:

$$V = \frac{4}{3}\pi r^3 = \frac{4}{3} \times 3.1416 \times \left(\frac{36 \times 10^{-9}\,\text{m}}{2}\right)^3 = 2.44 \times 10^{-23}\,\text{m}^3$$

$$V = 2.44 \times 10^{-23}\,\text{m}^3 \times \left(\frac{100\,\text{cm}}{1\,\text{m}}\right)^3 \times \left(\frac{1\,\text{L}}{1000\,\text{cm}^3}\right)$$

$$V = 2.44 \times 10^{-20}\,\text{L}$$

The concentration of acetylcholine in a vesicle is given by:

$$[\text{Acetylcholine}] = \frac{\dfrac{10\,000\ \text{molecules}}{6.02 \times 10^{23}\ \text{molecules/mol}}}{2.44 \times 10^{-20}\,\text{L}} = 0.68\ \text{M}$$

9. A typical hormone binds to its receptor with an affinity (K_D) of approximately 1×10^{-9} M. Consider an in vitro (test tube) system in which the total hormone concentration is approximately 1 nM and the total concentration of receptor sites is 0.1 nM. What fraction of the receptor sites is bound with hormone? If the concentration of receptors is decreased to 0.033 nM, what fraction of receptor is bound with the hormone?

Answer: For simple equilibrium binding of hormone to receptor the following equilibrium applies:

$$[\text{HR}] \rightleftharpoons [\text{H}] + [\text{R}]$$

where [HR], [H], and [R] refer to the concentrations of hormone-receptor complex, free hormone (i.e., unbound hormone), and uncomplexed receptor. The equilibrium dissociation constant for this reaction is:

$$K_D = \frac{[\text{H}][\text{R}]}{[\text{HR}]}$$

We are given the total concentration of receptor sites. In the presence of hormone, total receptor partitions into free receptor, R, and HR. Thus, $[R_{total}] = [R] + [HR]$. The total hormone concentration is $[H_{total}] = [H] + [HR]$. We are asked to calculate the fraction of receptor sites bound so we looking for $f_{bound} = [HR]/[R_{total}]$ using these three equations. Using K_D, we can write [HR] as a function of $[R_{total}]$ and $[H_{total}]$ as follows:

$$K_D[\text{HR}] = [\text{H}][\text{R}]$$
$$[\text{H}] = [H_{total}] - [\text{HR}] \text{ and } [\text{R}] = [R_{total}] - [\text{HR}]$$
$$K_D[\text{HR}] = \{[H_{total}] - [\text{HR}]\}\{[R_{total}] - [\text{HR}]\}$$
$$[\text{HR}]^2 - [\text{HR}]\{[H_{total}] + [R_{total}] + K_D\} + [H_{total}][R_{total}] = 0$$

The solution to this quadratic equation is:

$$[\text{HR}] = \frac{[H_{Total}] + [R_{Total}] + K_D \pm \sqrt{\left([H_{Total}] + [R_{Total}] + K_D\right)^2 - 4[H_{Total}][R_{Total}]}}{2}$$

The correct solution is the minus root. (When there is no hormone present, [HR] must be zero. For the above equation to equal zero in this situation, the minus root must apply.)

The answers are $f_{bound} = 0.488$ at 0.1 nM receptor and $f_{bound} = 0.496$ at 0.033 nM receptor.

This seems reasonable. The K_D is the concentration of free hormone that would half-saturate receptors. The free hormone concentration in both cases will be very close to 1 nM because the receptor concentrations are smaller than this number. If receptors were completely saturated, the free hormone concentration would be 1 nM – 0.1 nM or 1 nM – 0.033 nM, which are both close to 1 nM.

11. Given that β-strands provide a more genetically economical way for a polypeptide to cross a membrane, why has nature chosen α-helices as the membrane-spanning motif for G-protein–coupled receptors? That is, what other reasons can you imagine to justify the use of α-helices?

Answer: The statement that β-strands are a more genetically economical way for a polypeptide to cross a membrane refers to the fact that a β-strand is in a more extended conformation than an α-helix. Thus, fewer amino acids are required to span the distance across the membrane. However, recall that the peptide bond is polar, and that secondary structural elements are stabilized by hydrogen bonds to the backbone atoms. In an α-helix, the hydrogen bonds between groups on the same strand of polypeptide chain, whereas

β-structures require stabilizing hydrogen bonds to be formed between adjacent runs of β-conformation. Thus, for single-spanning proteins, there would be no possibility for shielding the polarity of the polypeptide backbone from the hydrophobic core of the membrane if a β-conformation were adopted. This is not to say that β-conformations do not exist in integral membrane proteins. Indeed, there is a class of pores known as β-barrel proteins, in which β-strands are perpendicular with respect to the membrane and hydrogen bonded to adjacent β-strands. However, the majority of membrane-spanning regions of integral membrane proteins are α-helical, thereby satisfying hydrogen-bonding requirements of the polar backbone.

13. (Integrates with Chapter 10) Consider the data in Figure 11.49a. Recast Equation 10.2 to derive a form from which you could calculate the equilibrium electrochemical potential at which no net flow of potassium would occur. This is the Nernst equation. Calculate the equilibrium potential for K⁺ and also for Na⁺, assuming T = 37°C.

Answer: Equation 10.2 is $\Delta G = RT\ln([C_2]/[C_1]) + Z\mathcal{F}\Delta\psi$. For no net flow of potassium to occur, the system must be at equilibrium in which case $\Delta G = 0$. Making this substitution and solving for $\Delta\psi$, we find that

$$\Delta\psi = -(RT/Z\mathcal{F}) \times \ln([C_2]/[C_1])$$

Given $R = 8.3145$ J/mol, $\mathcal{F} = 96485$ J/V·mol, and $T = 37°C = (273 + 37 =)$ 310 K, and from Figure 11.49a, K⁺ inside and outside is 400 mM and 20 mM, respectively. Substituting these numbers into the equation above gives $\Delta\psi = -80$ mV. Since there is more potassium inside, the inside is at a potential -80 mV relative to the outside. For sodium (50 mM inside and 400 mM outside) $\Delta\psi = +55.6$ mV (with the inside more positive than the outside). The value for chloride is -60 mV. (Note: The values at 25°C are -77 mV and $+53.4$ mV for potassium and sodium, respectively.)

15. Use the information in Problems 13 and 14, together with Figure 11.50, to discuss the behaviour of potassium, sodium, and chloride ions as an action potential propagates along an axon.

Answer: The value for the membrane potential calculated in Problem 14 is equal to the chloride Nernst potential calculated in Problem 13. This implies that chloride is distributed according to its Nernst potential, but both potassium and sodium are not. They are not at their Nernst potentials because the sodium-potassium pump is maintaining at concentration differences far from their Nernst potentials. This means, however, that when there is a change in membrane permeability for either of these ions, the membrane potential will change toward the Nernst membrane potentials.

When the membrane is depolarized to about -40 mV, this triggers an opening of sodium channels. Sodium now finds itself permeable to the membrane and flows into the cell down its concentration gradient. As it does this, the membrane potential moves toward the Nernst potential for sodium (around 50 mV). It doesn't quite reach this potential because at about 30 mV, sodium channels begin to close and potassium channels open. Opening of potassium channels drives the membrane potential toward the Nernst potential for potassium at about -80 mV. The membrane potential actually overshoots its resting potential (-60 mV). Eventually, the membrane potential is restored as potassium channels close.

17. In the cell signalling pathway shown in Figure 11.4, what would be the effect if Ras were mutated so that it had no GTPase activity?

Answer: Signal transduction pathways include both on and off switches to ensure that signals last for appropriate lengths of time. The consequence of activation of a signal transduction pathway is to elicit a physiological response to some environmental or developmental condition. The response will somehow address the condition and examples of this might be responses to blood glucose or serum calcium levels. Once the response to the signal is made, the condition setting off the signal is reassessed. If the condition is still uncorrected, an additional signal is required.

On and off switches in signal transduction pathways often include kinases and phosphatases that phosphorylate and dephosphorylate a target protein. In the case of G proteins, they are activated by GTP binding, but they inactivate themselves by intrinsic GTPase activity. If Ras lacked GTPase activity but could still bind GTP and become active (as an inhibitor or activator of some downstream protein), then the signal would be stuck in the on position. In this case, Ras would be capable of signalling in the absence of hormone stimulation. As it turns out, mutant forms of Ras are commonly associated with human cancers. The mutants lead to constitutively active Ras as a consequence of inactivation of GTPase activity.

Questions for Self-Study

1. Name three classes of chemical species that act as hormones.

2. List the three receptor superfamilies that mediate transmembrane signal processing and give a brief description how signal processing occurs.

3. What two enzymatic activities are responsible for regulating cAMP levels?

4. cAMP is an example of a second messenger. Name five other second messengers.

5. A large family of second messengers can be derived from phospholipase C activity on phosphatidylinositol and its derivatives. Explain.

6. Protein kinase C is sensitive to what two intercellular signals?

7. Membrane-bound guanylyl cyclases and soluble guanylyl cyclases are stimulated by very different signals. What are they?

8. Match a term with its definition.
   a. Node of Ranvier
   b. Synapse
   c. Schwann cell
   d. Interneuron
   e. Sensory neuron
   f. Dendrite
   g. Axon

   1. Connects to sensory receptor
   2. Carries nerve impulses away from cell body
   3. Moves nerve impulses to the cell body
   4. Insulating layer around axons
   5. Gap between an axon and a dentrite
   6. Moves signals from one neuron to another
   7. Gap between Schwann cells along an axon's length

9. True or false:
   a. Typically, action potentials are induced by a hyperpolerization of the membrane voltage. _____
   b. The resting potential of an axon is determined by the concentration gradients of all impermeable ions. _____
   c. During an action potential, the membrane voltage changes from approximately −60 mV to +40 mV because of changes in sodium permeability. _____
   d. Potassium permeability changes alone are responsible for returning the action potential back to resting values. _____
   e. Action potentials attenuate with distance. _____

10. Fill in the blanks. In cholinergic synpases, small vesicles termed _____ _____ are localized on the inside of the synaptic knob and contain large amounts of the neurotransmitter _____. When an action potential arrives at the synaptic knob, voltage-gated _____ channels open. This is followed by fusion of vesicles with the plasma membrane and release of neurotransmitter into the synaptic cleft. Neurotransmitter induces action potentials in postsynaptic cells by binding to receptors. There are two kinds of receptors, _____ and _____, distinguished by their responses to a toxic alkaloid in toadstools or to nicotine. Neurotransmitter action is usually short-lived because it is rapidly hydrolyzed by the enzyme _____.

11. Match the following:
    a. Endorphin
    b. Catecholamine
    c. Glycine
    d. Glutamate
    e. Malathion
    f. d-tubocurarine

    1. Binds to nicotinic receptors and blocks their opening
    2. Insecticide that blocks muscarinic receptor
    3. Excitatory amino acid transmitter
    4. Epinephrine
    5. Peptide neurotransmitter
    6. Inhibitory amino acid transmitter

Answers

1. Steroids, amino acid derivatives, and peptides.

2. 7-transmembrane segmented receptors are integral membrane proteins composed of seven helical segments, an extracellular hormone-binding domain, and an intracellular G-protein–binding domain. GTP-binding proteins or G proteins bind GTP and are released from the transmembrane receptor upon hormone binding. Depending on the type of G protein, the G-protein–GTP complex activates or inhibits adenylyl cyclase, leading to changes in cyclic AMP levels. Single-transmembrane segment catalytic receptors are integral membrane proteins with an extracellular hormone-receptor domain, a transmembrane segment, and an intracellular domain with either tyrosine kinase or guanylyl cyclase activity. Ligand gated-oligomeric ion channels open or close in response to ligand binding. Many such ion channels are regulated by neurotransmitters.

3. Adenylyl cyclase and phosphodiesterase.

4. cGMP, inositol phosphates, diacylglycerol (DAG), calcium, phosphatidic acid, ceramide, nitric oxide, cyclic ADP-ribose.

5. Phospholipase C activity produces diacylglycerol (DAG) and phosphoinositol. Depending on the phosphorylation state of phosphatidylinositol, inositol-1-P, inositol-1,4-P, or inositol-1,4,5-P may be released. Inositol-1,4,5-P leads to inositol-1,3,4,5-P, inositol-1,3,4-P, inositol-pentaphosphate, and inositol hexaphosphate. DAG may also be converted to phosphatidic acid.

6. Calcium and diacylglycerol.

7. Membrane-bound guanylyl cyclases are stimulated by a variety of peptide hormones. Soluble guanylyl cyclases are stimulated by nitric oxide.

8. a. 7; b. 5; c. 4; d. 6; e. 1; f. 3; g. 2.

9. a. F; b. F; c. T; d. F; e. F.

10. Synaptic vesicles; acetylcholine; calcium; muscarinic; nicotinic; acetylcholinesterase.

11. a. 5; b. 4; c. 6; d. 3; e. 2; f. 1.

Additional Problems

1. Caffeine (1,3,7-trimethylxanthine), theophylline (1,3-dimethylxanthine found in teas), and theobromine (3,7-dimethylxanthine found in chocolate) mimic the action of hormones that cause an increase in cAMP. Why?

2. Anabolic steroids have been used to increase athletic performance because these hormones lead to increase in mass and strength of muscle. However, their use for this purpose is banned in many competitions and random tests are often conducted to determine if an athlete has taken anabolic steroids. (Notable examples of athletes who have tested positive for drug use include Ben Johnson, Diego Maradona, and Hulk Hogan.) The tests are conducted on urine samples and steroid use can be detected even if active steroid use had been discontinued at some time prior to testing. From the properties of steroid hormones, can you suggest why synthetic steroids might have long biological half-lives?

3. Explain why the GTP analogs GMP-PNP and GMP-PCP are activators of adenylyl cyclase.

4. Draw the structure of inositol and explain why it can be metabolized into a large number of active compounds.

5. Based on the description of calmodulin target proteins and the Baa helix and referring to the wheel plot of melittin in the answer to Additional Problem 9 of Chapter 10, suggest a possible function for melittin.

6. The cellular membrane potential is established by ion-pumping mechanisms that are electrogenic. How can an electrical potential across a synthetic membrane be established in the absence of electrogenic pumps?

7. How does hyperpolarization lead to inhibition of action potentials?

8. Electrical recordings from an unstimulated neuromuscular junction reveal small, transient fluctuations in the membrane voltage termed miniature end-plate potentials. The magnitude of these end-plate potentials is reduced in size with curare. Further, their frequency is altered with changes in the membrane potential, with hyperpolarization of the presynaptic membrane decreasing frequency and depolarization increasing frequency. Based on these observations, explain how miniature end-plate potentials arise.

9. In myelinated axons, sodium channels are clustered in the nodes of Ranvier where gaps in the myelin sheath leave the axon exposed. How does a nerve impulse propagate along a myelinated axon and is the spacing of nodes of Ranvier at all important for this process?

10. What mechanism insures that nerve stimuli move in one direction along a neuron?

Abbreviated Answers

1. These agents inhibit phosphodiesterase, the enzyme responsible for cAMP metabolism to AMP. With phosphodiesterase inhibited, levels of cAMP increase and remain high for prolonged periods of time. (They also interfere with adenosine receptors.)

2. Steroids are fat-soluble substances that can partition into hydrophobic substances like fats and be retained there for long periods of time. Further, the steroid ring is very stable and only slowly metabolized by reduction to more water-soluble forms that are excreted by the kidney.

3. These GTP analogs bind to the GTP-binding site on G proteins; however, because they lack the normal phosphate ester linkage they are not hydrolyzed, resulting in prolonged stimulation of adenylyl cyclase.

4. Inositol can be converted to a large number of phosphorylated derivatives that have different biological functions. The structure of inositol is shown below.

5. The α-helical wheel plot of melittin shows a helix with hydrophobic residues on one face and a collection of hydrophilic residues on another face, with several basic amino acids at one end of the peptide. Melittin is a component of bee venom and shows hemolytic activity. In addition, it binds to calmodulin and can block calmodulin stimulation of calmodulin-binding proteins.

6. An electrical potential across a semipermeable membrane can be formed by placing a salt, composed or a permeable cation or anion and an impermeable counterion, on one side of the membrane. For example, consider a salt composed of a negatively charged, large, impermeable protein and a small cation like sodium. Upon dissolving the salt in solution on one side of the membrane, the salt dissociates into the large protein anion and Na^+. Sodium freely diffuses across the membrane because it moves down its concentration gradient. But because the impermeable anion cannot follow, sodium exiting from the membrane produces a charge imbalance across the membrane creating a voltage gradient.

7. An action potential is initiated above a certain threshold voltage for sodium channels. This threshold is slightly less negative than the normal resting potential of the cell. Hyperpolarization drives the membrane to a more negative value and a greater voltage change is required to reach the threshold voltage.

8. Miniature end-plate potentials arise from random release of packets of acetylcholine as synaptic vesicles fuse with the presynaptic membrane and release their contents into the synaptic cleft. Curare blocks end-plate potentials by blocking acetylcholine receptors. Hyperpolarization lowers the frequency of their occurrence, whereas depolarization increases it by altering the presynaptic calcium flux and thus reducing or increasing spontaneous synaptic vesicle release.

9. For an action potential to be propagated along an axon, a change in the membrane potential must be large enough to exceed the threshold voltage for sodium-channel opening. Once a voltage change due to an action potential occurs in a local region of the axon, it must be conducted to nearby regions of the axon to cause a depolarization of the membrane to a value above the threshold value. The myelin sheath greatly increases the transverse resistance, causing current, induced by an action potential, to be carried down the axon. As the current moves down the axon, it is attenuated; however, the myelin sheath reduces attenuation and the nodes of Ranvier are spaced such that the attenuated current is still large enough to cause a local depolarization of the membrane exceeding the threshold voltage. In effect, action potentials jump from node to node. Between nodes the stimulus is carried as a passive electrical current.

10. If an axon is stimulated electrically to initiate an action potential, the action potential will be conducted in both directions along an axon. However, the transmission of information across a synaptic cleft occurs only in one direction.

Summary

Hormones are chemical signal molecules that control and coordinate the many and diverse processes that occur in different parts of an organism. Steroid hormones regulate metabolism, salt and water balances, inflammatory processes, and sexual function. Epinephrine and norepinephrine regulate smooth muscle contraction and relaxation, blood pressure, cardiac rate, and other processes. Peptide hormones likewise regulate processes in all body tissues, as well as the release of other hormones. Hormones bind with very high affinity to their receptors.

Non-steroid hormones bind exclusively to outward-facing membrane receptors and activate signal transduction pathways that mobilize second messengers, including cyclic AMP, cyclic GMP, Ca^{2+}, inositol-1,4,5-trisphosphate, diacylglycerol, and nitric oxide. The receptors that mediate transmembrane signalling include three receptor superfamilies: 1) the 7-transmembrane segment receptors, which transmit their signals via GTP-binding proteins; 2) the single-transmembrane segment catalytic receptors, which possess tyrosine kinase or guanylyl cyclase activity; and 3) oligomeric ion channels.

The first second messengers to be discovered were calcium and cAMP. cAMP is produced by adenylyl cyclase and hydrolyzed by phosphodiesterase. The activity of cAMP is mediated by G proteins, which exchange GDP for GTP upon binding of hormone to the associated receptor protein. G_α(GTP) dissociates from $G_{\beta\gamma}$ and binds to adenylyl cyclase to activate the synthesis of cAMP. Inhibitory G proteins act in a similar manner to inhibit adenylyl cyclase. The toxic effects of cholera toxin are due to ADP-ribosylation and consequently activation of G_s, whereas pertussis toxin ADP-ribosylates and inactivates G_i. The small G proteins, typified by the protein product of the Ras gene, function in a manner similar to the heterotrimeric G proteins. Mutant forms of the Ras protein have been implicated in the tumorigenic activity of certain tumor viruses.

A diverse array of second messengers is generated by breakdown of membrane phospholipids. Phospholipase C hydrolyzes phosphatidylinositol-4,5-bisphosphate to produce inositol-1,4,5-trisphosphate (IP_3) and diacylglycerol (DAG). IP_3 stimulates an increase in intracellular $[Ca^{2+}]$, whereas DAG activates protein kinase C. Activation of phospholipase C enzymes is mediated by G proteins or by receptor tyrosine kinases. IP_3 has a half-life of only a few seconds. It is catabolized by phosphatases and/or kinases to produce a series of other inositol-phosphate metabolites which may themselves be second messengers in certain cellular processes. Second messengers may also be produced by breakdown of phosphatidylcholine. Action of phospholipase A_2 on PC produces arachidonic acid, which can be metabolized to eicosanoid compounds, and phospholipases C and D can produce DAG and phosphatidic acid, respectively. Sphingomyelinase action on sphingomyelin produces ceramide, which stimulates a protein kinase, and gangliosides and their breakdown products modulate the activity of protein kinases and G-protein–coupled receptors.

Calcium ion is an important second messenger, which is released by action of IP_3 into the cytoplasm from intracellular stores, including calciosomes and ER. Extracellular calcium can enter the cell via ligand-gated, voltage-gated, or second messenger–regulated channels. Ca^{2+} binds to a series of calcium-binding proteins, such as calmodulin, which act to modulate enzyme and ion channel activity within the cell. Calmodulin target proteins possess a basic amphiphilic α-helix, to which calmodulin binds specifically and with high affinity. Ca^{2+} is also an activator of protein kinase C, which elicits a variety of cellular responses by phosphorylation of target proteins at Ser and Thr residues. Protein kinase C contains a pseudosubstrate sequence that masks the active site to inhibit PKC activity in the absence of DAG and Ca^{2+}. Many protein kinases and protein phosphatases are regulated by such intrasteric control. Protein phosphatases may either be specific for Ser- and Thr-phosphates or for Tyr-phosphates. The tumour-promoting activity of okadaic acid, the major cause of diarrhetic shellfish poisoning, arises from its potent inhibition of protein phosphatases.

The single-transmembrane segment receptor proteins display either a tyrosine kinase or guanylyl cyclase activity. Additionally, soluble tyrosine kinases and guanylyl cyclases also participate in cellular-signalling processes. Receptor tyrosine kinases are integral transmembrane proteins, whereas non-receptor tyrosine kinases, which are related to retroviral transforming proteins, are peripheral, lipid-anchored proteins. Receptor tyrosine kinases are membrane-associated allosteric enzymes, since hormone binding induces oligomerization of receptors in the membrane, activating phosphorylation of the cytoplasmic domains and stimulating tyrosine kinase activity by the receptors.

Polypeptide hormones are synthesized as inactive precursors and undergo cellular processing which produces the active hormone. Processing events common to all polypeptide hormones include 1) proteolytic cleavage of a hydrophobic N-terminal signal sequence; 2) proteolytic cleavage at sites defined by pairs of basic amino acids; 3) proteolytic cleavage at the site of a single Arg residue; and 4) post-translational modification of individual amino acids, including C-terminal α-amidation, phosphorylation, glycosylation or acetylation of the N-terminal residue.

Membrane-bound guanylyl cyclases are single-TMS receptors, which synthesize cGMP in response to hormone binding. Peptides, which activate membrane-bound guanylyl cyclases, include atrial natriuretic peptides. Soluble guanylyl cyclases are receptors for nitric oxide, which is synthesized by NO· synthase. NO· acts as a neurotransmitter and as a second messenger, inducing relaxation of vascular smooth muscle and mediating penile erection. It also enables macrophages to kill tumour cells and bacteria. NO· is unique among second messengers, because, as a dissolved gas, it is capable of rapid diffusion across cell membranes without the assistance of carriers. NO· has a half-life of 1–5 seconds and is degraded by non-enzymatic pathways. NO· activates guanylyl cyclase by binding to the heme prosthetic group to form a nitrosoheme.

Steroid hormones exert their effects in two ways: 1) in the nucleus, steroids act as transcription regulators, modulating gene expression; 2) steroids also can act at the cell membrane, directly regulating ligand-gated ion channels and other processes. Specialized receptor proteins carry steroids to the nucleus. These receptor proteins, members of a gene superfamily, each contain a hydrophobic steroid binding domain near the C-terminus and a central, hydrophilic DNA-binding domain. Receptor proteins for thyroid hormones are highly homologous with steroid receptors.

The nervous system is composed of neurons and neuroglia or glial cells. There are several types of glial cells that serve various purposes in the nervous system. Schwann cells envelope neurons and form an insulating layer. Phagocytic glial cells remove cellular debris from nervous tissue and other glial cells form linings in the cavities of the brain and in the spinal column. Neurons contain three distinct regions: the cell body, which contains the nucleus, mitochondria, ribosomes, endoplasmic reticulum, and other organelles; the axon, a long extension of the cell body whose primary function is to carry nerve impulses from the cell body to the cell periphery; and, dendrites, short, branched structures that carry impulses to the cell body from the periphery. Certain axons have myelin sheath derived from Schwann cells. The Schwann cells wrap around the axon to produce an insulating layer with periodic gaps called the nodes of Ranvier where the axon is exposed. The distal end of the axon ends in a synaptic knob or synaptic bulb.

There are three kinds of neurons: sensory neurons that transduce sensory signals into nervous signals; interneurons that pass signals from one neuron to another; and motor neurons that pass signals to muscles. The signals carried by neurons are electrical signals that arise from changes in the electrical potential across the neuron membrane as a result of changes in permeability of the membrane to various ions. The Nernst equation predicts the contribution to the membrane electrical potential for a single permeable ion unequally distributed across a membrane. The sign and magnitude of the electrical potential are given by $\Delta\psi = (RT/\mathcal{F})\times\ln[C_2]/[C_1]$ where $[C_2]$ and $[C_1]$ are the molar concentrations of the ion on both sides of the membrane, R is the gas constant, T is the temperature in degrees Kelvin, and $\mathcal{F}$ is Faraday's constant. For multiple ions, the Goldman equation is used, where $\Delta\psi = (RT/\mathcal{F})\ln\{([\Sigma P_C[C_{outside}] + \Sigma P_A[A_{inside}])/(\Sigma P_C[C_{inside}] + \Sigma P_A[A_{outside}])\}$ and P_A and P_C are the permeabilities of anions and cations to the membrane. Nerve impulses are called action potentials and they arise when the membrane becomes permeable to specific ions. A resting cell maintains a membrane potential of about −60 mV (with the inside negative relative to the outside), due in large part to the Na^+–K^+ pump. When a cell is depolarized, the membrane potential is made more positive (the opposite, to hyperpolarize, is to change the membrane potential to a more negative value) by about 20 mV, and voltage-gated ion channels specific for sodium are opened. Because sodium is in high concentration external to the cell and the inside of the cell is at a negative potential, sodium rushes into the cell, causing the cell to depolarize to a membrane potential close to the value predicted for the Nernst potential for sodium. At this point, the sodium channels close and potassium-specific voltage-gated channels open, allowing potassium to rush out of the cell down its electrochemical gradient to hyperpolarize the cell to a value below the resting membrane potential. Eventually, potassium channels close and the voltage returns to the resting potential. Action potentials are propagated very rapidly, are not attenuated with distance, and show a fixed amplitude. Because the amplitude is fixed, the information content is the number and frequency of action potentials. The voltage-gated sodium channels are integral membrane proteins. Tetrodotoxin from the puffer fish, and saxitoxin from two species of marine dinoflagellates responsible for "red tides," bind to the sodium channels and prevent their opening. Veratridine from a plant of the lily family and batrachotoxin, a compound from the skin secretions of a Colombian frog, can block sodium channels in the open position. Voltage-gated potassium channels are also intrinsic membrane proteins that can be specifically blocked by 4-aminopyridine, tetraethylammonium ion, dendrotoxin I (a 60-residue peptide from the black mamba snake), mast cell degranulating peptide (a 22-residue peptide from bee venom), and charybdotoxin (a 37-residue peptide from scorpion venom).

Transmission from one neuron to another involves information transfer across the synaptic cleft. There are two kinds of synapses: electrical synapses with a very small gap, approximately 2 nm, separating the presynaptic cell from the postsynaptic cell; and chemical synapses, with 20 nm to 50 nm gaps. Chemical substances called neurotransmitters are released by the presynaptic cell, diffuse across the synaptic cleft, and bind to receptors in the postsynaptic cell. Neurotransmitters include acetylcholine, various amino acids, catecholamines, peptides, and gaseous compounds. The cholinergic synapse employs acetylcholine as a neurotransmitter. The presynaptic cell contains synaptic vesicles filled with acetylcholine. A voltage-gated calcium channel in the presynaptic membrane opens in response to the arrival of an action potential and allows calcium to enter the cell. Calcium, complexed to calmodulin, binds to a 75-kD protein, synapsin-I, allowing synaptic vesicle fusion to the plasma membrane and acetylcholine release into the synaptic cleft. Acetylcholine release can be specifically blocked by several toxins produced by *Clostridium botulinum,* the bacteria responsible for botulism poisoning. α-latrotoxin, a black widow spider venom protein, stimulates acetylcholine release.

Acetylcholine released into the synaptic cleft binds to acetylcholine receptors in the postsynaptic membrane, leading to membrane depolarization, and initiation of an action potential in the postsynaptic cell. There are two classes of acetylcholine receptors that are distinguished by their responses to muscarine, a toxic toadstool alkaloid, and nicotine. Nicotinic receptors are K^+–Na^+ channels located in motor endplates of skeletal muscles. Nicotine binding causes the receptor to lock into the open conformation. The nicotinic acetylcholine receptors are ligand-gated ion channels that undergo a conformational change upon acetylcholine binding that results in the opening of a channel equally permeable to both K^+ and Na^+. The effects of sodium on the membrane voltage are greater than those of potassium, and as a result, the postsynaptic cell depolarizes and an action potential is initiated. The channel remains open for only a few milliseconds then closes, and as long as acetylcholine remains bound to the receptor, it will not reopen. To re-sensitize the receptor, acetylcholine must be removed. This occurs when the concentration of acetylcholine in the synaptic cleft drops to below 10 nM in response to acetylcholinesterase-dependent degradation of acetylcholine. Repackaging of acetylcholine into synaptic vesicles occurs in the presynaptic cell. Empty synaptic vesicles are produced by endocytosis of the presynaptic membrane. A proton pump, a V-type ATPase, produces a proton gradient across the vesicle membrane by pumping protons into the vesicle and acetylcholine transport protein uses this gradient to concentrate acetylcholine in the vesicles. Agents that prevent nicotinic acetylcholine receptors from opening include d-tubocurarine, cobratoxin, and α-bungarotoxin.

The muscarinic receptors, located in smooth muscle and glands, are stimulated by muscarine. Binding of acetylcholine to muscarinic receptors results in 1) inhibition of adenylyl cyclase, 2) stimulation of phospholipase C, and 3) opening of potassium channels. All of these effects are mediated by G proteins. As mentioned, muscarine stimulates these receptors. A potent antagonist is atropine from the deadly nightshade plant.

Acetylcholine receptors can be activated by the acetylcholine analogs, decamethonium and succinylcholine. These agents lead to long-term stimulation of acetylcholine receptors because they are broken down only slowly. Organophosphorus compounds are potent inhibitors of acetylcholinesterase, a serine esterase with an active site serine that is a target for DIFP, malathion, and parathion (commonly used insecticides), and sarin and tabun (nerve gases). Physostigmine and neostigmine are mild inhibitors of acetylcholinesterase that have been used in the treatment of myasthenia gravis.

The amino acids glutamate and aspartate are also excitatory neurotransmitters that are stored in presynaptic vesicles and released into the presynaptic cleft by calcium-dependent exocytosis. Synaptic vesicles are filled with glutamate in a manner similar to acetylcholine-filled vesicles. A proton pump creates a proton gradient that provides the driving force for glutamate accumulation. To remove glutamate from the synaptic cleft, glutamate is taken into glial cells and converted to glutamine. Glutamine is transported to the presynaptic neuron and recycled by the mitochondria back to glutamate. Glutamate receptors include N-methyl-D-aspartate (NMDA), kainate, and AMPA receptors, examples of ligand-gated ion channels, and metabotropic receptors which are G-protein–mediated receptors that are coupled to phosphotidylinositol metabolism. The NMDA receptors the best characterized glutamate receptor. It functions as a Ca^{2+}, Na^+, and K^+ channel that is closed by Mg^{2+} in a voltage-dependent manner. The hallucinogenic drug phencyclidine (PCP, a.k.a angel dust) is a specific antagonist of the NMDA receptor.

γ-aminobutyric acid (GABA) and glycine are inhibitory neurotransmitters that function by hyperpolarizing the postsynaptic neuron. The receptors are ligand-gated chloride channels. GABA receptors are localized in the brain and opened by ethanol. Glycine receptors are found in the spinal cord and are blocked specifically by strychnine.

The catecholamine neurotransmitters include L-dopa, dopamine, norepinephrine, and epinephrine, all derived from the amino acid tyrosine. Norepinephrine is the neurotransmitter in junctions between sympathetic nerves and smooth muscle. Excessive production of dopamine or hypersensitivity of dopamine receptors is responsible for schizophrenia, while lowered production of dopamine is found in Parkinson's disease. Inhibitors of catecholamine uptake and vesicular repackaging have been used to treat clinical depression. Monoamine oxidase inhibitors block degradation of norepinephrine. The tricyclics act on norepinephrine transporters, reserpine inhibits proton-monoamine exchange protein from reloading synaptic vesicles with norepinephrine, and cocaine blocks the reuptake transporters of monoamine neurotransmitters in the presynaptic membrane.

Peptide neurotransmitters include endorphins and enkephalins, natural opioid substances that act as pain relievers; endothelins, regulatory peptides that act on smooth muscle and connective tissue; vasoactive intestinal peptide, and many more. Vasoactive intestinal peptide causes an increase in cAMP via a G-protein–mediated pathway.

Chapter 12

Enzymes—Kinetics and Specificity

● ●

Chapter Outline

- ❖ Enzymes
    - ⅄ Biological catalysts that function in dilute, aqueous solutions under mild conditions (e.g., pH) and low temperatures to increase reaction rate
    - ⅄ Catalytic power: Ratio of catalyzed rate to uncatalyzed rate
    - ⅄ Specificity
- ❖ Nomenclature
    - ⅄ Common names
    - ⅄ International Commission on Enzymes (EC numbers): Six classes
- ❖ Terms
    - ⅄ Holoenzyme: Protein and prosthetic group
    - ⅄ Apoenzyme: Protein-lacking prosthetic group
    - ⅄ Prosthetic group: Firmly bound coenzyme
    - ⅄ Coenzyme: Organic compound cofactor
- ❖ Chemical kinetics
    - ⅄ Rate law: $v = -dA/dt = k[A]^n$
        - • k = rate constant
        - • n = order of reaction,
            - • $n = 1$, first order $[A]$
            - • $n = 2$, second order $[A]^2$ or $[A][B]$
    - ⅄ Molecularity: Number of molecules that must simultaneously react
- ❖ Reaction rates
    - ⅄ Limited by activation barrier: Free energy needed to reach transition state
    - ⅄ Arrhenius equation $k = Ae^{-\Delta G^*/RT}$: ΔG^* = Free energy of activation
    - ⅄ Influenced by
        - • Temperature
        - • Catalysts
- ❖ Enzyme kinetics
    - ⅄ Saturatable: Zero-order kinetics at high $[S]$
    - ⅄ Michaelis–Menten: $v_0 = (V_{max}[S])/(K_m+[S])$
        - • $K_m = (k_{-1}+k_2)/k_1$
        - • $[S] = K_m$ when $v_0 = V_{max}/2$
- ❖ Enzyme quantities
    - ⅄ One international unit: Amount to catalyze formation of one micromole of product in one minute
    - ⅄ Turnover number = $k_{cat} = k_2 = V_{max}/[E_T]$
    - ⅄ k_1 sets upper limit on catalytic efficiency: Reaction can go no faster than rate at which E and S form ES
    - ⅄ k_{cat}/K_m = catalytic efficiency
- ❖ Plots
    - ⅄ Direct plot: v versus $[S]$: $v_0 = (V_{max}[S])/(K_m+[S])$
        - • Rectangular hyperbola
        - • Asymptotically approaches V_{max} when $[S]$ high
        - • $[S] = K_m$ when $v_0 = V_{max}/2$

- Lineweaver–Burk (double-reciprocal): $1/v_0$ versus $1/[S]$: $1/v_0 = (K_m/V_{max})(1/[S])+1/V_{max}$
  - Linear
  - Slope = K_m/V_{max}
  - y-intercept $=1/V_{max}$
  - x-intercept $= -1/K_m$
- Hanes–Woolf: $[S]/v_0$ versus $[S]$: $[S]/v_0=(1/V_{max})[S]+(K_m/V_{max})$
  - Linear
  - Slope = $1/V_{max}$
  - y-intercept = K_m/V_{max}
  - x-intercept = $-K_m$
- ❖ pH dependence: Enzymes generally active over pH range
- ❖ Temperature dependence of enzyme-catalyzed reactions
  - Below 50°C: Q_{10}: Ratio of activities at two temperatures 10° apart: For typical enzyme $Q_{10} = 2$
  - Above 50°C: Typically enzyme denatures
- ❖ Inhibition
  - Reversible inhibition: Non-covalent
    - Competitive inhibition: Inhibitor and substrate compete for same binding site
      - V_{max} unchanged
      - $K_m = K_m(1+[I]/K_I)$
    - Non-competitive inhibition
      - Pure non-competitive inhibition: S and I bind at different sites
        - K_m unchanged
        - $V_{max. app} = V_{max}/(1 + [I]/K_I)$
      - Mixed non-competitive inhibition: I binding influences S binding
        - $K_I < K_{I'}$: $V_{max,app}$ decreased: $K_{m,app}$ increased
        - $K_{I'} < K_I$: $V_{max,app}$ decreased: $K_{m,app}$ decreased
      - Uncompetitive: I bonds to ES complex
        - $V_{max,app}$ decreased: $K_{m,app}$ decreased
      -
  - Irreversible inhibition: Covalent
    - Suicide substrate or Trojan Horse substrate
    - Site-specific affinity label
- ❖ Bisubstrate reactions: Two substrates converted to two products
  - Sequential or single displacement
    - Random: Creatine kinase: Either substrate binds to enzyme; either product is released
    - Ordered: NAD$^+$-dependent dehydrogenases: Leading substrate binds first
  - Ping-Pong or double-displacement: Aminotransferase: Leading substrate binds: Enzyme modified: Product released: Second substrate binds: Enzyme unmodified: Second product released
- ❖ Enzyme specificity
  - Induced fit: Conformational change with substrate binding
  - Active site binds transition state molecule
  - Conformational changes by first substrate binding may be required for second substrate binding
- ❖ Catalytic biomolecules
  - Enzymes: Proteins
  - Ribozymes: RNA
    - RNase P RNA component
    - Self-splicing RNAs
    - Ribosomal RNA: Peptidyl transferase property of rRNA
  - Abzymes: Antibodies

Chapter Objectives

Michaelis–Menten Enzyme Kinetics

One of the keys to understanding Michaelis–Menten enzyme kinetics is to remember the model and the assumptions. The enzyme–substrate complex is in rapid equilibrium with free substrate. Product formation involves a fast catalytic step followed by a slow release of product. The velocity, v, is the initial velocity of the reaction measured immediately upon addition of substrate when product concentration is very small. The Michaelis–Menten equation is not a complicated equation and is easy to understand.

$$v = (V_{max}[S])/(K_m + [S])$$

It is easy to remember that K_m has units of concentration because the denominator of the Michaelis–Menten equation is the term $K_m + [S]$. V_{max} is equal to the product of k_2 and $[E_T]$. V_{max} is reached when substrate concentration is large. How large? Large relative to K_m. The equation is an example of a rectangular hyperbola. In a plot of v vs $[S]$, V_{max} is approached asymptotically as $[S]$ increases and K_m is the substrate concentration that supports $v = V_{max}/2$.

Graphical Representation

The Lineweaver–Burk double-reciprocal plot uses $1/v$ and $1/[S]$ as variables because they are linearly related and give rise to straight lines. A minor disadvantage to double-reciprocal plots is that they use inverse space: as $[S]$ increases, $1/[S]$ decreases. Values of v at low $[S]$ tend to dominate the plot. With this in mind, it is easy to remember that the $1/v$ intercept is equal to $1/V_{max}$, because the intercept occurs at the smallest real value of $1/v$. Smaller values of $1/v$ occur only to the left of the $1/v$-axis, where $1/[S]$ is negative. (Negative concentrations do not exist in the real world.) The $1/[S]$ intercept is equal to $-1/K_m$. Alternative variables related linearly are $[S]/v$ vs. $[S]$, used in Hanes–Woolf plots. Concentrate on direct plots (i.e., v vs. $[S]$) and on double-reciprocal plots. Examples of a double-reciprocal plot and a Hanes–Woolf plot are presented in Figures 12.9 and 12.10 below.

$$\frac{1}{v} = \frac{K_m}{V_{max}}\left(\frac{1}{[S]}\right) + \frac{1}{V_{max}}$$

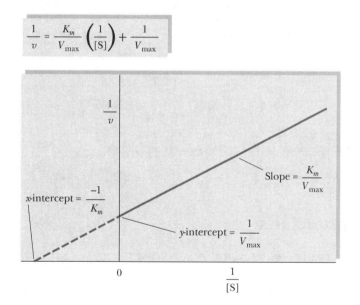

Figure 12.9 The Lineweaver–Burk double-reciprocal plot, depicting extrapolations that allow the determination of the x- and y-intercepts and slope.

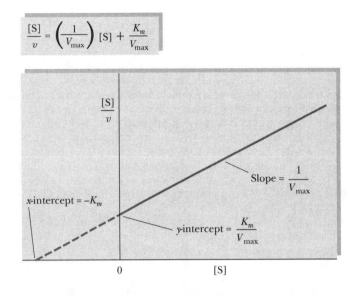

$$\frac{[S]}{v} = \left(\frac{1}{V_{max}}\right)[S] + \frac{K_m}{V_{max}}$$

Figure 12.10   A Hanes–Woolf plot of $[S]/v$ versus $[S]$, another straight-line rearrangement of the Michaelis–Menten equation.

Inhibitors

Competitive inhibition occurs whenever an inhibitor competes with a substrate for the substrate binding site in a reversible manner. How will the presence of a competitive inhibitor affect enzyme kinetics? Clearly, at high $[S]$, S will out-compete the inhibitor. Thus, V_{max} is unaffected. The apparent K_m is increased to $K_m(1 + [I]/K_I)$. (The term $[I]/K_I$ is the inhibitor concentration normalized to the inhibitor dissociation constant, K_I.)

In non-competitive inhibition, the inhibitor binds reversibly to a site different than the substrate binding site, but the inhibitor-bound enzyme is inactive. The easiest case to remember is pure non-competitive inhibition. Here, I binds to its enzyme-binding site without regard to the state of occupancy of the substrate-binding site. In other words, E and ES bind I with equal affinity. The consequence is a decrease in the apparent V_{max} to $V_{max}/(1 + [I]/K_I)$; however, K_m is unaffected. Mixed non-competitive inhibition occurs when I binding to E and ES differ. Both K_m and V_{max} are affected.

Bisubstrate Reactions

Single-displacement or sequential reactions occur as follows:

$$A + B + E \rightarrow AEB \rightarrow PEQ \rightarrow E + P + Q$$

The two substrates may bind in a specific order or in random order.
Ping-Pong or double-displacement reactions proceed as follows:

$$A + E \rightarrow EA \rightarrow E'P \rightarrow E' + P; \ E' + B \rightarrow E'B \rightarrow EQ \rightarrow E + Q$$

Problems and Solutions

1.   *According to the Michaelis–Menten equation, what is the v/Vmax ratio when [S] = 4 Km?*

Answer: 0.8.

3.   *For a Michaelis–Menten reaction, k₁ = 7 × 10⁷ M⁻¹s⁻¹, k₋₁ = 1 × 10³ s⁻¹, and k₂ = 2 × 10⁴ s⁻¹. What are the values of Ks and Km? Does substrate binding approach equilibrium or does it behave more like a steady-state system?*

Answer: When $k_1 = 7 \times 10^7/\text{M·s}$, $k_{-1} = 1 \times 10^3/\text{s}$, $k_2 = 2 \times 10^4/\text{s}$:

$K_s = K_{-1}/k_1$ $K_m = (k_{-1} + k_2)/k_1$
$K_s = [1 \times 10^3/\text{s}]/[7 \times 10^7/\text{M·s}]$ $K_m = ([1 \times 10^3/\text{s}] + [2 \times 10^4/\text{s}])/[7 \times 10^7/\text{M·s}]$
$K_s = 1.43 \times 10^{-5}$ M $K_m = 3 \times 10^{-4}$ M

$K_s = 1.43 \times 10^{-5}$ M; $K_m = 3 \times 10^{-4}$ M

Once the ES complex forms, the substrate may be either converted to product or released as S. Formation of product is governed by a first-order rate constant, k_2, which is 20 times larger than the first-order rate constant for dissociation of ES (i.e., k_{-1}). Thus, the enzyme behaves like a steady-state system. Only in the case where k_2 is rate-limiting, will substrate binding approach equilibrium.

5. Using Figure 12.7 as a model, draw curves that would be obtained from v versus [S] plots when
   a. twice as much enzyme is used.
   b. half as much enzyme is used.
   c. a competitive inhibitor is added.
   d. a pure non-competitive inhibitor is added.
   e. an uncompetitive inhibitor is added.
For each example, indicate how V$_{max}$ and K$_m$ change.

Answer: Figure 12.7 is a direct plot of initial velocity versus substrate.

a.   With twice as much enzyme, the plot should asymptotically approach a value of V_{max} that is twice the value shown in the figure. But, since the K_m is unchanged, it will reach 1/2 its V_{max} at the same value of [S] independent of enzyme concentration.

b.   Half as much enzyme will reach a V_{max} value half that shown in Figure 12.7, but it will have the same K_m.

c.   A competitive inhibitor will not influence V_{max}, so the plot will asymptotically approach V_{max}, but the K_m will be larger by a factor of $(1 + [I]/K_I)$, where [I] is the inhibitor concentration and K_I is the dissociation constant for inhibitor binding to the enzyme.

d.   For a pure non-competitive inhibitor, K_m will be unchanged, but V_{max} will be lower by a factor of $1/(1 + [I]/K_I)$.

e.   For an uncompetitive inhibitor, K_m will be decreased by the factor $1/(1 + [I]/K_{I'})$, and V_{max} will be decreased by the same factor, where $K_{I'}$ is the inhibitor dissociation constant for binding to the enzyme–substrate complex.

Plots for (a) and (b) are shown below along with a control plot (in the middle). It is clear that while each reach a different V_{max}, they all show the same K_m.

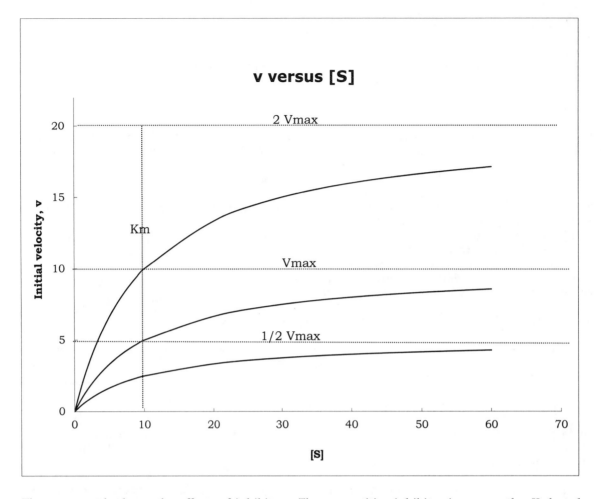

The next graph shows the effects of inhibitors. The competitive inhibitor increases the K_m but does not affect the V_{max}. For pure non-competitive inhibition, V_{max} is depressed, whereas K_m is unchanged. Finally, for uncompetitive inhibition, both K_m and V_{max} are affected but in interesting ways. V_{max} is decreased but so is K_m. If you think of K_m apparent as the concentration of substrate at which the enzyme is at one-half V_{max}, it would appear that a lower K_m suggests better functioning of the enzyme!

As a cautionary note: The value of [S] at which the enzyme is at one-half V_{max} is the K_m when the enzyme is tested without inhibitors. When inhibitors are tested, it is more appropriate to refer to this value as the apparent K_m. The relationships between K_m and apparent K_m's are given in Table 12.6 of the textbook.

v versus [S]

7. *The following graphical patterns obtained from kinetic experiments have several possible interpretations depending on the nature of the experiment and the variables being plotted. Give at least two possibilities for each.*

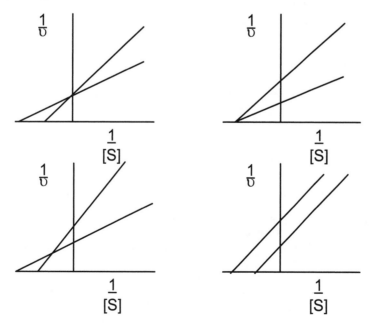

Answer: In the top left graph, the results may be due to a competitive inhibitor. The line with the steeper slope is from enzyme kinetic measurements in the presence of an inhibitor, whereas the other line is enzyme kinetic data without inhibitor. In competitive inhibition, V_{max}, the reciprocal of the $1/\upsilon$ intercept, is independent of the presence of inhibitor. However, $K_{m,app}$ increases, as reflected in the decrease (in absolute magnitude) of the $1/[S]$ intercept which equals $1/K_{m,app}$. In competitive inhibition, I and S compete for the same enzyme-binding site. The apparent K_m increases because in the presence of inhibitor, higher concentrations of substrate are required to half-saturate the enzyme. The lines are described by the following equation:

$$\frac{1}{\upsilon} = \frac{K_m\left(1+\dfrac{[I]}{K_I}\right)}{V_{max}} + \frac{1}{V_{max}}$$

An alternative interpretation of the data is that the inhibitor binds to and forms a complex with the substrate. In this case, the equation

$$\frac{1}{\upsilon} = \frac{K_m}{V_{max}} \times \frac{1}{[S]} + \frac{1}{V_{max}}$$

must be modified to take this inhibitor–substrate interaction into account. In this equation, [S] is the initial concentration of substrate available to the enzyme. The concentration of substrate used to construct the plots is the total substrate concentration, $[S_T]$. Under normal conditions, $[S_T] = [S]$, but in this case, $[S_T] = [S] + [SI]$ because some of the substrate is complexed to I. We can derive an expression for [S] as follows:

From $[S_T]=[S]+[SI]$, we have

$[S]=[S_T]-[SI]$, and using

$K_I=\dfrac{[I][S]}{[SI]}$, we see that

$[SI]=\dfrac{[I][S]}{K_I}$

Substituting [SI] above and solving for [S], we find:

$[S]=\dfrac{[S_T]}{1+\dfrac{[I]}{K_I}}$

By substituting into $\dfrac{1}{\upsilon}$ the equation, it becomes:

$$\frac{1}{\upsilon} = \frac{K_m(1+\dfrac{[I]}{K_I})}{V_{max}} \times \frac{1}{[S_T]} + \frac{1}{V_{max}}$$

This equation is identical to the case of competitive inhibition.

The top right graph may be a case of pure, non-competitive inhibition which is described by the following equation

$$\frac{1}{\upsilon} = \frac{K_m\left(1+\dfrac{[I]}{K_I}\right)}{V_{max}} \times \frac{1}{[S]} + \frac{\left(1+\dfrac{[I]}{K_I}\right)}{V_{max}}$$

In this case, the inhibitor binds to the enzyme and to the enzyme–substrate complex with equal affinity. The binding of I to E has no effect on the binding of S to E. Thus, K_m is unaffected because the inhibitor-free enzyme is capable of normal catalysis. V_{max} is decreased to $V_{max}/(1 + [I]/K_I)$. In effect, the inhibitor lowers the active enzyme concentration. The data can also be explained as the result of experiments conducted at two different enzyme concentrations. (In this case, no inhibition whatsoever is involved.) Another possibility, involving an inhibitor, is that the inhibitor binds irreversibly to E and inactivates it. This is the same as lowering the total enzyme concentration. Another possibility is that we may be looking at a case of random, single-displacement bisubstrate reaction. Look at Figure 12.20 and compare it to this plot. In this plot, the top line would be from data generated at a fixed concentration of the second substrate, whereas the second (lower) line from conditions in which the second substrate concentration is higher. Binding of substrate A is not affected by binding of B and vice versa. Finally, an inhibitor that simply inactivated the enzyme irreversibly would give similar data. The inhibitor, in effect, lowers the concentration of active enzyme, which would give the same K_m but lower V_{max}.

The bottom left graph may be an example of mixed non-competitive inhibition in which the inhibitor I binds to both E and ES but unequally. In this case, I binds to ES with higher affinity (i.e., lower K_I) than to S. V_{max} is decreased and $K_{m,app}$ is increased. Alternatively, this may be an example of a single-displacement bisubstrate mechanism characterized by the following equation

$$\frac{1}{v} = \frac{1}{V_{max}}\left(K_m^A + \frac{K_S^A K_m^B}{[B]}\right) \times \frac{1}{[A]} + \frac{1}{V_{max}}\left(1 + \frac{K_m^B}{[B]}\right)$$

Compare this to Figure 12.19. The line with the shallower slope would be data collected at higher second substrate concentration.

The bottom right graph is characteristic of uncompetitive inhibition. Uncompetitive inhibitors bind only to the enzyme–substrate complex, ES. As a consequence, V_{max} is decreased by the factor $(1 + [I]/K_I)$ but so is K_m, apparent. The enzyme appears to function better in terms of substrate concentration (it half-saturates at lower concentrations), but its V_{max} is lower. This happens because I binding to ES shifts the equilibrium to the right, making it easier to half-saturate with substrate. Alternatively, the graph is typical of double-displacement (ping-pong) bisubstrate mechanisms as shown in Figure 12.22.

9. *Measurement of the rate constants for a simple enzymatic reaction obeying Michaelis–Menten kinetics gave the following results:*

$$k_1 = 2 \times 10^8 \ M^{-1}s^{-1}$$
$$k_{-1} = 1 \times 10^3 \ s^{-1}$$
$$k_2 = 5 \times 10^3 \ s^{-1}$$

    a. *What is K_s, the dissociation constant for the enzyme–substrate complex?*
    b. *What is K_m, the Michaelis constant for this enzyme?*
    c. *What is k_{cat} (the turnover number) for this enzyme?*
    d. *What is the catalytic efficiency (k_{cat}/K_m) for this enzyme?*
    e. *Does this enzyme approach "kinetic perfection"? That is, does k_{cat}/K_m approach the diffusion-controlled rate of enzyme association with substrate?*
    f. *If a kinetic measurement was made using 2 nanomoles of enzyme per millilitre and saturating amounts of substrate, what would V_{max} equal?*
    g. *Again, using 2 nanomoles of enzyme per millilitre of reaction mixture, what concentration of substrate would give $v = 0.75 V_{max}$?*
    h. *If a kinetic measurement was made using 4 nanomoles of enzyme per millilitre and saturating amounts of substrate, what would V_{max} equal? What would K_m equal under these conditions?*

Answer: a.   The dissociation constant K_s is simple the ratio of k_{-1} to k_1, the forward and reverse rate constants for formation of the ES complex. An easy way to remember this is that the units of dissociation constants are concentration. (If fact, a functional definition of the dissociation constant is the concentration of free ligand that half-saturates the binding site.) Given units for the rate constants, it is clear that $K_s = k_{-1}/k_1$.

$$K_s = \frac{k_{-1}}{k_1} = \frac{1 \times 10^3 s^{-1}}{2 \times 10^8 M^{-1}s^{-1}}$$
$$K_s = 0.5 \times 10^{-5} M \text{ or } 5 \ \mu M$$

b.   The Michaelis constant, K_m, is $(k_{-1}+k_2)/k_1$. Again, an easy way to remember this is to recall that K_m is the substrate concentration at which the enzyme is functioning at one-half its maximum velocity. Thus, K_m must have units of concentration.

$$K_m = \frac{k_{-1} + k_2}{k_1} = \frac{1 \times 10^3 s^{-1} + 5 \times 10^3 s^{-1}}{2 \times 10^8 M^{-1}s^{-1}}$$
$$K_m = 3 \times 10^{-5} M \text{ or } 30 \ \mu M$$

c.   The turnover number, k_{cat}, is given by $V_{max}/[E_T]$, which is simply equal to k_2. Thus, k_{cat} is $5 \times 10^3 \ s^{-1}$.

d.   The catalytic efficiency is the turnover number divided by K_m, both of which we have determined.

$$\frac{k_{cat}}{K_m} = \frac{5 \times 10^3 s^{-1}}{3 \times 10^{-5} M}$$

$$\frac{k_{cat}}{K_m} = 1.67 \times 10^8 M^{-1} s^{-1}$$

e.   The very fastest we could expect the enzyme to function is given by the rate constant for diffusion of a small molecule, which is in the range 10^8 to 10^9 $M^{-1}s^{-1}$. The catalytic efficiency of the enzyme is within this range so, yes, this enzyme does approach kinetic perfection.

f.   With saturating amounts of substrate, the enzyme functions at V_{max}. Given k_2 and the enzyme concentration, V_{max} is calculated as follows:

$$V_{max} = k_2 \times [E_{total}] = 5 \times 10^3 s^{-1} \times \frac{2 \times 10^{-9} mol}{mL}$$

$$V_{max} = 1 \times 10^{-5} mol / mL \cdot s$$

g.   We must solve the Michaelis–Menten equation for [S], given $v = 0.75\ V_{max}$.

$$v = \frac{V_{max} \times [S]}{K_m + [S]}$$

$$v(K_m + [S]) = V_{max} \times [S]$$

$$[S](V_{max} - v) = vK_m$$

$$[S] = \frac{vK_m}{(V_{max} - v)}$$

Given $v = 0.75\ V_{max}$ and $K_m = 30\ \mu M$

$$[S] = \frac{0.75\ V_{max} \times 30\ \mu M}{(V_{max} - 0.75\ V_{max})}$$

$$[S] = 90 \mu M$$

h.   We are asked here to determine V_{max} given twice the enzyme amount used in (f). The V_{max} is simply proportional to the enzyme concentration and, so, is twice the value determined in (f).

$$V_{max} = k_2 \times [E_{total}] = 5 \times 10^3 s^{-1} \times \frac{4 \times 10^{-9} mol}{mL}$$

$$V_{max} = 2 \times 10^{-5} mol / mL \cdot s$$

The K_m is, however, unchanged at $30\ \mu M$.

11.   The citric acid cycle enzyme fumarase **catalyzes the conversion of fumarate to form malate:**
Fumarate + H₂O ⇌ malate
The turnover number, k$_{cat}$, for fumarase is 800 s^{-1}. The K$_m$ of fumarase for its substrate fumarate is 5 µM.
   a.   In an experiment using 2 nanomole/mL of fumarase, what is V$_{max}$?
   b.   The cellular concentration of fumarate is 47.5 µM. What is v when [fumarate] = 47.5 µM?
   c.   What is the catalytic efficiency of fumarase?
   d.   Does fumarase approach "catalytic perfection"?

Answer: a.   We can determine V_{max}, given k_{cat} (i.e., k_2) and the concentration of fumarase as follows:

$$V_{max} = k_2 \times [E_{total}] = 800\ s^{-1} \times \frac{2 \times 10^{-9} mol}{mL}$$

$$V_{max} = 1.6 \times 10^{-6} mol / mL \cdot s$$

$$V_{max} = 1.6\ \mu mol / mL \cdot s$$

b. To determine v given the substrate constant, K_m, and V_{max} (just calculated), we can use the Michaelis–Menten equation as follows:

$$v = \frac{V_{max} \times [S]}{K_m + [S]}$$

Given $V_{max} = 1.6 \ \mu mol / mL \cdot s$ (from (a)), $K_m = 5 \ \mu M = 18 \ \mu M$, $[S] = 47.5 \ \mu M$

$$v = \frac{1.6 \ \mu mol / mL \cdot s \times 47.5 \ \mu M}{5 \ \mu M + 47.5 \ \mu M}$$

$$v = 1.45 \ \mu mol \ mL^{-1} s^{-1}$$

c. The catalytic efficiency is the turnover number divided by K_m, both of which we know.

$$\frac{k_{cat}}{K_m} = \frac{800 \ s^{-1}}{5 \ \mu M}$$

$$\frac{k_{cat}}{K_m} = 1.60 \times 10^8 M^{-1} s^{-1}$$

d. The very fastest we could expect the enzyme to function is given by the rate constant for diffusion of a small molecule, which is in the range 10^8 to 10^9 $M^{-1}s^{-1}$. The catalytic efficiency of this enzyme is in this range so, yes, fumarase approaches perfection.

13. *Acetylcholinesterase catalyzes the hydrolysis of the neurotransmitter acetylcholine:*
Acetylcholine + H₂O → acetate + choline
*The **K_m** of acetylcholinesterase for its substrate acetylcholine is 9 × 10⁻⁵ M. In a reaction mixture containing 5 nanomoles/mL of acetylcholinesterase and 150 µM acetylcholine, a velocity v₀ = 40 µmol/mL·s was observed for the acetylcholinesterase reaction.*
　　*a. Calculate the **V_max** for this amount of enzyme.*
　　*b. Calculate **k_cat** for acetylcholinesterase.*
　　*c. Calculate the catalytic efficiency (**k_cat/K_m**) for acetylcholinesterase.*
　　d. Does acetylcholinesterase approach "catalytic perfection"?

Answer:　a.　Again, we are given K_m, the initial velocity or a reaction at a given substrate concentration. We can use this information and the Michaelis–Menten equation to calculate V_{max} as follows:

$$v = \frac{V_{max} \times [S]}{K_m + [S]}$$

$$V_{max} \times [S] = v \times (K_m + [S])$$

$$V_{max} = \frac{v \times (K_m + [S])}{[S]}$$

Given $v = 40 \ \mu mol \ mL^{-1} s^{-1}$, $K_m = 9 \times 10^{-5}$ M = 90 μM, $[S] = 150 \ \mu M$

$$V_{max} = \frac{40 \ \mu mol \ mL^{-1} s^{-1} \times (90 + 150) \ \mu M}{150 \ \mu M}$$

$$V_{max} = 64 \ \mu mol \ mL^{-1} s^{-1}$$

b. To calculate k_{cat}, given the enzyme concentration and V_{max}, recall that $k_{cat} = k_2$, which is determined as follows.

$$k_2 = \frac{V_{max}}{E_{total}}$$

Given $V_{max} = 64 \ \mu mol \ mL^{-1} s^{-1}$ and $E_{total} = 5$ nanomol/mL

$$k_2 = \frac{64 \times 10^{-6} mol \ mL^{-1} s^{-1}}{5 \times 10^{-9} \ mol/mL}$$

$$k_2 = k_{cat} = 1.28 \times 10^4 \ s^{-1}$$

c. The catalytic efficiency is the turnover number divided by K_m, both of which we know.

$$\frac{k_{cat}}{K_m} = \frac{1.28 \times 10^4 \text{ s}^{-1}}{9 \times 10^{-5} \text{ M}}$$

$$\frac{k_{cat}}{K_m} = 1.42 \times 10^8 \text{ M}^{-1}\text{s}^{-1}$$

d. The very fastest we could expect the enzyme to function is given by the rate constant for diffusion of a small molecule, which is in the range 10^8 to 10^9 M^{-1} s^{-1}. The catalytic efficiency of this enzyme is in this range so, yes, acetylcholinesterase approaches perfection.

15. Equation 12.9 presents the simple Michaelis–Menten situation where the reaction is considered to be irreversible ([P] is negligible). Many enzymatic reactions are reversible, and P does accumulate.

a. Derive an equation for v, the rate of the enzyme-catalyzed reaction S→P in terms of a modified Michaelis–Menten model that incorporates the reverse reaction that will occur in the presence of product, P.

b. Solve this modified Michaelis–Menten equation for the special situation when v = 0 (that is, S ⇌ P is at equilibrium, or in other words, K_{eq} = [P]/[S]).

(J.B.S. Haldane first described this reversible Michaelis–Menten modification, and his expression for K_{eq} in terms of the modified Michaeli–Menten equation is known as the Haldane relationship.)

Answer: Equation 12.9 is simply modified to include conversion of P back to S. The model we need to work with is:

$$E + S \rightleftharpoons ES \rightleftharpoons E + P$$

And, we must consider rate constants k_1, k_{-1}, k_2, and now k_{-2} for formation of ES by combination of E + P. The rate of change of the concentration of ES is given by the following:

$$\frac{d[ES]}{dt} = k_1[E][S] + k_{-2}[E][P] - k_{-1}[ES] - k_2[ES]$$

If we assume [ES] reaches steady state, then $\frac{d[ES]}{dt} = 0$

This allows us to solve for [ES] in terms of the rate constants, [S] and [P]

$$[ES] = [E]\frac{k_1[S] + k_{-2}[P]}{k_{-1} + k_2} \quad (1)$$

The total amount of enzyme is given by:

$$[E_{total}] = [E] + [ES] \quad (2)$$

Substituting (1) into (2) and solving for [E]:

$$[E] = \frac{[E_{total}]}{1 + \frac{k_1[S] + k_{-2}[P]}{k_{-1} + k_2}} \quad (3)$$

The velocity of the S to P reaction is given by:

$$v = k_2[ES] \text{ or } k_2([E_{total}] - [E])$$

Substituting for [E] using (3) we get:

$$v = k_2\left([E_{total}] - \frac{[E_{total}]}{1 + \frac{k_1[S] + k_{-2}[P]}{k_{-1} + k_2}}\right)$$

Rearranging this equation, we get:

$$v = k_2[E_{total}] \left(\frac{1 + \dfrac{k_1[S] + k_{-2}[P]}{k_{-1} + k_2} - 1}{1 + \dfrac{k_1[S] + k_{-2}[P]}{k_{-1} + k_2}} \right)$$

$$v = k_2[E_{total}] \left(\frac{\dfrac{k_1[S] + k_{-2}[P]}{k_{-1} + k_2}}{1 + \dfrac{k_1[S] + k_{-2}[P]}{k_{-1} + k_2}} \right)$$

$$v = \left(\frac{\dfrac{k_1 k_2[E_{total}][S]}{k_{-1} + k_2} + \dfrac{+k_2[E_{total}]k_{-2}[P]}{k_{-1} + k_2}}{1 + \dfrac{k_1[S] + k_{-2}[P]}{k_{-1} + k_2}} \right)$$

We define $k_2[E_{total}] = V^f_{max}$, $-k_{-2}[E_{total}] = V^r_{max}$
(Note the minus sign in the last identity.)

$$\frac{k_1}{k_{-1} + k_2} = \frac{1}{K^S_M} \text{ and } \frac{k_2}{k_{-1} + k_2} = \frac{1}{K^P_M}$$

The equation simplifies to:

$$v = -\frac{\dfrac{V^f_{max}[S]}{K^S_M} - \dfrac{V^r_{max}[P]}{K^P_M}}{1 + \dfrac{[S]}{K^S_M} + \dfrac{[P]}{K^P_M}}$$

b. When $v = 0$, the above equation should give the equilibrium constant for the reaction.

$$0 = \frac{\dfrac{V^f_{max}[S]}{K^S_M} - \dfrac{V^r_{max}[P]}{K^P_M}}{1 + \dfrac{[S]}{K^S_M} + \dfrac{[P]}{K^P_M}}$$

$$\frac{V^f_{max}[S]}{K^S_M} - \frac{V^r_{max}[P]}{K^P_M} = 0, \text{ or}$$

$$\frac{V^f_{max}[S]}{K^S_M} = \frac{V^r_{max}[P]}{K^P_M}, \text{ or}$$

$$K_{eq} = \frac{[P]}{[S]} = \frac{V^f_{max}K^P_M}{V^r_{max}K^S_M}$$

17. Use Figure 12.12 to answer the following questions.
a. Is the enzyme whose temperature versus activity profile is shown in Figure 12.12 likely to be from an animal or a plant? Why?
b. What do you think the temperature versus activity profile for an enzyme from a thermophilic prokaryote growing in a 27°C pool of water would resemble?

Answer: a. The enzyme whose activity versus temperature is shown in Figure 12.12 has a temperature maximum at 37°C. In addition, the profile is quite sharp, suggesting that the enzyme is maximized for function at or near this temperature. Many animals are endothermic, maintaining a constant body temperature, and this enzyme's activity profile would be consistent with an enzyme from an animal of this kind. Plants, on the other hand, typically experience a broader range of temperatures.

b. For an enzyme from a thermophile, one might expect a similar activity profile but one whose maximum is at higher temperatures.

Questions for Self-Study

1. Enzymes have three distinctive features that distinguish them from chemical catalysts. What are they?

2. Chose from the list following each enzyme systematic name the term that best fits the enzyme class.
   a. Oxidoreductase
      1. Cleavage using water   2. *Cis–trans* conversion   3. Uses NAD or NADP
   b. Transferase
      1. C–C bond formation   2. Methylation reaction   3. Hydrolysis
   c. Hydrolase
      1. O_2 functions as acceptor   2. Acetyl-group transfer   3. Cleavage of peptide bond
   d. Isomerase
      1. Methyltransferase   2. Aldose to ketose conversion   3. Peptide-bond hydrolysis

3. Match the terms in the first column with the descriptions in the second column.
   a. $A \rightarrow P$ 1. K_m
   b. v 2. V_{max}
   c. $d[P]/dt = d[S]/dt$ 3. First-order reaction
   d. k in $v = k[A][B]$ 4. Michaelis constant
   e. k_{-1}/k_1 5. V_{max}/E_{Total}
   f. $(k_{-1} + k_2)/k_1$ 6. The velocity or rate of a reaction.
   g. v at $[S] = \infty$ 7. Enzyme:substrate dissociation constant
   h. $[S]$ when $v = V_{max}/2$ 8. $1/V_{max}$
   i. k_{cat} 9. Equilibrium
   j. $1/v$ when $1/[S] = 0$ 10. Second-order rate constant

4. Fill in the blanks. The energy barrier preventing thermodynamically favourable reactions from occurring is known as the ____ ____ ____. In general, catalysts ____ this energy barrier by providing an alternate reaction pathway leading from substrate to product. The intermediate along this reaction pathway that has the highest free energy is known as the ____ ____.

5. True or false:
   a. For competitive inhibition, the apparent K_m is larger than K_m by the factor $(1 + [I]/K_I)$. _____
   b. For non-competitive inhibition, the apparent V_{max} is larger than V_{max} by the factor $(1 + [I]/K_I)$. ____
   c. A plot of V_{max} versus temperature is linear for a typical enzyme. ____
   d. Ordered, single-displacement reactions refer to bisubstrate reactions in which two substrates bind to the enzyme before catalysis occurs. ____
   e. The reaction catalyzed by the enzyme glutamate:aspartate aminotransferase is a good example of a double-displacement or Ping-Pong reaction. ____

6. What is a ribozyme? What is an abzyme?

Answers

1. Enormous catalytic power, specificity, and the ability to be regulated.

2. a. 3; b. 2; c. 3; d. 2.

3. a. 3; b. 6; c. 9; d. 10; e. 7; f. 1 or 4; g. 2; h. 1 or 4; i. 5; j. 8.

4. Energy of activation; lower; transition state.

5. a. T; b. F; c. F; d. T; e. T.

6. A ribozyme is a catalytic RNA. An abzyme is a catalytic antibody.

Additional Problems

1. A researcher was studying the kinetic properties of β-galactosidase using an assay in which o-nitrophenol-β-galactoside (ONPG), a colourless substrate, is converted to galactose and o-nitrophenolate, a brightly coloured, yellow compound. Upon addition of 0.25 mM substrate to a fixed amount of enzyme, o-nitrophenolate (ONP) production was monitored as a function of time by spectrophotometry at $\lambda = 410$ nm. The following data were collected:

Time (sec)	A_{410} nm
0	0.000
15	0.158
30	0.273
45	0.360
60	0.429
75	0.484
90	0.529
150	0.652
210	0.724
270	0.771
330	0.805
390	0.830
450	0.849
510	0.864

   a. Convert A_{410} nm to concentration of o-nitrophenolate, [ONP], using $\varepsilon = 3.76$ mM^{-1}cm^{-1} as the extinction coefficient.

   b. Plot [ONP] versus time.

   c. Determine the initial velocity of the reaction.

   d. Explain why the curve is nearly linear initially and later approaches a plateau.

   e. Describe how K_m and V_{max} for β-galactosidase can be determined with additional experimentation.

2. Under what conditions can an enzyme assay be used to determine the relative amounts of an enzyme present?

3. For many reactions, it is often difficult to measure product formation, so coupled assays are often used. In a coupled enzyme assay, the activity of an enzyme is determined by measuring the activity of a second enzyme that uses as substrate the product of a reaction catalyzed by the first enzyme. The utility of coupled assays is that the product of the second enzyme is easy or convenient to measure. You are asked to design a coupled assay to measure the relative amounts of a particular enzyme in several samples. In qualitative terms with respect to K_m and V_{max} for both enzymes, explain how an appropriate coupled assay is set up.

4. In the case of a competitive inhibitor, explain how the inhibitor dissociation constant, K_I, can be determined from enzyme kinetic data.

5. Is K_m a good measure of the dissociation constant for substrate binding to enzyme? Explain.

6. Derive an expression for v as a function of [S] for mixed, non-competitive inhibition.

7. In Figure 12.16a, the presence of inhibitor decreases V_{max}; however, it also decreases $K_{m,app}$. This seems to suggest that in the presence of an inhibitor, the remaining active enzyme's performance is improved since it saturates at a lower substrate concentration. Can you explain this paradox?

Abbreviated Answers

1. a. The concentration of ONP, [ONP], is calculated using Beer's Law, $A = \varepsilon \cdot C \cdot l$, where ε is the extinction coefficient, C is the concentration, and l is the path length (1 cm in this case). [ONP] = A_{410} nm/$(\varepsilon \cdot l$ cm).

Time (sec)	A_{410} nm	[ONP] (mM)
0	0.00	0.00
15	0.158	0.042
30	0.273	0.073
45	0.36	0.096
60	0.429	0.114
75	0.484	0.129
90	0.529	0.141
150	0.652	0.173
210	0.724	0.193
270	0.771	0.205
330	0.805	0.214
390	0.83	0.221
450	0.849	0.226
510	0.864	0.230

b.   The plot of [ONP] versus time is shown below:

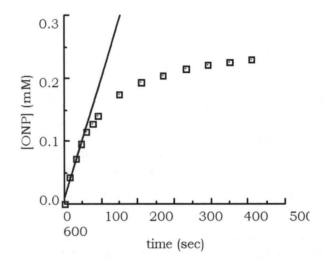

c.   The initial velocity is equal to the slope of a line drawn through the initial points as shown above and has a value of 0.00188 mM/sec.

d.   The enzyme is converting substrate to product, and the curve is the time course of this process. The initial points are linear because the enzyme is obeying Michaelis–Menten kinetics. At later times, two things happen to cause the rate of product formation, given by the slope of a tangent drawn along the graph, to decrease: [S] decreases; and [P] increases. The curve is approaching 2.5 mM, the initial value of substrate, indicating that nearly all of the initial substrate has been converted to product.

e.   By repeating the experiment at different initial substrate concentrations, the initial velocities at varying substrate concentrations can be measured. These data form a v versus [S] data set, which can be used to determine K_m and V_{max}.

2.   At substrate concentrations high relative to K_m, an enzyme functions at or near V_{max}. V_{max}, given by $V_{max} = k_2 E_T$, is proportional to the total enzyme concentration.

3.   The following reaction sequence represents a coupled enzyme assay.

$$\begin{array}{cc} E_1 & E_2 \\ S \rightarrow P_1 \rightarrow P_2 \end{array}$$

We are interested in determining the relative amount of E_2 by measuring the rate of production of P_2. The concentration of the substrate for E_1, namely S, must be large relative to K_{m1} in order for E_1 to function at

V_{max}. Also, the rate at which E_2 produces P_2 must be constant. This requires that $[P_1]$ be at a steady-state concentration. The rate of change of $[P_1]$ is given by

$$\frac{d[P_1]}{dt} = V_{max,E_1} - \frac{V_{max,E_2}[P_1]}{K_{m2} + [P_1]}$$

For $[P_1]$ to be at steady state, $\frac{d[P_1]}{dt} = 0$, and solving for $[P_1]$, we find:

$$[P_1]_{steady\ state} = \frac{K_{m2} \times V_{max,E_1}}{V_{max,E_2} - V_{max,E_1}} \quad \text{which is positive only when}$$

$$V_{max,E_2} > V_{max,E_1}$$

Thus, [S] must be high enough to saturate E1 and $k_2 \cdot [E_{2,T}]$ must be greater than $V_{max,E1}$.

4.   For competitive inhibition, $K_{m,app} = K_m(1 + [I]/K_I)$. By measuring $K_{m,app}$ at several different inhibitor concentrations and plotting $K_{m,app}$ against [I], the slope of the resulting straight line divided by the y-intercept (equal to K_m) is $1/K_I$.

5. K_m and K_D are defined as follows:

$$K_m = \frac{k_{-1} + k_2}{k_1}, \text{ and } K_D = \frac{k_{-1}}{k_1}$$

When k_{-1} is large relative to k_2, $K_m \approx K_D$

6.   The following reactions occur for mixed, non-competitive inhibition:

$$E + S \rightleftarrows ES \rightarrow P;\ E + I \rightleftarrows EI;\ ES + I \rightleftarrows IES$$

Binding of I to E and to ES are governed by:

$$K_I = \frac{[E][I]}{[EI]};\ K_I' = \frac{[ES][I]}{[IES]}$$

These equations can rearranged to give:

$$[EI] = \frac{[E][I]}{K_I};\ [IES] = \frac{[ES][I]}{K_I'}$$

The rate of change of [ES] is given by:

$$\frac{d[ES]}{dt} = -k_2[ES] - k_{-1}[ES] + k_1[E][S]$$

Using this equation and making the steady-state assumption, we find:

$$[ES] = \frac{k_1[E][S]}{k_2 + k_{-1}} = \frac{[E][S]}{K_m}$$

The total concentration of enzyme, E_T, is given by:

$$[E_T] = [E] + [ES] + [EI] + [IES]$$

Substituting the expressions for [ES], [EI], and [IES] above, we find:

$$[E_T] = [E] + \frac{[E][S]}{K_m} + \frac{[E][I]}{K_I} + \frac{[E][S][I]}{K_m K_I'}, \text{ and solving for [E], we find:}$$

$$[E] = \frac{\dfrac{[E_T] \times K_m}{(1 + \dfrac{[I]}{K_I'})}}{K_m \dfrac{(1 + \dfrac{[I]}{K_I})}{(1 + \dfrac{[I]}{K_I'})} + [S]}$$

The rate of product formation is given by:

$$v = k_2[ES] = k_2 \frac{[E][S]}{K_m}$$

Finally, substituting the expression for [E] above we find:

$$v = \frac{\dfrac{k_2[E_T]}{(1 + \dfrac{[I]}{K_I'})} \times [S]}{K_m \times \dfrac{(1 + \dfrac{[I]}{K_I})}{(1 + \dfrac{[I]}{K_I'})} + [S]} = \frac{V_{max,app}[S]}{K_{m,app} + [S]}$$

Clearly, $V_{max,app}$ is always less than V_{max}. $K_{m,app}$ may be less than, equal to, or greater than K_m depending on the magnitude of K_I relative to K_I'.

7.   In Figure 12.16a, I binds to ES with greater affinity (lower dissociation constant) than to E. Therefore, the addition of I is expected to affect the E + S $\leftrightarrows$ ES equilibrium by shifting it to the right, allowing more ES to form at lower [S].

Summary

Enzymes are the catalysts of metabolism, allowing living systems to achieve kinetic control over the thermodynamic potential within organic reactions. Enzymes have three distinctive attributes that are essential to their biological purpose: enormous catalytic power, great selectivity in catalyzing only very specific reactions, and the ability to be regulated so that their activity is compatible with the momentary needs of the cell. Formally, enzymes are classified by a system of nomenclature based on the particular reaction they catalyze, although certain trivial names for enzymes often enjoy common usage. Enzymes may be simple proteins or they may be proteins complexed with non-protein components called cofactors. Cofactors include metal ions and organic molecules known as coenzymes.

An enzyme accelerates the rate of a process by lowering the thermodynamic barrier to reaction, known as the free energy of activation. The reactant in an enzyme-catalyzed reaction is called the substrate. The fact that graphs of enzyme activity as a function of substrate concentration show a limiting plateau or saturation level was the important clue that an enzyme (E) actually binds its substrate (S) to form an enzyme–substrate (ES) complex that can react to yield product (P). Enzyme kinetic analysis is based on the notion put forth by Michaelis and Menten that the E and S reversibly interact, and ES can react to form P. Briggs and Haldane extended this model by assuming that the system E + S $\leftrightarrows$ ES $\rightarrow$ P quickly reaches a steady state condition where $d[ES]/dt = 0$. The standard Michaelis–Menten equation for an enzymatic reaction is then derived:

$$v = \frac{V_{max}[S]}{K_m + [S]}$$

V_{max} is the maximal velocity attained when [S] is so great as to not be rate limiting; K_m is a constant reflecting the relative affinity and reactivity of the enzyme-substrate interaction. Because graphs of

v versus [S] are not linear, the Michaelis–Menten expression is often rearranged to give equations that yield linear relationships between rate and substrate concentration.

Because their activity is highly dependent on maintenance of their native protein structure, enzymes are very sensitive to pH and temperature. Enzyme inhibition has been an important means for investigating enzymes and their mode of action. Such studies have also contributed to human health through the science of pharmacology, since many drugs exert their action as inhibitors of enzymes. Some inhibitors act by competing with the substrate for binding to the active site of the enzyme, altering the apparent K_m. Other inhibitors uniquely affect the apparent V_{max} while still others affect both $K_{m,app}$ and $V_{max,app}$. Inhibitors, which react covalently with the enzyme, can lead to irreversible inhibition of its activity.

Most enzymatic reactions involve more than one substrate. These multi-substrate reactions can be analyzed kinetically to determine whether two (or more) substrates are bound before reaction occurs (so-called sequential or single-displacement reactions), or whether one substrate binds and reacts with the enzyme before the other substrate is bound (Ping-Pong or double-displacement reactions). Exchange reactions are another useful tool in enzyme kinetic analysis.

Recent discoveries have broadened our view of biocatalysis. Certain RNA molecules have the essential features of enzymes: rate enhancement, catalytic turnover, and specificity of reaction. This finding has important implications to our view of molecular or pre-biotic evolution. Further, biocatalysts in the form of antibodies have been "tailor-made" by using transition state analogs of a reaction as antigens. The antibodies elicited in response to these analogs act as biocatalysts by facilitating entry of the reactants into a reactive transition-state intermediate. The creation of "designer enzymes" has become a realistic possibility.

Chapter 13

Mechanisms of Enzyme Action

• •

Chapter Outline

❖ Transition-state intermediate
  ⋏ Energy difference between ES and EX‡ is smaller than that between S and X‡
  ⋏ Enzyme stabilizes transition state more than substrate
❖ Catalytic mechanisms or factors
  ⋏ Destabilization of ES complex
    • Entropy loss upon formation of ES complex
    • Destabilization of S because E designed to bind transition state
      ● Structural strain: E binds transition state better than S
      ● Desolvation: Desolvated ionic groups show increased reactivity
      ● Electrostatic effects: Charge proximity
  ⋏ Stabilization of EX‡ complex: Transition-state analogs are potent inhibitors
  ⋏ Covalent catalysis
    • Nucleophilic catalysis
      ● Nucleophilic centres on enzymes: Amines, carboxylates, hydroxyls, imidazole, thiol
      ● Electrophilic targets on substrates: Phosphoryl, acyl, glycosyl groups
    • Electrophilic catalysis: Coenzymes
  ⋏ General acid–base catalysis
    • Specific acid–base catalysis: H^{+} or OH^{-} involved: No dependence on buffer concentration
    • General acid–base catalysis
      ● AH (protonated acid) donates
      ● B^{-} (unprotonated base) accepts protons
    • Low-barrier hydrogen bond: H bond between groups with matching pK_a values
      ● LBHB formation stabilizes transition state
      ● LBHB may facilitate hydrogen tunnelling
  ⋏ Metal ion catalysis
    • Metalloenzymes: Metal ion tightly bound
    • Metal-activated enzymes: Metal ion loosely bound
    • Metal functions
      ● Stabilize formation of negative charge
      ● Powerful nucleophile at neutral pH
  ⋏ Proximity and orientation
❖ Serine proteases
  ⋏ Enzyme diversity
    • Trypsin, chymotrypsin, elastase: Digestive enzymes
    • Thrombin: Blood clotting
    • Subtilisin: Bacterial enzyme
    • Plasmin, TPA: Blood clot breakdown
    • Acetylcholinesterase (not a protease): Degrades neurotransmitter acetylcholine

- Digestive enzyme specificity: Cleavage (hydrolysis) of peptide bond on carbonyl side
  - Chymotrypsin: Phe, Trp, Tyr: Hydrophobic pocket near catalytic triad
  - Trypsin: Lys, Arg: Aspartic acid at bottom of hydrophobic pocket
  - Elastase: Small neutral amino acids: Mouth of pocket closed by threonine and valine
- Burst kinetics: Rapid release of amino end: Carboxyl end attached to enzyme and slowly hydrolyzed
- Catalytic triad: His[57], Asp[102], Ser[195]
  - Ser[195]: Acyl-enzyme intermediate formed by hydroxylate attack on carbonyl carbon of peptide bond
  - His[57]
    - General base: Deprotonates Ser[195]: Deprotonates water
    - General acid: Protonates carbonyl oxygen: Protonates peptide nitrogen
  - Asp[102]: Orients His[57]
- ❖ Aspartic proteases
  - Enzyme diversity
    - Pepsin, chymosin: Digestive enzymes
    - Cathepsin D and cathepsin E: Protein degradation in lysosomes
    - Renin: Blood pressure regulation
    - AIDS HIV-1 protease: Viral life cycle
  - Catalytic dyad: Two aspartic acids
    - Low-barrier hydrogen bond between two aspartic acids and catalytic water
    - Substrate participates in flow of electrons to and from substrate to aspartic acids
- ❖ Chorismate Mutate: Chorismate to prephenate
  - Claisen rearrangement
  - Enzymatic activity: N-terminus of P protein
  - Dimerization via antiparallel coiled-coil: 7-residue repeat of leucines
  - Transition-state analog: Consistent with chair transition state
    - Near attack conformation promoted by electrostatic and hydrophobic interactions of active-site residues

Chapter Objectives

General Considerations

To appreciate why reactions can be slow, you must understand that even the most favourable path from reactant to product passes through some transition-state intermediate. Formation of the transition-state intermediate is an energy-requiring process, and the energy necessary for its formation—the activation energy—is an energy barrier that must be overcome for the reaction to occur. Enzyme-catalyzed reactions also have an activation energy, but it is not the energy difference between the substrate and the transition state that matters; rather, it is the energy difference between the enzyme-substrate complex and the enzyme–transition-state complex. Enzymes increase reaction rates because the energy barrier between ES and EX‡ is less than the barrier between S and X‡ (See Figure 13.1).

Understand the catalytic mechanisms used by enzymes to achieve enormous rate accelerations, which include 1) Entropy loss in ES formation; 2) destabilization of ES due to strain, desolvation, or electrostatic effects; 3) near-attack conformations; 4) covalent catalysis; 5) general acid or base catalysis; 6) low-barrier hydrogen bonds; 7) metal ion catalysis; and 8) proximity and orientation.

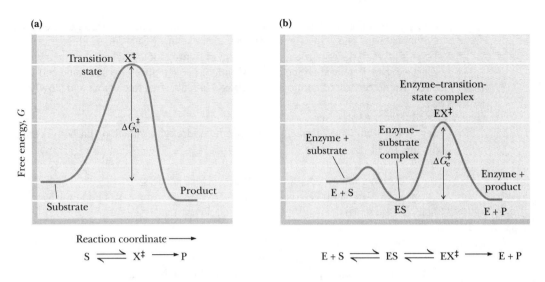

(a)

Free energy, *G*

Transition state X‡

$\Delta G_u^{\ddagger}$

Product

Substrate

Reaction coordinate ⟶

$S \rightleftharpoons X^{\ddagger} \longrightarrow P$

(b)

Enzyme–transition-state complex

EX‡

Enzyme + substrate

Enzyme–substrate complex

$\Delta G_e^{\ddagger}$

Enzyme + product

E + S

ES

E + P

$E + S \rightleftharpoons ES \rightleftharpoons EX^{\ddagger} \longrightarrow E + P$

Figure 13.1 Enzymes catalyze reactions by lowering the activation energy. Here the free energy of activation for (a) the noncatalyzed reaction, $\Delta G_u^{\ddagger}$, is larger than that for (b) the enzyme-catalyzed reaction, $\Delta G_e^{\ddagger}$.

Serine Proteases—Covalent Catalysis

The serine proteases and related enzymes are arguably the best-characterized group of enzymes. The key to catalysis is a catalytic triad of His[57], Asp[102], and Ser[195] (in chymotrypsin). Understand the role of this serine in catalysis: the fact that it is transiently, covalently modified during catalysis, accounting for the burst kinetics—a rapid release of one product followed by a slow release of the second product. The mechanism based on this catalytic triad is found in a number of enzymes, including trypsin, chymotrypsin, elastase, thrombin, subtilisin, plasmin, tissue plasminogen activator, and acetylcholinesterase, to name a few. We have already encountered a few of the digestive serine proteases in Chapter 5 as tools used in primary sequence determination of proteins. Substrate specificity is determined by a substrate-binding pocket that is distinct from the catalytic triad.

Aspartic Proteases—Low-Barrier Hydrogen Bonds

Pepsin, chymosin, cathepsin D and E, rennin, and HIV-1 protease are examples of aspartic proteases. The mechanism of action was initially thought to be acid–base catalysis with two aspartic acid residues functioning as a general acid and a general base. The pH profile of enzymes with this type of catalysis is bell-shaped, indicating the involvement of a proton donor and acceptor. Aspartic acid residues participate in low-barrier hydrogen bonds with a water molecule to form a cyclic structure. Substrate joins the structure and a flow of electrons first to the substrate to form a tetrahedral intermediate and then from the substrate to cleave the peptide bond releases the carboxyl group. Flow of electrons from the amino group of the cleaved bond results in a second tetrahedral intermediate formed with the enzyme, which is resolved by a water molecule.

Chorismate Mutase: Stabilization of Transition State

This enzyme participates in the pathway leading to biosynthesis of phenylalanine by converting chorismate to prephenate. The reaction mechanism involves stabilization of a transition state: The chair conformation of the substrate, which is stabilized by electrostatic and hydrophobic interactions from active-site amino acid residues. The transition state is a near-attack conformation that positions reactive groups nearby.

Problems and Solutions

1. *Tosyl-L-phenylalanine chloromethylketone (TPCK) specifically inhibits chymotrypsin by covalently labelling His[57].*
   a. Propose a mechanism for the inactivation reaction, indicating the structure of the product(s).
   b. State why this inhibitor is specific for chymotrypsin.

c. Propose a reagent based on the structure of TPCK that might be an effective inhibitor of trypsin.

Answer: a. The structure of tosyl-L-phenylalanine chloromethylketone (TPCK) and the reaction mechanism leading to covalent labelling of His[57] are shown below:

b. The phenyl group of TPCK binds to the specificity pocket of chymotrypsin by hydrophobic interactions. This brings the chloromethylke to group into the active site.

c. Trypsin shows specificity for peptide bonds in which the carbonyl carbon is from a positively charged amino acid such as arginine or lysine. Reagents specific for trypsin may be produced by replacing the phenylalanine residue of TPCK with arginine or lysine.

3. Pepstatin (below) is an extremely potent inhibitor of the monomeric aspartic proteases, with K_I values of less than 1 nM.

   a. On the basis of the structure of pepstatin, suggest an explanation for the strongly inhibitory properties of this peptide.
   b. Would pepstatin be expected to also inhibit the HIV-1 protease? Explain your answer.

Answer: The structure of pepstatin is:

It contains 5 peptide bonds joining together the following groups: methylbutanoic acid; valine; valine; 4-amino-3-hydroxy methylheptanoic acid (statine); alanine; and, 4-amino-3-hydroxymethyl heptanoic acid. Thus, pepstatin has a structure very similar to a 6-residue polypeptide chain of hydrophobic amino acids. The active site of pepsin can accommodate a chain of up to 7 residues in length. Further, pepsin cleaves peptide bonds between hydrophobic amino acids. Pepstatin binds tightly to the active site because of the nature of its hydrophobic side chains. Assuming that the catalytic site is in the middle of the hydrophobic-binding pocket, pepstatin will be positioned with a carbon–carbon single bond at the active site.

Thus, a hydroxyl group replaces a carbonyl. The high pK_a of the hydroxyl will resist catalysis.

b. The HIV-1 protease cleaves between Tyr and Pro in the sequence Ser–Gln–Asn–Tyr–Pro–Ile–Val. The structure of HIV-1 protease is similar to that of mammalian aspartic proteases. The active site is a cleft between two identical subunits with two aspartic acids contributed from both subunits at the heart of the catalytic mechanism. The mammalian aspartic protease preferentially cleaves between hydrophobic amino acids residues. The sequence shown above has only two hydrophobic residues on the C-terminus. We might expect that the catalytic pocket of HIV-1 protease to be lined with hydrophilic groups that will accommodate the relatively hydrophilic N-terminal residues. Thus, we do not expect the highly hydrophobic pepstatin to inhibit HIV-I protease. The inhibitor dissociation constants (K_I) of pepsin and HIV-1 for pepstatin are 1 nM and 1 μM, respectively, reflecting the fact that pepstatin binds tightly to pepsin but relatively poorly to HIV-1.

5. The k$_{cat}$ for alkaline phosphatase–catalyzed hydrolysis of methylphosphate is approximately 14/sec at pH 8 and 25°C. The rate constant for the uncatalyzed hydrolysis of methylphosphate under the same conditions is approximately 10^{-15}/sec. What is the difference in the activation free energies of these two reactions?

Answer: Using equation 13.3, we can calculate the difference in activation energies between the uncatalyzed and catalyzed reaction:

$$\frac{k_e}{k_u} = \frac{K_S}{K_T}$$

Where K_S is the dissociation constants for enzyme-substrate complex, and

K_T is the dissociation constants for enzyme-transition state complex.

In general, $K = e^{\frac{-\Delta G}{RT}}$, and

$$\frac{k_e}{k_u} = \frac{K_S}{K_T} = \frac{e^{\frac{-\Delta G_S}{RT}}}{e^{\frac{-\Delta G_T}{RT}}} = e^{\frac{(\Delta G_T - \Delta G_S)}{RT}} \quad \text{or}$$

$$\Delta G_T - \Delta G_S = RT \ln \frac{k_e}{k_u} = RT \ln \frac{\dfrac{14}{\sec}}{\dfrac{1 \times 10^{-15}}{\sec}}$$

$$\Delta G_T - \Delta G_S = 8.314 \times 298 \times 37.18$$

$$\Delta G_T - \Delta G_S = 92 \frac{kJ}{mol}$$

7. Consult a classic paper by William Lipscomb (1982. Accounts of Chemical Research 15:232–238), and on the basis of this article write a simple mechanism for the enzyme carboxypeptidase A.

Answer: Lipscomb's paper begins with a discussion of factors that influence enzyme catalysis and discusses entropy changes, transition-state binding, chemical catalysis, and other effects. He then goes on to look for these in the mechanism of carboxypeptidase A. It is clear that entropy changes are involved in substrate binding because the enzyme restricts rotational and translational degrees of freedom of the substrate upon binding. In the active site, regions around the Zn^{2+} and several charged amino acids compensate for loss of substrate entropy by releasing waters of solvation. Transition-state binding was difficult to access, but the active site contains a number of reactive groups including Glu-270, Tyr-248, and Zn^{2+} that contribute to catalysis. The pH optimum of the enzyme, 7.5, suggested involvement of either a water molecule and or Glu-270, whose pK_a would have to be shifted to around neutrality from a typical value for a side-chain carboxylate of around 4.5. The enzyme hydrolyzes peptide bonds starting at the C-terminus of its substrate. The mechanism proposed by Lipscomb involves binding of the carboxy terminus to Arg145 and further restriction of the scissile peptide bone with a hydrogen bond to Tyr248. The pathway for catalysis involves general acid–base chemistry in which glu270 promotes the attack of water on the carbonyl carbon of the scissile peptide bond. Zinc is thought to either stabilize a negatively charged oxyanionic intermediate or help activate a water molecule. The figure below shows these points.

9. **As noted on page 447, a true transition state can bind to an enzyme active site with a K_T as low as 7×10^{-26} M. This is a remarkable number, with interesting consequences. Consider a hypothetical solution of an enzyme in equilibrium with a ligand that binds with a K_D of 10^{-27} M. If the concentration of free enzyme, [E], is equal to the concentration of the enzyme–ligand complex, [EL], what would [L], the concentration of free ligand, be? Calculate the volume of solution that would hold 1 molecule of free ligand at this concentration.**

Answer: For the reaction EL $\rightleftharpoons$ E + L, the equilibrium dissociation constant is:

$$K_D = \frac{[E][L]}{[EL]}$$

If the concentration of enzyme–ligand complex, [EL] is equal to the free enzyme concentration, [E], we see that

$$K_D = [L]$$

That is, the equilibrium dissociation constant is equal to the free ligand concentration that half-saturates the ligand-binding molecule. (At half saturation [EL] = [E].) Thus, [L] = K_D = 1×10^{-27} M.
   The volume that would contain one molecule is:

$$1 \times 10^{-27} \frac{mol}{L} \times \frac{6.02 \times 10^{23}\, molecules}{mol} \times x = 1\ molecule$$

Solving for x, we find:

$$x = \frac{1\ molecule}{1 \times 10^{-27} \dfrac{mol}{L} \times \dfrac{6.02 \times 10^{23}\, molecules}{mol}} = 1661\ L$$

11. **The incredible catalytic power of enzymes can perhaps best be appreciated by imagining how challenging life would be without just one of the thousands of enzymes in the human body. For example, consider life without fructose-1,6-bisphosphatase, an enzyme in the gluconeogenesis pathway in liver and kidneys (see Chapter 21), which helps produce new glucose from the food we eat:**

Fructose-1,6-bisphosphate + H₂O → Fructose-6-P + Pᵢ

The human brain requires glucose as its only energy source, and the typical brain consumes about 120 g (or 480 calories) of glucose daily. Ordinarily, 2 pieces of sausage pizza could provide more than enough potential glucose to feed the brain for a day. According to a national fast-food chain, 2 pieces of sausage pizza provide 1340 calories, 48% of which is from fat. Fats cannot be converted to glucose in gluconeogenesis, so that leaves 697 calories potentially available for glucose synthesis. The first-order rate constant for the hydrolysis of fructose-1,6-bisphosphate in the absence of enzyme is 2 × 10⁻²⁰/sec. Calculate how long it would take to provide enough glucose for 1 day of brain activity from 2 pieces of sausage pizza without the enzyme.

Answer: If a typical brain consumes 120 g of glucose, this corresponds to

$$\frac{120 \text{ g}}{180 \frac{\text{g}}{\text{mol}}} = 0.667 \text{ mol glucose}$$

We will assume that all this glucose comes from gluconeogenesis, and hence all of it must pass through fructose-1,6-bisphosphatase. Further, we will assume that it all derives from the liver (gluconeogenesis is most active in the liver) and an average volume of a human liver is around 1500 mL. (See *Alcohol and Alcoholism* Vol. 35, No. 5, pp. 531–532, 2000). Next we need to know the concentration of fructose-1,6-bisphosphate in liver. This is difficult to determine because the concentration might be expected to vary depending on physiological conditions. We could get an estimate by looking for the K_m of the enzyme. This can be found using SwissProt, looking for the human enzyme, and then following links to NiceZyme view of the protein linked via the enzyme's E.C. number, and then to BRENDA, a comprehensive enzyme information system. There were several listings with an average of around 2 μM. It is typically the case that the K_m for enzymes is within the physiological concentration range of its substrates and so we will assume a concentration of 2 μM for fructose-1,6-bisphosphate.

Using the first-order rate constant for non-enzymatic hydrolysis of fructose-1,6-bisphosphate, we find that fructose-6-phosphate is being supplied at the following rate:

$$\text{rate} = \frac{2 \times 10^{-20}}{\text{s}} \times 2 \times 10^{-6} M = 2 \times 10^{-26} \frac{M}{\text{s}}$$

Converting this to moles per second we must multiply by the volume (1500 mL or 1.5 L), which gives:

$$2 \times 10^{-26} \frac{M}{\text{s}} \times 1.5 \text{ L} = 3 \times 10^{-26} \frac{\text{mol}}{\text{s}}$$

To produce 0.667 moles would take:

$$\frac{0.667 \text{ mol}}{3 \times 10^{-26} \frac{\text{mol}}{\text{s}}} = 2.2 \times 10^{25} \text{ s} \times \frac{\text{min}}{60 \text{ sec}} \times \frac{\text{hr}}{60 \text{ min}} \times \frac{\text{day}}{24 \text{ hr}} \times \frac{\text{yr}}{356 \text{ days}}$$

$$= 7 \times 10^{17} \text{ yrs!}$$

The following graphs show the temperature and pH dependencies of 4 enzymes, A, B, X, and Y. Problems 13 through 17 refer to these graphs.

(a)

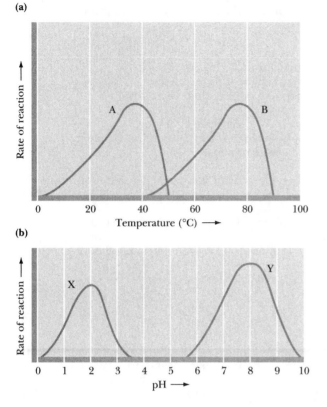

(b)

13.   **Which statement is true concerning enzymes X and Y?**
   a.   **They could not possibly be at work in the same part of the body at the same time.**
   b.   **They have different temperature ranges at which they work best.**
   c.   **At a pH of 4.5, enzyme X works slower than enzyme Y.**
   d.   **At their appropriate pH ranges, both enzymes work equally fast.**

Answer: The correct answer is (a). Referring to the pH plot, it is clear that the enzymes have different pH ranges. So, it seems unlikely they function in the same environment. Answer (b) is not correct as it refers to enzymes A and B and not X and Y. Answers (c) and (d) are incorrect.

15.   **At which temperatures might A and B both work?**
   a.   **above 40°C**
   b.   **below 50°C**
   c.   **above 50°C and below 40°C**
   d.   **between 40°C and 50°C**

Answer: The correct answer is (d). The activity curves for both enzymes overlap in the range 40°C to about 50°C.

17.   **At 35°C, the rate of the reaction catalyzed by enzyme A begins to level off. Which hypothesis best explains this observation?**
   a.   **The temperature is too far below optimum.**
   b.   **The enzyme has become saturated with substrate.**
   c.   **both a and b**
   d.   **neither a nor b**

Answer: The correct answer is (b). Clearly, (a) is not true for enzyme A as its temperature optimum is around 37°C. This also eliminates (c). If the "level off" in the question refers to leveling off of activity when substrate concentration increases, then (b) is the only correct answer.

Questions for Self-Study

1. List the six catalytic mechanisms or factors that contribute to the performance of enzymes.

2. What is a transition-state analog?

3. Match an item in the first column to one in the second column.
   a. Covalent catalysis
   b. Specific acid–base catalysis
   c. General acid–base catalysis
   d. Metalloenzyme
   e. Metal-activated enzyme

   1. Sensitive to changes in [metal ion]
   2. Formation of modified amino acid residue
   3. Tightly bound Zn^{2+}
   4. Catalysis involves specific H^+ donor
   5. Rate is pH dependent but [Buffer] independent

4. What three amino acids form the catalytic triad of the serine proteases?

5. The aspartic proteases show a bell-shaped curve of enzyme activity versus pH centred around pH = 3. How is this information consistent with the involvement of two aspartic acid residues in catalysis?

6. The active sites of many enzymes are organized to stabilize the conformation of substrates that bring the reacting atoms of the substrates in van der Waals contact and at bond angles resembling the transition state. What are these conformations called and how might they aide in catalysis?

7. What conditions are necessary for two groups to form low-barrier hydrogen bonds?

Answers

1. Entropy loss in ES formation; destabilization of ES due to strain, desolvation, or electrostatic effects; covalent catalysis; general acid or base catalysis; metal ion catalysis; proximity and orientation.

2. A transition-state analog is a molecule that is chemically and structurally similar to the transition state.

3. a. 2; b. 5; c. 4; d. 3; e. 1.

4. Aspartic acid, histidine, and serine.

5. The fact that the centre of the curve is around pH = 3.0 indicates that an acidic amino acid such as aspartic acid or glutamic acid is involved. The bell-shape is consistent with the involvement of both a general acid and a general base—i.e., two distinct groups.

6. The conformation of the substrate is termed a near-attack conformation and it is along a reaction path leading to the transition state.

7. The hydrogen bond distances must be relatively short and the hydrogen-bonded pairs must have pK_a values that are close to each other.

Additional Problems

1 The pH profile of pepsin is bell-shaped, indicating the involvement of a general acid and a general base in catalysis with pK_a values around 4.3 and 1.4, respectively. The two candidates for these roles are two aspartic acid residues, Asp^{32} and Asp^{215}. However, the pK_a values of aspartic acid residues in polypeptides range from 4.2 to 4.6. How might the pK_a of an aspartic acid residue be influenced by protein structure?

2. State the specificity exhibited by the serine proteases trypsin, chymotrypsin, and elastase, and explain how this specificity is determined by the protein.

3. a. *p*-nitrophenyl acetate is slowly hydrolyzed by chymotrypsin to *p*-nitrophenol and acetic acid. One nice property of this compound is that the product, *p*-nitrophenol, when ionized, is brightly yellow-coloured, making it convenient to follow enzyme activity spectrophotometrically. Draw [*p*-nitrophenylate] produced as a function of time.
    b. On the same graph, draw [acetate] production as a function of time.
    c. Why are the two plots different?

4. Discuss the importance of histidine in enzyme catalysis.

5. a. Papain is a sulfhydryl protease from papaya that shows broad specificity. (It is used as a component of meat tenderizers.) During catalysis, an acyl-enzyme intermediate is formed as an acylthioester. The active residue is Cys[25], which is readily modified by iodoacetate, a potent inhibitor of papain. How might the role of Cys[25] in papain be similar to Ser[95] in chymotrypsin?
    b. Suggest a mechanism by which iodoacetate inhibits papain.

Abbreviated Answers

1. The pK_a of the side-chain carboxyl group of aspartic acid is around 4.3. Thus, the general acid in pepsin has a pK_a in the normal range of pK_a values exhibited by aspartic acids. For an aspartic acid to function as a general base with pK_a = 1.4, its pK_a must be lowered considerably. How might this be achieved? In a protein, the polypeptide chain may fold in a manner to place an aspartic acid in an environment that influences its pK_a. One way to lower the pK_a is to have positive-charge residues nearby stabilizing the negatively charged carboxylate form of the aspartic acid side chain.

2. Chymotrypsin cleaves peptide bonds in which the carbonyl group is donated by amino acids with bulky, hydrophobic groups such as Phe, Trp, and Tyr. Trypsin's specificity is for Arg and Lys—large, positively charged amino acids. Elastase hydrolyzes after Ala and Gly. The substrate-binding pocket in chymotrypsin is a deep, hydrophobic pocket adjacent to the catalytic site. A similar pocket is found in trypsin but with an aspartic acid residue located deep in the pocket (in a position occupied by a serine residue in chymotrypsin). In elastase, the substrate-binding pocket is filled by a valine residue and a threonine residue. Analogous positions in chymotrypsin and trypsin are occupied by glycine residues.

3. a. and b.

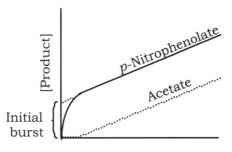

c. Initially, rapid production of *p*-nitrophenolate occurs without accompanying acetate production. Only at later times are the rates of production of *p*-nitrophenolate and acetate identical. This "burst" of activity produces a molar equivalent of *p*-nitrophenolate. Hydrolysis of *p*-nitrophenylacetate is a two-step process. First, the acetate group is transferred from the substrate to Ser[195] on the enzyme and *p*-nitrophenolate is released. Subsequently, acetate is hydrolyzed from Ser[195]. The second step is the rate-limiting step. The acetate production curve exhibits an initial lag corresponding to formation of acyl-Ser[195].

4. Histidine is the only amino acid with a pK_a around neutral pH. It can function as a general acid or general base, as seen for His[57] in the serine proteases.

5. a. Chymotrypsin catalysis involves a nucleophilic attack of the carbonyl carbon of the peptide bond by Ser[195] forming an acylester intermediate. This was facilitated by Ser[195] losing a proton to nearby His[57]. In papain, the active-site residue is a cysteine. Cysteine has a much lower pK_a than serine and will more readily function as a nucleophile. An acylthioester is formed as an intermediate in catalysis in papain.

b.

Summary

Enzymes accelerate reaction rates by reducing the activation energies for biochemical reactions. To do so, enzymes must stabilize the transition-state complex, EX‡, more than they stabilize the enzyme–substrate complex, ES. Put another way, enzymes are designed by nature to bind the transition state more tightly than the substrate or product. Enzyme-catalyzed reactions are typically 10^7 to 10^{14} times faster than their uncatalyzed counterparts. The catalytic mechanisms which contribute to the prowess of enzymes include a) entropy loss in ES formation; b) destabilization of ES due to strain, desolvation, or electrostatic effects; and c) covalent catalysis, general acid-base catalysis, metal ion catalysis, and proximity and orientation effects. When a substrate binds to an enzyme, the (usually large) intrinsic binding energy is compensated by entropy loss and destabilization in the ES complex, but not in the EX‡ complex. The transition state for any reaction is a "moving target"—a transient species that exists for only 10^{-14} – 10^{-13} s. The short lifetime of the transition state prevents quantitative studies of this complex, but the dissociation constant for the EX‡ complex can be estimated to be on the order of 10^{-15} M. Transition-state analogs are stable molecules that resemble the transition state for a particular reaction, and that therefore bind very tightly to their respective enzymes. Since they are only approximations of the transition-state structure, transition-state analogs cannot, however, bind as tightly as the transition state itself.

Some enzyme reactions derive rate acceleration from the formation of a covalent bond with the substrate. Many of the side chains of amino acids in proteins offer suitable nucleophilic centres for catalysis, including amines, carboxylates, hydroxyls, and imidazole and thiol groups. Electrophilic catalysis may also occur, but usually involves coenzyme adducts that possess or generate electrophilic centres. General acid–base catalysis, in which a proton is transferred from a suitable donor/acceptor to or from the substrate in the transition state, may also provide significant rate accelerations. General acid–base catalysis is most effective when the pK_a of the donating or accepting group is near the ambient pH. Metal ions may also exert catalytic power in enzyme reactions. Metals may act as electrophilic catalysts, stabilizing the increased electron density or negative charge, which may develop in a reaction. They may also act to coordinate and thus increase the acidity of nucleophilic groups at the active site. Enzymes also provide significant rate acceleration via proximity and orientation effects—i.e., by providing an active site environment in which all the reacting groups are proximal and oriented optimally for the desired reaction.

The serine proteases, including trypsin, chymotrypsin, elastase, thrombin, subtilisin, plasmin, tissue plasminogen activator, and many similar enzymes, cleave peptide chains in a mechanism involving a covalent intermediate and general acid–base catalysis. The active sites of serine proteases contain a highly conserved catalytic triad consisting of Asp^{102}, His^{57}, and Ser^{195}. Asp^{102} functions to immobilize and orient His^{57}, which accepts a proton from Ser^{195}, facilitating attack by Ser^{195} on the acyl carbon of the scissile bond. The mechanisms of the serine proteases were elucidated in studies of hydrolysis of model organic esters. The observation of burst kinetics—the rapid release of one of the reaction products in an amount equal to the enzyme concentration, followed by a slower, steady state product release—provided evidence for a multi-step reaction sequence and the eventual identification of covalent acyl enzyme intermediates.

Aspartic proteases are active at acidic pH and their catalytic mechanism involves two aspartic acid residues. A number of important enzymes are aspartic proteases, including pepsin and chymosin (digestive enzymes), cathepsin D and E (lysosomal proteins), renin (blood physiology), and the HIV-1 protease (processing of HIV polyprotein). Catalysis involves formation of a low-barrier hydrogen bond with the two aspartic acid residues, water, and the peptide bond substrate. The low-barrier hydrogen bond forms a network that facilitates movement of electrons to and from the substrate and water. The HIV-1 protease, which cleaves the polyproteins produced by the AIDS virus, is an aspartic protease and is a dimer of identical subunits, which mimics the two-lobed monomeric structure of pepsin and other aspartic proteases.

Chorismate mutase catalyzes the conversion of chorismate to prephenate, an intermediate in biosynthesis of phenylalanine. Its chemistry is Claisen rearrangement, which is catalyzed by stabilization of a near-attack conformation in which the substrate is in the chair conformation, stabilized by numerous hydrogen bonds and ionic interactions. A near-attack conformation is a conformation reached along a reaction pathway in which reacting atoms are at van der Waals contact and at an angle that represents the transition state. The uncatalyzed reaction in water occurs via the same pathway, but the presence of the enzyme makes formation of the near-attack conformation much more likely to occur.

Chapter 14

Enzyme Regulation

• •

Chapter Outline

❖ Enzyme regulation
  ⅄ Approach to equilibrium
  ⅄ K_m of enzymes in the range of in vivo substrate concentrations
  ⅄ Genetic controls
  ⅄ Covalent modification
  ⅄ Allosteric regulation
    • Allosteric regulation of phosphofructokinase
  ⅄ Others Zymogens: Proenzymes or zymogens: Activated by proteolysis
    • Proinsulin: Insulin
    • Chymotrypsinogen: Chymotrypsin
    • Blood-clotting factors: Serine protease cascade converting fibrinogen to fibrin
  ⅄ Isozymes: Lactate dehydrogenase: A_4, A_3B_2, A_2B_2, A_1B_3, B_4
  ⅄ Modular proteins: cAMP-dependent protein kinase: R_2C_2
❖ General properties of regulatory proteins
  ⅄ Kinetic properties
    • Do not follow simple Michaelis–Menten kinetics
    • Activity sigmoidal: Higher order dependence on substrate concentration
    • Cooperativity
  ⅄ Allosteric inhibition
  ⅄ Often regulated by activation
  ⅄ Oligomeric organization
  ⅄ Effectors alter distribution of conformational isomers
❖ Cooperativity models
  ⅄ Monod, Wyman, Changeux (1965): Symmetry model
    • Two conformations: T (tense or taut) and R (relaxed)
    • R state high affinity/T state lower affinity
    • Positive homotropic effectors: Substrate binding shifts equilibrium to R
    • Heterotropic effectors
      • Positive effector: Binds to R state
      • Negative effector: Binds to T state
  ⅄ Koshland, Nemethy, Filmer (1966): Sequential model: Induced fit: S-binding induces conformational change
❖ Covalent modification through phosphorylation
  ⅄ Protein kinases: Converter enzymes that add phosphate from ATP
    • Target amino acids: Ser, Thr, or Tyr
    • Target amino acids within a consensus sequence
      • Intrasteric control: Pseudosubstrate sequence (lacking phosphate target amino acid) binds to kinase and inactivates it
  ⅄ Protein phosphatase: Converter enzymes that hydrolyze phosphate
❖ Other covalent modifications: Adenylylation, uridylylation, ADP-ribosylation, methylation, disulfide bond formation, and others
❖ Pyruvate dehydrogenase: Cooperative enzyme that catalyzes the conversion of pyruvate into acetyl coenzyme A

- Structure
  - Complex of three enzymes, all with different catalytic activities
    - Pyruvate dehydrogenase (E.C. 1.2.4.1)
      - Requires TPP as a cofactor
    - Dihydrolipoyl transacetylase (E.C. 2.3.1.12)
      - Requires lipoate and coenzyme A as cofactors
    - Dihydrolipoyl dehydrogenase (E.C. 1.8.1.4)
      - Requires FAD and NAD^+ as cofactors
- Regulation of pyruvate dehydrogenase
  - Allosteric regulation
    - Allosterically activated by coenzyme A
    - Competitively inhibited by acetyl-coenzyme A (competes with substrate for active site)
    - Allosterically activated by NAD^+
    - Inhibited by NADH
    - Allosterically inhibited by ATP
    - Allosterically activated by AMP
  - Covalent regulation
    - Inhibited by phosphorylation by pyruvate dehydrogenase kinase
    - Activated by dephosphorylation by pyruvate dehydrogenase phosphatase
  - Calcium- and magnesium-activated pyruvate dehydrogenase in muscle
- Oxygen-binding proteins hemoglobin and myoglobin
  - Hemoglobin: Transports oxygen from lung to tissue: Sigmoidal oxygen binding
  - Myoglobin: Oxygen-storage protein: Simple oxygen-binding curve
- Oxygen-binding group
  - Ferrous iron
  - Protoporphyrin ring
  - Histidine F8 5th iron coordinate
  - 6th Iron coordinate
    - In oxy-protein: Oxygen
    - In deoxy-protein: Nothing
    - In met-protein: Water: Iron is ferric (met): Does not bind oxygen
- Myoglobin: Monomeric protein
- Hemoglobin: Dimer of dimers: $(\alpha\beta)_2$
  - Sigmoidal oxygen binding: Cooperativity: Oxygen is positive homotropic regulator
  - Negative heterotropic effectors: Protons, carbon dioxide, chloride, 2,3-BPG
    - Protons lower oxygen affinity: Bohr effect: Oxygen unloaded at low pH
    - Carbon dioxide
      - Covalently modifies α-amino groups as carbamate: Carbamate forms salt link to stabilize T state
      - Carbon dioxide also converted to carbonic acid: Source of protons for Bohr effect
    - 2,3-bisphosphoglycerate: Binds to Hb: Stabilizes T state and thus lowers oxygen affinity
  - Physiology
    - Fetal hemoglobin: Binds 2,3-BPG poorly: High-affinity oxygen binding allows fetal Hb to get oxygen from adult Hb
    - Sickle-cell anemia: Amino acid substitution responsible for hemoglobin polymerization
- Oxygen binding in Hb accompanied by conformational changes
  - Oxygen binding to heme iron moves iron into porphyrin plane
  - Histidine F8 accompanies this movement by moving helix F, EF corner, and FG corner
  - Deoxy Hb is T state and oxy Hb is R state conformations: MWC model
  - Oxygen binding to α-chain indices conformational change that is transmitted to β-chain: Sequential model

Chapter Objectives

Enzymes are proteins that act as biological catalysts, but unlike inorganic catalysts, enzymes exhibit incredible specificity and can be regulated in numerous ways. Know the factors controlling enzymatic activity including product build-up and approach to equilibrium, availability of substrates and cofactors, regulation of enzyme production and degradation, covalent modification, allosteric regulation, biosynthesis of enzymes as zymogens, isozymes, and regulation by modulator proteins. Keep in mind that enzymes as proteins may be capable of assuming different conformations and that the substrate-binding site may undergo local conformational change upon substrate binding.

Allosteric Regulation

In order to understand allosteric regulation, you must first understand standard Michaelis–Menten kinetics. Plots of v versus [S] are hyperbolic, approaching V_{max} as [S] becomes large and having K_m defined as the substrate concentration where $v = 0.5 \times V_{max}$. Allosteric proteins exhibit sigmoidal plots of v versus [S]. The shape of the sigmoidal curve may be influenced by inhibitors or activators that bind at sites distinct from the substrate-binding site yet still influence catalysis.

Myoglobin and Hemoglobin

These were the first proteins whose structures were solved by X-ray crystallography, and they serve as a paradigm for understanding allosteric regulation. Be sure to understand the physiological function of these two proteins: myoglobin is an oxygen-storage protein, whereas hemoglobin is an oxygen-transporting protein. Comparison of the structures of myoglobin and hemoglobin is a classic study in the four levels of protein structure: amino acid sequence, secondary structure, three-dimensional structure, and, for hemoglobin, quaternary structure. To a first approximation, hemoglobin appears to be simply a tetramer of myoglobin-like subunits, but the subunits are in fact not identical and hemoglobin binds O_2 cooperatively. Oxygen-saturation curves for myoglobin and hemoglobin are presented below in Figure 14.13. Be sure to understand cooperativity and the affects of H^+, CO_2, and 2,3-bisphosphoglycerate on O_2-binding curves for hemoglobin.

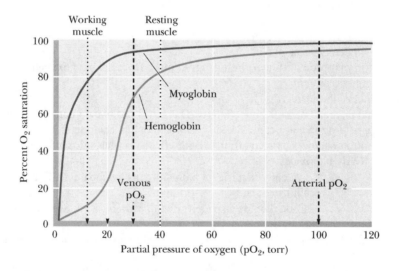

Figure 14.13 O_2-binding curves for hemoglobin and myoglobin.

Allosteric Models

Be familiar with the two models for allosteric behaviour: the symmetry model of Monod, Wyman, and Changeux; and the sequential model of Koshland, Nemethy, and Filmer. The symmetry model postulates the existence of two conformational states, **R** (relaxed) and **T** (taut), that differ in their affinity for substrate with **R** having a higher affinity than **T**. Cooperativity arises because substrate-binding shifts the **R/T** equilibrium toward the **R** state. Allosteric activators and inhibitors bind at specific sites distinct from the substrate-binding site but influence substrate binding by influencing the **R/T** equilibrium. Inhibitor binding favours the **T** state, whereas activator binding favours the **R** state. In the sequential model, ligand-binding sites are in communication with each other such that the state of occupancy of a ligand-binding site influences the state of occupancy of other sites.

Problems and Solutions

1.   List 6 general ways in which enzyme activity is controlled.

Answer: Enzyme activity may be controlled by:

a.   Accumulation of product as the reaction approaches equilibrium. As substrate is converted to product, [P] increases.

b.   Availability of substrates and cofactors.

c.   Regulation of the amounts of enzyme synthesized or degraded by cells.

d.   Covalent modifications catalyzed by modifying enzymes or converter enzymes may activate or inhibit an enzyme or alter its kinetic properties.

e.   Allosteric regulation leading to either inhibition or activation.

f.   Regulation by interaction with modulator proteins.

g.   Activation or inactivation by proteolysis.

h.   Isozymes.

3.   (Integrates with Chapter 12) Draw both Lineweaver–Burk plots and Hanes–Woolf plots for an MWC allosteric enzyme system, showing separate curves for the kinetic response in (a) the absence of any effectors, (b) the presence of allosteric activator A, and (c) the presence of allosteric inhibitor I.

Answer: First, let us derive the expression for substrate binding in the case of a two-state model. The protein is assumed to exist in two conformational states, **R** and **T**, and to have n binding sites. Further, it is assumed that the **T** state does not bind substrate. The following equilibrium applies:

$$R_0 \leftrightarrows T_0, \text{ and } L = \frac{[T_0]}{[R_0]}$$

where L is the equilibrium constant for the **R** to **T** transition and the subscript refers to the number of substrate-binding sites occupied. Substrate binding occurs as follows:

$$R_0 + S \leftrightarrows R_1$$
$$R_1 + S \leftrightarrows R_2$$
$$.$$
$$.$$
$$.$$
$$R_{n-1} + S \leftrightarrows R_n$$

Substrate binding is described by so-called macroscopic association constants of the form:

$$K_i = \frac{[R_i]}{[R_{i-1}][S]}$$

Substrate binding, normalized to total protein concentration is given by:

$$\upsilon = \frac{[R_1] + 2[R_2] + \cdots + n[R_n]}{[T_0] + [R_0] + [R_1] + [R_2] + \cdots + [R_n]}$$

The macroscopic association constants can be rearranged to give each $[R_i]$ as a function of K_i, $[R_0]$, and [S] as follows:

$$[R_i] = K_i \times [R_{i-1}][S] = K_i K_{i-1} \times [R_{i-2}][S]^2 = \cdots = [S]^i [R_0] \prod_i K_i$$
$$\text{Where } \prod_i K_i = K_1 K_2 \cdots K_i$$

Substituting the expressions for $[R_i]$s into the equation for υ we have:

$$v = \frac{\sum_{i=1}^{n} i \times [S]^i [R_0] \prod_i K_i}{[T_0] + [R_0] + \sum_{i=1}^{n} [S]^i [R_0] \prod_i K_i}$$

Now, the macroscopic association constants refer to substrate binding to any site as opposed to a specific site. The association constant for binding to a specific site is the microscopic association constant, K^*. The two are related as follows:

$$K_i = \frac{(n+1-i)}{i} K^*$$

Substituting for K_i and using $[T_0] = L[R_0]$, the expression for v becomes:

$$v = \frac{\sum_{i=1}^{n} i \times [S]^i \prod_i \frac{(n+1-i)}{i} K^*}{1 + L + \sum_{i=1}^{n} [S]^i \prod_i \frac{(n+1-i)}{i} K^*}$$

The numerator and the denominator are equal to:

$$n[S]K^*(1+[S]K^*)^{n-1} \text{ and } L+(1+[S]K^*)^n$$

Upon substituting these terms above, v simplifies to:

$$v = \frac{n[S] \times K^*(1+[S]K^*)^{n-1}}{L+(1+[S]K^*)^n}, \text{ or}$$

$$v = \frac{n\alpha(1+\alpha)^{n-1}}{L+(1+\alpha)^n}$$

Where $\alpha = K^*[S]$. (Because $K^*_a = 1/K^*_d$, the term α is a normalized concentration; it is simply $[S]$ divided by the dissociation constant K^*_d.

This equation can be generalized to take into account heterotropic interactions. Heterotropic interactions refer to binding of molecules at sites other than substrate-binding sites that influence the **R** to **T** transition. For simplicity, let us assume that an inhibitor I binds to the **T** state at a single site, whereas an activator A binds to the **R** state at a single site. If we define $\beta = [I]/K_I$ and $\gamma = [A]/K_A$, where $[I]$ and $[A]$ refer to inhibitor and activator concentrations, and K_I and K_A are inhibitor- and activator-dissociation–binding constants, the expression for v becomes:

$$v = \frac{n\alpha(1+\alpha)^{n-1}}{L\frac{(1+\beta)^n}{(1+\gamma)^n} + (1+\alpha)^n}$$

Lineweaver–Burk plots and Hanes–Woolf plots are shown below for a two-site protein ($n = 2$) with: $L = 0$ (no cooperativity); $L = 1000$ ($\beta = 0$, $\gamma = 0$); $L = 1000$, $\beta = 1$ ($\gamma = 1$); and, $L = 1000$, $\gamma = 1$ ($\beta = 0$).

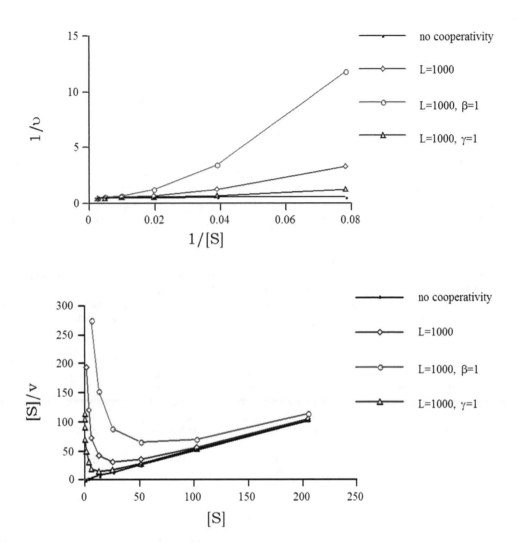

5. The equation $\dfrac{Y}{(1-Y)} = \left(\dfrac{pO_2}{P_{50}}\right)^n$ **allows the calculation of Y (the fractional saturation of hemoglobin with O₂), given P₅₀ and n (see box on page 496). Let P₅₀ = 26 torr and n = 2.8. Calculate Y in the lungs, where pO₂ = 100 torr, and Y in the capillaries, where pO₂ = 40 torr. What is the efficiency of O₂ delivery under these conditions (expressed as Y_lungs − Y_capillaries)? Repeat the calculations, but for n = 1. Compare the values for Y_lungs − Y_capillaries for n = 2.8 versus Y_lungs − Y_capillaries for n = 1 to determine the effect of cooperative O₂ binding of oxygen delivery by hemoglobin.**

Answer: Y = fractional saturation of hemoglobin. For P_{50} = 26 torr, n = 2.8, calculate Y at pO_2 = 100 torr and at pO_2 = 40 torr.

$$\frac{Y}{1-Y} = (\frac{pO_2}{P_{50}})^n$$

$$Y = (1-Y)(\frac{pO_2}{P_{50}})^n = (\frac{pO_2}{P_{50}})^n - (\frac{pO_2}{P_{50}})^n \times Y, \text{ and solving for Y we find:}$$

$$Y = \frac{(\frac{pO_2}{P_{50}})^n}{1+(\frac{pO_2}{P_{50}})^n} = \frac{(pO_2)^n}{(pO_2)^n + (P_{50})^n}$$

For $n = 2.8$, $P_{50} = 26$ torr: $Y_{lungs} = 0.98$ at $pO_2 = 100$
$Y_{capillaries} = 0.77$ at $pO_2 = 40$

Efficiency of O_2 delivery = $Y_{lungs} - Y_{capillaries} = 0.21$

For $n = 1.0$, $P_{50} = 26$ torr: $Y_{lungs} = 0.79$ at $pO_2 = 100$
$Y_{capillaries} = 0.61$ at $pO_2 = 40$

Efficiency of O_2 delivery = $Y_{lungs} - Y_{capillaries} = 0.18$

At an oxygen tension of 100 torr, hemoglobin with $n = 2.8$ is nearly completely saturated. Under the same condition, hemoglobin with $n = 1.0$ is only 79% saturated. Thus, for the case of $n = 2.8$, hemoglobin can carry a maximum load of oxygen away from the lung. In the tissues at a $pO_2 = 40$ torr, hemoglobin with $n = 2.8$ versus $n = 1.0$ can change its fractional saturation by 0.21 and 0.18, respectively. When expressed as a percentage of the initial load ([efficiency $\div$ Y_{lung}] $\times$ 100%), O_2 delivery by hemoglobin with $n = 2.8$ and $n = 1.0$ is 21% and 23%, a modest difference.

7. Consult Table 14.2 and do the following.
   a. Suggest a consensus amino acid sequence within phosphorylase kinase that makes it a target of protein kinase A (the cAMP-dependent protein kinase).
   b. Suggest an effective amino acid sequence for a regulatory domain pseudosubstrate sequence that would exert intrasteric control on phosphorylase kinase by blocking its active site.

Answer: a.   cAMP-dependent protein kinase A phosphorylates serine or threonine in a sequence Arg–(Arg or Lys)–any amino acid–(Ser or Thr) or [–R(R/K)X(S/T)]. We must search for a region within the sequence of phosphorylase kinase to see if one is present. To get the sequence, do a full-text search at SwissProt (http://web.expasy.org/protscale). From the results page activate KPB1_HUMAN (P46020), which will bring you an information page for human glycogen phosphorylase kinase. (The features section actually tells you where in the sequence protein kinase A phosphorylates. But let's see if we can find the sequence on our own.)

After looking over all this wonderful information about this enzyme, scroll down to the bottom of the sequence and activate the FASTA format link (P46020 in FASTA format). Copy the all the data (except any line beginning with a ">" as these are comments lines) and paste it into a Microsoft Word document and edit it (using the Replace command in the Edit menu) by replacing paragraph marks (under "special") with "deletes". This action should convert the sequence into a single word as shown below.

MRSRSNSGVRLDGYARLVQQTILCHQNPVTGLLPASYDQKDAWVRDNVYSILAVWGLGLAYRKNADRDEDKAK
AYELEQSVVKLMRGLLHCMIRQVDKVESFKYSQSTKDSLHAKYNTKTCATVVGDDQWGHLQLDATSVYLLFLA
QMTASGLHIIHSLDEVNFIQNLVFYIEAAYKTADFGIWERGDKTNQGISELNASSVGMAKAALEALDELDLFGVK
GGPQSVIHVLADEVQHCQSILNSLLPRASTSKEVDASLLSVVSFPAFAVEDSQLVELTKQEIITKLQGRYGCCRFL
RDGYKTPKEDPNRLYYEPAELKLFENIECEWPLFWTYFILDGVFSGNAEQVQEYKEALEAVLIKGKNGVPLLPELY
SVPPDRVDEEYQNPHTVDRVPMGKLPHMWGQSLYILGSLMAEGFLAPGEIDPLNRRFSTVPKPDVVVQVSILAET
EEIKTILKDKGIYVETIAEVYPIRVQPARILSHIYSSLGCNNRMKLSGRPYRHMGVLGTSKLYDIRKTIFTFTPQFIDQ
QQFYLALDNKMIVEMLRTDLSYLCSRWRMTGQPTITFPISYSMLDEDGTSLNSSILAALRKMQDGYFGGARVQT
GKLSEFLTTSCCTHLSFMDPGPEGKLYSEDYDDNYDYLESGNWMNDYDSTSHARCGDEVARYLDHLLAHTAPH
PKLAPTSQKGGLDRFQAAVQTTCDLMSLVTKAKELHVQNVHMYLPTKLFQASRPSFNLLDSPHPRQENQVPSVR
VEIHLPRDQSGEVDFKALVLQLKETSSLQEQADILYMLYTMKGPDWNTELYNERSATVRELLTELYGKVGEIRH
WGLIRYISGILRKKVEALDEACTDLLSHQKHLTVGLPPEPREKTISAPLPYEALTQLIDEASEGDMSISILTQEIMVY
LAMYMRTQPGLFAEMFRLRIGLIIQVMATELAHSLRCSAEEATEGLMNLSPSAMKNLLHHILSGKEFGVERSVRP
TDSNVSPAISIHEIGAVGATKTERTGIMQLKSEIKQVEFRRLSISAESQSPGTSMTPSSGSFPSAYDQQSSKDSRQ
GQWQRRRLDGALNRVPVGFYQKVWKVLQKCHGLSVEGFVLPSSTTREMTPGEIKFSVHVESVLNRVPQPEYR
QLLVEAILVLTMLADIEIHSIGSIIAVEKIVHIANDLFLQEQKTLGADDTMLAKDPASGICTLLYDSAPSGRFGTMTY
LSKAAATYVQEFLPHSICAMQ

My single "word" has 1223 characters. Next, using Microsoft Word search for sequences like RR?S, RR?T, RK?S, RK?T. (The ? is a wild card meaning any character will be accepted.) RRFS and RRLS were the only two found.

MRSRSNSGVRLDGYARLVQQTILCHQNPVTGLLPASYDQKDAWVRDNVYSILAVWGLGLAYRKNADRDEDKAK
AYELEQSVVKLMRGLLHCMIRQVDKVESFKYSQSTKDSLHAKYNTKTCATVVGDDQWGHLQLDATSVYLLFLA
QMTASGLHIIHSLDEVNFIQNLVFYIEAAYKTADFGIWERGDKTNQGISELNASSVGMAKAALEALDELDLFGVK
GGPQSVIHVLADEVQHCQSILNSLLPRASTSKEVDASLLSVVSFPAFAVEDSQLVELTKQEIITKLQGRYGCCRFL
RDGYKTPKEDPNRLYYEPAELKLFENIECEWPLFWTYFILDGVFSGNAEQVQEYKEALEAVLIKGKNGVPLLPELY
SVPPDRVDEEYQNPHTVDRVPMGKLPHMWGQSLYILGSLMAEGFLAPGEIDPLN**RRFS**TVPKPDVVVQVSILAE
TEEIKTILKDKGIYVETIAEVYPIRVQPARILSHIYSSLGCNNRMKLSGRPYRHMGVLGTSKLYDIRKTIFTFTPQFID
QQQFYLALDNKMIVEMLRTDLSYLCSRWRMTGQPTITFPISYSMLDEDGTSLNSSILAALRKMQDGYFGGARVQ
TGKLSEFLTTSCCTHLSFMDPGPEGKLYSEDYDDNYDYLESGNWMNDYDSTSHARCGDEVARYLDHLLAHTAP
HPKLAPTSQKGGLDRFQAAVQTTCDLMSLVTKAKELHVQNVHMYLPTKLFQASRPSFNLLDSPHPRQENQVPSV
RVEIHLPRDQSGEVDFKALVLQLKETSSLQEQADILYMLYTMKGPDWNTELYNERSATVRELLTELYGKVGEIRH
WGLIRYISGILRKKVEALDEACTDLLSHQKHLTVGLPPEPREKTISAPLPYEALTQLIDEASEGDMSISILTQEIMVY
LAMYMRTQPGLFAEMFRLRIGLIIQVMATELAHSLRCSAEEATEGLMNLSPSAMKNLLHHILSGKEFGVERSVRP
TDSNVSPAISIHEIGAVGATKTERTGIMQLKSEIKQVEF**RRLS**ISAESQSPGTSMTPSSGSFPSAYDQQSSKDSRQ
GQWQRRRRLDGALNRVPVGFYQKVWKVLQKCHGLSVEGFVLPSSTTREMTPGEIKFSVHVESVLNRVPQPEYR
QLLVEAILVLTMLADIEIHSIGSIIAVEKIVHIANDLFLQEQKTLGADDTMLAKDPASGICTLLYDSAPSGRFGTMTY
LSKAAATYVQEFLPHSICAMQ

The correct one happens to be RRLS with the serine located at 1018.

b. To regulate phosphorylase kinase with a pseudosubstrate sequence we must first look at Table 14.2 for its consensus target sequence: —KRKQIS*VRGL. The serine in this sequence is phosphorylated by the kinase reaction. A suitable regulatory domain pseudosubstrate sequence would mimic the target sequence but have an amino acid substitution at serine. A convenient substitution is A (alanine) for S (serine) since both amino acids are about the same size. Thus, a potential pseudosubstrate sequence might be KRKQIAVRGL.

9. You land a post as scientific investigator with a pharmaceutical company that would like to develop drugs to treat people with sickle-cell anemia. They want ideas from you! What molecular properties of Hb S might you suggest as potential targets of drug therapy?

Answer: Hemoglobin S differs from normal hemoglobin by a single amino acid change in the β chain: a Glu to Val at position 6. This change replaces an acidic, and therefore negatively charged amino acid, for a hydrophobic amino acid. The problem with sickle-cell hemoglobin is that at low oxygen tension, it polymerizes into long polymers that cause red blood cells to assume an elongated, inflexible shape, which causes them to move poorly through small-diameter capillaries. You might suggest developing a drug that binds to this region of hemoglobin and lowers its hydrophobicity. You might think about some N-terminal chemistry that alters the characteristics of the N-terminus, which is located only six amino acid residues away.

One of the few drugs currently being used to treat sickle-cell anemia is hydroxyurea. However, hydroxyurea does not address the defective hemoglobin. It induces formation of fetal hemoglobin and the presence of fetal hemoglobin lessens sickling.

11. Lactate, a metabolite produced under anaerobic conditions in muscle, lowers the affinity of myoglobin for O₂. This effect is beneficial, because O₂ dissociation from Mb under anaerobic conditions will provide the muscle with oxygen. Lactate binds to Mb at a site distinct from the O₂-binding site at the heme. In light of this observation, discuss whether myoglobin should be considered an allosteric protein.

Answer: Lactate production is a consequence of anaerobic metabolism of pyruvate (fermentation). Pyruvate's aerobic fate is to be fed into the citric acid cycle, a process that requires oxygen. Thus, build-up of lactate is a signal that pyruvate is not being metabolized sufficiently fast. Since myoglobin is a store of oxygen, regulation of oxygen affinity by lactate makes physiological sense.

Is myoglobin an allosteric protein given this observation? Allostery refers to regulation of enzymatic activity or ligand binding by another molecule at another binding site on the protein. A consequence of allostery is modulation of protein structure either by shifting the equilibrium between two conformational states (T and R) or modulating the properties of neighbouring binding sites (induced fit). That lactate influences oxygen affinity of myoglobin by binding to a site distinct from the oxygen-binding site is consistent with allostery. Additionally, oxymyoglobin and deoxymyoglobin exhibit different affinities for lactate. These would indicate that myoglobin is a allosteric protein. The title of a paper by Giardia et al.

(Functional modulation by lactate of myoglobin A monomeric allosteric hemoprotein (1996) *J. Biol. Chem.* 29:16999–17001) clearly indicates how they view the question.

Allostery has traditionally been thought of as a property of multimeric proteins, like hemoglobin.

13.   CTP synthetase catalyzes the synthesis of CTP from UTP:

$$UTP + ATP + glutamine \rightleftarrows CTP + glutamate + ADP + P_i$$

The substrates UTP and ATP show positive cooperativity in their binding to the enzyme, which is an α_4-type homotetramer. However, the other substrate, glutamine, shows negative cooperativity. Draw substrate saturation curves of the form v versus [S]/K_{0.5} for each of these three substrates that illustrate these effects.

Answer: If the enzyme exhibits positive cooperativity for UTP and ATP, then the Hill coefficient must be greater than 1 but likely less than 4. (Since the enzyme is a homotetramer, it would only have a Hill coefficient of 4 if it were perfectly cooperative.) The $K_{0.5}$ values for the three substrates are expected to be different, but values for UTP and ATP might be similar (but not necessarily equal). The Hill coefficients for UTP and ATP need not be identical. Finally, since the enzyme exhibits negative cooperativity for glutamine, the Hill coefficient in this case should be less than 1. The question asks for plots of v versus [S] normalized to $K_{0.5}$ values, and this will allow all three plots to be presented on the same graph. The graph below includes the case of no cooperativity.

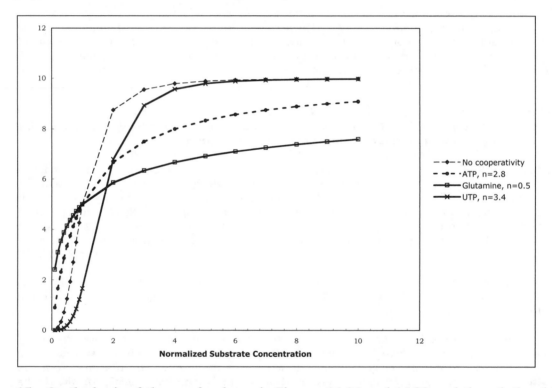

15.   On the basis of the graphs shown in Figures 14.21 and 14.22 and the relationship between blood pH and respiration (Chapter 2), predict the effect of hyperventilation on Hb:O₂ affinity.

Answer: Hyperventilation will increase arterial pO_2 and decrease pCO_2. The decrease in pCO_2 causes a change in blood pH by the following mechanism catalyzed by carbonic anhydrase:

$$H^+ + HCO_3^- \rightleftarrows H_2CO_3 \rightleftarrows H_2O + CO_2$$

Lower pCO_2 pulls the equation to the right resulting in a decrease in [H⁺] and an increase in pH. Looking at Figure 14.21, this will result in an increase in affinity of Hb for oxygen and a modest increase in the percent saturation of hemoglobin. Figure 14.22 indicates that CO_2 lowers hemoglobin's affinity for oxygen. The mechanism is carbamate formation on alpha amino groups. This negatively charged adduct will form a salt link that stabilizes the deoxy or T state. Lowering of pCO_2 will remove carbamate and also favour the oxy state. Thus, hyperventilation is expected to increase oxygen affinity.

Questions for Self-Study

1. What is the essential difference between the "lock and key" hypothesis of enzyme substrate interaction and the "induced fit" hypothesis?

2. List six factors that affect or modulate the activity of enzymes.

3. How are the proteins trypsinogen, chymotrypsinogen, pepsinogen, procarboxypeptidase, and proelastase related to active enzymes?

4. Lactate dehydrogenase is a tetramer that catalyzes the interconversion of lactate and pyruvate. There are two different subunits, A and B, that can interact to form either homotetramers of heterotetramers with different kinetic properties. Write the five possible tetrameric combinations. What kind of enzyme regulation does lactate dehydrogenase typify?

5. Fill in the blanks. Oxygen binding to myoglobin is _____ by pH, whereas decreasing pH _____ the affinity of hemoglobin for oxygen. This is known as the _____ effect. One physiological source of protons that will decrease pH in tissue is produced by the enzyme carbonic anhydrase, which catalyzes the following reaction: _____. One of the substrates of this reaction, namely _____ _____, by itself lowers the oxygen affinity of hemoglobin by reacting with free α-amino groups to produce a _____—a negatively charged species that can form salt bridges and stabilize the _____ form of hemoglobin. Another compound that will stabilize this form of hemoglobin is _____, which binds at a single site on hemoglobin.

6. Circle the correct words in the brackets: Fetal hemoglobin has [higher or lower] affinity for oxygen than does adult hemoglobin because it has [higher or lower] affinity for 2,3-bisphosphoglycerate.

7. The enzyme aspartate transcarbamolyase catalyzes the condensation of carbamoyl phosphate and aspartic acid to form N-carbamoylasparate. A plot of initial velocity versus aspartate concentration is not a rectangular hyperbola as found for enzymes that obey Michaelis–Menten kinetics. Rather, the plot is sigmoidal. Further, CTP shifts the curve to the right along the substrate axis and makes the sigmoidal shape more pronounced. ATP shifts the curve to the left and makes the sigmoidal shape less pronounced. What kind of enzyme is aspartate transcarbamoylase and what roles do CTP and ATP play in enzyme activity?

8. Match the items in the left hand column with items in the right-hand column.
   a. Symmetry Model
   b. Monod, Wyman, and Changeux
   c. K system
   d. V system
   e. Koshland, Nemethy, and Filmer
   f. Induced fit
   g. Hill coefficient
   h. Increases [R conformation]
   i. Decreases [R conformation]
   j. Homotropic effector

   1. Second non-catalytic substrate–binding site
   2. Substrate-binding concentration dependence
   3. Negative effector
   4. Conformation [substrate] dependent
   5. $K_{0.5}$ changes in response to effectors
   6. V_{max} regulated
   7. Sequential model
   8. $R_0 \rightarrow T_0$
   9. Two conformational states
   10. Positive effector

Answers

1. The "lock and key" hypothesis depicts the enzyme as a rigid template into which the substrate fits. In the "induced fit" hypothesis enzymes are highly flexible, dynamic molecules and the shape of the enzyme's active site is modified by substrate binding.

2. Product inhibition, substrate availability, genetic controls such as induction and repression, covalent modifications, allosteric regulation by effector molecules, zymogens, isozymes, and modulator proteins.

3. These proteins are precursors of the enzymes trypsin, chymotrypsin, pepsin, carboxypeptidase, and elastase. They are converted to active enzymes by hydrolysis of peptide bonds.

4. A_4, A_3B, A_2B_2, AB_3, B_4; isozymes.

5. unaffected; lowers; Bohr; $CO_2 + H_2O \rightarrow H_2CO_3 \rightarrow H^+ + HCO_3^-$; carbon dioxide; carbamate; T (or tense or taut); 2,3-bisphosphoglycerate.

6. Higher; lower

7. Aspartate transcarbamoylase is a regulatory enzyme. CTP is a negative heterotropic effector and ATP is a positive heterotropic effector.

8. a. 8 or 9; b. 8 or 9; c. 5; d. 6; e. 7; f. 4; g. 2; h. 10; i. 3; j. 1.

Additional Problems

1. Enzyme activity may be controlled in several ways (see answer to Self-Study Question 2 above). It is clear that some of these regulatory mechanisms are effective nearly instantly, whereas others are slowly activated. With respect to duration, certain controls are short-lived, whereas others are long-lasting. Compare and contrast enzyme control mechanisms with respect to these parameters.

2. The heme-binding site of both myoglobin and hemoglobin is a pocket in the hydrophobic core of these proteins. This pocket is lined with hydrophobic amino acid side chains, with the exception of histidine F8 (the 8th residue of helix F). Generally, hydrophilic residues such as histidine are not located in hydrophobic interiors. What are the important functions of histidine F8 that require it to be buried in a hydrophobic environment?

3. The histidine discussed above is the so-called distal histidine. A second histidine, the proximal histidine, is located on the opposite side of the heme ring. How does the proximal histidine influence ligand specificity?

4. Free heme is an effective oxygen-binding molecule but it has two shortcomings: its iron is readily oxidized, and it forms a heme–O_2–heme complex that has low solubility. How has incorporation of heme into a protein corrected these heme flaws?

5. Discuss the role of amino acid substitution in adapting fetal hemoglobin and adult hemoglobin to different physiological functions.

6. It is rather easy to determine if an accidental cut involves a vein or an artery. Arterial cuts produce crimson-coloured blood, whereas venous cuts produce darker, bluish-tinted blood. Explain.

7. a. A lecturer wants to demonstrate the spectral changes upon oxygenation and deoxygenation of hemoglobin. So, pure hemoglobin, obtained as a lyophilized (freeze-dried) powder from a biochemical supply company, is resuspended in a buffered salt solution. The resulting solution is brownish-red in colour, indicating a mixture of oxyhemoglobin and met-hemoglobin. What is met-hemoglobin and how can it be converted to oxyhemoglobin?
   b. The conversion is made to oxyhemoglobin, and the lecturer now decides to produce deoxyhemoglobin by placing the solution under partial vacuum to lower the O_2 tension. This is only moderately successful. Can you suggest modifications to the procedure that will favour deoxyhemoglobin formation?

8. The expression $\upsilon = \dfrac{n\alpha(1+\alpha)^{n-1}}{L+(1+\alpha)^n}$ derived in the answer to Problem 3 above assumes that substrate binds to the **R** state but not the **T** state. If this assumption is changed allowing substrate binding to both states, the equation becomes:

$$\upsilon = \frac{\alpha n(1+\alpha)^{n-1} + Lc\alpha n(1+c\alpha)^{n-1}}{L(1+\alpha)^n + (1+\alpha)^n}$$

where c = K_R/K_T, the ratio of dissociation constants for substrate binding to the **R** and **T** states. (a) Under what conditions is substrate binding to protein dominated by T-state binding? (b) Plot v versus α for varying L and fixed c. (c) Plot v versus α for varying L and fixed c.

9. Using the Hill plot show below, estimate K_1 and K_4 for hemoglobin and K for myoglobin. Estimate the Hill coefficient for myoglobin and for hemoglobin at low, intermediate, and high values of pO_2.

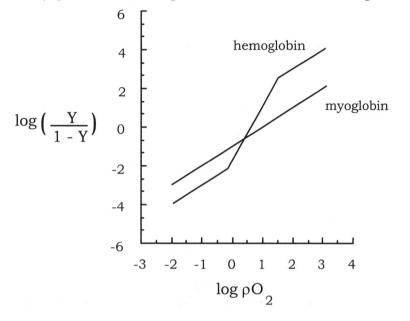

Abbreviated Answers

1. Variations in [product], [S], and [cofactors] have immediate consequences for enzyme activity. The same is true for allosteric regulation. Further, these controls last as long as the signals are present. Genetic controls, such as induction and repression leading to an increase or decrease in enzyme synthesis, are fast, although not immediate, and can be long-lasting. Clearly, degradation is long-lasting. However, a delicate balance between synthesis and degradation can lead to a very responsive system of control. Covalent modification may lead to rapid and long-lasting changes in enzyme activity. Balancing the activity of modifying enzymes against enzymes that can reverse these modifications creates a sensitive system of enzyme control. Finally, zymogens and isozymes are examples of enzyme control mechanisms that can be extremely long-lasting.

2. This histidine, known as the distal histidine because it is on the opposite side of the oxygen-binding site where the so-called proximal histidine is located (see following question), is one of the iron coordinates in both myoglobin and hemoglobin. In hemoglobin, movement of the distal histidine in a single subunit of Hb can influence the accessibility of the oxygen-binding site in the other subunits.

3. The proximal histidine is located close enough to the heme iron so as to prevent carbon monoxide from binding to hemoglobin with optimum geometry.

4. By forming a protein–heme complex, the apparent solubility of heme is greatly increased. Thus, higher concentrations can be maintained without the problem of limited solubility, especially in the presence of oxygen. Because the heme is partially buried in a hydrophobic pocket, it is protected from oxidation. Oxidation produces met-Hb which does not transport oxygen.

5. Oxygen is supplied to the fetal blood system via the placenta, where gas exchange occurs between fetal and maternal circulatory systems. Thus, the fetus must successfully compete with adult, maternal hemoglobin for oxygen. This is possible because fetal hemoglobin has a higher affinity for oxygen than adult hemoglobin. The β-chains of adult-Hb are replaced by γ-chains in fetal-HB. A critical function of β-chains is formation of the 2,3-BPG-binding site at the β/β interface of the $(\alpha\beta)$ dimer junction. The binding site is composed of eight positive charges, four from each β chain, of which three are from side

chains and the fourth is from the N-terminus. In fetal-HB, the 2,3-BPG-binding site is considerably weaker due to an amino acid substitution, Ser^{143} for His^{143}, at the 2,3-BPG-binding site. As a consequence, fetal-HB binds 2,3-BPG less avidly and therefore has a high oxygen affinity.

6. In arterial blood, hemoglobin is oxygenated, whereas in venous blood, deoxy-hemoglobin predominates. The change in colour upon change in oxygenation state is due to an alteration in the iron coordination. In oxyHb, iron is six-fold coordinated with the sixth position occupied by oxygen. In deoxyHb, iron is five-fold coordinated.

7. a. Met-hemoglobin is hemoglobin with its iron atom in the +3 oxidation state as ferric (Fe^{3+}) iron. It can be converted to oxyhemoglobin by treatment with a reducing agent such as sodium hydrosulfite (sodium dithionite).

b. A couple of things come to mind. Since it is pure hemoglobin, it may lack 2,3-bisphosphoglycerate (2,3-BPG), accounting for the tenacity of oxygen binding. Alternatively, the pH of the solution could be lowered and CO_2 added to decrease oxygen affinity.

8. a. When the product Lc is much greater than 1, T-state binding dominates. Typically, $K_R > K_L$ and so c > 1.

b. and c. The upper four curves shown below are for c = 0.1 and L = 1, 10, 100, and 1,000. The lower three curves are for L = 10,000 and c = 0.1, 0.03, and 0.01.

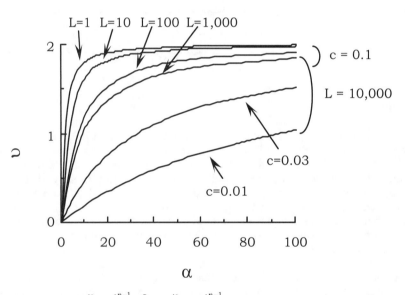

9. From the Hill equation, $\upsilon = \dfrac{\alpha n(1+\alpha)^{n-1} + Lc\alpha n(1+c\alpha)^{n-1}}{L(1+\alpha)^n + (1+\alpha)^n}$, it can be seen that when Y is equal to 1/2,

K = x-intercept = $n(\log pO_2)$. The x-intercept is determined graphically as shown below.

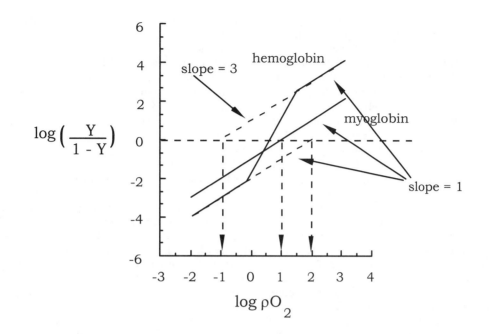

Summary

Enzymes display an extraordinary specificity with regard to the substrates they act upon and the reactions they catalyze. Molecular recognition through structural complementarity is the basis of this specificity. The active sites of enzymes are pockets or clefts in the protein structure whose shape and charge distribution are complementary to the substrate's own properties. In turn, substrate binding induces changes in protein conformation so that the substrate is embraced by the enzyme and catalytic groups are brought to bear. In effect, the enzyme–substrate complex mimics the transition–state intermediate of the reaction.

Regulation of enzyme activity can be achieved at several levels: enzyme synthesis or degradation, reversible covalent modifications catalyzed by converter enzymes, non-covalent interactions with cellular metabolites (allosteric regulation), zymogen activation, isozymes, or modular proteins.

Allosteric regulation occurs when regulatory metabolites modulate the activity of allosteric enzymes by binding at sites distinct from the active site. Such effectors may activate (positively regulate) or inhibit (negatively regulate) enzyme activity. Often, an allosteric enzyme catalyzes the first step in an essential metabolic pathway. The end product of the pathway may be a feedback inhibitor (negative regulator) of this allosteric enzyme. Allosteric enzymes are characterized by sigmoid v versus [S] kinetic patterns. The sigmoid shape of such kinetic curves suggests that the enzymatic rate is proportional to $[S]^n$, where $n > 1$. Allosteric enzymes are oligomeric and possess multiple ligand-binding sites.

Comparison of the two oxygen-binding hemoproteins, myoglobin and hemoglobin, illustrates the differences between normal and allosteric proteins. Myoglobin (Mb) is a monomer that has one heme and binds one O_2. Hemoglobin (Hb) is an $\alpha_2\beta_2$ tetramer, has 4 hemes and binds 4 O_2. Mb functions as an oxygen-storage protein in muscle, while Hb serves as the vertebrate oxygen-transport protein. The oxygen-binding curve for Mb resembles the substrate saturation curves seen for normal, "Michaelis–Menten" enzymes, but the Hb O_2-binding curve is sigmoid, indicating that the binding of O_2 to Hb is cooperative. Cooperative binding means that the binding of one O_2 to a Hb molecule enhances the binding of additional O_2 molecules by the same Hb. O_2 binding by these hemoproteins draws the heme Fe^{2+} atom closer into the porphyrin ring system. This small shift in the position of the iron atom is not particularly important to the biological function of Mb, but in Hb, it triggers the molecular events which underlie its allosteric properties and it has profound consequences for the physiological function of Hb.

Oxygenation markedly affects the quaternary structure of the Hb molecule. In a functional sense, the Hb molecule is composed of two equivalent $\alpha\beta$-dimers. Oxygenation causes the two $\alpha\beta$-dimers to rotate relative to one another. Specific Hvbonds and salt bridges which stabilize the deoxy form of Hb are ruptured when O_2 binds. Hb adopts either of two conformational states, the deoxy-, or **T**, state, and the oxy-, or **R**, state. The transition from the deoxy-Hb conformational state to the oxy-Hb state opens the molecule so that O_2 now gains access to previously inaccessible heme groups of the β-chains. This mechanism explains the cooperative O_2 binding exhibited by Hb.

H^+, CO_2, and 2,3-bisphosphoglyceric acid (BPG) all promote dissociation of O_2 from Hb by binding preferentially to the deoxy state. BPG binds one-to-one with Hb. The BPG-binding site lies within the central cavity of Hb. BPG electrostatically crosslinks the β-chains, stabilizing the deoxy-Hb conformation. Fetal Hb (Hb *F*) differs from normal Hb (Hb *A*) in having two γ-chains in place of the β-chains. An important difference is that each γ-chain has one less positively charged amino acid R-group than the β-chain in the BPG-binding site, so Hb *F* binds BPG less effectively than Hb *A*. Since BPG is bound less effectively, O_2 is bound more avidly by Hb *F*, thereby allowing the fetus to extract O_2 from the maternal blood circulation. In sickle-cell Hb (Hb *S*), Glu at position $\beta6$ is replaced by Val, introducing a new hydrophobic site on the surface of Hb molecules that makes them stick together to form filaments.

The Monod, Wyman, and Changeux model for the behaviour of allosteric proteins postulates that allosteric proteins are oligomers composed of identical subunits. The protein can exist in either of two conformational states, the **T** or "taut" state, and the **R** or "relaxed" state. The distribution of the protein between the two conformational states is characterized by the equilibrium constant, L:L = $\mathbf{T_o/R_o}$. The different states have different affinities for the various ligands. Usually, it is assumed that the substrate S binds "only" to the **R** state; the positive allosteric effector A binds "only" to the **R** state; and the negative allosteric effector I binds "only" to the **T** state. Given these parameters, the sigmoid rate response of allosteric enzymes to substrate concentration and the effects exerted by allosteric effectors are understood. The system described above is called a "K" system, because the substrate concentration giving half-maximal velocity, defined as $K_{0.5}$, varies, while V_{max} remains constant. In the "*V*" system of allosteric control, **R** and **T** states have the same affinity for S, but the **R** state is catalytically active, while the **T** state is not. A and I still differ in their relative affinities for **R** and **T**. Both the *K* and the *V* systems assume that the oligomeric allosteric protein undergoes a concerted conformational transition so that all subunits have identical conformations at the same time. The Koshland, Nemethey, and Filmer model rests on the "induced fit" hypothesis. That is, via tightly linked subunit interactions, the binding of ligand to one subunit can influence the ligand-binding affinity of neighbouring subunits. Therefore, an oligomeric protein could pass through a sequential series of conformations with differing ligand affinities, and different subunits may not necessarily have the same conformation at the same time.

Chapter 15

Molecular Motors

• •

Chapter Outline

❖ Molecular motors: Energy-transducing molecules that convert chemical energy into mechanical energy
❖ Muscle contraction: Actin/myosin-based system
  ⅄ Muscle cells: Multinucleated long cells known as muscle fibres
  ⅄ Myofibrils: Linear arrays of muscle proteins within muscle fibres
  ⅄ Sarcomere: Repeat unit along myofibril
  ⅄ Sarcolemma: Specialized plasma membrane surrounding muscle fibres
    • Transverse (or t) tubules: Extensions of plasma membrane (sarcolemma) that contact myofibrils
    • Sarcoplasmic reticulum: Specialized endoplasmic reticulum membrane that surrounds myofibrils
❖ Sarcomeres: Basic structural units of contraction: Repeat regions along myofibrils
  ⅄ Z line to Z line: Attachment site of F-actin
  ⅄ I band: Centred around Z lines: F-actin of opposite polarity on each side, tropomyosin and troponin
  ⅄ A band: Centred within sarcomere: Composed of myosin
  ⅄ H zone: Centred on M disc within A bond: Opposite myosin polarity on neither side of M disc
    • Region of A band outside H zone: Actin and myosin overlap
❖ Thin filaments
  ⅄ Filamentous (F) actin: Polymers of globular (G) actin
    • Polar filaments
    • Stimulates ATPase activity of myosin
  ⅄ Tropomyosin: Heterodimeric protein: Coiled coils of alpha helix
    • Dimers form head-to-tail polymers
    • Polymers bind to F-actin
    • Stoichiometry: 7 Actin per tropomyosin heterodimer
  ⅄ Troponin
    • Troponin T: Binds to tropomyosin
    • Troponin I: Binds to tropomyosin and actin
    • Troponin C: Binds to Troponin I
❖ Thick filaments: Bipolar myosin filaments
  ⅄ Myosin composition
    • Two heavy chains
    • Two LC1 (light chains): Essential light chains
    • Two LC2: Regulatory light chains
  ⅄ Myosin structure
    • Heavy chain tails associate to form filaments
      • 7-residue repeats form coiled-coil
    • Heads: Heavy and light chains: ATPase activity

- ❖ Muscle contraction: Sliding filament model
  - ⅄ Muscle tension (when accompanied by muscle shortening; i.e., non-isometric contractions) is a result of thin filaments sliding relative to thick filaments
    - • Sarcomere length decreases
    - • I band and H zone decrease
  - ⅄ Sliding depends on ATP and calcium
    - • ATP: Myosin heads are actin-activated ATPase
      - ● ATP dissociates myosin from actin
      - ● Myosin hydrolyzes ATP but requires actin to release products
      - ● Release of products is accompanied by conformational change
      - ● ATP binding reverses conformational change
- ❖ Cytoskeleton
  - ⅄ Functions
    - • Cell shape, mechanical strength, movement, transport of organelles, separation of chromosomes
  - ⅄ Components
    - • Microtubule, microfilaments, intermediate filaments
- ❖ Microtubule-based systems
  - ⅄ Microtubules
    - • Hollow tubes composed of the heterodimeric protein tubulin: $\alpha\beta$-tubulin dimer
    - • Tubulin subunits add onto the (+)-end
- ❖ Motor proteins: Myosins, kinesins, dyneins
  - ⅄ Kinesin 1: Tetramer of two heavy and two light chains
    - • Heavy chain N-terminal motor domain (binds to microtubules), coiled-coil stalk, C-terminal light chain–binding sites and cargo-binding site
    - • Light chains
  - ⅄ Dyneins: Microtubule motors: Axonemal and cytoplasmic varieties
    - • Cytoplasmic dynein: Dimer of heavy chains and several light chains
      - ● Heavy chain: Motor domain and microtubule-binding stalk domain
  - ⅄ Myosin V: Multimer of 16 chains
    - • Heavy chains form dimers: Domains include motor head, calmodulin binding neck and long tail with light chains
  - ⅄ Organelle movement along microtubules: microtubules point + end toward cell periphery
    - • Cytosolic dyneins move vesicles from + end to – end (back towards cell centre)
    - • Kinesis move from – end toward + end
  - ⅄ Motor characteristics
    - • Dyneins, myosins, and kinesins are processive: Move along track without releasing
    - • Movement governed by ATP binding and hydrolysis
      - ● Kinesins move hand-over-hand
- ❖ Motor molecules that move along DNA and RNA: Translocases
  - ⅄ Translocase that unwind DNA are helicases
  - ⅄ Translocases related to RecA protein
  - ⅄ Translocase movement is processive and driven by ATP hydrolysis
    - • Processivity by two different mechanisms
      - ● Hexameric helicases form rings around DNA
      - ● Rep helicase move hand-over-hand
        - ○ Basis is negative cooperativity between DNA-binding sites
- ❖ Rotary motors in bacteria
  - ⅄ Extracellular protein filaments: Polymers of flagellin: Function as propellers
  - ⅄ Membrane localized motors
    - • Attached to flagellin
    - • Use proton gradient for energy source
    - • Reversal of motor causes change in direction of swimming

Chapter Objectives

Microtubules

Microtubules are hollow cylindrical structures composed of the heterodimeric protein tubulin. Know the basic structure of the microtubule, the fact that it is composed of 13 protofilaments made up of a head-to-tail arrangement of tubulin dimers and that the structure has two distinct ends, the plus end and the minus end. These designations come from the fact that subunit addition to a microtubule occurs predominantly on the plus end. Microtubules function as cytoskeletal elements and as the principal polymeric structure in cilia and eukaryotic flagella. In cilia and flagella, microtubules are arranged in a characteristic 9 + 2 array known as the axoneme. A key, non-tubulin component of the axoneme is the microtubule-dependent ATPase dynein. The axoneme is a mechanochemical energy transducer converting the chemical energy released upon hydrolysis of ATP by dynein into the energy of axonemal movement. Cytoplasmic microtubules are involved in a number of cell functions including movement of particles within cells. This is best typified by axonal transport in neurons. Axonal microtubules like cytoplasmic microtubules are arranged with their plus ends toward the periphery of the cell or, in this case, toward the axon ends, whereas their minus ends are toward the cell body. Movement of organelles and vesicles from the plus end of a microtubule to the minus end is mediated by cytosolic dyneins. Movement in the opposite direction is dependent on kinesins, ATPases similar to cytosolic dyneins.

Muscle Cell Anatomy

Skeletal muscle cells contain fibre bundles termed myofibrils, which are composed predominantly of actin and myosin filaments. The myofibrils are divided into functional units called sarcomeres. Know how the basic anatomy of a sarcomere is composed of actin filaments and myosin filaments and how the two interdigitate. A sarcomere is a banded structure bordered by two Z lines. The A band marks the location of myosin filaments and is centred in the sarcomere. The bipolar myosin filaments contain a central portion devoid of myosin heads. The actin filaments are located in the I band and in part of the A band as they interdigitate with the myosin fibres. The region of the A band not containing interdigitated actin filaments is termed the H zone. The central bare region of the myosin bipolar filaments is centred in the H zone. During contraction, the I band shortens because actin and myosin filaments increase their regions of overlap. As a consequence, the H band shortens. The t-tubules are extensions of the sarcolemma that reach into the muscle cell interior and terminate close to the sarcoplasmic reticulum. Calcium ion release from the sarcoplasmic reticulum is the key event in initiation of muscle contraction and calcium release is set off by electrical signals propagated from the cell surface to the sarcoplasmic reticulum via the t-tubules.

Thin Filaments

The thin filaments are filaments of globular actin studded at regular intervals with a troponin complex of TnT, TnI, and TnC and lined with tropomyosin. Myosin-binding sites on F-actin can be covered and exposed by movement of tropomyosin in a calcium-dependent manner mediated by TnC. The thin filaments attach to the Z lines by association with α-actinin, which is a protein homologous to spectrin, the major structural protein of the red blood cell cytoskeleton. The ends of actin filaments are capped with β-actinin and two other components, γ-actinin, and paratropomyosin, are also found associated with the thin filament.

Thick Filaments

Myosin is the principal component of the thick filaments. A myosin molecule is composed of two heavy chains and two pairs of light chains, LC1 and LC2. Myosin is an asymmetric molecule with two heads (on one end) and a tail. The thick filaments are bundles of myosins, interacting in a tail-to-tail fashion to give rise to a "dumbbell"-like filament with a bare zone in the middle (tails only) and the heads sticking out around each end. The heads are the business end of the molecule; they have ATPase activity and are responsible for muscle contraction. The thick filaments contain additional proteins including creatine kinase and several proteins found in the M disc, a structure within the H zone important for organizing myosin filaments. The thick filaments are linked to the Z lines by β-connectin.

Sliding Filaments and Myosin ATPase Cycle

Myosin is an actin-activated ATPase that cycles between two conformational states. You should be familiar with the ATPase cycle of myosin and how it leads to force generation. In the resting state, the nucleotide-binding site of myosin is filled with ADP and P_i. Calcium, released upon stimulation, binds to TnC and induces a conformational change that causes movement of tropomyosin. This results in exposure of myosin-binding sites on actin. Myosin binds to actin, releases P_i, and subsequently undergoes a conformational change and release of ADP. The conformational change results in movement of the actin filament relative to myosin in a power stroke. ATP will now bind to the nucleotide-binding site, causing myosin to dissociate from actin. Myosin then hydrolyzes ATP as it returns to the resting conformation.

Calcium Ion Regulation

Calcium release is mediated through a series of calcium channels. The t-tubules contain dihydropyridine-sensitive calcium channels, whereas calcium channels in the terminal cisternae of the sarcoplasmic reticulum are sensitive to ryanodine. Uptake of calcium leading to muscle relaxation is mediated by calcium pumps.

Problems and Solutions

1. The cheetah is generally regarded as nature's fastest mammal, but another amazing athlete in the animal kingdom (and almost as fast as the cheetah) is the pronghorn antelope, which roams the plains of Wyoming. Whereas the cheetah can maintain its top speed of 70 mph for only a few seconds, the pronghorn antelope can run at 60 mph for about an hour! (It is thought to have evolved to do so in order to elude now-extinct ancestral cheetahs that lived in North America.) What differences would you expect in the muscle structure and anatomy of pronghorn antelopes that could account for their remarkable speed and endurance?

Answer: Clearly, the pronghorn antelope must be a master of oxidative phosphorylation and because of this must be capable of supplying muscle with oxygen-rich blood. The organs involved in oxygen homeostasis, namely the circulatory system (including the heart, blood, and blood vessels), are optimized for this task. The animal has a large, powerful heart, blood with a high hematocrit and red cells with high amounts of hemoglobin, and well-vascularized muscle and lung tissue. The animal is light and compact and of efficient design. In addition, muscle cells contain large numbers of mitochondria and numerous short muscle fibres.

3. ATP stores in muscle are augmented or supplemented by stores of phosphocreatine. During periods of contraction, phosphocreatine is hydrolyzed to drive the synthesis of needed ATP in the creatine kinase reaction:

$$Phosphocreatine + ADP \rightarrow creatine + ATP$$

Muscle cells contain 2 different isozymes of creatine kinase, 1 in the mitochondria, and 1 in the sarcoplasm. Explain.

Answer: Creatine is phosphorylated at the expense of ATP in the mitochondria and then exported to the sarcoplasm. In the sarcoplasm, it functions as a store of high-energy phosphate bonds to be used during intense muscle activity to replenish ATP supplies. Creatine phosphorylation in the mitochondria is accomplished by a mitochondrial creatine kinase. Phosphorylation of ADP by phosphocreatine in the sarcoplasm is accomplished by a sarcoplasmic enzyme. Free creatine and phosphocreatine thus form a circuit with phosphocreatine leaving the mitochondria and creatine entering.

5. Skeletal muscle can generate approximately 3–4 kg of tension or force per square centimetre of cross-sectional area. This number is roughly the same for all mammals. Since many human muscles have large cross-sectional areas, the force that these muscles can (and must) generate is prodigious. The gluteus maximus—on which you are probably sitting as you read this—can generate a tension of 1200 kg! Estimate the cross-sectional areas of all of the muscles in your body and the total force that your skeletal muscles could generate if they all contracted at once.

Answer: A person might have a maximum of 50% of her or his total body mass as muscle. For a 70 kg person, the muscle would account for approximately 35 kg. Assuming a density of 1 g/mL (muscle is slightly more dense than water but not by much), the 35 kg is approximately 35 000 mL or 35 000 cm^3. If this total mass of muscle were in the shape of a cylinder 1 cm thick the cylinder's cross-sectional area would be 35 000 cm^2.

   We are informed that the gluteus maximus can generate 1200 kg of force and that the average force is 3–4 kg per cm^2. If muscle generates 3–4 kg of tension per cm^2 then 35 000 cm^2 can generate between 1.05×10^5 and 1.40×10^5 kg of force.

7. Use the number you obtained in Problem 6 to calculate how many tubulin monomers would be found in a microtubule that stretched across the length of a liver cell. (See Table 1.2 for the diameter of a liver cell.)

Answer: The length of a liver cell is 20 000 nm. So, a microtubule 20 000 nm long would have:

$$\frac{20\ 000\ \text{nm}}{5.12\ \dfrac{\text{nm}}{\text{monomer}}} = 3906\ \text{monomers}$$

But, there are 13 protofilaments per cross-section.

Thus, there are

3906 monomers $\times$ 13 = 50 781 monomers.

9. As noted in this chapter, the myosin molecules in thick filaments of muscle are offset by approximately 14 nm. To how many residues of a coiled-coil structure does this correspond?

Answer: A coiled coil has a pitch of 0.51 nm and 3.5 residues per turn (slightly different from the 0.54 pitch of an alpha helix with 3.6 residues per turn). The number of residues of coiled coil represented by 14 nm is given by:

$$\frac{14\ \text{nm}}{0.51\ \dfrac{\text{nm}}{\text{turn}}} = 27.5\ \text{turns} \times \frac{3.5\ \text{residues}}{\text{turn}} = 96\ \text{residues}$$

11. Use the equations of Chapter 3 to determine the free energy of hydrolysis of ATP by the sarcoplasmic reticulum Ca-ATPase if the concentration of ATP is 3 mM, the concentration of ADP is 1 mM, and the concentration of P_i is 2 mM.

Answer:

For hydrolysis of ATP:

$$\Delta G = \Delta G_0' + RT \times \ln\frac{[\text{ADP}][P_i]}{[\text{ATP}]} = 8.31541\ \frac{\text{J}}{\text{mol K}} \times 298\ \text{K} \times \ln\frac{\left(1\times10^{-3}\right)\times\left(2\times10^{-3}\right)}{3\times10^{-3}}$$

$$\Delta G = -30.5 + 8.31541\ \frac{\text{J}}{\text{mol K}} \times 298\ \text{K} \times \ln\frac{\left(1\times10^{-3}\right)\times\left(2\times10^{-3}\right)}{3\times10^{-3}}$$

$$\Delta G = -48\ 620\ \frac{\text{J}}{\text{mol}}$$

13. For each of the motor proteins in Table 15.2, calculate the force exerted over the step size given, assuming that the free energy of hydrolysis of ATP under cellular conditions is −50 kJ/mol.

Answer: Hydrolysis of ATP releases −50 kJ of energy per mol of ATP and accounts for movement of the various motor molecules by one step. This movement was accomplished by a force acting through a step distance.

$$\text{Energy} = \text{Force} \times \text{distance}$$

A Joule of energy is a Newton of force acting through 1 metre of distance. Thus, 50 kJ is equivalent to 50 000 newton·metre.

$$\text{Force} = \frac{\text{Energy}}{\text{distance}}$$

$$\text{Force}_{\text{Kinesin 1}} = \frac{50\ \text{kJ}}{8\ \text{nm}} = \frac{50\ 000\ \text{newton}\cdot\text{m}}{8\ \times\ 10^{-9}\ \text{m}} = 6.25\times10^{12}\ \text{newtons}$$

$$\text{Force}_{\text{Myosin V}} = \frac{50\ \text{kJ}}{36\ \text{nm}} = \frac{50\ 000\ \text{newton}\cdot\text{m}}{36\ \times\ 10^{-9}\ \text{m}} = 1.39\times10^{12}\ \text{newtons}$$

$$\text{Force}_{\text{Dynein}} = \frac{50\ \text{kJ}}{28\ \text{nm}} = \frac{50\ 000\ \text{newton}\cdot\text{m}}{28\ \times\ 10^{-9}\ \text{m}} = 1.79\times10^{12}\ \text{newtons}$$

15. In which of the following tissues would you expect to find smooth muscle?
 a. *arteries*
 b. *stomach*
 c. *urinary bladder*
 d. *diaphragm*
 e. *uterus*
 f. *the gums in your mouth*

Answer: If you take a deep breath before answering this question, you might realize that you have voluntary control over your diaphragm, suggesting that it is not composed of smooth muscle. All the others have smooth muscle.

17. (Essay question.) You are invited by the National Science and Engineering Research Council (NSERC) to attend a scientific meeting to set the agenda for funding of basic research related to molecular motors for the next 10 years. Only basic research will be funded, ruling out studies on human subjects. You are asked to suggest the research area most worthy of scientific research. Your presentation must include (1) a brief background on what we currently know about the subject, (2) identification of a key research topic about which more needs to be known, and (3) a justification of why additional knowledge in this area is critical for advancing the field (that is, why investigations in this area are especially important). You are not being asked to provide the methods or experiments that might be used to address the problem—only the concept. Base your presentation on what you have learned in this chapter (you may consult and include references from the Further Reading section), and limit your presentation to 300 words.

Answer: Start out by reading a few brief reviews on the subject of molecular motors. It would make a great deal of sense to focus on one area like myosins or RNA helicases to make this a manageable assignment. Good luck.

Questions for Self-Study

1. Fill in the blanks. Cytoskeletal elements composed of hollow, cylindrical structures 24 nm in diameter are known as _____. These polymers are made up of the protein _____, a dimeric protein composed of _____ and _____. These cytoskeletal elements are the major structural elements of cilia and flagella. An ATPase, _____, is responsible for production of a sliding motion between polymers that is converted to a bending motion typical of ciliary or flagellar motion. A cytosolic variety of this ATPase is found in axons where it mediates the movement of organelles and vesicles from the plus end of a microtubule to the minus end. (The plus end is the end at which dimer subunits are _____ to the microtubule.) Another ATPase, _____, mediates movement of organelles and vesicles in the opposite direction.

2. What are the four kinds of muscle? Which is multinucleated?

3. On the microscopic level, skeletal and cardiac muscles display light and dark bands. What is the general name given to muscle with banding patterns?

4. Fill in the blanks. The basic structural units of skeletal muscle contraction are _____. They are arranged as linear arrays into small fibres called _____. The fibres are covered by a specialized endoplasmic reticulum called _____ _____. The ends of the fibres are bounded by extension of the muscle cell plasma membrane or _____. The extensions form _____ _____ that connect the specialized sarcoplasmic reticulum with the plasma membrane.

5. In the diagram presented below, label the following: I band, Z line, A band, H zone, location of thin filaments only, location of thick filaments only, overlap of thin and thick filaments.

6. Sort the terms below into thick filament or thin filament components.
    a. G-actin
    b. Heavy chains
    c. Troponin I
    d. Regulatory light chain
    e. Tropomyosin
    f. S1 fragments
    g. HMM
    h. Creatine kinase
    i. β-Actinin
    j. Troponin C
    k. Light meromyosin
    l. Troponin T
    m. Essential light chain
    n. Myosin

7. In skeletal muscle, cycles of contraction and relaxation are a result of a calcium cycle. Describe this calcium cycle.

Answers

1. Microtubules; tubulin; α-tubulin; β-tubulin; dynein; added; kinesin.

2. Skeletal (multinucleated), cardiac, smooth, and myoepithelial.

3. Striated.

4. Sarcomeres; myofibrils; sarcoplasmic reticulum; sarcolemma; transverse (or T) tubules.

5.

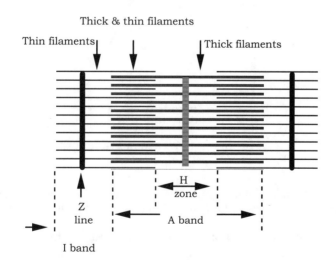

6. | Thick filament terms | Thin filament terms |
    | --- | --- |
    | b. Heavy chains | a. G-actin |
    | d. Regulatory light chain | c. Troponin I |
    | f. S1 fragments | e. Tropomyosin |
    | g. HMM | i. β-Actinin |
    | h. Creatine kinase | j. Troponin C |
    | k. Light meromyosin | l. Troponin T |
    | m. Essential light chain | |
    | n. Myosin | |

7. Calcium is released from the sarcoplasmic reticulum in response to electrical stimulation. This results in an increase in the concentration of sarcoplasmic calcium, which leads to calcium binding to troponin C and movement of troponin I and tropomyosin. The result of tropomyosin movement is to expose myosin-binding sites on actin. Relaxation occurs when the sarcoplasmic calcium ion concentration is lowered as a result of active transport of calcium back into the sarcoplasmic reticulum by calcium pumps.

Additional Problems

1. Design a simple experiment to determine the association constant for assembly of tubulin dimers to the ends of a microtubule.

2. The concentration of tubulin dimers determined above is the critical dimer concentration for assembly of microtubules. At equilibrium, dimers are being added to the polymer, but if dimer assembly causes the free tubulin dimer concentration to fall below the critical concentration, the microtubule will disassemble, thereby releasing free dimers to increase the concentration of dimers. The plus end and the minus end of microtubules have different critical dimer concentrations with the minus end being higher than the plus end. How does this lead to treadmilling?

3. The tenderloin is a muscle that runs along the back of an animal and is the source of filet mignon, a tender cut of meat, so tender in fact that when cooked, it can be cut with a fork. Can you suggest a reason why this muscle is so tender?

4. The graph below shows tension developed by a sarcomere held at various fixed lengths, where 100 refers to the natural resting length of the sarcomere. Based on your knowledge of sarcomere microanatomy, explain the line segments (ab), (bc), (cd), and (de).

5. Myosin heads can be used to stain actin filaments in non-muscle cells for the purpose of identification of a filament as an actin filament and to establish the direction of polarity. Explain.

6. It is customary to sever the spinal cord of a recently sacrificed fish in order to prevent the fish from becoming stiff. Why?

Abbreviated Answers

1. If we assume that the thermodynamics of elongation is more favourable than initiation, then, in conditions that favour microtubule formation, microtubules will be in equilibrium with free tubulin dimers or:

$$MT_{n-1} + T \rightleftarrows MT_n \text{ where}$$

$$K = \frac{[MT_n]}{[MT_{n-1}][T]}$$

Recognizing that $[MT_{n-1}] = [MT_n]$ we see that $K_A = [T]^{-1}$. If we could measure the concentration of free tubulin dimer in equilibrium with microtubules we could determine K. This can be accomplished by simply centrifuging the sample at a speed that will sediment microtubules but not tubulin dimers. By measuring the concentration of tubulin in the supernatant, we can determine K.

2.   Consider a solution of tubulin polymerizing into microtubules. As the concentration of free dimers decreases to the critical concentration of minus end assembly, addition of dimers to the minus end stops. However, since the critical concentration of plus end assembly is lower than minus end assembly, dimers will continue to add to the plus end. This depletes the concentration of free subunits below the critical concentration of minus end assembly, causing subunits to dissociate from the minus end. The system reaches a steady state at which minus end disassembly is balanced by plus end assembly.

3.   There are a couple of reasons. First, the muscle is composed of a relatively small number of very large muscle fibres with little connective tissue. Second, the muscle is not an extremely active muscle like the muscles of the shoulder. Finally, the filet is a cross-sectional cut out of the muscle across the long axis of the muscle fibres. The meat can be easily cut into smaller pieces by simply separating muscle fibres with a fork.

4.   At position (e), the sarcomere has been stretched so that thick and thin filaments no longer overlap and no tension is possible. Moving from (e) to (d), the length corresponds to an increase in overlap between thick and thin filaments and therefore a decrease in sarcomere length. At (d), actin filaments maximally overlap the region of thick filaments containing heads. At point (c), the thin filaments from opposite sides of the sarcomere come in contact. Moving from (d) to (c), no change in the number of cross-bridges overlapping with thin filaments occurs and the sarcomere can generate maximum tension. Sarcomere length between (c) and (b) result in overlap of thin filaments from opposite sides of the sarcomere. The drop in tension in moving from (b) to (a) results when actin filaments from opposite sides of the sarcomere begin to overlap with myosin heads on the opposite side of the thick filament. The following diagrams illustrate these points.

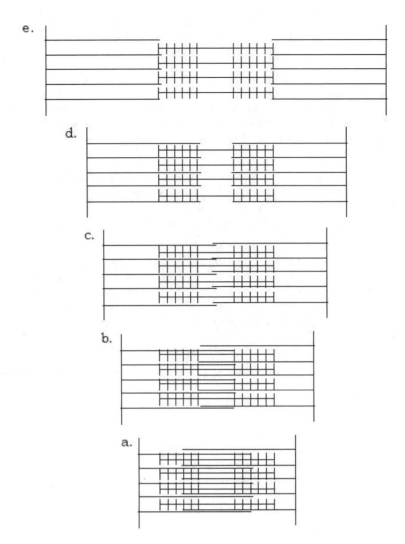

5. The S1 fragment of myosin will bind to actin fibres and decorate them in a characteristic arrowhead pattern. The tips of the arrowheads point away from the Z line in a sarcomere.

6. Fish become stiff because of *rigour mortis* as a result of a release of calcium and depletion of ATP stores. After death, the nerves quickly deteriorate and begin to randomly fire, leading to muscle stimulation and rapid depletion of ATP stores. By severing the spinal cord and icing the fish, the depletion of ATP stores can be delayed.

Summary

All organisms (at least at some stage in life) are capable of movement or motion. The energy for these processes is chemical energy that is transduced into mechanical energy by motor proteins. Motor proteins found in microtubule-based motile systems and those found in actin-dependent systems utilize hydrolysis of ATP, whereas the rotary motor found in bacterial flagella uses the energy of a proton gradient.

Microtubules are self-assembling structures that are fundamental components of cilia and eukaryotic flagella. Microtubules are formed by polymerization of tubulin, a dimeric protein comprised of similar 55 kD subunits. By the GTP-dependent process of treadmilling, tubulin units are added at the plus end of the microtubule and removed from the minus end. With their plus ends oriented toward the cell periphery and the minus ends toward the centre of the cell, microtubules form a significant part of the cytoskeleton. The motion of cilia and flagella results from the ATP-driven sliding or walking of dyneins along one microtubule while remaining firmly attached to an adjacent microtubule. Within eukaryotic cells, cellular dyneins and kinesin proteins are responsible for microtubule-based transport of organelles and vesicles.

Actin and myosin are two proteins responsible for various kinds of motion in a number of cell types. The best characterized system is muscle. Muscle contraction is essential to higher organisms for limb movement, locomotion, beating of the heart, and other functions. Four different kinds of muscle are found in higher organisms: skeletal, cardiac, smooth muscle, and myoepithelial cells. The latter three types are called myocytes and contain a single nucleus, whereas the cells of skeletal muscle—the muscle fibres—are multinucleate. Skeletal and cardiac muscle are striated. The sarcolemmal membrane contains extensions called transverse tubules which surround the sarcomeres and which enable the sarcolemmal membrane to contact the ends of each myofibril in the muscle fibre. Between t-tubules, the sarcomere is covered by the sarcoplasmic reticulum membrane. The terminal cisternae of the SR are joined to the t-tubules by foot structures. The trigger signal for muscle contraction is an increase in cytoplasmic [Ca^{2+}]. Relaxation occurs when [Ca^{2+}] is reduced.

Electron micrographs of banding patterns in skeletal muscle are consistent with a model for contraction in which thick and thin filaments slide along each other. Actin is the principal component of muscle thin filaments. It consists of a monomeric protein, G-actin, which polymerizes to form long filaments of right-handed helical F-actin. Other components of thin filaments include tropomyosin and the troponin complex. Myosin is the principal component of muscle thick filaments and consists of a globular head and a long, helical tail. The tails intertwine to form a left-handed coiled coil. The myosin heads exhibit ATPase activity, and it is the hydrolysis of ATP by the myosin heads that drives muscle contraction. Repeating structures in the myosin tails, including 7-residue, 28-residue, and 196-residue repeating units facilitate the formation of myosin–solvent and myosin–myosin interactions that stabilize the packing of myosin molecules in the thick filaments.

The molecular events of skeletal muscle contraction are powered by the ATPase activity of myosin. Actin increases the ATPase activity of myosin by 200-fold. Further, myosin and actin spontaneously associate to form an actomyosin complex, but ATP decreases the affinity of myosin for actin. In the absence of actin, ATP is rapidly cleaved at the myosin active site, but the hydrolysis products—ADP and P_i—are not released. Actin activates myosin ATPase by stimulating the release of P_i and then ADP. Thus, ATP hydrolysis and the association and dissociation of actin and myosin are coupled. The coupling involves a conformational change in the myosin head, driven by the free energy of hydrolysis of ATP, so that dissociation of myosin and actin, hydrolysis of ATP, and rebinding of myosin and actin occur with a net movement of the myosin head along the actin filament. Each such conformation change moves the thick filament approximately 100 Å along the thin filament.

Flagellated bacterial cells produce motility by rotating extracellular protein filaments, termed flagella and composed of the protein flagellin, using a rotary motor, which harnesses the energy of proton gradients to produce movement.

Chapter 16

Nutrition and the Organization of Metabolism

• •

Chapter Outline

❖ Metabolic diversity
  ⅄ Autotrophs: Utilize carbon dioxide as carbon source
  ⅄ Heterotrophs: Require carbon in organic molecules
  ⅄ Phototrophs: Use light as source of energy
  ⅄ Chemotrophs: Use chemical reactions as source of energy
❖ Role of oxygen
  ⅄ Obligate aerobes: Require oxygen
  ⅄ Obligate anaerobes: No need for oxygen: Oxygen poisonous
  ⅄ Facultative anaerobes: Adapt to anaerobic conditions
❖ Metabolic processes: Two types
  ⅄ Catabolism
    • Exergonic: Energy transduced into ATP
    • Oxidative degradation of complex molecules into simpler compounds
    • Electrons captured by NAD^+
  ⅄ Anabolism
    • Complex biomolecules produced from simpler precursors
    • Synthesis driven by energy, typically ATP hydrolysis
    • NADPH serves as source of electrons
  ⅄ Convergence of pathways
    • Stage 1: Nutrient macromolecules broken down into building block monomers
    • Stage 2: Building block monomers degraded to limited set of simpler intermediates
    • Stage 3: Combustion of intermediates to CO_2 and H_2O
  ⅄ ATP is energy connection between catabolism and anabolism
  ⅄ NAD^+ and NADPH are oxidizing and reducing agents in metabolism
  ⅄ Regulation
    • Anabolism and catabolism separately regulated
    • Competing pathways often localized in different cellular compartments
    • Anabolic and catabolic pathways (involving same end points) differ in at least one or more steps
      • Allows pathways to be regulated separately
      • Avoids simultaneous functioning of both pathways
❖ Enzymes organization
  ⅄ Separate, soluble entities: Intermediates supplied by diffusion
  ⅄ Multi-enzyme complexes: Intermediates passed between components of complex
  ⅄ Membrane-bound enzymes or complexes
❖ Experimental methods
  ⅄ Metabolic inhibitors
  ⅄ Genetic mutations
  ⅄ Isotopic traces
    • Radioactive isotopes: Detected when isotope decays by release of energy
    • Stable, heavy isotopes: Alter density of product
  ⅄ NMR: Signal sensitive to electronic environment of atomic nucleus

❖ Nutrition: Use of foods by organisms: Five components
  ⅄ Proteins: Source of amino acids
    • Essential amino acids
    • Degradation of amino acids
      • Glucogenic: Some amino acids can be used to produce glucose
      • Ketogenic: Some amino acids can be used to produce fatty acids
  ⅄ Carbohydrates: Metabolic energy derived from catabolism of carbohydrates
  ⅄ Lipids
    • Metabolic energy sources
    • Components of membranes
    • Sources of essential fatty acids: Linoleic and linolenic acids
  ⅄ Fibre: Cellulose, hemicellulose, lignins
  ⅄ Vitamins: Two classes
    • Water soluble: Used as coenzymes or coenzyme precursors (except vitamin C)
    • Fat soluble

Chapter Objectives

Understand the terms metabolism, catabolism, and anabolism. Know the classification of organisms, with respect to carbon and energy requirements, into photoautotrophs, photoheterotrophs, chemoautotrophs, and chemoheterotrophs. (What are you? Your houseplants?) Understand the terms obligate aerobes, facultative anaerobes, and obligate anaerobes.

The remainder of the textbook will concentrate on details of metabolism and take a step-by-step tour of individual pathways. This chapter gives the big picture. For example, oxygen moves in a cycle from photoautotrophic cells as O_2 to heterotrophic cells, from heterotrophic cells to heterotrophic cells as oxy-compounds, and from heterotrophic cells back to photoautotrophic cells as CO_2 and H_2O. Carbon cycles between photoautotrophs and heterotrophs as CO_2 and organic compounds.

Understand the role of ATP in metabolism. ATP is an energy-rich compound used to coupled exergonic to endergonic processes. In general, catabolic pathways are exergonic and produce ATP, whereas anabolic pathways are endergonic and consume ATP. The cofactors NAD^+ and NADPH play key roles in oxidation–reduction reactions. Catabolic pathways are often oxidative in nature with NAD^+ serving as the oxidant. In contrast, anabolic pathways are reductive with NADPH serving as a reductant.

Intermediary metabolism can be overwhelming at first glance, but appreciate the fact that the pathways converge to or diverge from a small number of key intermediates. In catabolism, large macro-molecules such as proteins, polysaccharides, and lipids are broken down into their component building blocks, which are catabolized into a small set of common metabolic intermediates that may be degraded to simple end products (e.g., CO_2, NH_3, H_2O). Alternatively, these intermediates can be used in anabolism to resynthesize macromolecules. Resynthesis pathways may share a number of intermediates with degradive pathways, but at least one step is different. This allows for independent regulation of the competing actions. How is regulation achieved? Clearly, reactions must be sensitive to concentrations of substrates and products but more sophisticated controls are often imposed at key reactions. These controls include allosteric regulation, covalent modification, and alterations of the level of enzyme or in the type of enzyme.

Problems and Solutions

1. If 3×10^{14} kg of CO_2 are cycled through the biosphere annually, how many human equivalents (70-kg persons composed of 18% carbon by weight) could be produced each year from this amount of CO_2?

Answer: The amount of carbon in a 70 kg person is 0.18 × 70 kg = 12.6 kg

$$\text{Carbon dioxide is } \frac{12}{12+16+16} \times 100\% = 27.3\% \text{ by weight in carbon}$$

So, 3×10^{14} kg of CO_2 represents $(3 \times 10^{14}$ kg$) \times 0.273 = 8.18 \times 10^{13}$ kg

$$\frac{8.18 \times 10^{13} \text{ kg}}{12.6 \dfrac{\text{kg}}{\text{person}}} = 6.5 \times 10^{12} \text{ people}$$

That is, 6 500 000 000 000 or 6.5 trillion people.

3. Name the 3 principal inorganic sources of oxygen atoms that are commonly available in the inanimate environment and readily accessible to the biosphere.

Answer: Most photosynthetic organisms use H_2O as a source of electrons to reduce CO_2 during carbon fixation. Thus, water is an abundant source of oxygen that is readily available. During the course of this process, oxygen gas (O_2) is liberated into the atmosphere. Aerobic organisms utilize O_2 as an electron acceptor during oxidation of reduced carbon compounds; CO_2 is released. This CO_2 is used by photosynthetic autotrophs to produce biomolecules. Oxygen thus cycles between H_2O, O_2, and CO_2.

5. Name the 3 principal modes of enzyme organization in metabolic pathways.

Answer: A metabolic pathway consists of all of the individual reactions involved in transforming a substrate into an end product. The reactions or steps are almost always catalyzed by enzymes. The enzymes may be separate proteins localized within a cell or cellular compartment but otherwise soluble. The product of one reaction is made available to the next reaction by diffusion. Alternatively, two or more enzymes may be organized into a multi-enzyme complex. Here, the enzymes catalyze sequential steps in the pathway. In this organization, the product of one enzyme is released directly to the next enzyme in the pathway. Finally, enzymes and enzyme complexes may be confined to a particular membrane within the cell. The purpose may be to provide a bridge between compartments, or to localize an enzymatic activity in a two-dimensional surface. Substrates confined to move in or along the membrane are only required to do a two-dimensional search to encounter enzyme.

7. (Integrates with Chapters 1 and 3) What are the metabolic roles of ATP, NAD⁺, and NADPH?

Answer: The living state requires a constant source of energy for biosynthesis, for movement, for replication—in short, for all of the activities characterizing the living state. The immediate source of energy depends on the cell type (see Problem 2) and includes light energy, chemical energy, or both. However, independent of the source of energy, all cells transduce energy into the chemical energy of the phosphoric anhydride bonds of ATP. ATP is the energy currency of cells. Hydrolysis of the high-energy bonds of ATP may be used to drive biosynthetic pathways and to support all of the other activities of the living state. Thus, ATP serves to couple exergonic processes to endergonic processes. For example, ATP synthesized during catabolic, exergonic pathways is used in hydrolysis reactions to drive anabolic, endergonic pathways.

The major catabolic pathways common to virtually all cells are based on oxidation of carbon compounds. For example, the conversion of glucose to C_2O and H_2O includes three oxidative sequences. In glycolysis, glucose is converted to pyruvate. Next, pyruvate is oxidized to acetyl-coenzyme A. Finally, acetyl-coenzyme A is metabolized to CO_2 and H_2O in the citric acid cycle. These three oxidative sequences of necessity are accompanied by electron transfers and NAD⁺ serves as the primary electron acceptor.

In contrast, anabolic pathways are often reductive; the immediate reductant or electron donor is NADPH. Thus, this reduced, phosphorylated form of NAD⁺ plays a role in metabolism exactly opposite to that of NAD⁺.

9. What are the advantages of compartmentalizing particular metabolic pathways within specific organelles?

Answer: Compartmentalization provides an easy solution to the problem of regulating two opposing pathways. For example, the catabolic pathway for fatty acid metabolism, known as β-oxidation, occurs in the mitochondria. In contrast, fatty acid biosynthesis largely occurs in the cytosol. Compartments may also provide a particular set of conditions favourable to only certain reactions. There is a group of enzymes known as acid hydrolases that are localized in lysosomes. These enzymes include proteases, nucleases, lipases, and glycosidases and they function at acidic pH. The enzymes are confined by a membrane barrier, and their activity is enhanced by the acidic pH maintained within lysosomes. If inadvertently released into the cytosol, these enzymes fail to cause damage to cellular components because the cytosol is maintained at a higher pH.

11. Compare and contrast mass spectrometry and NMR in terms of their potential advantages and disadvantages for metabolomic analysis.

Answer: Mass spectrometry is a very sensitive detection technique that requires small amounts of a compound. It can be used to identify unknown compounds, quantify known compounds, and determine the structure and chemical properties of compounds. It is used in studies on compounds ranging from low molecular weight metabolites to proteins. Mass spectrometry is often combined with a variety of separation techniques like gas chromatography, liquid chromatography, and electrophoresis. It is not an *in vivo* technique nor does it give three-dimensional information.

NMR has a variety of uses ranging from *in vivo* to *in vitro*. It is a non-invasive technique that can be applied to organisms, cells, biological fluids, or pure or partially purified samples. It can be used to monitor chemical reactions and dynamic processes. It can also provide structural information.

13. Define the following terms:
   a. genome
   b. transcriptome
   c. proteome
   d. metabolome

Answer: The genome is the total complement of genetic material of an organism. In the case of eukaryotes, it refers to the total sequence of bases in DNA of chromosomes in a haploid cell. Eukaryotic cells often contain additional genetic material such as mitochondrial and/or chloroplast DNA. For all organisms, the genome refers to double-stranded DNA. Virus genomes comprise a variety of nucleic acids such as single-stranded or double-stranded DNA or RNA.

The transcriptome is the full complement of mRNAs from a cell or particular tissue at a particular time or under a particular set of conditions. It represents expressed genes.

The proteome is the collections of all the proteins present in a cell, organism, or tissue at a particular time or under a particular set of conditions.

The metabolome is the set of small molecule compounds found in a cell, organism, or a tissue at a particular time and under a particular set of conditions. The metabolome is clearly dependent on the proteome but compounds in the cell's environment influence it. The proteome derives from translated mRNAs but protein half-lives can have a dramatic influence on it. The transcriptome derives from genes found in the genome but not all genes are expressed at the same time and to the same level. Further, mRNAs exhibit a range of half-lives and hence biological stability.

15. For each of the following metabolic pathways, describe where in the cell it occurs and identify the starting material and end product(s):
   a. citric acid cycle
   b. glycolysis
   c. oxidative phosphorylation
   d. fatty acid synthesis

Answer: The citric acid cycle occurs in the mitochondria in eukaryotic cells and in the cytoplasm of prokaryotic cells. It is a cycle that has as input two-carbon acetyl groups attached to coenzyme A (acetyl-CoA). The acetyl group is attached to oxaloacetate, a 4-carbon compound, to produce citrate, which is metabolized back to oxaloacetate in the cycle. Two carbons enter the cycle and two carbons exit it as CO_2. The cycle is oxidative, and electrons from it are used to reduce NAD^+ and FAD (to NADH and $FADH_2$).

Glycolysis occurs in the cytosol where glucose is converted to two molecules of pyruvate, a 3-carbon compound.

Oxidative phosphorylation is the formation of ATP (from ADP and P_i) that depends on a variety of membrane complexes to move electrons from NADH and $FADH_2$ to some terminal electron acceptor such as O_2 in the case of aerobes. The process occurs on the inner mitochondrial membrane in eukaryotes and on the plasma membrane of prokaryotes.

Fatty acid synthesis is a process that occurs in the cytosol. It uses two-carbon acetyl units in an activated 3-carbon form –malonly CoA to synthesize fatty acids.

17. Consult Table 16.4, and consider the information for ^{32}P and ^{33}S. Write reactions for the decay events for these 2 isotopes, indicating clearly the products of the decays, and calculate what percentage of each would remain from a sample that contained both and decayed for 100 days.

Answer: Table 16.4 informs us that both ^{32}P and ^{33}S decay by β emission. A β particle is a high-speed electron emitted from the nucleus during nuclear decay. How can the nucleus, which is made up on neutrons and protons, generate a negatively charged particle? The only possibilities are to change either a neutron or a proton into a β particle and something else. During β decay, a neutron is converted into a proton and a β particle. The β particle is then ejected from the nucleus. After this event has occurred, the nucleus gains a proton at the expense of a neutron. A change in proton number means the nucleus becomes an atom of a different element.

For phosphorus, ^{32}P starts out with 15 protons (making it phosphorus) and 17 neutrons (making it ^{32}P). Upon β decay, there are now 16 protons (making it sulfur) and 16 neutrons making it ^{32}S.

$$^{33}P \rightarrow \beta^- + \,^{32}S$$

For sulfur, ^{35}S starts out with 16 protons (making it sulfur) and 19 neutrons (making it ^{35}S). Upon β decay, there are now 17 protons (making it chlorine) and 18 neutrons making it ^{35}Cl.

$$^{33}P \rightarrow \beta^- + \,^{32}S$$

The amount of isotope remaining after 100 days is calculated using the following equation:

$$\frac{A}{A_o} = e^{\frac{-0.693t}{t_{1/2}}}$$

The term A_0 is the amount of isotope at time zero, A the amount of isotope after time, t, and $t_{1/2}$ is the half-life of the isotope. The value 0.693 is simply the natural log of 2. The equation can be easily derived recognizing that radioactive decay is first order in A, with some rate constant k. Thus,

$$\frac{dA}{dt} = -kA$$

$$\text{Rearranging } \frac{dA}{A} = -kdt$$

Now, integrating between A_0 at $t = 0$ and A at t, we get

$$\ln \frac{A}{A_0} = -kt \text{ or}$$

$$\frac{A}{A_0} = e^{-kt} \quad (1)$$

We can express k as a function of $t_{1/2}$ by recognizing that $A = \dfrac{A_0}{2}$

when $t = t_{1/2}$. Thus,

$$\ln \frac{\frac{A_0}{2}}{A_0} = -kt_{1/2}$$

$$k = \frac{\ln 2}{t_{1/2}} = \frac{\ln 2}{t_{1/2}} = \frac{0.693}{t_{1/2}}$$

Substituting this into (1), we get:

$$\frac{A}{A_0} = e^{-\frac{0.693t}{t_{1/2}}}$$

For ^{32}P with a half-life of 14.3 days, after 100 days we have:

$$\frac{A}{A_0} = e^{-\frac{0.693 \times 100 \text{ days}}{14.3 \text{ days}}} = 7.86 \times 10^{-3}$$

The percent remaining is 0.786%

For ^{35}S with a half-life of 87.1 days, after 100 days we have:

$$\frac{A}{A_0} = e^{-\frac{0.693 \times 100 \text{ days}}{87.1 \text{ days}}} = 0.451$$

The percent remaining is 45.1%

Questions for Self-Study

1. The entries in the last four columns of Table 16.1 have been rearranged in an incorrect order. Correct them.

Classification	Carbon Source	Energy Source	Electron Donors	Examples
Phototrophs	Organic compounds	Oxidation–reduction reactions	Organic compounds	Non-sulfur purple bacteria
Photoheterotrophs	CO_2	Oxidation–reduction reactions	H_2O, H_2S, S, other inorganic compounds	All animals, most microorganisms, non-photosynthetic plant tissue such as roots, photosynthetic cells in the dark
Chemotrophs	Organic compounds	Light	Organic compounds e.g., glucose	Green plants, algae, cyanobacteria, photosynthetic bacteria
Chemoheterotrophs	CO_2	Light	Inorganic compounds: H_2, H_2S, NH_4^+, NO_2^-, Fe^{2+}, Mn^{2+}	Nitrifying bacteria; hydrogen, sulfur, and iron bacteria

2. Match the terms in the two columns:
   a. Obligate aerobes
   b. Facultative anaerobes
   c. Obligate anaerobes
   d. Aerobes
   e. Anaerobes

   1 Use O_2 as electron acceptor
   2. Cannot use O_2 as electron acceptor
   3. O_2 required for life
   4. Use O_2 but can adapt to lack of O_2
   5. Cannot use or tolerate O_2

3. For each of the items listed below, state whether they are indicative of an anabolic (A) pathway or a catabolic (C) pathway.
   a. Consumes ATP
   b. Involves the cofactor NAD^+
   c. Results in reduction of compounds using NADPH
   d. Energy-yielding
   e. Production of glucose by photoautotroph
   f. Results in decrease in molecular complexity

4. Metabolic regulation of anabolic and catabolic pathways is accomplished by regulating the activities of enzymes. What three levels of enzymatic control are most common?

5. Anabolic pathways are endergonic, whereas catabolic pathways are exergonic. What role does ATP play in coupling the two kinds of pathways?

6. How are radioactive isotopes and stable, heavy isotopes used in biochemical research?

Answers

1.

Classification	Carbon Source	Energy Source	Electron Donors	Examples
Phototrophs	CO_2	Light	H_2O, H_2S, S, other inorganic compounds	Green plants, algae, cyanobacteria, photosynthetic bacteria
Photoheterotrophs	Organic compounds	Light	Organic compounds	Non-sulfur purple bacteria
Chemotrophs	CO_2	Oxidation–reduction reactions	Inorganic compounds: H_2, H_2S, NH_4^+, NO_2^-, Fe^{2+}, Mn^{2+}	Nitrifying bacteria; hydrogen, sulfur, and iron bacteria
Chemoheterotrophs	Organic compounds	Oxidation–reduction reactions	Organic compounds e.g., glucose	All animals, most microorganisms, non-photosynthetic plant tissue such as roots, photosynthetic cells in the dark

2. a. 3; b. 4; c. 5; d. 1; e. 2.

3. a. A; b. C; c. A; d. C; e. A; f. C.

4. Allosteric regulation, covalent modification, and enzyme synthesis and degradation.

5. Steps in anabolic pathways are often driven by hydrolysis of ATP. One result of catabolism is the phosphorylation of ADP to ATP.

6. Both types of isotopes are used to label compounds. Radioactive isotopes are unstable and release energy upon decay. The presence of a radioactively labelled compound can be detected by the energy emitted upon radioactive decay. Stable, heavy isotopes increase the density or mass of a compound into which they are incorporated.

Additional Problems

1. Table 16.4 lists the properties of various radioisotopes. For ^{14}C, the following information is given: Type—radioactive, Radiation Type—β^-, Half-life—5700 yr. Explain this information.

2. Calculate the percent density difference between double-stranded DNA containing ^{14}N (the normal isotope) and ^{15}N (the heavy isotope). Assume that the average molecular weight of a base pair in dsDNA is 625 and that the DNA is 50% A:T rich.

3. A gasoline-powered, internal-combustion engine, and a polar bear metabolizing blubber run very similar reactions overall to produce energy; however, the details are quite different. Explain.

4. NMR spectroscopy has been used to measure cellular pH by determining the chemical shift of cellular P_i. Phosphorus NMR is particularly convenient because ^{31}P has a large magnetic moment and is the naturally occurring isotope of phosphorus. But, why is inorganic phosphate studied? Why not one of the phosphates of ATP? Typically [ATP] is greater than [P_i].

Abbreviated Answers

1. The designation "radioactive" indicates that ^{14}C is unstable and will be converted into another isotope or element. Radiation type β^- informs us that the conversion occurs by beta emission; an electron is emitted from the nucleus. The atomic mass remains constant (the atomic mass is the sum of neutrons and protons); however, the atomic number increases by 1 to 7 and ^{14}C is converted to ^{14}N, a stable isotope. The emitted electron may be detected by liquid scintillation counting or by exposure to film. In liquid scintillation counting, the electron excites fluorescent molecules that emit visible light upon returning to their ground state. The amount of light is measured using a photomultiplier. In film

exposure, the electron reduces silver grains in the film. Under certain conditions, the number of grains reduced is proportional to the number of decay events. The half-life refers to the time it takes for one-half of the radioisotope to decay. So, after 5700 years only half of the starting material remains.

2. Our first task is to determine the number of nitrogens in an "average base-pair." A, G, C, and T have 5, 5, 3, and 2 nitrogens, respectively. Therefore A:T and G:C base pairs have 7 and 8 nitrogens and an average base pair in a 50% A:T–rich dsDNA has 7.5 nitrogens. The molecular weight of a ^{14}N-containing base-pair is 625. For a ^{15}N-containing base-pair, the molecular weight is

$$625 - (14 \times 7.5) + (15 \times 7.5) = 632.5$$

The percent density difference is given by:

$$\% \text{ difference} = \frac{632.5 - 625}{625} \times 100\% = 1.2\%$$

3. The engine and the polar bear both rely on carbon oxidation reactions for energy. The general equation that describes both reactions is:

$$(\text{—CH}_2\text{—})_n + O_2 \rightarrow CO_2 + H_2O$$

In an engine, gasoline vapour mixed with oxygen is ignited by a spark to initiate carbon oxidation. (The reaction is often not complete and CO or carbon monoxide and other partially oxidized carbon compounds are produced.) The polar bear takes a different approach. Fat, with an average carbon not unlike a typical hydrocarbon found in gasoline, is metabolized via β-oxidation, the citric acid cycle, and electron transport to produce CO_2; O_2 is consumed during electron transport to produce H_2O.

4. The chemical shift of phosphorus depends on, among other things, the local magnetic environment in which the phosphorus is located. Protonation of phosphate groups will result in a chemical shift. The advantage to using inorganic phosphate to monitor intracellular pH is that phosphorus has a pK_a around neutral pH. The pK_as of phosphate in nucleotides are approximately one pH unit lower.

Summary

From a chemical perspective, living organisms are open thermodynamic systems far displaced from equilibrium. Further, cellular constituents are characteristically in a chemically more reduced state than the inanimate matter that surrounds them. Nevertheless, cells must somehow extract energy and reducing power from the environment and use this energy and reducing power to maintain the complex chemical activities that collectively constitute the living state. The sum of all these processes is metabolism.

Maps of intermediary metabolism portray hundreds of enzymatic reactions, but these represent only the principal metabolic pathways. It is estimated that the cells of higher organisms carry out literally thousands of metabolic reactions, each catalyzed by a specific enzyme. Despite the great variations and adaptations found in organisms, virtually all have the same basic set of major metabolic pathways, a fact providing strong evidence that they evolved from a common ancestor. Still, considerable metabolic diversity exists between organisms in terms of the sources of carbon and energy that they exploit. Photoautotrophs require only light as a source of energy and CO_2 as a source of carbon; photoheterotrophs use light as a sole source of energy but must have an organic supply of carbon in order to synthesize their complement of biomolecules. Chemoautotrophs can live on CO_2 as their sole source of carbon provided an oxidizable inorganic substrate, such as Fe^{2+}, NO_2^- or NH_4^+, is available to supply energy. Chemoheterotrophs are organisms needing an organic carbon source for both energy and biomolecular synthesis. The flows of energy, carbon, and oxygen within the biosphere are intimately related. Phototrophs use solar energy to fix CO_2 into more reduced organic compounds; the electrons for this reduction come from water and O_2 is evolved. Heterotrophs feed on the organic products of photosynthesis, harvesting the energy in these compounds in oxidative reactions that release carbon dioxide, consume O_2, and form H_2O.

Metabolism consists of two major realms: the degradative pathways of catabolism and the biosynthetic pathways of anabolism. A metabolic pathway is composed of a sequence of enzymatic reactions, transforming some precursor to a specific end product via a consecutive series of intermediates. The enzymes of a particular pathway may exist either as physically separate entities, as a stable multi-enzyme complex, or as a membrane-associated system. Metabolic pathways often contain many individual steps for energetic reasons: energy transactions typically fall in the range of 0–50 kJ/mol, to fit within the prevailing free energy change for ADP phosphorylation/ATP hydrolysis in cells. Catabolic pathways exist to degrade a wide variety of fuel molecules—fats, carbohydrates, proteins— but these pathways converge to a few end products, namely acetyl-CoA and certain citric acid cycle intermediates. Water, ammonium, and carbon dioxide are the ultimate end products of catabolism. In contrast, anabolic pathways diverge from a limited set of building blocks (amino acids, sugars, nucleotides, and acetyl-CoA) to the end results of their synthetic activity, the astounding variety of complex biomolecules. Corresponding pathways of catabolism and anabolism differ for essential reasons. First, thermodynamics dictates that more energy is required for the synthesis of a biomolecule than can be realized from its degradation. Second, in order to have independent regulation of opposing metabolic sequences, the sequences must consist, at least in part, of unique reactions mediated by separate enzymes that serve as distinct sites for regulation.

ATP is the energy currency of the cell. ATP is a major product of catabolism; in turn, ATP is a principal substrate for anabolism, providing the chemical energy that serves as the driving force for biosynthesis. Electrons released in oxidative reactions of catabolism are collected in the pyridine nucleotide coenzymes, NADH and NADPH. The electrons carried in these two coenzymes have very different fates. Those in NADH are passed to O_2 to form H_2O in an energetic process known as oxidative phosphorylation, which couples NADH oxidation to ATP synthesis. In contrast, the electrons in NADPH provide the reducing power necessary to drive reductive anabolic reactions.

Metabolism is a tightly regulated, integrated process. Metabolic regulation is achieved by controlling the activity of key enzymes on one of a number of levels: allosteric regulation, covalent modification, and enzyme synthesis/degradation. The reactions comprising various metabolic pathways have been revealed through a growing arsenal of experimental methods. Early approaches relied on cell-free assays of metabolic intermediates and the enzymatic reactions transforming them. Enzyme inhibitors were a useful tool in these studies. Genetic mutations result in specific metabolic blocks that are very informative about metabolic reactions. Isotopic tracers are particularly good probes of metabolism since isotopically labelled compounds have essentially the same chemical behaviour as their unlabelled counterparts. Isotopes can be traced through their radioactivity or their difference in mass (or density). NMR spectroscopy has the power to reveal detailed information about the chemical fate of substances in a non-invasive, non-destructive way. Evidence regarding the compartmentation of metabolic processes within specific organelles has established that the flow of intermediates in metabolism is channelled spatially as well as chemically.

Nutrition is the use of foods by organisms. Nutrients include proteins, carbohydrates, lipids, fibres, and vitamins. Proteins serve as a source of essential amino acids. Excess amino acids may be converted to glucose, fatty acids, or completely degraded. Catabolism of carbohydrates represent an important source of metabolic energy. Lipid degradation is also an important source of metabolic energy; however, lipids also provide essential fatty acids. Fibres, including cellulose, hemicellulose, and lignin, play important roles in digestion and absorption. Vitamins are nutrients, which are required in the diet, usually in trace amounts, if they cannot be synthesized by the organism itself. Except for vitamin C, the water-soluble vitamins are all components or precursors of coenzymes, low molecular weight species that bring unique functionalities to certain enzymes. The fat-soluble vitamins are not related to coenzymes, but still have essential roles in various biological processes.

Chapter 17

Glycolysis

• •

Chapter Outline

- ❖ Glycolysis: Embden–Meyerhof pathway: Glucose to pyruvate
- ❖ Energy-consuming phase: Five reactions: Two ATP consumed
  - ⅄ Production of glucose-6-P: ATP consumed: 1st priming step
    - Hexokinase
      - Low K_m for glucose
      - Reacts with many different 6-carbon sugars
      - Glucose-6-P allosteric inhibitor
    - Glucokinase: Liver enzyme
      - High K_m for glucose: Functions only when glucose abundant
      - No allosteric inhibition
      - Enzyme levels regulated by insulin
    - Advantages to phosphorylated sugar
      - Impermeable: Remains inside cell
      - Glucose concentration gradient maintained
      - Glucose carbon skeleton committed to metabolism
  - ⅄ Fructose-6-P formation: Aldose–ketose isomerization
    - Phosphoglucoisomerase
    - Prepares C-1 for second phosphorylation
    - Prepares C-3 for eventual cleavage
  - ⅄ Fructose-1,6-bisphosphate formation: ATP consumed: 2nd priming step
    - Phosphofructokinase
    - Commits carbon skeleton to glycolysis
    - Allosteric regulation
      - Inhibitors
        - ATP: Increases K_m for Fructose-6-P
        - Citrate
      - Activators
        - AMP: Reverses inhibition of ATP: Formed by adenylate kinase from ADP
        - Fructose-2,6-bisphosphate: Increase affinity for F-6-P: Decreases ATP inhibition
  - ⅄ Formation of DHAP and glyceraldehyde-3-P
    - Fructose bisphosphate aldolase
    - Reverse of aldol condensation
    - Two classes of aldolases
      - Class I: Lysine forms Schiff base with carbonyl carbon: NaBH$_4$ inhibits
      - Class II: Zinc-containing enzyme: EDTA inhibits
  - ⅄ Trios phosphate isomerase
    - DHAP/glyceraldehyde-3-P interconversion
    - Ketose to aldose isomerization

❖ Energy yielding phase: Five reactions: Four ATP produced per glucose
   ⅄ Glyceraldehyde-3-phosphate dehydrogenase: Product 1,3-bisphosphoglycerate
      • Oxidation/reduction
         • NAD^+ reduced to NADH
         • Glyceraldehyde oxidized to glycerate
      • Carboxylic acid/phosphoric acid mixed anhydride formed
      • Site of arsenate poisoning
   ⅄ Phosphoglycerate kinase: ATP produced
      • Substrate-level phosphorylation
      • 1,3-bisphosphoglycerate also used to form 2,3-BPG by mutase
   ⅄ 3-Phosphoglycerate to 2-phosphoglycerate conversion
      • Phosphoglycerate mutase
      • 2,3-BPG cofactor
   ⅄ Enolase reaction
      • 2-Phosphoglycerate to PEP
      • Dehydration reaction
   ⅄ Pyruvate kinase reaction
      • PEP to pyruvate
      • ADP to ATP
      • Regulation
         • Activated by AMP, F-1,6-BP
         • Inhibited by ATP, acetyl-CoA, alanine
         • Covalent phosphorylation inhibits pyruvate kinase
❖ Fate of NADH and pyruvate
   ⅄ Aerobic respiration
      • Pyruvate to acetyl-Coenzyme A to citric acid cycle to carbon dioxide
      • NADH to electron transport
   ⅄ Anaerobic metabolism: Fermentation
      • Lactic acid fermentation: Pyruvate to lactic acid regenerates NAD^+
      • Ethanol fermentation
         • Pyruvate to acetaldehyde
         • Acetaldehyde to ethanol regenerates NAD^+
❖ Metabolism of other sugars
   ⅄ Fructose
      • Fructokinase at C-1: Aldolase forms DHAP and glyceraldehyde: Triose kinase to produce glyceraldehyde-3-P
      • Hexokinase at C:6 to produce fructose-6-P
   ⅄ Mannose: Hexokinase: Mannose-6-P isomerase to fructose-6-P
   ⅄ Galactose: Leloir pathway
      • Galactokinase at C-1 to produce galactose-1-P
      • Galactose-1-P + UDP–glucose to glucose-1-P and UDP–galactose
      • UDP–galactose epimerase: UDP–glucose
   ⅄ Glycerol
      • Glycerol kinase
      • Glycerol phosphate dehydrogenase to DHAP
   ⅄ Hypoxic stress: Response to oxygen limitation
      • Increase in glycolytic enzymes
      • Regulated by hypoxia inducible factor (HIF): Transcription factor active in low oxygen
         • DNA-binding protein: Binds to hypoxia responsive elements and activates
         • Hydroxylated by prolyl hydroxylase when oxygen plentiful: Hydroxylated HIF is ubiquitinated and degraded
         • Hydroxylated by factor-inhibiting HIF (FIH) blocks association with coactivator p300

Chapter Objectives

Glycolysis

Glycolysis is the metabolic pathway leading from glucose to two molecules of pyruvate. Before jumping into the details, it may be instructive to look at some basic chemistry. Glucose and pyruvic acid are shown below.

The carboxylate carbon and the keto carbon of pyruvate are at a more oxidized state, whereas the methyl carbon is at a more reduced state relative to an "average" carbon of glucose. Therefore, this conversion, from glucose to pyruvate, must be accompanied by an additional reduction reaction. (In effect, the production of one of the oxidized carbons of pyruvate is balanced by production of the reduced carbon.) What gets reduced is NAD^+. When pyruvate is further metabolized to lactic acid or ethanol and CO_2, NADH is used to reduce the carbonyl carbon to an alcoholic carbon. The net result is regeneration of NAD^+, which allows glycolysis to continue. Glycolysis produces ATP and the energy for the reaction is the result of an internal oxidation/reduction.

Understand the basic organization of glycolysis into an energy-consuming phase and an energy-producing phase (see Figure 17.1). The two kinases, hexokinase (or glucokinase) and phosphofructokinase are key enzymes in phase I. Know how each is regulated but focus on phosphofructokinase. Phase II is the pay-back portion of glycolysis. Key enzymes in this phase include glyceraldehyde-3-phosphate dehydrogenase, responsible for oxidation of the carbon skeleton; phosphoglycerate kinase, which catalyzes a substrate-level phosphorylation of ADP; and pyruvate kinase, responsible for the second substrate-level phosphorylation.

The Fate of Pyruvate

The ability to produce pyruvate from glucose depends on availability of NAD^+. But this coenzyme is in limiting amounts in cells, and thus must be recycled for glycolysis to continue. In fermentation, the end product of glycolysis, namely pyruvate, is used as a substrate to recycle NAD^+. Understand alcoholic fermentation and lactic acid fermentation. An advantage to relying on these processes is the ability to produce ATP rapidly. The disadvantages include the production of problematic waste products containing reduced carbons.

Phosphorylation of glucose and conversion to 2 molecules of glyceraldehyde-3-phosphate; 2 ATPs are used to prime these reactions.

Conversion of glyceraldehyde-3-phosphate to pyruvate and coupled formation of 4 ATP and 2 NADH.

Figure 17.1   The glycolytic pathway

Problems and Solutions

1. List the reactions of glycolysis that
   a. are energy-consuming (under standard-state conditions);
   b. are energy-yielding (under standard-state conditions);
   c. consume ATP;
   d. yield ATP;
   e. are strongly influenced by changes in concentration of substrate and product because of their molecularity;
   f. are at or near equilibrium in the erythrocyte (see Table 17.2).

Answer: Energy-consuming reactions have positive values of ΔG, whereas energy-yielding reactions have negative values of ΔG. Under standard conditions, the same rules apply but to values of $\Delta G^{\circ\prime}$. Using Table 17.1, we can classify reactions into these two types as follows:

a.

Energy-Consuming Reaction	Enzyme	$\Delta G^{\circ\prime}$ kJ/mol
Glucose-6-phosphate → fructose-6-phosphate	phosphoglucoisomerase	+1.67
Fructose-1,6-bisphosphate → dihydroxyacetone-P + glyceraldehyde-P	fructose biphosphate aldolase	+23.9
Dihydroxyacetone-P → glyceraldehyde-P	triose phosphate isomerase	+7.56
Glyceraldehyde-P + P_i + NAD^+ → 1,3-bisphosphoglycerate+ NADH + H^+	glyceraldehyde-3-P dehydrogenase	+6.30
3-phosphoglycerate → 2-phosphoglycerate	phosphoglycerate mutase	+4.4
2-phosphoglycerate → phosphoenolpyruvate + H_2O	enolase	+1.8

b.

Energy-Yielding Reaction	Enzyme	$\Delta G^{\circ\prime}$ kJ/mol
α-D-glucose + ATP^{4-} → glucose-6-phosphate + ADP^{3-}	hexokinase, glucokinase	−16.7
Fructose-6-phosphate + ATP^{4-} → fructose-1,6-bisphosphate + ADP^{3-} + H^+	phosphofructokinase	−14.2
1,3-bisphosphoglycerate + ADP^{3-} → 3-P-glycerate + ATP^{4-}	phosphoglycerate kinase	−18.9
Phosphoenolpyruvate + ADP^{3-} + H^+ → 1,3-bisphosphoglycerate+ NADH + H^+	pyruvate kinase	−31.7
Pyruvate + NADH + H^+ → lactate + NAD^+	lactate dehydrogenase	−25.2

c.

ATP-Utilizing Reaction	Enzyme	$\Delta G^{\circ\prime}$ kJ/mol
α-D-glucose + ATP^{4-} → glucose-6-phosphate + ADP^{3-}	hexokinase, glucokinase	−16.7
Fructose-6-phosphate + ATP^{4-} → fructose-1,6-bisphosphate + ADP^{3-} + H^+	phosphofructokinase	−14.2

d.

ATP-Producing Reaction	Enzyme	$\Delta G^{\circ\prime}$ kJ/mol
1,3-bisphosphoglycerate + ADP^{3-} → 3-P-glycerate + ATP^{4-}	phosphoglycerate kinase	−18.9
Phosphoenolpyruvate + ADP^{3-} + H^+ → 1,3-bisphosphoglycerate+ NADH + H^+	pyruvate kinase	−31.7

e. What reactions are strongly influenced by concentration? In general,

$$\Delta G = \Delta G^{\circ\prime} + RT \times \ln \frac{\Pi_i[P_i]}{\Pi_i[R_i]}$$

Reactions that generate an increase or decrease in the number of products over reactants are expected to be sensitive to concentration changes. This is the case for reactions catalyzed by two enzymes: fructose bisphosphate aldolase and glyceraldehyde-3-phosphate dehydrogenase.

f. Reactions that are at or near equilibrium have values of ΔG close to zero. Using this criterion, the reactions catalyzed by the following enzymes must be close to equilibrium: phosphoglucoisomerase, phosphofructokinase, fructose bisphosphate aldolase, triose phosphate isomerase, phosphoglycerate kinase, phosphoglycerate mutase, and enolase.

3. In an erythrocyte undergoing glycolysis, what would be the effect of a sudden increase in the concentration of (a) ATP; (b) AMP; (c) fructose-1,6-bisphosphate; (d) fructose-2,6-bisphosphate; (e) citrate; (f) glucose-6-phosphate?

Answer: Erythrocytes lack mitochondria and derive energy largely from glycolysis. Glycolysis is regulated at the two steps catalyzed by phosphofructokinase and pyruvate kinase. Phosphofructokinase is a key enzyme that serves as a "valve" regulating the movement of glucose units into glycolysis. Prior to formation of fructose-1,6-bisphosphate, there are other options (e.g., pentose phosphate pathway, glycogen synthesis) to glycolysis. The phosphofructokinase reaction commits glucose to glycolysis. This enzyme is subject to a number of regulatory mechanisms. At low ATP levels, the enzyme has a low K_m for fructose-6-phosphate; however, at high ATP levels, the enzyme behaves cooperatively and has an increased K_m for fructose-6-phosphate and a sigmoidal dependence of activity on fructose-6-phosphate concentration. This behaviour is a result of allosteric regulation by ATP. Phosphofructokinase has an additional ATP-binding site distinct from the substrate site. ATP binding to the allosteric site causes activity to be less sensitive to fructose-6-phosphate. This allosteric inhibition by ATP is reversed by competitive binding of AMP. The inhibitory effect of ATP is enhanced by citrate. This citric acid cycle intermediate is produced in the mitochondria, and when mitochondrial concentrations are high, citrate may be exported to the cytosol to be used in fatty acid biosynthesis. Cytosolic citrate also functions as an inhibitor of glycolysis by binding to phosphofructokinase and enhancing the allosteric effects of ATP. Since erythrocytes lack mitochondria, citrate is not expected to play an important role in regulation of glycolysis. Phosphofructokinase is also allosterically regulated by fructose-2,6-bisphosphate whose concentration is regulated by the enzymatic activities: phosphofructokinase 2 and fructose-2,6-bisphosphatase. High concentrations of fructose-2,6-bisphosphate is a signal to increase glycolysis by increasing the affinity of phosphofructokinase for its substrate, fructose-6-phosphate, and by decreasing the inhibitory effects of ATP.

The second key enzyme in regulation of glycolysis is pyruvate kinase. This enzyme has allosteric binding sites for AMP and fructose-2,6-bisphosphate leading to activation of the enzyme. Further, the enzyme is allosterically inhibited by ATP (and by alanine, and acetyl-coenzyme A).

With these points in mind, we predict that increased concentrations of ATP will lead to inhibition of glycolysis, and increased concentrations of AMP will stimulate glycolysis. An increase in fructose-1,6-bisphosphate will stimulate glycolysis. Fructose-2,6-bisphosphate is a signal to increase the rate of glycolysis. Citrate will inhibit glycolysis. Finally, increased concentrations of glucose-6-phosphate may stimulate glycolysis. Glucose-6-phosphate is isomerized to fructose-6-phosphate, a substrate of phosphofructokinase. Depending on the ATP, AMP, citrate, and fructose-2,6-bisphosphate levels, phosphofructokinase may be quite responsive to increased levels of fructose-6-phosphate. (The first reaction of glycolysis, phosphorylation of glucose to glucose-6-phosphate may be sensitive to glucose-6-phosphate levels as well. In muscle, the enzyme catalyzing this reaction is inhibited by glucose-6-phosphate, whereas in liver the enzyme is not.)

5. For each of the following reactions, name the enzyme that carries out this reaction in glycolysis and write a suitable mechanism for the reaction.

Answer: The first reaction is reaction 4 of glycolysis catalyzed by fructose bisphosphate aldolase. There are two classes of aldolase enzymes found in nature: Class I aldolase and Class II aldolase. Class I aldolase catalysis involves the formation of a Schiff base intermediate, and because of this, $NaBH_4$ is a potent inhibitor of this enzyme. Class II aldolase has an active-site Zn^{2+} that is required for catalysis. Divalent cation chelating agents, like EDTA, will inhibit Class II aldolases.

Catalysis for a Class I aldolase begins with Schiff base formation between an active-site lysine and the keto carbon of fructose-1,6-bisphosphate with elimination of water. The hydroxyl group of carbon 4 loses a proton to a nearby cysteine followed by elimination of the enolate anion. The resulting enamine is reprotonated, and DHAP is released by hydrolysis as shown below.

For Class II aldolases, an active-site Zn^{2+} acts as an electrophile to polarize the carbonyl group of the substrate and stabilizes the enolate intermediate as shown below.

F-1,6-bisP

Glyceraldehyde-3-phosphate

DHAP

The second reaction is catalyzed by glyceraldehyde-3-phosphate dehydrogenase. The complete reaction is:

Glyceraldehyde-3-phosphate   1,3-bisphosphoglycerate

The reaction mechanism involves nucleophilic attack of the carbonyl carbon by a cysteine to form a hemithioacetal, which transfers a hydride to NAD+ to form a thioester. The thioester is subsequently attacked by phosphate to produce 1,3-bisphosphoglycerate. This sequence of reactions is shown below.

NAD+   NADH + H+

7. (Integrates with Chapters 4 and 13) How might iodoacetic acid affect the glyceraldehyde-3-phosphate dehydrogenase reaction in glycolysis? Justify your answer.

Answer: The reaction mechanism of glyceraldehyde-3-phosphate dehydrogenase involves nucleophilic attack of the carbonyl carbon of glyceraldehyde-3-phosphate by a cysteine sulfhydryl group to form a hemithioacetyl. Iodoacetic acid is a very good alkylating agent and will react with cysteines as follows:

cysteine   I⁻ H⁺   cysteine

Iodoacetic acid will modify a cysteine sulfhydryl group whose function is critical to catalysis.

9.   *Sucrose can enter glycolysis by either of 2 routes:*

Sucrose phosphorylase: Sucrose + P_i $\leftrightarrows$ fructose + glucose-1-phosphate

Invertase: Sucrose + H_2O $\leftrightarrows$ fructose + glucose

Would either of these reactions offer an advantage over the other in the preparation of sucrose for entry into glycolysis?

Answer: The reaction catalyzed by sucrose phosphorylase produces glucose-1-phosphate, which enters glycolysis as glucose-6-phosphate, by the action of phosphoglucomutase. Therefore, glucose-6-phosphate produced by this route, bypasses the hexokinase reaction, normally employed, in which ATP hydrolysis occurs.

11. *(Integrates with Chapter 3) Triose phosphate isomerase catalyzes the conversion of dihydroxyacetone-P to glyceraldehyde-3-P. The standard free energy change, $\Delta G°'$, for this reaction is 17.6 kJ/mol. However, the observed free energy change (ΔG) for this reaction in erythrocytes is 12.4 kJ/mol.*

   a.   *Calculate the ratio of [dihydroxyacetone-P]/[glyceraldehyde-3-P] in erythrocytes from ΔG.*
   b.   *If [dihydroxyacetone-P] = 0.2 mM, what is [glyceraldehyde-3-P]?*

Answer: The reaction under examination is Dihydroxyacetone-P $\rightarrow$ glyceraldehyde-3-P.

The observed free energy change (ΔG) is calculated from the standard free energy change ($\Delta G°$) using the following equation:

$$\Delta G = \Delta G°' + RT \times \ln \frac{[\text{Products}]}{[\text{Reactants}]}$$

In this case, we have

$$\Delta G = \Delta G°' + RT \times \ln \frac{[\text{glyceraldehyde-3-phosphate}]}{[\text{dihydroxyacetone phosphate}]}$$

Since the question asks us for the ratio of [dihydroxyacetone-P]/glyceraldehyde-3-P], rearrange, using the property $\log (x) = - \log (1/x)$ to give

$$\Delta G = \Delta G°' - RT \times \ln \frac{[\text{dihydroxyacetone phosphate}]}{[\text{glyceraldehyde-3-phosphate}]}$$

Solving for the desired ratio, we have

$$\frac{[\text{dihydroxyacetone phosphate}]}{[\text{glyceraldehyde-3-phosphate}]} = e^{\frac{(\Delta G°' - \Delta G)}{RT}}$$

Substituting the numbers, and using 37°C as the temperature at which erythrocytes find themselves:

$$\frac{[\text{dihydroxyacetone phosphate}]}{[\text{glyceraldehyde-3-phosphate}]} = e^{\frac{(17.6-12.4)}{8.314\times10^{-3}\times310}} = e^{2.018}$$

$$\frac{[\text{dihydroxyacetone phosphate}]}{[\text{glyceraldehyde-3-phosphate}]} = 7.52$$

This answer tells us that the chemical reaction as written above lies to the left, which we already knew from the positive value for its ΔG.

b.   Given that the dihydroxyacetone-P concentration in erythrocytes is 0.2 mM, we can calculate the concentration of glyceraldehyde-3-P from the answer for part (a) above.

$$[\text{glyceraldehyde-3-phosphate}] = \frac{[\text{dihydroxyacetone phosphate}]}{7.52} = \frac{0.2 \text{ mM}}{7.52}$$

$$[\text{glyceraldehyde-3-phosphate}] = 0.027 \text{ mM} = 27 \ \mu\text{M}$$

13. (Integrates with Chapter 3) The standard free energy change ($\Delta G°'$) for hydrolysis of phosphoenolpyruvate (PEP) is −61.9 kJ/mol. The standard free energy change ($\Delta G°'$) for ATP hydrolysis is −30.5 kJ/mol.

   a. What is the standard free energy change for the pyruvate kinase reaction:
   ADP + phosphoenolpyruvate → ATP + pyruvate
   b. What is the equilibrium constant for this reaction?
   c. Assuming the intracellular concentrations of [ATP] and [ADP] remain fixed at 8 mM and 1 mM, respectively, what will be the ratio of [pyruvate]/[phosphoenolpyruvate] when the pyruvate kinase reaction reaches equilibrium?

Answer: a. The reaction ADP + phosphoenolpyruvate → ATP + pyruvate is the sum of two coupled reactions:

   Reaction 1: Phosphoenolpyruvate + H₂O → pyruvate + Pᵢ;
   = −61.9 kJ/mol

and

   Reaction 2: ADP + Pᵢ → ATP + H₂O;
   = +30.5 kJ/mol

The value of $\Delta G°'$ for the latter reaction is positive (+) because we have written it in the direction of ATP synthesis, rather than in the direction of hydrolysis, for which the value of $\Delta G°'$ is given in the problem.

   The total change in the standard free energy of coupled reactions is given by the sum of the free energy changes of the individual reactions. Accordingly, we have for the reaction in question,

$$\Delta G°'_{Total} = \Delta G°'_1 + \Delta G°'_2 = -61.9\,\frac{kJ}{mol} + 30.5\,\frac{kJ}{mol} = -31.4\,\frac{kJ}{mol}$$

b. The equilibrium constant, K'_{eq}, is derived from the standard free energy change using the following equation:

$$\Delta G°' = -RT \times \ln K'_{eq}$$

which upon rearranging, yields

$$K'_{eq} = e^{-\frac{\Delta G°'}{RT}}$$

Substituting the appropriate numerical values, with the product $RT = 2.48$ at 25°C, we have

$$K'_{eq} = e^{-\frac{(-31.4)}{2.48}} = 3.19 \times 10^5$$

The equilibrium position of this reaction obviously lies far to the right.

c. The equilibrium constant is the ratio of products to reactants at equilibrium. For this reaction,

$$K'_{eq} = \frac{[ATP][pruvate]}{[ADP][PEP]} = \frac{[ATP]}{[ADP]} \times \frac{[pruvate]}{[PEP]} = \frac{8\text{ mM}}{1\text{ mM}} \times \frac{[pruvate]}{[PEP]}, \text{ or}$$

$$\frac{[pruvate]}{[PEP]} = \frac{K'_{eq}}{8} = \frac{3.19 \times 10^5}{8} = 3.94 \times 10^4$$

15. (Integrates with Chapter 3) The standard free energy change ($\Delta G°'$) for hydrolysis of 1,3-bisphosphoglycerate (1,3-BPG) to 3-phosphoglycerate (3-PG) and Pᵢ is −49.6 kJ/mol:
1,3-BPG + H₂O → 3-PG + Pᵢ
The standard free energy change ($\Delta G°'$) for ATP hydrolysis is −30.5 kJ/mol:
ATP + H₂O → ADP + Pᵢ

   a. What is the standard free energy change for the phosphoglycerate kinase reaction:
   ADP + 1,3-BPG → ATP + 3-PG
   b. What is the equilibrium constant for this reaction?

> **c. If the steady-state concentrations of [1,3-BPG] and [3-PG] in an erythrocyte are 1mM and 120 mM respectively, what will be the ratio of [ATP]/[ADP], assuming the phosphoglycerate kinase reaction is at equilibrium?**

Answer: a.   The reaction ADP + 1,3-BPG → ATP + 3-PG is derived as the sum of two coupled reactions:

Reaction 1: 1,3-BPG + H_2O → 3-PG + P_i;
  = −49.6 kJ/mol

and

Reaction 2: ADP + P_i → ATP + H_2O;
  = + 30.5 kJ/mol

The value of $\Delta G^{\circ\prime}$ for the latter reaction is positive (+) because we have written it in the direction of ATP synthesis, rather than in the direction of hydrolysis, for which the value of $\Delta G^{\circ\prime}$ is given in the problem.

The total change in the standard free energy of coupled reactions is given by the sum of the free energy changes of the individual reactions. Accordingly, we have for the reaction in question,

$$\Delta G^{\circ\prime}{}_{Total} = \Delta G^{\circ\prime}{}_1 + \Delta G^{\circ\prime}{}_2 = -49.6\,\frac{kJ}{mol} + 30.5\,\frac{kJ}{mol} = -19.1\,\frac{kJ}{mol}$$

b.   The equilibrium constant, K_{eq}, is derived from the standard free energy change using the following equation:

$$\Delta G^{\circ\prime} = -RT \times \ln K'_{eq}$$

which upon rearranging, yields

$$K'_{eq} = e^{-\frac{\Delta G^{\circ\prime}}{RT}}$$

Substituting the appropriate numerical values, with the product $RT = 2.48$ at 25°C, we have

$$K'_{eq} = e^{-\frac{(-19.1)}{2.48}} = 2227$$

(At 37°C, the value is 1651).

c.   The equilibrium constant is the ratio of products to reactants at equilibrium. For this reaction,

$$K'_{eq} = \frac{[ATP][3-PG]}{[ADP][1,3-BPG]} = \frac{[ATP]}{[ADP]} \times \frac{[3-PG]}{[1,3-BPG]}$$

$$K'_{eq} = \frac{[ATP]}{[ADP]} \times \frac{120\ mM}{1\ mM}, \text{ or}$$

$$\frac{[ATP]}{[ADP]} = \frac{K'_{eq}}{120} = \frac{2227}{120} = \frac{2227}{120} = 18.6$$

(At 37°C, the value is 13.8).

> **17.   Taking into consideration the equilibrium constant for the adenylate kinase reaction (page 570), calculate the change in concentration in AMP that would occur if 8% of the ATP in an erythrocyte (red blood cell) were suddenly hydrolyzed to ADP. In addition to the concentration values in Table 17.2, it may be useful to assume that the initial concentration of AMP in erythrocytes is 5 mM.**

Answer: The values given for ADP and ATP from Table 17.2 are 0.14 mM and 1.85 mM, respectively, and the equilibrium constant for the adenylate kinase is 0.44. Using this information and equation 17.7 (see below) we can calculate the [AMP].

$$K_{eq} = \frac{[\text{ATP}][\text{AMP}]}{[\text{ADP}]^2}$$

$$[\text{AMP}] = \frac{K_{eq} \times [\text{ADP}]^2}{[\text{ATP}]} = \frac{0.44 \times \left(0.14 \times 10^{-3}\right)^2}{1.85 \times 10^{-3}} = 4.7 \times 10^{-6} \approx 5~\mu\text{M}$$

The same equation is used to calculate the new concentration of AMP after 8% of the initial ATP is hydrolyzed to ADP. This will lower ATP by (0.08×1.85 mM =) 0.148 mM and increase ADP by the same amount, more than doubling the ADP concentration.

$$K_{eq} = \frac{[\text{ATP}][\text{AMP}]}{[\text{ADP}]^2}$$

$$[\text{AMP}] = \frac{K_{eq} \times [\text{ADP}]^2}{[\text{ATP}]} = \frac{0.44 \times \left(0.14 \times 10^{-3} + 0.148 \times 10^{-3}\right)^2}{1.85 \times 10^{-3} - 0.148 \times 10^{-3}} = 21.4 \times 10^{-6} \approx 20~\mu\text{M}$$

A small amount of ATP hydrolysis nearly doubles [ADP] but it increases [AMP] four-fold.

19.   As noted on page 583, the galactose-1-phosphate uridylyltransferase reaction proceeds via a Ping-Pong mechanism. Consult Chapter 12, page 428, to refresh your knowledge of Ping-Pong mechanisms, and draw a diagram to show how a Ping-Pong mechanism would proceed for the uridylyl transferase.

Answer: Galactose-1-phosphate uridylyltransferase catalyzes the following reaction:

UDP–glucose + α-D-galactose-1-P $\rightleftarrows$ α-D-glucose-1-P + UDP–galactose

UDP–glucose binds to the active site and UMP is transferred to an active-site histidine to make a covalent adduct. Glucose-1-P is subsequently released. Galactose-1-P then binds and UMP is transferred to it to produce UDP–galactose. The reaction is shown below.

Step 1

UDP-Glucose

Glucose-1-P

Step 2

Galactose-1-P

UDP-Galactose

Questions for Self-Study

1. True or false:
   a. Another name for glycolysis is the Embden–Meyerhof pathway. _____
   b. Glycolysis is confined to the mitochondrial matrix. _____
   c. In the first phase of glycolysis, glucose is converted to two molecules of glyceraldehyde-3-phosphate and NAD^+ is reduced. _____
   d. The only difference between hexokinase and glucokinase is sugar specificity. _____
   e. Phosphofructokinase hydrolyzes ATP. _____
   f. Conversion of glucose-6-P to fructose-6-P and conversion of glyceraldehyde-3-P to dihydroxyacetone-P are aldose to ketose conversions. _____

2. Phosphofructokinase is the key enzyme regulating glycolysis. For the following compounds, indicate their effects on phosphofructokinase activity.
   a. ATP
   b. AMP
   c. Citrate
   d. Fructose-2,6-bisphosphate
   e. Fructose-6-phosphate

3. The ability of a cell to continue glycolysis in the presence of adequate supplies of glucose and a need for ATP is critically dependent on the reaction catalyzed by glyceraldehyde-3-phosphate dehydrogenase. Why? What is the reaction catalyzed by this enzyme?

4. Which two reactions in the second phase of glycolysis are examples of substrate-level phosphorylations?

5. a. The production of lactate or ethanol and carbon dioxide from glucose are examples of what process?
   b. What is the purpose of this process?

6. Fill in the blanks. The _____ pathway is followed by galactose to enter glycolysis. Galactose is first converted to galactose-1-phosphate by _____ in an ATP-dependent reaction. Galactose-1-phosphate is exchanged for the glucose-1-phosphate moiety of a uridine nucleotide derivative producing _____. This compound is acted on by a glucose-4-epimerase converting it to _____.

7. Conversion of 1,3-bisphosphoglycerate to 2,3-bisphosphoglycerate (a allosteric effector of hemoglobin) and the conversion of 3-phosphoglycerate to 2-phosphoglycerate are examples of reactions catalyzed by what kind of enzymes?

Answers

1. a. T; b. F; c. F; d. F; e. F; f. T.

2. a. inhibits; b. blocks ATP inhibition; c. inhibits; d. stimulates; e. stimulates.

3. The enzyme converts glyceraldehyde-3-phosphate and phosphate to 1,3-bisphosphoglycerate with accompanying reduction of NAD^+ to NADH. The reaction is critical because the levels of NAD^+ are limiting.

4. The reactions catalyzed by phosphoglycerate kinase and pyruvate kinase.

5. a. Fermentation; b. Fermentation provides a pathway for regeneration of NAD^+ from NADH that does not involve oxygen or another external electron acceptor.

6. Leloir; galactokinase; UDP–galactose; UDP–glucose.

7. Mutases

Additional Problems

1. Why is it advantageous to phosphorylate glucose immediately after being transported into cells?

2. Describe the basic chemistry of interconversion of glucose-6-phosphate to fructose-6-phosphate and of dihydroxyacetone phosphate to glyceraldehyde-3-phosphate.

3. What reaction is catalyzed by the enzyme fructose bisphosphate aldolase? Class I aldolases are irreversibly inactivated by $NaBH_4$ but inactivation requires the presence of either fructose-1,6-bisphosphate or dihydroxyacetone phosphate. The enzyme can be treated with $NaBH_4$ in the presence of glyceraldehyde-3-phosphate and upon removal of $NaBH_4$ the enzyme is active. Explain.

4. Describe the reaction catalyzed by phosphoglycerate mutase. What other molecules are required for activity?

5. What key differences exist between hexokinase and glucokinase to ensure that glucose is properly apportioned between muscle and liver?

6. Draw the structures of glycerol and of glyceraldehyde. Anaerobic organisms, grown in the absence of oxygen, can use glyceraldehyde as a source of metabolic energy but not glycerol. However, metabolism of glycerol starts with glycerol kinase converting glycerol to 3-phosphoglycerol, which is subsequently metabolized to glyceraldehyde-3-phosphate. Why is glycerol catabolism a problem for anaerobic organisms yet conversion of glyceraldehyde to pyruvate possible?

7. Mannose is a 2′ epimer of glucose. However, only one additional enzyme is required to get mannose into glycolysis. Outline a reasonable pathway by which mannose enters glycolysis.

Abbreviated Answers

1. Phosphorylation of glucose makes it essentially impermeable to the cell membrane and traps glucose inside the cell. Phosphorylation also keeps the [glucose] low inside cells, allowing uptake to occur down a glucose concentration gradient. Finally, phosphorylation commits glucose to some form of metabolism.

2. Both reactions are isomerizations of aldoses to ketoses.

3. Fructose bisphosphate aldolase interconverts fructose-1,6-bisphosphate with dihydroxyacetone phosphate and glyceraldehyde-3-phosphate. Class I aldolases form a Schiff base during catalysis. (See answer to problem 5, above.) The Schiff base forms at the keto carbon of either fructose-1,6-bisphosphate or dihydroxyacetone phosphate and $NaBH_4$ will reduce the Schiff base to a stable adduct. Once modified in this fashion, the enzyme is irreversibly inactivated. Treating the enzyme with either $NaBH_4$ alone or with $NaBH_4$ and glyceraldehyde-3-phosphate has no effect because a Schiff base is not formed.

4. Phosphoglycerate mutase moves the phosphate group from C-3 of 3-phosphoglycerate to C-2 to produce 2-phosphoglycerate. The yeast and rabbit muscle enzymes use 2,3-bisphosphoglycerate as a cofactor. The cofactor transfers a phosphate group to an active-site histidine to form a phosphohistidine intermediate. The phosphate group is then transferred to C-2 of 3-phosphoglycerate at the active site to form enzyme-bound 2,3-bisphosphoglycerate. The product, 2-phosphoglycerate, is formed when phosphate is subsequently transferred from C-3 to an enzyme histidine. The cofactor 2,3-bisphosphoglycerate is also used as an allosteric inhibitor of hemoglobin. It is formed from 1,3-bisphosphoglycerate by bisphosphoglycerate mutase.

5. Hexokinase has a low K_m for glucose, approximately 0.1 mM, and is inhibited by glucose-6-phosphate. Thus, cells containing hexokinase, such as muscle, will continue to phosphorylate glucose even when blood–glucose levels are low. However, if glucose is not metabolized immediately and glucose-6-phosphate levels build up, hexokinase is inhibited. Glucokinase, found in the liver, has a much higher K_m for glucose, approximately 10 mM, ensuring that liver cells phosphorylate glucose only when blood–glucose levels are high. In addition, glucokinase is not inhibited by glucose-6-phosphate. This allows liver cells to continue to accumulate glucose. In a later chapter, we will see that excess glucose is stored as glycogen.

6.   The structures of glycerol and glyceraldehyde are shown below.

glycerol   glyceraldehyde

Glycerol is metabolized by first being phosphorylated by glycerol kinase to *sn*-glycerol-3-phosphate, which is converted to dihydroxyacetone phosphate (DHAP) by glycerol phosphate dehydrogenase. DHAP is subsequently isomerized to glyceraldehyde. Since glycerol is converted into glyceraldehyde, it is curious that anaerobic organisms can utilize one of these compounds but not the other. The problem lies with the enzyme glycerol phosphate dehydrogenase. This enzyme uses NAD^+ as coenzyme. Thus, glyceraldehyde production by this pathway results in NAD^+ reduction. A second NAD^+ is reduced when glyceraldehyde is metabolized via glycolysis. One NAD^+ is regenerated when pyruvate is converted to lactate or ethanol and CO_2 but since two were reduced, one NADH remains. In the absence of oxygen or some other suitable electron acceptor, NAD^+ levels drop as all of the coenzyme is trapped in the reduced form NADH.

7.   Mannose is phosphorylated by hexokinase to produce mannose-6-phosphate, which is isomerized by phosphomannose isomerase to fructose-6-phosphate, a glycolytic intermediate.

Summary

Glycolysis—the degradation of glucose and other simple sugars—is a catabolic process carried out by nearly all cells. An anaerobic process, it provides precursor molecules for aerobic catabolic pathways, such as the critic acid cycle, and serves as an emergency energy source when oxygen is limiting. Glycolysis consists of two phases. The first series of five reactions breaks glucose down to two molecules of glyceraldehyde-3-phosphate. The second phase converts these two molecules of glyceraldehyde-3-P into two molecules of pyruvate. The overall pathway produces two molecules of ATP per glucose consumed. In aerobic organisms, including humans, pyruvate is oxidatively decarboxylated to produce a molecule of acetyl-coenzyme A, which fuels the citric acid cycle (and subsequent electron transport). Under anaerobic conditions, the pyruvate formed in glycolysis can be reduced to lactate (in oxygen-starved muscles or in microorganisms) or ethanol (in yeast) in fermentation processes. During glycolysis, a portion of the metabolic energy of the glucose molecule is converted into ATP. The subsequent entry of pyruvate into the TCA cycle provides more energy in the form of ATP and reduced coenzymes.

The initial reaction of glycolysis involves phosphorylation of glucose at C-6, a reaction that consumes an ATP molecule in order to make more ATP later. Hexokinase is the primary catalyst for this reaction, but, when glucose levels rise in the liver, glucokinase becomes active and shares the responsibility for phosphorylation of glucose. The second reaction of glycolysis is the isomerization of glucose-6-phosphate to fructose-6-phosphate, carried out by phosphoglucoisomerase in a reaction involving the transient formation of an ene-diol intermediate. The new primary alcohol group created at C-1 on the carbon skeleton is the site of another phosphorylation in the next reaction, catalyzed by phosphofructokinase. Like the hexokinase/glucokinase reaction, this reaction also consumes a molecule of ATP. The phosphofructokinase reaction is the most elaborately regulated reaction in the glycolytic pathway. ATP is an allosteric inhibitor of phosphofructokinase, whereas AMP can reverse the inhibition due to ATP. Although ATP levels in cells rarely change by more than 10%, the action of adenylate kinase facilitates relatively large changes in AMP levels in response to hydrolysis of ATP. The phosphofructokinase reaction is also inhibited by citrate, providing a critical link between regulation of glycolysis and the citric acid cycle. Fructose-2,6-bisphosphate is a potent allosteric activator that increases the affinity of the enzyme for the substrate fructose-6-phosphate.

The 6-carbon substrate skeleton is cleaved to two 3-carbon units in the fructose bisphosphate aldolase reaction. The products are dihydroxyacetone phosphate and glyceraldehyde-3-phosphate. Two types of fructose bisphosphate aldolase enzymes exist in nature. Animal tissues produce a Class I aldolase that forms a covalent Schiff base adduct with substrate and is thus inhibited by $NaBH_4$. Bacteria and fungi produce a Class II aldolase that does not form Schiff base adducts with substrate, but which contains an active site Zn^{2+} ion that acts as an electrophile to polarize the carbonyl group of the substrate and stabilize the enolate intermediate in the aldolase reaction. The dihydroxyacetone phosphate produced by the aldolase reaction is converted to another molecule of glyceraldehyde-3-phosphate by the fifth reaction of the pathway, triose phosphate isomerase. Although these last two reactions are energetically unfavourable, the earlier priming reactions bring the equilibrium constant for the first five reactions of glycolysis close to 1.

The second phase of glycolysis begins with the oxidation of glyceraldehyde-3-phosphate to produce a high-energy phosphate metabolite, 1,3-bisphosphoglycerate, and a reduced coenzyme, NADH, in the glyceraldehyde-3-phosphate dehydrogenase reaction. The reaction mechanism involves nucleophilic attack by a cysteine–SH group at the active site on the carbonyl carbon of glyceraldehyde-3-phosphate to form a hemithioacetal intermediate, followed by hydride transfer to NAD^+ and nucleophilic attack by phosphate to displace the product from the enzyme. In the seventh step of the pathway, phosphoglycerate kinase, transfers a phosphoryl group from 1,3-bisphosphoglycerate to ADP to form an ATP, an example of substrate-level phosphorylation. Since each glucose molecule sends two molecules of 1,3-bisphosphoglycerate into the phosphoglycerate kinase reaction, this step pays off the ATP debt created by the two priming reactions of glycolysis. The phosphoglycerate mutase reaction converts 3-phosphoglycerate to 2-phosphoglycerate and the enolase reaction then converts 2-phosphoglycerate to phosphoenolpyruvate, a high-energy phosphate that can drive the synthesis of another ATP molecule in the pyruvate kinase reaction, the final reaction of the glycolytic pathway. Pyruvate kinase is subject to regulation and possesses allosteric sites for activation by AMP and fructose-2,6-bisphosphate and inhibition by ATP, acetyl-CoA, and alanine. Phosphorylation of pyruvate kinase by cAMP-dependent protein kinase makes pyruvate kinase more sensitive to inhibition by ATP and alanine and raises the K_m for PEP. Other sugars, including fructose, mannose, and galactose, can enter the glycolytic pathway if they can be converted by appropriate enzymes into glycolysis intermediates.

Chapter 18

The Tricarboxylic Acid Cycle

• •

Chapter Outline

- ❖ TCA cycle (tricarboxylic acid): Citric acid cycle: Krebs cycle
  - ⊥ Input: Acetyl units
  - ⊥ Output: Carbon dioxide, ATP (or GTP), reduced cofactors
  - ⊥ Related activities
    - Electron transport: Recycles cofactors
    - Oxidative phosphorylation: Transduces energy into ATP
- ❖ Pyruvate dehydrogenase complex: Major source of acetyl units from glucose
  - ⊥ Reaction
    - Pyruvate to acetyl CoA and carbon dioxide
    - NAD^+ reduced
  - ⊥ Enzyme complex: Three enzyme activities
    - Pyruvate dehydrogenase
    - Dihydrolipoyl transacetylase
    - Dihydrolipoyl dehydrogenase
  - ⊥ Coenzymes
    - Thiamine pyrophosphate
    - Coenzyme A
    - Lipoic acid
    - NAD^+
    - FAD: protein bound
  - ⊥ Regulation
    - Acetyl-CoA, NADH inhibitors
    - AMP activates: GTP inhibits
    - Covalent modification (mammalian enzyme): Phosphoenzyme inhibited
      - Pyruvate dehydrogenase kinase: Activate by acetyl-CoA and NADH
      - Pyruvate dehydrogenase phosphatase: Calcium activated
- ❖ Citrate synthase
  - ⊥ Perkin condensation: Acetyl CoA + oxaloacetate to citrate
  - ⊥ Regulation
    - NADH: Allosteric inhibitor
    - Succinyl CoA: Allosteric inhibitor: Intracycle inhibitor
- ❖ Aconitase
  - ⊥ Citrate to aconitate to isocitrate: Dehydration-rehydration
  - ⊥ Iron–sulfur cluster
  - ⊥ Site of action of fluoroacetate: Trojan horse inhibitor: Requires conversion to fluorocitrate
- ❖ Isocitrate dehydrogenase
  - ⊥ Oxidative decarboxylation of isocitrate: Forms α-ketoglutarate
  - ⊥ NAD^+ reduced
  - ⊥ Regulation
    - NADH, ATP allosteric inhibitors
    - ADP, NAD^+ allosteric activator
    - Covalent modification (*E. coli* enzyme): Phosphoenzyme inhibited

- Kinase activated by TCA cycle intermediates
- Phosphatase activated by TCA cycle intermediates
❖ α-ketoglutarate dehydrogenase: Multienzyme complex: Similar to pyruvate dehydrogenase complex
  ⮦ Oxidative decarboxylation of α-ketoglutarate: Produces succinyl-CoA
  ⮦ NAD^+ reduced
  ⮦ Regulation
    • NADH inhibits
❖ Succinyl-CoA synthetase: Succinate thiokinase
  ⮦ Substrate-level phosphorylation
    • GTP in mammals: Nucleoside diphosphate kinase moves P to ATP
    • ATP in plants and bacteria
❖ Succinate dehydrogenase
  ⮦ FAD reduced
  ⮦ Membrane-bound enzyme: Covalently bound FAD
  ⮦ Electron transport: Electrons moved to coenzyme Q
❖ Fumarase: Hydration of fumarate: Produces malate
❖ Malate dehydrogenase
  ⮦ NAD^+ reduced
  ⮦ Oxaloacetate produced
❖ TCA intermediates connected to biosynthetic pathways
  ⮦ α-ketoglutarate: Precursor of Glu
    • Glu: Precursor of
      • Pro, Arg, Gln
  ⮦ Succinyl CoA: Porphyrin ring synthesis
  ⮦ Fumarate: Precursor of Asp
  ⮦ Oxaloacetate: Precursor of Asp
    • Asp: Precursor of pyrimidine nucleotides, Asn, Met, Lys, Thr, Ile
    • PEP: Precursor of
      • Phe, Tyr, Trp (plants and microorganism)
      • 3-phosphoglycerate: Precursor of
        o Ser, Gly, Cys
      • Glucose
❖ Anaplerotic reactions: Produce TCA cycle intermediates
  ⮦ Pyruvate carboxylase
  ⮦ PEP carboxykinase
  ⮦ Malic enzyme
❖ Glyoxylate cycle: Plants and bacteria: Uses acetyl units to produce oxaloacetate: Oxaloacetate to pyruvate: Pyruvate to glucose
  ⮦ Citric acid cycle to isocitrate
  ⮦ Isocitrate lyase produces glyoxylate and succinate
  ⮦ Succinate to oxaloacetate via citric acid cycle
  ⮦ Malate synthase: Glyoxylate + acetyl CoA to malate

Chapter Objectives

Citric Acid Cycle

The citric acid cycle is a central metabolic cycle to which catabolism of monosaccharides, amino acids, and fatty acids converge. We see that pyruvate, the end product of glycolysis, is introduced as an acetyl unit attached to coenzyme A catalyzed by pyruvate dehydrogenase. (A carbon is lost as CO_2.) The pyruvate dehydrogenase reaction is worth understanding, because we encounter almost identical biochemistry in α-ketoglutarate dehydrogenase catalysis of α-ketoglutarate to succinyl-CoA. Pyruvate is decomposed to CO_2 and a two-carbon acetyl group, which is attached to thiamine pyrophosphate. The acetyl group is transferred to coenzyme A via lipoic acid and in the process, lipoic acid is reduced. To reoxidize lipoic acid, electrons are transferred to protein-bound FAD and then to NAD^+.

The citric acid cycle begins with condensation of acetyl-CoA and oxaloacetate to produce citric acid, a tricarboxylic acid (see Figure 18.2). The cycle then converts citrate to oxaloacetate and two molecules of CO_2. You should understand that the basic chemistry is oxidation. (Input is an acetyl group, outputs are carbon dioxide.) Oxidations are always accompanied by reductions and the reductions that take place include three steps at which NAD^+ is reduced to NADH: isocitrate to α-ketoglutarate conversion catalyzed by isocitrate dehydrogenase, α-ketoglutarate to succinyl-CoA conversion catalyzed by α-ketoglutarate dehydrogenase (similar in reaction mechanism to pyruvate dehydrogenase), and malate to oxaloacetate conversion catalyzed by malate dehydrogenase. The first two reactions are responsible for the two CO_2 molecules produced by the cycle. An additional reduction occurs during the conversion of succinate to fumarate catalyzed by succinate dehydrogenase. This enzyme plays two metabolic roles, one in the TCA cycle and the other as a component of the electron transport chain.

There are a number of important points to remember about the citric acid cycle that will help you with other aspects of biochemistry.

1. When amino acid metabolism is covered, we will see that a few of the citric acid cycle intermediates derive from and can be converted into amino acids. Examples include pyruvic acid/alanine, α-ketoglutarate/glutamic acid, and oxaloacetate/aspartic acid.
2. The citric acid cycle has a substrate-level phosphorylation catalyzed by succinyl-CoA synthetase. Synthetases are enzymes that drive product formation with NTP hydrolysis. So, succinyl-CoA synthetase can produce succinyl-CoA using hydrolysis of either GTP or ATP, depending on the source of the enzyme. (Citric acid synthase synthesizes citric acid but it does not utilize hydrolysis of ATP to drive the reaction.)
3. The steps from succinate to fumarate to malate to oxaloacetate are almost identical in chemistry to β-oxidation, the principal pathway of fatty acid catabolism.

Regulation of the Cycle

The citric acid cycle is regulated at pyruvate dehydrogenase by acetyl-CoA, CoA, NAD^+, NADH, and ATP; at citrate synthase by NADH, ATP, and succinyl-CoA; at isocitrate dehydrogenase by NAD^+, ADP, and ATP; and, at α-ketoglutarate dehydrogenase by NADH, AMP, and succinyl-CoA. The cycle is sensitive to NAD^+ levels, a measure of electron transport activity, to adenine nucleotides, a measure of energy charge, and to immediate substrates like acetyl-CoA or succinyl-CoA.

Citric Acid Cycle Outputs and Inputs

The whole point of the cycle is to consume acetyl units for energy with CO_2 as a byproduct. However, other pathways can produce TCA cycle intermediates and TCA intermediates can feed into other pathways. For example, acetyl units can be derived from catabolism of fatty acids and certain amino acids, whereas citrate is used to move carbons out of the citric acid cycle to synthesize fatty acids. Amino acids and citric acid cycle intermediates are interconvertible. Reactions leading to citric cycle intermediates are known as anaplerotic reactions.

Glyoxylate Cycle

The glyoxylate cycle allows plants and bacteria to convert acetyl units into sugar carbons. Parts of the cycle are identical to the TCA cycle. However, the key differences are conversion of isocitrate to succinate and glyoxylate by isocitrate lyase, and production of malate from glyoxylate and acetyl-CoA by malate synthase. This allows for the production of four-carbon units from two-carbon acetyl units. Later we will study gluconeogenesis, an anabolic pathway leading to synthesis of glucose from certain three- or four-carbon intermediates.

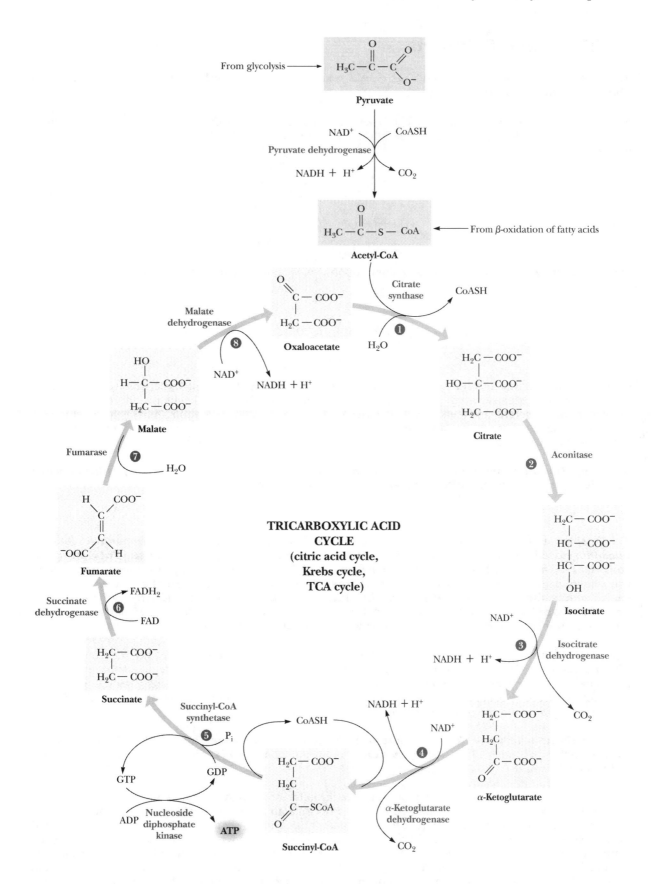

Figure 18.2 The tricarboxylic acid (TCA) cycle.

Problems and Solutions

1. Describe the labelling pattern that would result from the introduction into the TCA cycle of glutamate labelled at the C_γ with ^{14}C.

Answer: Glutamate may be converted to α-ketoglutarate either by transamination or by the action of glutamate dehydrogenase. In either case, glutamate with label at the C_γ will produce α-ketoglutarate labelled at C_γ as shown below.

The label is not lost in the first cycle and shows up in oxaloacetate at either of two positions.

No label is lost in the second round as well; however, in each subsequent cycle, 50% of the label is lost. This occurs because at the end of the second round, label is equally distributed among all the carbons of oxaloacetate. Since each cycle releases carbons from oxaloacetate, one half of the label is lost. The remaining label is redistributed equally among all the carbons and again one half is lost with subsequent cycles.

3. Using the same molecules from Problem 2, calculate the number of CO_2 produced when considering glycolysis, the PDH complex, and the Krebs cycle.

Answer: a. 4 CO_2; c. 2 CO_2; c. 2 CO_2.

5. (Integrates with Chapter 14) The serine residue of isocitrate dehydrogenase that is phosphorylated by protein kinase lies within the active site of the enzyme. This situation contrasts with most other examples of covalent modification by protein phosphorylation, where the phosphorylation occurs at a site remote from the active site. What direct effect do you think such active-site phosphorylation might have on the catalytic activity of isocitrate dehydrogenase? (See Barford, D., 1991. Molecular mechanisms for the control of enzymic activity by protein phosphorylation. Biochimica et Biophysica Acta 1133:55–62.).

Answer: Isocitrate dehydrogenase catalyzes the oxidative decarboxylation of isocitrate to α-ketoglutarate with reduction of NAD^+ to NADH. Phosphorylation of Ser[113] leads to enzyme inactivation because isocitrate no longer binds to the enzyme. Ser[113] normally forms a hydrogen bond with the γ-carboxyl group of isocitrate. Phosphorylated Ser[113] interferes with isocitrate binding by electrostatic repulsion of the carboxyl group and by steric hindrance.

7. In a tissue where the TCA cycle has been inhibited by fluoroacetate, what difference in the concentration of each TCA cycle metabolite would you expect, compared with a normal, uninhibited tissue?

Answer: Fluoroacetate is an example of a suicide inhibitor or a Trojan horse inhibitor. When tested *in vitro* against isolated enzymes of the TCA cycle, fluoroacetate has no effect. However, when used on isolated mitochondria or *in vivo*, fluoroacetate is a potent inhibitor of aconitase. Fluoroacetate is converted to fluoroacetyl-coenzyme A by acetyl-CoA synthetase, which is condensed with oxaloacetate by citrate synthase to produce 2R,3S-fluorocitrate. This isomer specifically inhibits aconitase. With aconitase inhibited, we might expect all TCA cycle intermediates to decrease in concentration. Citrate concentrations, however, will increase in concentration, but isocitrate and all subsequent metabolites will decrease in concentration. Fluoroacetate poisoning leads to a host of physiological changes including alterations in carbohydrate metabolism. Citrate accumulation leads to inhibition of phosphofructokinase. Low levels of oxaloacetate prevent cells from consuming acetyl units and these eventually lead to ketosis and lactidosis.

9. *Starting with citrate, isocitrate, α-ketoglutarate, and succinate, state which of the individual carbons of the molecule undergo oxidation in the next step of the TCA cycle. Which of the molecules undergo a net oxidation?*

Answer:

In the conversion of citrate to isocitrate, one carbon is reduced and one carbon is oxidized. Hence, there is no net change in the oxidation state in going from citrate to isocitrate. Production of α-ketoglutarate from isocitrate is the result of an oxidation. The enzyme that catalyzes this reaction, isocitrate dehydrogenase, uses NAD⁺ as a cofactor, which is reduced to NADH during the reaction. Likewise, conversion of α-ketoglutarate to succinate is an oxidation. In this case, the conversion is a two-step process. In the first step, α-ketoglutarate is converted to succinyl-CoA by α-ketoglutarate dehydrogenase. This is an oxidation (the carbon in a thiol ester bond is at the same oxidation state as a carbon in an ester bond), and so it must be accompanied by a reduction—in this case, NAD⁺ is reduced to NADH. Succinyl-CoA to succinate is a hydrolysis reaction that is coupled to production of a high-energy phosphate bond (as GTP or ATP). Finally, succinate to fumarate is catalyzed by succinate dehydrogenase. This enzyme has an enzyme-bound FAD coenzyme that is reduced when succinate is oxidized to fumarate.

11. *Based on the action of thiamine pyrophosphate in catalysis of the pyruvate dehydrogenase reaction, suggest a suitable chemical mechanism for the pyruvate decarboxylase reaction in yeast:*
pyruvate → acetaldehyde +CO₂

Answer:

13. Describe the labelling pattern that would result if $^{14}CO_2$ were incorporated into the TCA cycle via the pyruvate carboxylase reaction.

Answer: The pyruvate carboxylase reaction converts pyruvate and CO_2 to oxaloacetate, with label appearing on the β-carboxyl group of oxaloacetate. When this is used to synthesize citrate, the labelled carbon shows up as a carboxyl group up on the middle carbon, which is eliminated by the α-ketoglutarate dehydrogenase step as shown below.

15. Describe the labelling pattern that would result in the glyoxylate cycle if a plant were fed acetyl-CoA labelled at the –CH₃ carbon.

Answer: The glyoxylate cycle begins in the glyoxysome with synthesis of citrate and conversion to isocitrate. Next, isocitrate is converted to succinate and glyoxylate. The methyl carbon of acetyl-CoA ends up as a methylene carbon of succinate. This would be transported to the mitochondria where it would be converted to oxaloacetate. Since succinate has no chiral carbons, the labelled carbon appears as either the carbonyl carbon or the methylene carbon of oxaloacetate. This, however, occurs in the TCA cycle in the mitochondria. So, the labelling pattern will be as shown in Figure 18.20.

17. In most cells, fatty acids are synthesized from acetate units in the cytosol. However, the primary source of acetate units is the TCA cycle in mitochondria, and acetate cannot be transported directly from the mitochondria to the cytosol. Cells solve this problem by exporting citrate from the mitochondria and then converting citrate to acetate and oxaloacetate. Then, because cells cannot transport oxaloacetate into mitochondria directly, they must convert it to malate or pyruvate, both of which can be taken up by mitochondria. Draw a complete pathway for citrate export, conversion of citrate to malate and pyruvate, and import of malate and pyruvate by mitochondria.
   a. Which of the reactions in this cycle might require energy input?
   b. What would be the most likely source of this energy?
   c. Do you recognize any of the enzyme reactions in this cycle?
   d. What coenzymes might be required to run this cycle?

Answer: The uptake pathway is shown below. Clearly, the citrate lyase reaction is driven by hydrolysis of ATP. Citrate release by the mitochondria must be balanced by malate and pyruvate uptake to maintain charge neutrality. (Citrate is a tricarboxylic acid, whereas malate is a dicarboxylic acid and pyruvate a monocarboxylic acid.) Conversion of oxaloacetate to malate to pyruvate in the cytosol moves electrons from NADH to NAPDH and the latter is used in anabolic pathways. Malate to oxaloacetate to citrate is part of the citric acid cycle and pyruvate dehydrogenase feeds two-carbon acetyl units into the citric acid cycle. Citrate lyase in the cytosol provides acetyl units for fatty acid biosynthesis, which also requires reducing equivalents in the form of NADPH. NADPH is supplied by malic enzyme from electrons originating on NADH. Clearly, NAD^+ plays a key role in this process.

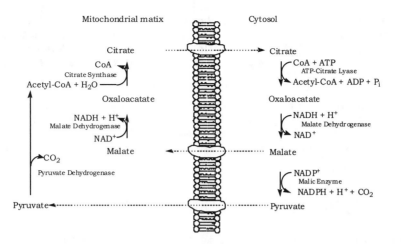

19. Glycolysis, the pyruvate dehydrogenase reaction, and the TCA cycle result in complete oxidation of a molecule of glucose to CO_2. Review the calculation of oxidation numbers for individual atoms in any molecule, and then calculate the oxidation numbers of the carbons of glucose, pyruvate, the acetyl carbons of acetyl-CoA, and the metabolites of the TCA cycle to convince yourself that complete oxidation of glucose involves removal of 24 electrons and that each acetyl-CoA through the TCA cycle gives up 8 electrons.

Answer: In this case, a simple set of rules for calculating oxidation numbers is to assign oxidation numbers to bonds with oxygen as −2 and hydrogen as +1 and bonds to carbon as zero. The oxidation number of a carbon and all its covalently bonded partners must sum to zero (in compounds that are neutrally charged and have no lone pair electrons.) For example, for CO_2, the oxidation number of carbon plus $2s(-2) = 0$ or, the oxidation number of carbon = +4 for the carbon in CO_2. Glucose is shown below. The oxidation number of C_1 is calculated as follows: $C_1 - 2 + 1 = 0$ or $C_1 = +1$. For carbons 2 through 5, $C_n + 1 + 1 - 2 = 0$ or $C_n = 0$. For C_6, $C_6 + 1 + 1 + 1 - 2 = 0$, $C_6 = -1$. For each carbon to change its oxidation number to that of CO_2, it must be increased in each case. For carbons 2 through 5, the increase is from 0 to 4 for a total of (4s4=) 16. Carbon 1 changes from +1 to +4 or for a change of 3. Carbon 6 changes from −1 to 4 for a change of 5. The sum is (16+3+5 =) 24.

For the acetyl group in acetyl-CoA, the methyl carbon's oxidation number is −3, and changing it to the oxidation number of carbon in carbon dioxide (+4) is a change of +7. The carbonyl carbon's oxidation number is +4 (−2 for oxygen and −2 for the sulfur in coenzyme A). However, in order to metabolize the acetyl group, the coenzyme adduct must be removed by hydrolysis. This will convert the carbonyl carbon to a carboxyl carbon with an oxidation number of +3 (−2 for two oxygens and +1 for a proton). Converting it to carbon dioxide is a change of +1 in oxidation number.

21. Aconitase is rapidly inactivated by 2R,3R-fluorocitrate, which is produced from fluoroacetate in the citrate synthase reaction. Interestingly, inactivation by fluorocitrate is accompanied by stoichiometric release of fluoride ion (i.e., 1 F-ion is lost per aconitase active site). This observation is consistent with "mechanism-based inactivation" of aconitase by fluorocitrate.

Suggest a mechanism for this inactivation, based on formation of 4-hydroxy-trans-aconitate, which remains tightly bound at the active site. To assess your answer, consult this reference: Lauble, H., Kennedy, M., et al., 1996. The reaction of fluorocitrate with aconitase and the crystal structure of the enzyme-inhibitor complex. Proceedings of the National Academy of Sciences 93:13699–13703.

Answer: 2R, 3R-fluorocitrate is converted by aconitase to 2-fluoro-*cis*-aconitate. This intermediate then rotates 180 degrees in the active site. Addition of hydroxide at the C4 position is followed by double bond migration from C3-C4 to C2-C3, to form 4-hydroxy-*trans*-aconitate. This product remains tightly bound at the aconitase active site, inactivating the enzyme. Studies by Trauble et al. have shown that the inhibitory product can be displaced by a 10^6-fold excess of isocitrate.

Questions for Self-Study

1. a.   Complete the following reaction and name the enzyme complex that catalyzes it.

    Pyruvate + CoA + _____ → acetyl-CoA + _____ + _____ + CO_2

    b.   This enzyme complex uses five coenzymes. Name the coenzymes.

2.   The citric acid cycle is also known as the Krebs cycle and the TCA (tricarboxylic acid) cycle. Identify the tricarboxylic acids in the cycle.

3.   Fill in the blanks. The citric acid cycle converts two-carbon _____ units into _____ _____. In the process, the carbons are _____ and coenzymes are _____. The coenzymes serve as mobile electron carriers connecting the citric acid cycle to the _____ _____ _____.

4. α-ketoglutarate can be produced by oxidative decarboxylation of a citric acid cycle intermediate or by deamination of an amino acid. Identify these two sources of α-ketoglutarate.

5.   The α-ketoglutarate dehydrogenase complex used five coenzymes during catalysis. One of them, lipoic acid, a carboxylic acid, is transiently covalently modified during catalysis. In particular, a disulfide bond is broken and reformed. Briefly outline this process.

6.   In an earlier chapter, we learned that thiol ester bonds are high-energy bonds. In the citric acid cycle, there is one substrate-level phosphorylation (of GDP) driven by cleavage of a thiol ester bond. Identify the reaction and the enzyme. (Hint: The enzyme is named for the reverse reaction.)

7.   Succinate dehydrogenase converts succinate to fumarate. This enzyme is a member of which two important metabolic sequences?

8.   The citric acid cycle results in net oxidation of carbons. The production of succinate leaves a four-carbon unit in the cycle that is converted to oxaloacetate. Order the compounds shown below from least oxidized to most oxidized and identify them.

9.   What is an anaplerotic reaction?

10. The citric acid cycle is regulated by metabolic signals at pyruvate dehydrogenase leading into the cycle and at three places in the cycle, citrate synthase, isocitrate dehydrogenase, and α-ketoglutarate dehydrogenase. List the metabolic signals and state how they affect the cycle.

11. Fill in the blanks. The _____ cycle is a metabolic sequence active in plants, particularly seedlings, in which acetyl units are converted to _____. In this cycle citrate is produced from oxaloacetate and acetyl-CoA and citrate is converted to isocitrate. These two steps are identical to two steps in the _____ cycle. However, the fate of isocitrate is different in the two cycles. In plants isocitrate is converted to succinate and the two-carbon compound _____. Succinate is subsequently metabolized to oxaloacetate. The two-carbon compound and a second acetyl group from acetyl-CoA are condensed to form a four-carbon compound that is metabolized to _____. Thus, the inputs to the cycle are _____ _____ _____, which are converted into a four-carbon compound.

Answers

1. a.   Pyruvate + CoA + NAD^+ → acetyl-CoA + NADH + H^++ CO_2; pyruvate dehydrogenase.
    b.   Thiamine pyrophosphate, coenzyme A, lipoic acid, NAD^+, and FAD.

2.   Citrate and isocitrate.

3.   Acetyl; carbon dioxide; oxidized; reduced; electron-transport chain.

4.   Isocitrate and glutamic acid.

5.   During catalysis, the disulfide bond is broken by transfer of an acetyl unit to lipoic acid in thiol ester linkage. The acetyl unit is then transferred to CoA leaving the disulfide bond as two sulfhydryl groups. An oxidation must occur for the disulfide to be reformed and this occurs at the expense of FAD reduction. (Subsequently, electrons are passed to NAD^+.)

6.   The reaction is conversion of succinyl-CoA to succinate and CoA with phosphorylation of GDP to GTP. The enzyme is succinyl-CoA synthetase. (Why is it a synthetase and not a synthase?)

7.   Citric acid cycle and electron transport.

8.   The compounds are succinate, fumarate, malate, and oxaloacetate. Fumarate and malate (boxed) are at the same oxidation state.

9.   It is a reaction that replenishes citric acid cycle intermediates.

10. NADH inhibits; NAD^+ stimulates; ATP inhibits; ADP and AMP stimulate; Succinyl-CoA inhibits; acetyl-CoA inhibits, CoA stimulates.

11. Glyoxylate; oxaloacetate; TCA (or citric acid); glyoxylate; malate; two acetyl units.

Additional Problems

1. a. Identify the following compounds.

$$
\begin{array}{lll}
CH_3 & COO^- & COO^- \\
| & | & | \\
C=O & CH_2 & CH_2 \\
| & | & | \\
COO^- & C=O & CH_2 \\
 & | & | \\
 & COO^- & C=O \\
 & & | \\
 & & COO-
\end{array}
$$

   b. If a Schiff base were produced between a side chain lysine and each of these compounds and then subsequently displaced by ammonia, to what would each of these compounds be converted?

2. The glyoxylate cycle is divided between specialized organelles known as glyoxysomes and the mitochondria. Describe the interplay between these two organelles that is necessary for the glyoxylate cycle to function.

3. The four steps in the citric acid cycle from succinate to oxaloacetate are similar in chemistry to the fatty acid catabolic pathway known as β-oxidation. In this pathway, a carbon in a fatty acid chain two positions away from the carboxylic acid group (the first position is α, next β, the last ω or omega) is oxidized to a keto group. Show that this also occurs when succinate is converted to oxaloacetate.

4. In glycolysis, phosphofructokinase is allosterically inhibited by citrate. What is a high concentration of citrate signalling and why is it important to turn off glycolysis under these conditions?

5. How is succinate dehydrogenase different than the other TCA cycle enzymes?

6. Succinyl-CoA synthetase is responsible for the only substrate-level phosphorylation found in the citric acid cycle. The mammalian enzyme uses GDP as a nucleotide and produces GTP. How is the high-energy phosphate bond of GTP utilized by cells?

7. If a labelled carbon atom of citric acid survives one turn of the cycle, it shows up in two positions in oxaloacetate. Which steps are responsible for this?

8. Pyruvate carboxylase is a biotin-containing enzyme that reacts pyruvate with CO_2 to produce oxaloacetate. In general terms, describe this reaction. What is the role of biotin in this reaction? Of what general type of reaction is this an example?

Abbreviated Answers

1. a. Pyruvate, oxaloacetate, and α-ketoglutarate.
   b. alanine, aspartic acid, glutamic acid.

2. The glyoxylate cycle begins with an acetyl unit from acetyl-CoA condensing onto oxaloacetate to produce citrate, which is converted to isocitrate. Although identical to steps in the citric acid cycle, which is carried out in mitochondria, these steps are carried out in glyoxysomes. Isocitrate is metabolized into glyoxylate and succinate by isocitrate lyase, and a second acetyl unit from acetyl-CoA is condensed onto glyoxylate to produce malate, which can be used to produce monosaccharides. Glyoxysomes are unable to generate oxaloacetate from succinate produced by isocitrate lyase and rely on the mitochondria. Succinate is exported to the mitochondria where it is metabolized via the citric acid cycle to oxaloacetate. Oxaloacetate is converted to aspartate by transamination with glutamate as an amino-group donor. The products of transamination, namely aspartic acid and α-ketoglutarate, are transported back to the glyoxysome where the reverse reaction is carried out to produce oxaloacetate and glutamate. Glutamate is exported back to the mitochondria and oxaloacetate is now available for the glyoxylate cycle.

3.

succinate   fumarate   malate   oxaloacetate

4.   High concentrations of citrate are an indication that the citric acid cycle is backing up. This can occur because ATP levels are satisfactory, NAD^+ is unavailable, or an alternate source of acetyl-units, perhaps from fatty acid catabolism, is available. There is no need to continue glycolysis and citrate inhibition at phosphofructokinase insures that glucose units are conserved.

5.   Succinate dehydrogenase is responsible for the conversion of succinate to fumarate in the citric acid cycle. This enzyme is also part of the electron-transport chain and moves electrons to coenzyme Q and is localized in the inner mitochondrial membrane. The other TCA cycle enzymes are located in the matrix.

6.   Signal transduction and protein synthesis both use hydrolysis of GTP. In addition, GTP can be used to phosphorylate ADP by nucleoside diphosphate kinase, which catalyzes the following reaction:

$$GTP + ADP \rightarrow ATP + GDP$$

7.   Both succinate and fumarate are symmetrical molecules with two sets of equivalent carbons. Label at succinate (or fumarate) thus shows up in two positions in later stages.

8.   Pyruvate carboxylase catalyzes a two-step reaction leading to oxaloacetate formation. In the first step, bicarbonate is attached to biotin in an ATP-dependent reaction. In the second step, the activated carboxyl group is transferred to pyruvate to produce oxaloacetate. Biotin functions as a carrier of activated carboxyl groups. The reaction is an example of an anaplerotic reaction because it leads to synthesis of a citric acid cycle intermediate.

Summary

Pyruvate produced in glycolysis can be oxidatively decarboxylated to acetyl-CoA and then oxidized in the tricarboxylic acid cycle (also known as the citric acid cycle or Krebs cycle). Electrons produced in this oxidative process are collected in reduced coenzymes (NADH and $FADH_2$), then passed through the electron transport pathway to oxygen (O_2), the final electron acceptor. Discovery of the cycle dates to Hans Krebs' studies of the oxidation of small organic acids by kidney and liver tissue, Szent-Gyorgyi's observation that addition of certain dicarboxylic acids increased the oxygen consumption of muscle tissue, and the demonstration by Martius and Knoop that citrate could be converted to isocitrate and α-ketoglutarate.

The oxidative decarboxylation of pyruvate is carried out by pyruvate dehydrogenase, a multi-enzyme complex composed of three types of protein subunits and five different coenzymes. Acetyl-CoA produced in this reaction enters the TCA cycle, combining with oxaloacetate in the citrate synthase reaction. This irreversible step commits acetate units to oxidation and to energy production. Citrate synthase is allosterically inhibited by NADH and by succinyl-CoA. Citrate is then isomerized to isocitrate by aconitase in a two-step process involving aconitate as an intermediate. This reaction converts a tertiary alcohol—a poor substrate for further oxidation—to a secondary alcohol, which can be readily oxidized. Fluoroacetate blocks the TCA cycle *in vivo*, although it has no apparent effect on any single reaction of the TCA cycle. Citrate synthase converts fluoroacetate to fluorocitrate, which strongly inhibits aconitase.

Isocitrate is oxidatively decarboxylated by isocitrate dehydrogenase in a two-step reaction involving oxidation of the C-2 alcohol of isocitrate to form oxalosuccinate, followed by a β-decarboxylation reaction that expels the central carboxyl group as CO_2, leaving the product α-ketoglutarate. NADH produced in this reaction links the TCA cycle and the electron-transport chain. Isocitrate dehydrogenase is allosterically inhibited by NADH and ATP and allosterically activated by ADP. A second oxidative decarboxylation occurs in the α-ketoglutarate dehydrogenase reaction, which involves a multi-enzyme complex similar in many respects to pyruvate dehydrogenase. The reaction produces NADH and succinyl-CoA—a thiol ester product. Succinyl-CoA is used in the next step to drive the synthesis of GTP (in animals) or ATP (in plants and bacteria). This reaction is catalyzed by succinyl CoA synthetase and is an example of substrate-level phosphorylation, the only such reaction in the TCA cycle. The mechanism is postulated to involve formation of succinyl phosphate at the active site, followed by transfer of the phosphoryl group to an active site histidine with release of succinate. Phosphate is then transferred to GDP to form GTP.

The TCA cycle is completed by converting succinate to oxaloacetate. The process involves an oxidation, a hydration reaction, and a second oxidation. Succinate dehydrogenase, a membrane-bound enzyme and a part of the electron-transport chain, catalyzes the oxidation of succinate to fumarate, linking this reaction to reduction of FAD. Fumarase then catalyzes the trans-hydration of fumarate to produce malate, and malate dehydrogenase completes the cycle by oxidizing malate to oxaloacetate. The latter reaction is strongly endergonic, but the reaction is pulled forward by the favourable citrate synthase reaction. The net reaction accomplished by the TCA cycle produces two molecules of CO_2, one ATP and four reduced coenzymes per acetate group oxidized. Carbon introduced to the cycle in any given citrate synthase reaction is not expelled as CO_2 in that same turn of the cycle. The carbonyl carbon of any given acetyl-CoA survives the first turn intact, but is completely lost as CO_2 in the second turn. The methyl carbon survives two full turns, and then undergoes 50% loss in the third turn, 25% loss in the fourth turn, etc. The TCA cycle provides a variety of intermediates for biosynthetic pathways, including citrate, α-ketoglutarate, succinyl-CoA, fumarate, and oxaloacetate. On the other hand, the cell also feeds some of these same molecules back into the TCA cycle from other reactions, replenishing TCA cycle intermediates in so-called anaplerotic reactions.

The main sites of regulation in the TCA cycle are pyruvate dehydrogenase, citrate synthase, isocitrate dehydrogenase, and α-ketoglutarate dehydrogenase. All these enzymes are inhibited by NADH, and ATP inhibits both pyruvate dehydrogenase and isocitrate dehydrogenase. The cycle is turned on when ADP/ATP and NAD^+/NADH ratios are high. Acetyl-CoA activates pyruvate carboxylase and succinyl-CoA inhibits both citrate synthase and α-ketoglutarate dehydrogenase.

Animals use the TCA cycle primarily for energy production and they essentially waste carbon units by giving off CO_2. As a result, they cannot effect net synthesis of carbohydrates from acetyl-CoA. Plants and bacteria, on the other hand, employ a modification of the TCA cycle—the glyoxylate cycle—to conserve carbon units and facilitate eventual biosynthesis of carbohydrates from two-carbon acetate units. In plants, isocitrate lyase and malate synthase—the enzymes of the glyoxylate cycle—are contained in specialized organelles called glyoxysomes. The glyoxylate cycle permits seeds to grow underground where photosynthesis is impossible. When the plant begins photosynthesis and can fix CO_2 to produce sugars, glyoxysomes disappear.

Chapter 19

Electron Transport and Oxidative Phosphorylation

• •

Chapter Outline

❖ Oxidative phosphorylation driven by electron transport
  ⅄ Membrane-associated processes
    • Plasma membrane of bacteria
    • Mitochondrial membrane of eukaryotes
      • Outer mitochondrial membrane: Permeable to $M_r < 10\ 000$ due to protein porin
      • Intermembrane space: Creatine kinase, adenylate kinase, cytochrome c
      • Inner mitochondrial membrane: Highly impermeable
        ○ High protein content
        ○ High content of unsaturated fatty acids
        ○ Cardiolipin and diphosphatidylglycerol: No cholesterol
        ○ Cristae: Folds that increase surface area
      • Matrix
        ○ TCA cycle enzymes (except succinate dehydrogenase)
        ○ Enzymes for catabolism of fatty acids
        ○ Circular DNA
        ○ Ribosomes, tRNAs
❖ Reduction potentials: Electrical potential generated when reactions involve movement of electrons
  ⅄ Standard reduction potentials: $\mathscr{E}_0'$
    • Measured using sample half-cell with oxidized and reduced forms at 1 M
    • Reference half-cell 1 M H^+ and H_2 gas at 1 atm
    • Electrons flow toward cell with larger positive reduction potential
    • Half-cell reactions written as reduction reaction: Electrons on reactant side
    • Positive values of $\mathscr{E}_0'$: Accept electrons: Oxidizing agents
    • Negative values of $\mathscr{E}_0'$: Donate electrons: Reducing agents
  ⅄ Standard free energy change related to standard reduction potential
    • $\Delta G^{\circ\prime} = -n\mathscr{F}\Delta\mathscr{E}_0'$
      • n = number of electrons
      • $\mathscr{F}$ = Faraday's constant: 96 485 J/V·mol
      • $\Delta\mathscr{E}_0' = \mathscr{E}_0'(\text{final}) - \mathscr{E}_0'(\text{initial})$
❖ Electron-transport chain
  ⅄ Electron mediators
    • Flavoproteins: Tightly bound FMN or FAD
    • Coenzyme Q (ubiquinone): 1 or 2 electron transfers: Mobile within membrane
    • Cytochromes: Fe^{2+}/Fe^{3+}
      • Cytochrome a: Isoprenoid (15-C) on modified vinyl and formyl in place of methyl
      • Cytochrome b: Iron-protoporphyrin IX
      • Cytochrome c: Iron-protoporphyrin IX linked to cysteine
    • Iron–sulfur proteins: Fe^{2+}/Fe^{3+}: Several types
    • Protein-bound copper: Cu^+/Cu^{2+}

- Electron-transport complexes: Four
  - Complex I: NADH–coenzyme Q reductase (NADH reductase)
    - Electron movement
      - [FMN] accepts electron pair from NADH
      - [$FMNH_2$] donates electrons to Fe-S
      - Fe-S donates electrons to coenzyme Q
    - Protons pumped from matrix to cytosol
    - Supports 3 ATP
  - Complex II: Succinate–coenzyme Q reductase (succinate dehydrogenase)
    - Components
      - FAD
      - Fe-S centres
    - No protons pumped
    - Supports 2 ATP
    - Similar complexes that reduce coenzyme Q
      - Glycerolphosphate dehydrogenase: No protons pumped
      - Fatty acyl–CoA dehydrogenase: No protons pumped
  - Complex III: Coenzyme Q–cytochrome c reductase
    - Components
      - Cytochromes b_L and b_H
      - Rieske protein: Fe-S protein
    - Q cycle
    - Protons pumped
  - Complex IV: Cytochrome c oxidase
    - Components
      - Cytochrome a and Cu_A
      - Cytochrome a_3 and Cu_B
    - Binuclear centre: O_2 consumption and H_2O production
    - Protons pumped
- Mitchell's chemiosmotic hypothesis: Proton gradient used to drive ATP synthesis
  - Protons per electron pair
    - From succinate 6
    - From NADH 10
  - Four protons per ATP
    - ADP uptake: 1 proton
    - ATP synthesis: 3 protons
  - One oxygen consumed per electron pair
  - P/O
    - From NADH: 2.5
    - From succinate: 1.5
- ATP synthase: F_1F_oATPase
  - F_1: ATP synthesis: Spherical particles on inner membrane
  - F_o: Proton channel in inner membrane
- Inhibitors of oxidative phosphorylation
  - Complex I: Rotenone, ptericidin, amytal, mercurial compounds
  - Complex II: 2-thenoyltrifluoroacetone, carboxin
  - Complex III: Antimycin, myxothiazol
  - Complex IV: Cyanide, azide, carbon monoxide
  - ATP synthase: Oligomycin, DCCD
- Uncouplers: Stimulate electron transport: Short-circuit proton gradient: Block ATP production
  - Proton ionophores: Lipid-soluble substance with dissociable proton
  - Thermogenin: Uncoupler protein: Generates heat using proton gradient
- Mitochondrial exchange and uptake
  - ATP/ADP translocate
    - ADP in: ATP out: 1 proton in

- ⊥ Glycerolphosphate shuttle
    - · Cytosolic glycerolphosphate dehydrogenase: NADH-dependent
    - · Mitochondrial glycerolphosphate dehydrogenase: FAD-dependent
    - · DHAP and glycerolphosphate exchanged
- ⊥ Malate-aspartate shuttle
    - · Cytosolic and mitochondrial malate dehydrogenases both use NADH
    - · Aspartate exchanged for glutamate
    - · Malate exchanged for α-ketoglutarate
- ❖ Cytochrome c and apoptosis
    - ⊥ Apoptosis: Programmed cell death
        - · Set off in response to various signals: Calcium, ROS, lipids, kinases
        - · Cytochrome c released by mitochondria
        - · ATP–ADP translocase (inner membrane) and voltage-dependent anion channel (outer membrane) form pores that pass cytochrome c
    - ⊥ Cytochrome c in cytosol
        - · Activates apoptosome
        - · Apoptosome activates caspases that destroy cell components

Chapter Objectives

Oxidation–Reduction Reactions

Electron transport involves sequential oxidation–reduction reactions. For any electron carrier, we can think of the carrier as participating in a reaction in which electrons are either produced or consumed. If electrons are consumed, the carrier is reduced, and if electrons are produced, the carrier is oxidized. But in reality, free electrons are not just present in solution waiting to react (electrons are not like a typical chemical substrate); rather, electrons are exchanged between pairs of reacting molecules. The pairs are an oxidant (or oxidizing agent) and a reductant (or reducing agent). An oxidant accepts electrons, is itself reduced, but oxidizes the reductant, the agent from which the electrons originated. A reductant donates electrons, is itself oxidized, but reduces an oxidant.

The tendency to donate or accept electrons is measured by standard reduction (redox) potentials. It should be clear how these measurements are made. A reference half-cell is connected to a sample half-cell by an agar salt bridge and a low-resistance pathway. (The agar salt bridge simply functions to complete the circuit between the half-cells connected by the low-resistance pathway.) The reference half-cell is H^+/H_2 at 1 M and 1 atmosphere. The reduction potential of this half-cell is 0 V by definition. (Clearly, no potential exists when the reference half-cell is connected to itself.) If the reaction in the sample cell consumes electrons, electrons will flow from the reference cell to the sample cell unless a voltage is applied to prevent this flow. In this case, a positive voltage is required. Thus, a positive standard redox potential indicates that the sample is an oxidant relative to the reference cell, and a negative standard redox potential indicates that the sample is a reductant relative to the reference cell. The two key formulas to remember:

$$\Delta G^{\circ\prime} = -n\mathscr{F}\Delta\mathscr{E}_0' \text{ and}$$
$$\mathscr{E} = \mathscr{E}_0' + (RT/n\mathscr{F})\ln([\text{oxidant}]/[\text{reductant}]).$$

Electron-Transport Chain

A simplified way of thinking about the electron-transport chain is to divide the chain into two types of components, mobile electron carriers and membrane-bound protein complexes. The mobile electron carriers include $NAD^+/NADH$, coenzyme Q or ubiquinone, cytochrome c, and oxygen. Substrates, such as malate (for malate dehydrogenase) or α-ketoglutarate (for α-ketoglutarate dehydrogenase) or succinate (for succinate dehydrogenase) can be thought of as mobile electron carriers as well; however, they are peripheral to the electron-transport chain. There are four membrane-bound complexes that simply move electrons from one mobile electron carrier to another. The first complex is NADH–coenzyme Q reductase or NADH reductase, which moves electrons from NADH to CoQ. CoQ can also be reduced by succinate–coenzyme Q reductase also known as succinate dehydrogenase, which uses succinate as a source of electrons. Coenzyme Q-cytochrome c reductase moves electrons from $CoQH_2$ to cytochrome c. Finally, cytochrome oxidase moves electrons from reduced cytochrome c to molecular oxygen.

Proton Gradient Formation

Electron transport accomplishes two things: it regenerates reduced cofactors such as NAD^+ and [FAD], and it produces ATP. Understand how the energy of electron transport is used to form a proton gradient, which is used in turn to phosphorylate ADP to ATP. Protons are pumped out of the mitochondria by NADH–coenzyme Q reductase. Protons are also expelled in the Q cycle involving coenzyme Q–cytochrome c reductase. The essential point is that coenzyme Q carries electrons and protons, whereas cytochrome c carries only electrons. Cytochrome c oxidase also moves protons, but the details of how this is achieved are unknown.

ATP Synthase

ADP phosphorylation and proton gradient dissipation are coupled by the ATP synthase or F_1F_o–ATPase. Understand how this protein complex is organized and situated in the inner mitochondrial membrane. The F_o portion (o is for oligomycin) is a proton pore, and the F_1 is an ATPase that functions in the reverse direction to produce ATP.

Inhibitors and Uncouplers

Appreciate the difference between an inhibitor and an uncoupler. Inhibitors block the action of some component of electron transport or ATP synthase. Uncouplers do not interfere with electron transport and in fact stimulate it. However, they provide an alternative pathway to dissipate the energy of electron transport.

Problems and Solutions

1. **For the following reaction,**
$$[FAD] + 2 \text{ cyt c } (Fe^{2+}) + 2 H^+ \rightarrow [FADH_2] + 2 \text{ cyt c } (Fe^{3+})$$
determine which of the redox couples is the electron acceptor and which is the electron donor under standard-state conditions. Calculate the value of $\Delta\mathscr{E}_0'$, and determine the free energy change for the reaction.

Answer: The reduction half-reactions and their standard reduction potentials for the reaction are (from Table 19.1):

$FAD + 2H^+ + 2e^- \rightarrow FADH_2$, $\mathscr{E}_0' = -0.219$ V*

cytochrome c $(Fe^{3+}) + e^- \rightarrow$ cytochrome c (Fe^{2+}), $\mathscr{E}_0' = 0.254$ V

The standard reduction potential is the voltage that is generated between a sample half-cell and reference half-cell (H^+/H_2). In effect, it is the voltage that must be applied to a circuit connecting a sample half-cell and the reference half-cell to prevent current from flowing. Using this convention, we see that if the FAD half-cell is connected to the reference half-cell, a slightly negative voltage of -0.219 V must be applied to prevent electrons from flowing from the reference cell into the sample cell. Conversely, $+0.254$ V must be applied when the cytochrome c half-cell is connected to the reference cell. Thus, electrons have a greater tendency to flow from the reference cell to cytochrome c than to FAD. Therefore, electrons must move from $FADH_2$ to cytochrome c. Thus, $FADH_2$ is the electron donor and cytochrome c (Fe^{3+}) is the electron acceptor.

$$\Delta\mathscr{E}_0' = \mathscr{E}_0'(\text{acceptor}) - \mathscr{E}_0'(\text{donor}) = \mathscr{E}_0'(\text{cyto } c) - \mathscr{E}_0'(\text{FAD})$$

$$\Delta\mathscr{E}_0' = +0.254 - (-0.219) = +0.473 \text{ V}$$

The free energy change for the reaction is given by:

$\Delta G^{o'} = -n\mathscr{F}\Delta\mathscr{E}_0'$, where n is the number of electrons, and

$$\mathscr{F} = \text{Faraday's constant} = 96.485\frac{\text{kJ}}{\text{V} \cdot \text{mol}}$$

$$\Delta G^{o'} = -2 \times 96.485\frac{\text{kJ}}{\text{V} \cdot \text{mol}} \times 0.473 \text{ V} = -91.3\frac{\text{kJ}}{\text{mol}}$$

* The value of -0.219 given for FAD in Table 19.1 is for free FAD. Protein-bound FAD has a standard reduction potential in the range of from 0.003 to -0.091, with 0.02 V being a typical value. Using 0.02V, $\Delta G^{o'} = 45.2$ kJ/mol.

3. *For the following redox reaction,*

$$NAD^+ + 2\ H^+ + 2\ e^- \rightarrow NADH + H^+$$

suggest an equation (analogous to Equation 19.12) that predicts the pH dependence of this reaction, and calculate the reduction potential for this reaction at pH 8.

Answer: The NAD^+ reduction shown above may be rewritten as:

$$NAD^+ + H^+ + 2\ e^- \rightarrow NADH$$

However, a source of electrons is needed for the reaction to occur. Therefore, let us assume that the reaction is in aqueous solution with a general reductant of the form:

$$Reductant \rightarrow Oxidant + 2e^-$$

The overall reaction is:

$$NAD^+ + H^+ + Reductant \rightarrow NADH + Oxidant$$

$$\Delta G = \Delta G^{o\prime} + RT\ln\frac{[Oxidant][NAD^+]}{[Reductant][NADH][H^+]}$$

$$= \Delta G^{o\prime} + RT\ln\frac{[Oxidant][NAD^+]}{[Reductant][NADH]} + RT\ln\frac{1}{[H^+]}$$

$$= \Delta G^{o\prime} + RT\ln\frac{[Oxidant][NAD^+]}{[Reductant][NADH]} - RT\ln[H^+]$$

But $\ln[H^+] = 2.303\log_{10}[H^+]$ and $pH \equiv -\log_{10}[H^+]$, so

$$-\ln[H^+] = -2.303\log_{10}[H^+] = 2.303 \times pH$$

Thus:

$$\Delta G = \Delta G^{o\prime} + RT\ln\frac{[Oxidant][NAD^+]}{[Reductant][NADH]} + 2.303 \times RT \times pH$$

In general, $\Delta G = -n\mathcal{F}\Delta\mathscr{E}$ or $\Delta\mathscr{E} = -\dfrac{\Delta G}{n\mathcal{F}}$ where n is the number of electrons, and

$\mathcal{F}$ = Faraday's constant = $96.485\ \dfrac{kJ}{V\cdot mol}$

$$\Delta\mathscr{E} = \Delta\mathscr{E}_o^{\prime} - \frac{RT}{n\mathcal{F}}\ln\frac{[Oxidant][NAD^+]}{[Reductant][NADH]} - 2.303 \times \frac{RT}{n\mathcal{F}} \times pH$$

To calculate the reduction potential, we assume that the reaction is being carried out under standard conditions. Thus, all reactants and products are at 1 M concentration. The above equation simplifies to:

$$\Delta\mathscr{E} = \Delta\mathscr{E}_o^{\prime} - 2.303 \times \frac{RT}{n\mathcal{F}} \times pH$$

5. *A wealthy investor has come to you for advice. She has been approached by a biochemist who seeks financial backing for a company that would market dinitrophenol and dicumarol as weight-loss medications. The biochemist has explained to her that these agents are uncouplers and that they would dissipate metabolic energy as heat. The investor wants to know if you think she should invest in the biochemist's company. How do you respond?*

Answer: The structures of dicumarol and dinitrophenol are:

Dicumarol   2,4-Dinitrophenol

The biochemistry of the suggestion is sound. (Beware: This is not an endorsement of the idea. Please continue reading.) Both compounds are uncoupling agents and act by dissipating the proton gradient across the inner mitochondrial membrane. Instead of being used to synthesize ATP, the energy of the proton gradient is dissipated as heat. As ATP levels decrease, electron transport will increase, and glucose or fatty acids will be metabolized in an attempt to meet the false metabolic demand.

The compounds are both lipophilic molecules and are capable of dissolving in the inner mitochondrial membrane. Their hydroxyl groups have low pK_a values because they are attached to conjugated ring systems. On the cytosolic (and higher pH) surface of the inner mitochondrial membrane, the compounds will be protonated, whereas on the matrix side they will be unprotonated.

So much for the theoretical biochemistry. In working with unfamiliar compounds, it is imperative to consult references to find out what is known about them. One good place to start is the MSDS (Material Safety Data Sheet). The MSDS is a summary of potential hazards of a compound provided by the manufacturer. Another good reference, and one found in virtually every biochemist's laboratory, is the Merck Index (Published by Merck & Co., Rahway, NJ). The Merck Index informs us, in the section on human toxicity under 2,4-dinitrophenol, that this compound is highly toxic, produces an increase in metabolism (good for a diet), increased temperature, nausea, vomiting, collapse, and, death (a drastic weight loss indeed). Under dicumarol, human toxicity is not mentioned; however, under the subsection "therapeutic category," we are informed that the compound is used as an anticoagulant in humans. Dicumarol was first discovered as the agent responsible for hemorrhagic sweet clover disease in cattle. It is produced by microorganisms in spoiled silage and causes death by bleeding. It is used therapeutically as an anticoagulant, but the therapy must be carefully monitored.

7.   Of the dehydrogenase reactions in glycolysis and the TCA cycle, all but one use NAD⁺ as the electron acceptor. The lone exception is the succinate dehydrogenase reaction, which uses covalently bound FAD of a flavoprotein as the electron acceptor. The standard reduction potential for this bound FAD is in the range of 0.003–0.091 V (Table 19.1). Compared to the other dehydrogenase reactions of glycolysis and the TCA cycle, what is unique about succinate dehydrogenase? Why is bound FAD a more suitable electron acceptor in this case?

Answer: Succinate dehydrogenase converts succinate to fumarate, an oxidation of an alkane to an alkene. The other oxidation reactions in the TCA cycle and in glycolysis either convert alcohols to ketones or ketones to carboxyl groups. These oxidations are sufficiently energetic to reduce NAD⁺. The standard redox potential (from Table 19.1) for reduction of fumarate to succinate is 0.031 V. In contrast, the redox potential for NAD⁺ is −0.320 V. Thus, under standard conditions, if NAD⁺ participated in the succinate–fumarate reaction, it would do so as a reductant (i.e., as NADH) passing electrons to fumarate to produce succinate, the exact opposite of what is accomplished in the TCA cycle. To remove electrons from succinate, an oxidant with a higher (more positive) redox potential is required. The covalently bound FAD of succinate dehydrogenase meets this requirement with a standard redox potential in the range of 0.003 to 0.091 V. (We will encounter another example of conversion of an alkane to an alkene with reduction of FAD in fatty acid metabolism or β-oxidation.)

9.   Consider the oxidation of succinate by molecular oxygen as carried out via the electron transport pathway.

$$\text{succinate} + \tfrac{1}{2} O_2 \rightarrow \text{fumarate} + H_2O$$

a.   What is the standard free energy change ($\Delta G°$), for this reaction if $\mathscr{E}_0'(Fum/Succ) = +0.031$ V and $\mathscr{E}_0'\left(\tfrac{1}{2} O_2/H_2O\right) = +0.816$ V.

b.   What is the equilibrium constant (K_{eq}) for this reaction?

c.   Assume that (1) the actual free energy release accompanying succinate oxidation by the electron-transport pathway is equal to the amount released under standard conditions (as calculated in part a); (2) this energy can be converted into the synthesis of ATP with an efficiency of 0.7 (that is, 70% of the energy released upon succinate oxidation is captured in ATP synthesis); and (3) the oxidation of 1 succinate leads to the phosphorylation of 2 equivalents of ATP.

Under these conditions, what is the maximum ratio of [ATP]/[ADP] attainable for oxidative phosphorylation when [Pi] = 1 mM? (Assume $\Delta G°'$ for ATP synthesis = +30.5 kJ/mol.)

Answer: a.   The relevant half-reactions are (from Table 19.1):

$$\text{Fumarate} + 2H^+ + 2e^- \rightarrow \text{succinate} \qquad \mathscr{E}_0' = +0.031$$

$$\tfrac{1}{2}O_2 + 2H^+ + 2e^- \rightarrow H_2O \qquad \mathscr{E}_0' = +0.816$$

Thus, O_2 is the electron acceptor and succinate is the electron donor.

$$\Delta\mathscr{E}_0' = \mathscr{E}_0'(\text{acceptor}) - \mathscr{E}_0'(\text{donor}) = \mathscr{E}_0'(O_2) - \mathscr{E}_0'(\text{succinate})$$

$$\Delta\mathscr{E}_0' = +0.816 - (0.031) = +0.785 \text{ V}$$

The free energy change for the reaction is given by:

$\Delta G^{o\prime} = -n\mathscr{F}\Delta\mathscr{E}_0'$, where n is the number of electrons, and

$$\mathscr{F} = \text{Faraday's constant} = 96.485 \frac{\text{kJ}}{\text{V}\cdot\text{mol}}$$

$$\Delta G^{o\prime} = -2 \times 96.485 \frac{\text{kJ}}{\text{V}\cdot\text{mol}} \times (0.785 \text{ V}) = -151.5 \frac{\text{kJ}}{\text{mol}}$$

b.   To calculate the equilibrium constant:

From $\Delta G^{o\prime} = -RT \ln K_{eq}$, we see that

$$K_{eq} = e^{\frac{-\Delta G^{o\prime}}{RT}}$$

$$K_{eq} = e^{\frac{-\Delta G^{o\prime}}{RT}} = e^{\frac{-(-151.5)}{(8.314\times10^{-3})(298)}} = 3.60 \times 10^{26}$$

c.   Assuming that $\Delta G = -151.3$ kJ/mol, the amount of energy used to synthesize ATP is:

$$-151.5 \frac{\text{kJ}}{\text{mol}} \times (0.70) = -106.1 \frac{\text{kJ}}{\text{mol}} \text{ for 2 ATP synthesized}$$

Per ATP, we have $53.05 \dfrac{\text{kJ}}{\text{mol}}$

Since $\Delta G = \Delta G^{o\prime} + RT \ln \dfrac{[\text{ATP}]}{[\text{ADP}][P_i]}$

$$\frac{[\text{ATP}]}{[\text{ADP}]} = [P_i] \times e^{\frac{\Delta G - \Delta G^{o\prime}}{RT}} = (1 \text{ mM}) \times e^{\frac{53.05 - 30.5}{(8.314\times10^{-3})(298)}}$$

$$\frac{[\text{ATP}]}{[\text{ADP}]} = 8.89$$

11.   Write a balanced equation for the reduction of molecular oxygen by reduced cytochrome c as carried out by complex IV (cytochrome oxidase) of the electron-transport pathway.
a.   What is the standard free energy change (ΔG^o), for this reaction if

$$\mathscr{E}_0' \text{ cyt c (Fe}^{3+}\text{)/cyt c (Fe}^{2+}\text{)} = +0.254 \text{ volts and } \mathscr{E}_0' (\tfrac{1}{2}O_2/H_2O) = +0.816 \text{ volts}$$

b.   What is the equilibrium constant (K_{eq}) for this reaction?
c.   Assume that (1) the actual free energy release accompanying cytochrome c oxidation by the electron-transport pathway is equal to the amount released under standard conditions (as calculated in part a), (2) this energy can be converted into the synthesis of ATP with an efficiency of 0.60 (that is, 60% of the energy released upon cytochrome c oxidation is captured in ATP synthesis), and (3) the reduction of 1 molecule of O_2 by reduced cytochrome c leads to the phosphorylation of 2 equivalents of ATP.
Under these conditions, what is the maximum ratio of [ATP]/[ADP] attainable for oxidative phosphorylation when [P_i] = 3 mM? (Assume $\Delta G^{o\prime}$ for ATP synthesis = +30.5 kJ/mol.)

Answer: The balanced equation for transfer of electrons from cytochrome c to oxygen is:

$$4 \text{ Cytochrome } c(Fe^{2+}) + O_2 + 4 \text{ H}^+ \rightarrow 4 \text{ Cytochrome } c(Fe^{3+}) + 2 \text{ H}_2O$$

a.   The relevant half-reactions are (from Table 19.1):

$$\text{Cytochrome } c(Fe^{2+}) + e^- \rightarrow \text{Cytochrome } c(Fe^{3+}) \qquad \mathscr{E}_0' = +0.254$$
$$\tfrac{1}{2}O_2 + 2 \text{ H}^+ + 2 \text{ e}^- \rightarrow \text{H}_2O \qquad \mathscr{E}_0' = +0.816$$

Thus, oxygen is the electron acceptor and cytochrome c is the electron donor.

$$\Delta \mathscr{E}_0' = \mathscr{E}_0'(\text{acceptor}) - \mathscr{E}_0'(\text{donor}) = \mathscr{E}_0'(O_2) - \mathscr{E}_0'(\text{cytochrome } c)$$

$$\Delta \mathscr{E}_0' = +0.816 - (+0.254) = +0.562 \text{ V}$$

The free energy change for the reaction is given by:

$$\Delta G^{o\prime} = -n\mathscr{F}\Delta\mathscr{E}_0' \text{, where } n \text{ is the number of electrons, and}$$

$$\mathscr{F} = \text{Faraday's constant} = 96.485 \frac{\text{kJ}}{\text{V} \cdot \text{mol}}$$

$$\Delta G^{o\prime} = -4 \times 96.485 \frac{\text{kJ}}{\text{V} \cdot \text{mol}} \times (0.562 \text{ V}) = -217 \frac{\text{kJ}}{\text{mol}}$$

b.   To calculate the equilibrium constant:

From $\Delta G^{o\prime} = -RT \ln K_{eq}$, we see that

$$K_{eq} = e^{\frac{-\Delta G^{o\prime}}{RT}}$$

The value of RT at 25°C is $(8.314 \times 10^{-3})(298) \frac{\text{kJ}}{\text{mol}} = 2.48 \frac{\text{kJ}}{\text{mol}}$

$$K_{eq} = e^{\frac{-\Delta G^{o\prime}}{RT}} = e^{\frac{-(-217)}{(8.314 \times 10^{-3})(298)}} = 1.08 \times 10^{38}$$

c.   Assuming that $\Delta G = -217$ kJ/mol, the amount of energy used to synthesize ATP is:

$$-217 \frac{\text{kJ}}{\text{mol}} \times (0.60) = -130.2 \frac{\text{kJ}}{\text{mol}} \text{ for 2 ATP synthesized}$$

Per ATP, we have $65.1 \dfrac{\text{kJ}}{\text{mol}}$

Since $\Delta G = \Delta G^{o\prime} + RT \ln \dfrac{[\text{ATP}]}{[\text{ADP}][P_i]}$

$$\frac{[\text{ATP}]}{[\text{ADP}]} = [P_i] \times e^{\frac{\Delta G - \Delta G^{o\prime}}{RT}} = (3 \text{ mM}) \times e^{\frac{65.1 - 30.5}{(8.314 \times 10^{-3})(298)}}$$

$$\frac{[\text{ATP}]}{[\text{ADP}]} = 3437$$

13.   *Assume that the free energy change (ΔG) associated with the movement of 1 mole of protons from the outside to the inside of a bacterial cell is −23 kJ/mol and 3 H^+ must cross the bacterial plasma membrane per ATP formed by the F_1F_o–ATP synthase. ATP synthesis thus takes place by the coupled process:*

$$3 \, H^+{}_{out} + ADP + P_i \leftrightarrows 3 \, H^+{}_{in} + ATP + H_2O.$$

a.   If the overall free energy change ($\Delta G_{overall}$) associated with ATP synthesis in these cells by the coupled process is −21 kJ/mol, what is the equilibrium constant (K_{eq}) for the process?
b.   What is $\Delta G_{synthesis}$, the free energy change for ATP synthesis, in these bacteria under these conditions?

c. *The standard free energy change for ATP hydrolysis is ΔG°'$_{hydrolysis}$ is –30.5 kJ/mol. If [P$_i$] = 2 mM in these bacterial cells, what is the [ATP]/[ADP] ratio in these cells?*

Answer: a.

$$\Delta G^{o\prime} = -RT \ln K_{eq} \ \text{ or}$$

$$K_{eq} = e^{\frac{-\Delta G^{o\prime}}{RT}}$$

$$= e^{\frac{-21}{(8.314\times10^{-3})(298)}} = e^{8.48} = 4.80\times10^{3} \ \text{M}^{-1}$$

b.   The overall free energy change for ATP synthesis accounts for proton movement and ATP synthesis. Because ΔG is a state property, we can write:

$$\Delta G_{overall} = \Delta G_{synthesis} + \Delta G_{proton\ movement} \ \text{ or}$$

$$\Delta G_{synthesis} = \Delta G_{overall} - \Delta G_{proton\ movement}$$

$$\Delta G_{synthesis} = -21\,\text{kJ} - 3\ \text{mol protons} \times \left(-23\frac{\text{kJ}}{\text{mol protons}}\right)$$

$$\Delta G_{synthesis} = -21\,\text{kJ} + 69\,\text{kJ} = 48\,\text{kJ}$$

c.

$$\Delta G_{hydrolysis} = \Delta G^{o\prime}_{hydrolysis} + RT \ln \frac{[\text{ADP}][\text{P}_i]}{[\text{ATP}]} \ \text{ or}$$

$$\ln \frac{[\text{ADP}][\text{P}_i]}{[\text{ATP}]} = \frac{\Delta G_{hydrolysis} - \Delta G^{o\prime}_{hydrolysis}}{RT}$$

$$\ln \frac{[\text{ADP}][\text{P}_i]}{[\text{ATP}]} = \frac{(-48)-(-30.5)}{(8.314\times10^{-3})(298)} = -7.06$$

$$\frac{[\text{ADP}][\text{P}_i]}{[\text{ATP}]} = e^{-7.06} = 8.56\times10^{-4}$$

$$\frac{[\text{ATP}]}{[\text{ADP}][\text{P}_i]} = \frac{1}{8.56\times10^{-4}}$$

$$\frac{[\text{ATP}]}{[\text{ADP}]} = \frac{[\text{P}_i]}{8.56\times10^{-4}} = \frac{2\times10^{-3}}{8.56\times10^{-4}} = 2.34$$

15.   Describe in your own words the path of electrons through the copper and iron centres of Complex IV.

Answer: In Complex IV, four electrons and two protons react with O_2 to produce 2 H_2O. This four-electron reduction is accomplished by moving electrons one at a time from cytochrome *c* to Cu_A to cytochrome *a*, and then to the binuclear centre composed of Cu_B and cytochrome a_3. The $Cu^{2+}{}_B$ of binuclear centre is reduced with the first electron from cytochrome *a*. Then, the iron centre of cytochrome a_3 is reduced by a second electron. With both elements of the binuclear centre reduced, oxygen binds and electrons are transferred to both atoms of O_2. The now activated oxygen is cleaved with addition of another electron and two protons to produce a water molecule bound to Cu_B and an anionic oxygen bound to the iron centre of cytochrome a_3. This oxygen atom is released as a water molecule upon reduction by a single electron and addition of two protons. In the diagram below, lone pairs are shown as paired black dots. When the two electrons are transferred to O_2, the two oxygens are now joined by a single bond.

$$\text{Fe}^{3+} \qquad \text{Cu}^{2+}$$
$$\downarrow e^-$$
$$\text{Fe}^{3+} \qquad \text{Cu}^{2+}$$
$$\downarrow e^-$$
$$O_2 \rightarrow \text{Fe}^{2+} \ \ddot{\underset{..}{O}}{=}\ddot{\underset{..}{O}} \quad \text{Cu}^{2+}$$
$$\text{Fe}^{3+}{-}{:}\ddot{\underset{..}{O}}{-}\ddot{\underset{..}{O}}{:}^- \quad \text{Cu}^+$$
$$\downarrow e^- 2\ H^+$$
$$\text{Fe}^{3+} \ -{:}\ddot{\underset{..}{O}}\cdot H{+}{:}\ddot{\underset{..}{O}}{:}{+}H\ \text{Cu}^+$$
$$\downarrow$$
$$\text{Fe}^{4+} \ -{:}\ddot{\underset{..}{O}}{:}_- \quad H_2O \ \ \text{Cu}^+$$
$$\downarrow e^- 2\ H^+$$
$$\text{Fe}^{3+} \ \ H_2O$$

17. In Problem 20 at the end of Chapter 18, you might have calculated the number of molecules of oxaloacetate in a typical mitochondrion. What about protons? A typical mitochondrion can be thought of as a cylinder 1 m in diameter and 2 m in length. If the pH in the matrix is 7.8, how many protons are contained in the mitochondrial matrix?

Answer: The volume of a mitochondrion is calculated as follows:

$$V = \pi \left(\frac{d}{2} \right)^2 \times \text{length}$$

$$V = 3.14 \left(\frac{1 \times 10^{-6}}{2} \right)^2 \times 2 \times 10^{-6}$$

$$V = 1.57 \times 10^{-18}\,\text{m}^3 \times \left(\frac{100\ \text{cm}}{1\ \text{m}} \right)^3 \times \left(\frac{1\ \text{L}}{1000\ \text{cm}^3} \right)$$

$$V = 1.57 \times 10^{-15}\,\text{L}$$

The hydrogen ion concentration is

$$\text{pH} = -\log[\text{H}^+] \text{ or}$$
$$[\text{H}^+] = 10^{-\text{pH}} = 10^{-7.8}$$
$$[\text{H}^+] = 1.58 \times 10^{-8}\text{M}$$

The number of molecules in the volume × concentration × Avogadro's number or

Number of molecules of H^+ = $1.57 \times 10^{-8}\text{L} \times 10^{-7.8}\text{M} \times 6.02 \times 10^{23}$

Number of molecules of H^+ = 15

Questions for Self-Study

1. How does the formula $\Delta G^{\circ\prime} = -n\mathcal{F}\Delta\mathcal{E}_0'$ predict the direction of electron flow between two reduction half-reactions under standard conditions?

2. The electron transport chain is composed of four complexes. For the statements below indicate which complex or complexes fit the description. The complexes are NADH–coenzyme Q reductase

(complex I); succinate–coenzyme Q reductase (complex II); coenzyme Q–cytochrome c reductase (complex III); and cytochrome c oxidase (complex IV).
a. Contains two copper sites
b. Contains protein-bound FAD
c. Produces water upon electron transport
d. Is involved in the Q cycle
e. Moves electrons from substrate directly into the electron-transport chain
f. Reduces Q
g. Is a citric acid cycle enzyme
h. Reduces a small protein localized on the outer surface of the inner mitochondrial membrane
i. Moves protons across the inner mitochondrial membrane
j. Moves electrons from a lipid-soluble mobile electron carrier to a water-soluble mobile electron carrier
k. Contains tightly bound FMN
l. Transfers electrons to oxygen
m. Moves electrons from NADH to CoQ
n. Moves electrons from cytochrome c to oxygen
o. Contains cytochromes

3. The energy difference for protons across the inner mitochondrial membrane is given by:

$$\Delta G = 2.303 RT \times \log \frac{H^+_{out}}{H^+_{in}} + Z \mathscr{F} \Delta \psi$$

How would this equation be modified by the following conditions?
a. If protons were uncharged species.
b. If the inner mitochondrial membrane was freely permeable to ions other than protons.
c. If the equation was written as a function of pH.

4. ATP synthase or F_1F_o–ATPase is composed of two complexes: a peripheral membrane complex and an integral membrane complex. What roles do the complexes play in oxidative phosphorylation?

5. What is the key difference between an electron transport inhibitor and an uncoupler? What are the consequences of each to electron transport, oxygen consumption, and ATP production?

Answers

1. In general, a reaction is spontaneous when $\Delta G < 0$. When the reaction is under standard conditions $\Delta G^{\circ\prime} < 0$. Thus, $\Delta \mathscr{E}_0' > 0$, $\mathscr{E}_0'_{final} - \mathscr{E}_0'_{initial} > 0$ or $\mathscr{E}_0'_{final} > \mathscr{E}_0'_{initial}$. Electrons will flow from the reduction half-reaction with the smaller standard reduction potential to the reduction half-reaction with the larger standard reduction potential.

2. a. IV; b. II; c. IV; d. III; e. II; f. I and II; g. II; h. III; i. I, III, and IV; j. III; k. I; l. IV; m. I; n. IV; o. III and IV.

3. a. $\Delta G = 2.303\ RT \times \log \frac{H^+_{out}}{H^+_{in}}$; b. $\Delta G = 2.303\ RT \times \log \frac{H^+_{out}}{H^+_{in}}$; c. $\Delta G = -2.303 RT (pH_{out} - pH_{in}) + Z \mathscr{F} \Delta \psi$

4. The peripheral membrane complex or, F_1 unit, is the site at which ADP and P_i are joined to form ATP. The integral membrane complex, F_o, is a proton channel.

5. An electron-transport inhibitor blocks the movement of electrons through a component of the transport chain. Inhibitors will block electron transport for electrons entering the chain above the blockage point but not for those entering below the blockage point. Oxygen consumption and ATP production will, depending on the source of electrons, be diminished or stopped. Uncoupling agents provide an alternate pathway through which protons can re-enter the mitochondrial matrix. Uncouplers stimulate electron transport and oxygen consumption but block ATP synthesis.

Additional Problems

1. Isolated, inner mitochondrial membranes do not transport electrons from NADH to O_2 unless cytochrome c is added. Why?

2. Describe one site in the electron-transport chain responsible for pumping hydrogen ions out of the mitochondria during electron transport.

3. Nigericin is an ionophore whose structure is shown below.

It is soluble in the inner mitochondrial membrane in either its acidic form with the carboxyl group protonated or as a potassium salt. Valinomycin is a cyclic compound composed of various L- and D-amino acids and lactic acid and functions as a potassium ionophore. The presence of nigericin, valinomycin, and potassium will effectively destroy the electrochemical potential of mitochondria. Why?

4. An uncoupling agent like dinitrophenol actually stimulates O_2 consumption. Why?

5. In the citric acid cycle, malate dehydrogenase catalyzes the following reaction:

$$\text{malate} + NAD^+ \rightarrow \text{oxaloacetate} + NADH$$

Given the following standard reduction potentials, calculate $\Delta G^{\circ\prime}$:

Reduction Half-Reaction	$\mathscr{E}_0'$ (V)
Oxaloacetate + 2H$^+$ + 2 e$^-$ → malate	−0.166
NAD$^+$ + H$^+$ + 2 e$^-$ → NADH	−0.320

In which direction will the reaction proceed under standard conditions? Which component functions as the oxidant? Reductant? Does this differ from the physiological direction?

Abbreviated Answers

1. Inner mitochondrial membranes contain all of the components necessary for electron transport except cytochrome c. Cytochrome c is a relatively small protein (M_r = 1800) that is localized on the outer surface of the inner mitochondrial membrane, and it is readily lost during purification procedures. Cytochrome c moves electrons between coenzyme Q–cytochrome c reductase and cytochrome c oxidase and must be present for electrons to flow from NADH to O_2.

2. There are three sites at which protons are pumped out of the mitochondria in response to electron transport: NADH dehydrogenase, coenzyme Q–cytochrome c reductase, and cytochrome c oxidase. The details of how protons are pumped by cytochrome c oxidase are unknown. Coenzyme Q–cytochrome c reductase is involved in the Q cycle. NADH dehydrogenase moves electrons from NADH to coenzyme Q using a flavoprotein and several Fe-S proteins to move electrons. In NADH dehydrogenase, the flavoprotein accepts electrons and protons from NADH on the matrix side of the inner mitochondrial membrane but donates electrons to a series of Fe-S proteins. CoQ is thought to play two roles in the movement of electrons through NADH dehydrogenase. It is the terminal electron acceptor for the complex. Additionally, CoQ is thought to participate at an intermediate stage of electron flow by accepting electrons

from one Fe-S component and donating electrons to another Fe-S component. In the process, CoQ binds protons from the matrix side of the membrane and releases protons into the intermembrane space.

3. Since valinomycin is specific for potassium, it will not affect the proton gradient by itself. In the presence of potassium, valinomycin will move potassium into the mitochondrial matrix until potassium is actually concentrated inside the mitochondria. This occurs because initially potassium moves down a potassium chemical gradient (assuming that the mitochondrial matrix has a low potassium concentration) until the potassium concentration is equal on both sides of the membrane. But potassium continues to accumulate, driven inside the cell by the electrical potential of the proton gradient. Net movement of potassium stops when the potassium concentration difference across the membrane is sufficient to produce a potassium electrical potential equal in magnitude and opposite in sign from the electrical potential of the proton gradient. However, the proton gradient still exists.

Nigericin alone will simply replace the proton gradient with a potassium gradient. The chemical potential of the proton gradient is effectively destroyed but an electrical potential, now due to potassium, is still present.

The combination of nigericin, valinomycin, and potassium will dissipate the proton gradient without creating a potassium gradient.

4. Uncouplers stimulate oxygen consumption because the protonmotive force exerts a backpressure on the electron-transport chain, making it progressively harder to pump protons into the inner membrane space against the electrochemical gradient. Uncouplers dissipate the protonmotive force, thereby relieving this backpressure and stimulating oxygen consumption. This phenomenon is known as respiratory control.

5. The relevant half-reactions are (from Table 19.1):

$$NAD^+ + 2H^+ + 2e^- \rightarrow NADH + H^+ \qquad \mathscr{E}_o' = -0.320$$
$$oxaloacetate + 2H^+ + 2e^- \rightarrow malate \qquad \mathscr{E}_o' = -0.166$$

Thus, oxaloacetate is the electron acceptor and NADH is the electron donor.

$$\Delta \mathscr{E}_o' = \mathscr{E}_o'(acceptor) - \mathscr{E}_o'(donor) = \mathscr{E}_o'(NAD^+) - \mathscr{E}_o'(oxaloacetate)$$

$$\Delta \mathscr{E}_o' = -0.320 - (0.166) = -0.154 \text{ V}$$

The free energy change for the reaction is given by:

$$\Delta G^{o\prime} = -n \cdot \mathscr{F} \Delta \mathscr{E}_o', \text{ where } n \text{ is the number of electrons, and}$$

$$\mathscr{F} = \text{Faraday's constant} = 96.485 \frac{kJ}{V \cdot mol}$$

$$\Delta G^{o\prime} = -2 \times 96.485 \frac{kJ}{V \cdot mol} \times (-0.154 \text{ V}) = +29.7 \frac{kJ}{mol}$$

A positive $\Delta G^{o\prime}$ indicates that the reaction, under standard conditions, is not favourable and will proceed in the reverse direction. Electrons will flow from NADH to oxaloacetate. Thus, NADH serves as a reductant and oxaloacetate serves as an oxidant. In the citric acid cycle, removal of oxaloacetate by citrate synthase lowers the concentration of oxaloacetate and drives the reaction toward NADH production.

Summary

Most of the metabolic energy obtained from sugars and similar metabolites entering glycolysis and the TCA cycle is funnelled into NADH and [FADH2] via oxidation–reduction reactions. Electrons stored in the form of reduced coenzymes and flavoproteins are then passed through an elaborate and highly organized chain of proteins and coenzymes, the so-called electron-transport chain, finally reaching O2, molecular oxygen, the terminal electron acceptor. In the course of electron transport, energy is stored in the form of a proton gradient across the inner mitochondrial membrane. This proton gradient then provides the energy to drive ATP synthesis in oxidative phosphorylation. Electron transport and oxidative phosphorylation are membrane-associated processes. Bacteria carry out these processes at (and across) the plasma membrane, and in eukaryotic cells they are carried out and localized in mitochondria.

Mitochondria are surrounded by a simple outer membrane and a more complex inner membrane. The proteins of the electron-transport chain and oxidative phosphorylation are associated with the inner mitochondrial membrane.

The tendency of the components of the electron-transport chain to transfer electrons to other species is characterized by an electron-transfer potential or standard reduction potential, $\mathscr{E}_0'$. These potentials are determined by measuring the voltages generated in reaction half-cells. Standard reduction potentials are measured relative to a reference half-cell. The H^+/H_2 half-cell normally serves as the reference half-cell and is assigned a standard reduction potential of 0.0 V. The sign of $\mathscr{E}_0'$ for a redox couple can be used to indicate whether reduction or oxidation occurs for that couple in any real reaction (involving two redox couples). The redox couple with the more negative $\mathscr{E}_0'$ will act as an electron donor, and the redox couple with the more positive $\mathscr{E}_0'$ will act as an electron acceptor. For redox couples with a large positive standard reduction potential, the oxidized form of the couple has a strong tendency to be reduced.

Fractionation of the membranes containing the electron-transport chain results in the isolation of four distinct complexes, including I) NADH–coenzyme-Q reductase, II) succinate–coenzyme Q reductase, III) coenzyme Q–cytochrome c reductase, and IV) cytochrome c oxidase. Oxidation of NADH and reduction of coenzyme Q by complex I is accompanied by transport of protons from the matrix to the cytoplasmic side of the inner mitochondrial membrane. Complex II, succinate–coenzyme Q reductase or succinate dehydrogenase, is an integral membrane protein, a TCA cycle enzyme and a flavoprotein. The net reaction carried out by this complex is oxidation of succinate and reduction of coenzyme Q, with intermediate oxidation–reduction of [FADH$_2$]. In complex III, reduced coenzyme Q passes its electrons to cytochrome c via a complex redox cycle involving three cytochromes, several Fe-S centres and proton transport across the inner mitochondrial membrane. Cytochrome c, a mobile electron carrier, passes electrons from complex III to complex IV, cytochrome c oxidase. Electron transfer in complex IV involves two hemes and two copper sites in cytochrome a and a_3. and results in proton transport across the inner mitochondrial membrane. In spite of their spatial proximity, the four major complexes of the electron-transport chain operate and migrate independently in the inner mitochondrial membrane.

The elucidation of the mechanism that couples electron transport and ATP synthesis was one of the great challenges (and triumphs) of modern biochemistry. Peter Mitchell's chemiosmotic hypothesis postulates that a proton gradient generated by the electron-transport chain is utilized to drive ATP synthesis. The mitochondrial complex that carries out ATP synthesis is called ATP synthase or F_1F_0–ATPase. The F_1 subunit of this complex is spherical in shape, consists of five major polypeptide chains and catalyzes ATP synthesis. The F_0 subunit forms the transmembrane pore or channel through which protons move to drive ATP synthesis. The essence of the Mitchell hypothesis was confirmed in a reconstitution experiment by E. Racker and W. Stoeckenius, using bacteriorhodopsin to generate a proton gradient and the ATP synthase to generate ATP. As shown by Paul Boyer, the energy provided by electron transport drives enzyme conformation changes that regulate the binding and release of substrates on ATP synthase. The mechanism involves catalytic cooperativity between three interacting sites. Many of the details of electron transport and oxidative phosphorylation have been gained from studying the effects of specific inhibitors, including rotenone, which inhibits NADH-UQ reductase, and cyanide, which blocks complex IV, cytochrome c oxidase. Uncouplers dissipate the proton gradient across the inner mitochondrial membrane that was created by electron transport. Endogenous uncouplers including thermogenin provide heat for the organism by uncoupling these processes. Molecular shuttle systems exist to carry the electrons of NADH into the mitochondrial matrix, because NADH and FADH$_2$ cannot be transported across the inner mitochondrial membrane. The two systems which operate in this manner are the glycerol phosphate shuttle and the malate-aspartate shuttle. ATP produced by oxidative phosphorylation is carried out of the mitochondria by an ATP/ADP translocase, which couples the exit of ATP with the entry of ADP.

The net yield of energy from glucose oxidation—either ~30 or ~32 ATP synthesized per glucose—depends upon the shuttle system used. The overall efficiency of metabolism (from glucose to the TCA cycle to electron transport and oxidative phosphorylation) is about 54%.

Chapter 20

Photosynthesis

● ●

Chapter Outline

❖ Photosynthesis: Two aspects
  ⅄ Light reactions: NADPH and ATP produced, oxygen evolved, water is electron donor
  ⅄ Dark reactions: Carbon dioxide fixed
❖ Chloroplasts: Plastids
  ⅄ Outer membrane: Porous
  ⅄ Intermembrane space
  ⅄ Inner membrane
  ⅄ Stroma: Volume within inner membrane but outside thylakoids
  ⅄ Thylakoid: Paired folds
    ◆ Lamella
    ◆ Thylakoid vesicles
    ◆ Grana: Stacks of thylakoid vesicles
    ◆ Thylakoid space (lumen)
❖ Photosynthetic pigments
  ⅄ Chlorophyll: Porphyrin-like molecule with Mg^{2+}
  ⅄ Secondary light-harvesting pigments: Broaden wavelength range
    ◆ Carotenoids
    ◆ Phycobilins
❖ Light energy
  ⅄ Absorption of energy
    ◆ $E = h\upsilon$: h = Planck's constant, υ = frequency of light
    ◆ $\upsilon = c/\lambda$: c = speed of light in a vacuum, λ = wavelength
    ◆ Light photons: Packet of energy or quantum: $E = h\upsilon$
  ⅄ Energy excites π electrons
  ⅄ Release of energy
    ◆ Heat
    ◆ Fluorescence: Light but at longer wavelength: Lower frequency: Less energetic
    ◆ Resonance energy transfer: Near neighbours exchange exciton: Förster resonance energy transfer
    ◆ Energy transduction: Molecule with excited electron becomes better reductant
❖ Characteristics of photosynthesis
  ⅄ Membrane-localized
  ⅄ Pigments organized into units
    ◆ Antennae molecules harvest light
    ◆ Reaction centre: Energy sink of photosynthetic unit
  ⅄ Eukaryotes: Two photosystems
    ◆ PSI: 700 nm: Excited electrons reduce $NADP^+$
    ◆ PSII: 680 nm: Splits water: Generates oxygen: Pumps protons: Reduces PSI
  ⅄ Prokaryotes: PSII-like but without oxygen evolution capacity
❖ Protein complexes: Two light harvesting complexes
  ⅄ PSI complex: Provides reducing power for NADPH production (used in Calvin cycle to fix CO_2)
  ⅄ PSII complex: Splits water producing oxygen (by-product) and electrons: Electrons moved to PSI via electron-transport chain

⁁ Cytochrome b_6/cytochrome f complex
- Moves electrons from PSII to PSI: Protons pumped (ATP produced): Non-cyclic flow of electrons
- Moves electrons from PSI to PSI: Protons pumped (ATP produced): Cyclic flow of electrons

❖ *Z* Scheme: Movement of electrons from water via PSII through cyto b_6/cyto f complex through PSI to NADP$^+$

❖ PSII activities: H_2O/plastiquinone oxidoreductase
⁁ P680 reaction centre complex cycles through S_0, S_1, S_2, S_3, S_4
- Each step removes one electron from water
- With S_4 oxygen is released

⁁ P680 to P680* to P680$^+$ by exciton absorption and electron release
⁁ Electron from P680 passes to pheophytin: Chlorophyll with 2 H$^+$ in place of Mg^{2+}
⁁ Pheophytin passes electron to plastoquinone
⁁ Plastoquinone (lipid mobile) passes electrons to cyto b_6/cyto f
⁁ P680$^+$ to P680: Electron from water through Mn complex and D (tyrosyl residue)

❖ Cyto b_6/cyto f activities: Plastoquinol/plastocyanin oxidoreductase
⁁ Cytochrome f: Moves electrons from plastoquinone to plastocyanin
- Plastocyanin: Copper atom involved in single-electron transfers
- Diffuses along inside of thylakoid along membrane

⁁ Cytochrome b_6 involved in cyclic electron transport: Cyclic photophosphorylation

❖ PSI activities: Plastocyanin/ferredoxin oxidoreductase
⁁ P700 to P700* to P700$^+$ by exciton absorption and electron release
⁁ Electron from P700 passes to quinone (A1)
⁁ Quinone (A1) passes electron to membrane-bound ferredoxins
⁁ Membrane-bound ferredoxins pass electrons to soluble ferredoxin
⁁ Soluble ferredoxin passes electrons to NADP$^+$: Ferredoxin/NADP$^+$ reductase

❖ Quantum yields
⁁ Eight photons per O_2 evolved: Four per PSI and four for PSII
⁁ One proton per photon: Eight protons pumped
⁁ Three protons per ATP
⁁ Two NADPH produced

❖ Photophosphorylation
⁁ Proton translocations
- Water to PSII
- Q cycle

⁁ $\Delta p = \Delta \psi - 2.3RT \times \Delta pH/(\mathscr{F})$
⁁ CF$_1$CF$_o$ATP synthase couples proton release to ATP production
⁁ Non-cyclic photophosphorylation: Electrons from water to NADP$^+$
⁁ Cyclic photophosphorylations: Electrons from PSI through cyto b_6 back to PSI

❖ Calvin–Benson cycle
⁁ Only known pathway of net CO_2 fixation
⁁ Immediate product 3-phosphoglycerate: Reduced to glyceraldehyde-3-P using NADPH
⁁ G-3-P used to produce 4-, 5-, 6-, and 7-C compounds
⁁ Hexose principle product

❖ Rubisco: CO_2 + ribulose-1,5-BP → two 3-PG
⁁ Fixes carbon dioxide to carbon skeleton
⁁ Most abundant enzyme in biosphere

❖ Regulation of CO_2 fixation
⁁ Changes in stromal pH
- Light pumps protons into thylakoid
  - Stromal pH increases to 8
    - o Rubisco carbamylation promoted
    - o Fructose-1,6-BPase activated
    - o Ribulose-5-P kinase activated
    - o G-3-P dehydrogenase activated

- Generation of reducing power
  - F-1,6-BPase activated by reduction
  - Sedoheptulose-1,7-BPase activated by reduction
  - Ribulose-5-P kinase activated by reduction
- Mg^{2+} efflux upon proton influx (charge balance)
  - Rubisco activated
  - F-1,6-BPase activated
- ❖ Photorespiration: Rubisco: Ribulose bisphosphate carboxylase/oxygenase
  - Oxygenase activity produces 3-PG + phosphoglycolate: O_2 consumed
  - Phosphoglycolate converted to glyoxylate: O_2 consumed
  - Glyoxylate to glycine to serine to 3-PB
  - Glycine to serine: CO_2 produced
- ❖ Hatch–Slack pathway: C4 plants: CO_2 delivery system
  - PEP + CO_2 to oxaloacetate to malate: Mesophyll cells
  - Malate to pyruvate + CO_2: Bundle sheath cells
  - Pyruvate and malate exchanged
- ❖ Crassulacean acid metabolism
  - Stomata closed during the day: Malate decarboxylated to produce CO_2
  - Stomata opened during the night: CO_2 + PEP to oxaloacetate and malate

Chapter Objectives

Photosynthesis

It is convenient to divide photosynthesis into light and dark reactions. Keep in mind that the light reactions harvest light energy and transduce it into the chemical energy of ATP and NADPH. ATP serves its usual role as energy currency. NADPH is a cellular reducing agent. In the dark reactions, CO_2 is fixed into organic compounds and reduced to a hydrated carbon. The objective is to produce carbohydrates from CO_2, the chemistry is carbon reduction, and the biochemistry is the Calvin cycle.

Light Reactions

Light energy is used to split water in a reaction called photolysis producing O_2, H^+, and electrons. The electrons move along an electron-transport chain leading to $NADP^+$. Analogous to the electron-transport chain in mitochondria, electron flow in chloroplasts (and other photosynthetic systems) is accompanied by H^+ gradient formation, which is used, in turn, to synthesize ATP. Get the big picture down and then fill in the detail.

The abstraction of electrons from water is an energy-requiring process, and in photosynthesis, the energy derives from sunlight. How is this energy harvested? Chlorophylls and accessory light-harvesting pigments are responsible. Production of O_2 from 2 H_2O generates 8 electrons. In the "Z" system, generation of each electron requires two quanta of light (only one quantum per electron is needed for the cyclic pathway of PSI). This explains why the pigment molecules are organized into photosynthetic units. The pigment molecules in a unit cooperate to collect light quanta and funnel the energy to a reaction centre. Photosynthetic eukaryotes have two separate but interacting photosystems, PS-I and PS-II. PS-II is responsible for O_2 production and has a reaction centre P680. PS-1 reduces $NADP^+$ if coupled to PSII or by itself can move electrons in a cycle beginning and ending at its reaction centre P700. The movement of electrons from water to $NADP^+$ requires excitation of PS-II, electron transport from PS-II to PS-I, excitation of PS-I, and electron transport from PS-I to $NADP^+$. Electron transport from PS-II to PS-I is accompanied by proton-gradient formation. This gradient is subsequently used to produce ATP. When we get to the Calvin cycle, we will see that there is a greater requirement for ATP than NADPH, and the additional ATP can be generated by cyclic photophosphorylation. This process involves only PS-I. An excited electron is fed from PS-I into the electron-transport chain leading from PS-II to PS-I and thus moves in a circle. However, cyclic electron flow is accompanied by proton-gradient formation and subsequent ATP production.

Dark Reactions

Rubisco is the key player in CO_2 fixation. Understand the carboxylase reaction leading to two phosphoglycerates. Rubisco also catalyzes an oxygenase reaction, which leads to photorespiration. The carboxylase reaction adds carbon at the oxidation state of a carboxylate group to ribulose-1,5-bisphosphate to produce phosphoglycerate. The carboxyl groups now must be reduced to aldehydes for carbohydrate synthesis to occur. The initial steps include phosphorylation to 1,3-BPG and reduction to glyceraldehyde-3-phosphate and P_i. (We saw these steps in gluconeogenesis and glycolysis.) The remainder of the Calvin cycle (Figure 20.24) converts glyceraldehyde to glucose, not an onerous task given our knowledge of gluconeogenesis, and regenerates ribulose-1,5-bisphosphate. This aspect of the cycle is reminiscent of the non-oxidative phase of the pentose phosphate pathway and uses isomerases, aldolases, transketolases, phosphatases, and a kinase to convert three-carbon sugars into five-carbon sugars.

Regulation

Calvin cycle activity is coordinated with the light reactions by three light-induced effects: light-induced pH changes, generation of reducing power, and Mg^{2+} efflux. Know the targets for these controls. Rubisco regulation by Mg^{2+} is dependent on CO_2 availability.

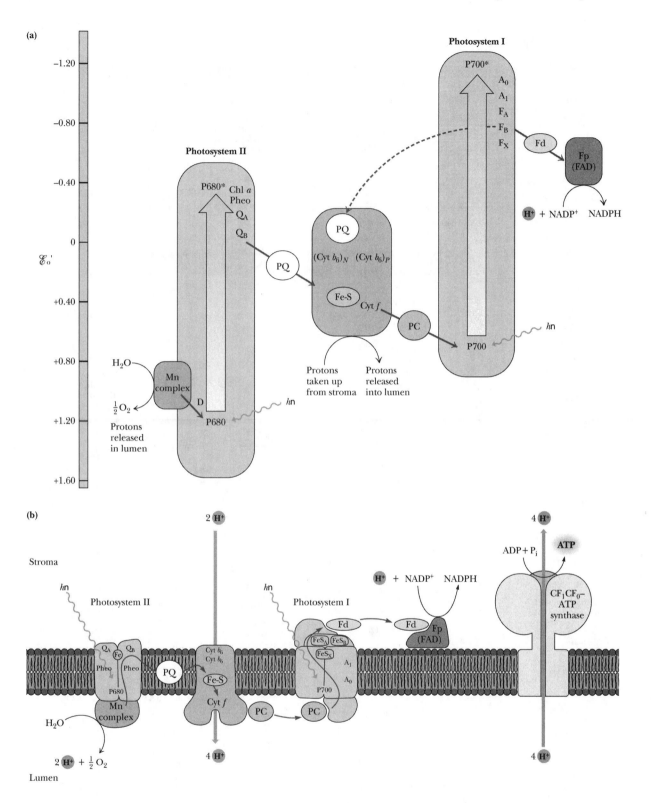

Figure 20.11 The Z scheme of photosynthesis.

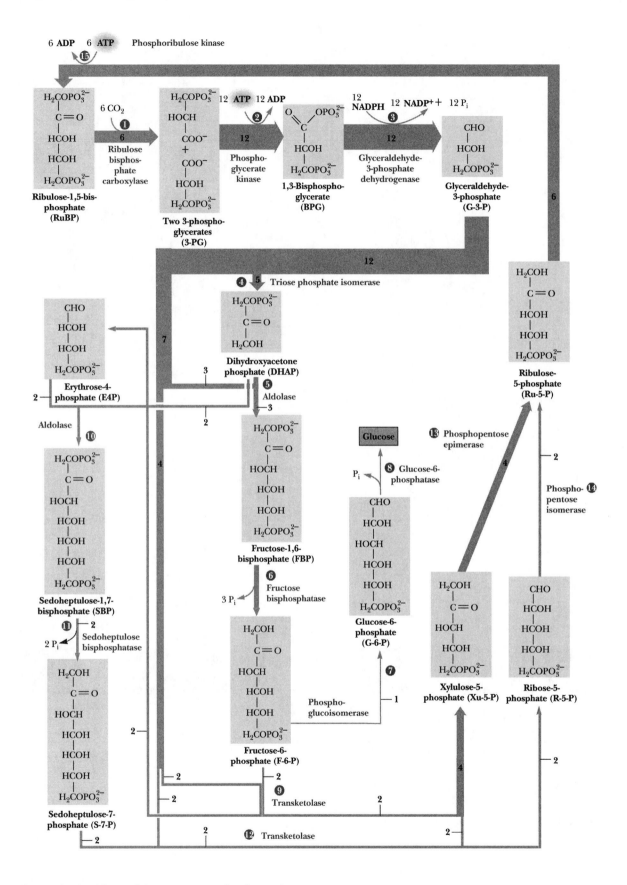

Figure 20.24 The Calvin–Benson cycle of reactions.

Problems and Solutions

1. In Photosystem I, P700 in its ground state has an $\mathscr{E}_0'$ = +0.4 V. Excitation of P700 by a photon of 700-nm light alters the $\mathscr{E}_0'$ of P700* to −0.6 V. What is the efficiency of energy capture in this light reaction of P700?

Answer: The energy of a photon of light is given by:

$$E = \frac{hc}{\lambda},$$

h = Planck's constant = $6.626 \times 10^{-34}\,\text{J} \cdot \text{sec}$

c = speed of light in a vacuum = $3 \times 10^8\,\dfrac{\text{m}}{\text{sec}}$

λ = wavelength of light. In this case, λ = 700 nm = $700 \times 10^{-9}\,\text{m}$

Thus, $E = \dfrac{(6.626 \times 10^{-34}\,\text{J} \cdot \text{sec}) \times (3 \times 10^8\,\frac{\text{m}}{\text{sec}})}{700 \times 10^{-9}\,\text{m}} = 2.84 \times 10^{-19}\,\text{J}$

And, a mole of photons represents

$(2.84 \times 10^{-19}\,\text{J}) \times 6.02 \times 10^{23} = 171\text{ kJ of energy}$

Absorption of this amount of energy changes the redox potential of photosystem I from +0.4 V to −0.6 V. We can think of this as an oxidation–reduction reaction in which an electron is transferred from a donor with $\mathscr{E}_0'$ = +0.4 V to an acceptor with $\mathscr{E}_0'$ = −0.6 V. The $\Delta G^{o\prime}$ for this reaction can be calculated using:

$\Delta G^{o\prime} = -n\mathscr{F}\Delta\mathscr{E}_0'$, where n is the number of electrons and

$\mathscr{F}$ = Faraday's constant = $96.485\,\dfrac{\text{kJ}}{\text{V} \cdot \text{mol}}$

$\Delta\mathscr{E}_0' = \Delta\mathscr{E}_0'(\text{acceptor}) - \Delta\mathscr{E}_0'(\text{donor})$

$\Delta\mathscr{E}_0' = -0.6 - (+0.4) = -1.0$ V

$\Delta G^{o\prime} = -1 \times 96.485\,\dfrac{\text{kJ}}{\text{V} \cdot \text{mol}} \times (-1.0\text{ V}) = -5.79\,\dfrac{\text{kJ}}{\text{mol}}$

$\Delta G^{o\prime} = -1 \times 96.485\,\dfrac{\text{kJ}}{\text{V} \cdot \text{mol}} \times (-0.030\text{ V}) = 96.5\,\dfrac{\text{kJ}}{\text{mol}}$

The efficiency $= \dfrac{96.5}{171} \times 100\% = 56.4\%$

3. (Integrates with Chapters 3 and 19) Assuming that the concentrations of ATP, ADP, and P$_i$ in chloroplasts are 3 mM, 0.1 mM, and 10 mM, respectively, what is the ΔG for ATP synthesis under these conditions? Photosynthetic electron transport establishes the proton-motive force driving photophosphorylation. What redox potential difference is necessary to achieve ATP synthesis under the foregoing conditions, assuming 1.3 ATP equivalents are synthesized for each electron pair transferred.

Answer:

$$\Delta G = \Delta G^{o\prime} + RT \times \ln\frac{[\text{ATP}]}{[\text{ADP}][\text{P}_i]}$$

At T = 25°C (298 K),

$\Delta G = 30.5\,\dfrac{\text{kJ}}{\text{mol}} + (8.314 \times 10^{-3}\,\dfrac{\text{kJ}}{\text{mol} \cdot \text{K}})(298\text{ K}) \times \ln\dfrac{3 \times 10^{-3}}{(0.1 \times 10^{-3})(10 \times 10^{-3})}$

$\Delta G = 30.5\,\dfrac{\text{kJ}}{\text{mol}} + 19.8\,\dfrac{\text{kJ}}{\text{mol}}$

$\Delta G = 50.3\,\dfrac{\text{kJ}}{\text{mol}}$

From $\Delta G = -n\mathscr{F}\Delta\mathscr{E}$, where n is the number of electrons and

$$\mathscr{F} = \text{Faraday's constant} = 96.485\,\frac{kJ}{V\cdot mol}$$

$$\Delta\mathscr{E} = -\frac{\Delta G}{n\mathscr{F}} = -\frac{1.3\times50.3\,\dfrac{kJ}{mol}}{2\times96.485\,\dfrac{kJ}{V\cdot mol}}$$

$$\Delta\mathscr{E} = -0.34\ V$$

5. If non-cyclic photosynthetic electron transport leads to the translocation of 3 H⁺/e⁻ and cyclic photosynthetic electron transport leads to the translocation of 2 H⁺/e⁻, what is the relative photosynthetic efficiency of ATP synthesis (expressed as the number of photons absorbed per ATP synthesized) for non-cyclic versus cyclic photophosphorylation? (Assume that the CF₁CF₀ATP synthase yields 3 ATP/14 H⁺).

Answer: In non-cyclic photosynthetic electron transport, photosystems I and II are excited by absorption of light quanta. Thus, two quanta are needed to excite one electron, which translocates 3 protons.

$$\frac{3\ H^+}{e^-}\times\frac{e^-}{2\ \text{quanta}} = \frac{3\ H^+}{2\ \text{quanta}}$$

But ATP is produced by

$$\frac{3\ ATP}{14\ H^+}\times\frac{3\ H^+}{2\ \text{quanta}} = \frac{9\ ATP}{28\ \text{quanta}} = \frac{0.32\ ATP}{\text{quanta}}$$

Quanta (number of photons) per ATP is the inverse of this

$$\frac{3.11\ \text{quanta}}{ATP}$$

In cyclic photosynthetic electron transport, photosystems I is excited by absorption of light quanta. Thus, one quanta are needed to excite one electron, which translocates 2 protons.

$$\frac{2\ H^+}{e^-}\times\frac{e^-}{1\ \text{quanta}} = \frac{2\ H^+}{\text{quanta}}$$

But ATP is produced by

$$\frac{3\ ATP}{14\ H^+}\times\frac{2\ H^+}{\text{quanta}} = \frac{6\ ATP}{14\ \text{quanta}} = \frac{0.43\ ATP}{\text{quanta}}$$

Quanta (number of photons) per ATP is the inverse of this

$$\frac{2.33\ \text{quanta}}{ATP}$$

7. Predict the consequences of a Y161F mutation in the amino acid sequence of the D1 and the D2 subunits of PSII.

Answer: The notation Y161F indicates a mutation changing the amino acid located at position 161 from tyrosine (Y) to phenylalanine (F). (The codons for tyrosine are UAU an UAC and those for phenylalanine are UUU and UUC. So, a simple one-base transversion of A to T would cause this change.) In photosynthesis, movement of electrons from H_2O to P680 involves manganese and tyrosine 161, which becomes a free radical in its oxidized form. Tyrosine's hydroxyl group participates in the mechanism of electron transfer to a nearby manganese ion. Replacing tyrosine with phenylalanine would clearly prevent this interaction from occurring. This would prevent P680, once activated by light to P680* and then to P680⁺ by electron transfer, from returning back to the ground state.

9. (Integrates with Chapters 17 and 19) Calculate $\Delta G°'$ for the NADP⁺-specific glyceraldehyde-3-P dehydrogenase reaction of the Calvin–Benson cycle.

Answer: In the Calvin cycle, glyceraldehyde-3-P dehydrogenase moves electrons from NADPH to 1,3-bisphosphoglycerate producing glyceraldehyde-3-phosphate and NADP⁺. The $\Delta G^{\circ\prime}$ is calculated as follows:

$$\Delta G^{\circ\prime} = -n\,\mathscr{F}\Delta \mathscr{E}_0^{\prime}, \text{ where } n \text{ is the number of electrons, and}$$

$$\mathscr{F} = \text{Faraday's constant} = 96.485\,\frac{\text{kJ}}{\text{V}\cdot\text{mol}}$$

$$\Delta \mathscr{E}_0^{\prime} = \mathscr{E}_0^{\prime}(\text{acceptor}) - \mathscr{E}_0^{\prime}(\text{donor})$$

$$\Delta \mathscr{E}_0^{\prime} = \mathscr{E}_0^{\prime}(1,3\text{BPG}) - \mathscr{E}_0^{\prime}(\text{NADPH})$$

$$\Delta \mathscr{E}_0^{\prime} = -0.290 - (-0.320) = 0.030\ \text{V}$$

$$\Delta G^{\circ\prime} = -2 \times 96.485\,\frac{\text{kJ}}{\text{V}\cdot\text{mol}} \times (0.030) = -5.79\,\frac{\text{kJ}}{\text{mol}}$$

11. **^{14}C-labelled carbon dioxide is administered to a green plant, and shortly thereafter the following compounds are isolated from the plant: 3-phosphoglycerate, glucose, erythrose-4-phosphate, sedoheptulose-1,7-bisphosphate, ribose-5-phosphate. In which carbon atoms will radioactivity be found?**

Answer: CO_2 fixation is catalyzed by ribulose bisphosphate carboxylase (rubisco) in the following reaction:

Thus, the first compound labelled is carbon 1 of 3-phosphoglycerate. In the Calvin cycle, this compound is used, ultimately, to produce glucose. Synthesis starts with the conversion of 3-phosphoglycerate to 1,3-bisphosphoglycerate by phosphoglycerate kinase. 1,3-bisphosphoglycerate is then converted to glyceraldehyde-3-phosphate by glyceraldehyde-3-phosphate dehydrogenase. Starting with carbon 1 of 3-phosphoglycerate labeled, this carbon is carbon 1 of 1,3-bisphosphoglycerate, and carbon 1 of both glyceraldehyde-3-phosphate and dihydroxyacetone phosphate (produced from glyceraldehyde-3-phosphate by triose phosphate isomerase action). Both glyceraldehyde-3-phosphate and dihydroxyacetone phosphate are used to produce glucose. The action of aldolase will combine these two three-carbon compounds to produce fructose-1,6-bisphosphate. This aldol condensation reaction joins carbon 1 of dihydroxyacetone phosphate to carbon 1 of glyceraldehyde-3-phosphate. Thus, carbons 3 and 4 of fructose-1-6-bisphosphate acquire label, which will show up in the same carbons in glucose.

In the Calvin cycle, transketolase is responsible for production of erythrose-4-phosphate. The four carbons of erythrose derive from carbons 3, 4, 5, and 6 of fructose-6-phosphate. Thus, we expect erythrose-4-phosphate to be labelled at carbons 1 and 2.

The transketolase reaction moves carbon 1 and the keto carbon of fructose to glyceraldehyde-3-phosphate to produce xylulose-5-phosphate, which may be converted to ribulose-5-phosphate by phosphopentose epimerase. By this path, label is expected at carbon 3 of ribulose-5-phosphate. (Ribulose is also labelled at carbons 1, 2, and 3. See below.)

The fate of sedoheptulose-1,7-bisphosphate in the Calvin cycle is as follows. This compound is synthesized from erythrose-4-phosphate and dihydroxyacetone phosphate by aldolase. Thus, we expect label at carbons 3, 4, and 5 from carbon 1 of dihydroxyacetone phosphate and carbons 1 and 2 of erythrose-4-phosphate, respectively. Transketolase can convert sedoheptulose to ribose-5-phosphate by transferring carbons 1 and 2 (the keto carbon) to glyceraldehyde-3-P. The ribose formed by this path derives from carbons 3, 4, and 5 of sedoheptulose and will be labelled at C-1, 2, and 3.

13. Write a balanced equation for the conversion of phosphoglycolate to glycerate-3-P by the reactions of photorespiration. Does this balanced equation demonstrate that photorespiration is a wasteful process?

Answer:

$$2 \text{ (\textbf{Phosphoglycolate} + \textbf{H}_2\textbf{O}} \rightarrow \text{Glycolate} + \textbf{P}_i\text{)}$$
$$2 \text{ (Glycolate} + \textbf{O}_2 \rightarrow \text{Glyoxylate} + \textbf{H}_2\textbf{O}_2\text{)}$$
$$2 \text{ (Glyoxylate} + \textbf{Serine} \rightarrow \text{Glycine} + \text{Hydroxypyruvate)}$$
$$2 \text{ Glycine} \rightarrow \textbf{Serine} + \textbf{CO}_2 + \textbf{NH}_3$$
$$2 \text{ (Hydroxypyruvate} + \textbf{NADH} + \textbf{H}^+ \rightarrow \text{Glycerate} + \textbf{NAD}^+\text{)}$$
$$2 \text{ (Glycerate} + \textbf{ATP} \rightarrow \textbf{3-phosphoglycerate} + \textbf{ADP)}$$

Net: 2 Phosphoglycolate + 2 H_2O + 2 O_2 + 2 ATP + 2 NADH + 2 H^+ + Serine →
$$\text{3-Phosphoglycerate} + CO_2 + NH_3 + 2 \text{ NAD}^+ + 2 \text{ ADP} + 2 H_2O_2 + 2 P_i$$

To clean up this reaction, we could use the glutamate dehydrogenase reaction to convert ammonium and α-ketoglutarate into glutamate.
$$NH_3 + \alpha\text{-Ketoglutarate} + \textbf{NADH} + \textbf{H}^+ \rightarrow \text{Glutamate} + H_2O + \textbf{NAD}^+$$

Net: 2 Phosphoglycolate + α-Ketoglutarate + H_2O + 2 O_2 + 2 ATP + 3 NADH + 3 H^+ + Serine →
$$\text{Glutamate} + \text{3-phosphoglycerate} + CO_2 + 3 \text{ NAD}^+ + 2 \text{ ADP} + 2 H_2O_2 + 2 P_i$$

Using an aminotransferase we could convert glutamate into serine and α-ketoglutarate with hydroxypyruvate as keto acceptor.
$$\text{glutamate} + \text{hydroxypyruvate} \rightarrow \alpha\text{-Ketoglutarate} + \text{Serine}$$

Net: 2 Phosphoglycolate + hydroxypyruvate + H_2O + 2 O_2 + 2 ATP + 3 NADH + 3 H^+ →
$$\text{3-phosphoglycerate} + CO_2 + 3 \text{ NAD}^+ + 2 \text{ ADP} + 2 H_2O_2 + 2 P_i$$

Finally, we could convert one phosphoglycerate into glycerate and then into hydroxypyruvate as follows: glutamate into serine and α-ketoglutarate with hydroxypyruvate as keto acceptor.
$$\text{3-Phosphoglycerate} + \text{ADP} \rightarrow \text{Glycerate} + \text{ATP}$$
$$\text{Glycerate} + \text{NAD}^+ \rightarrow \text{Hydroxypyruvate} + \text{NADH} + H^+$$

Net: 2 Phosphoglycolate + H_2O + 2 O_2 + ATP + 2 NADH + 2 H^+ →
$$\text{3-phosphoglycerate} + CO_2 + 2 \text{ NAD}^+ + \text{ADP} + 2 H_2O_2 + 2 P_i$$

15. The number of c-subunits in F_1F_0–type ATP synthases shows some variation from organism to organism. For example, the yeast ATP synthase contains 10 c-subunits, the spinach CF_1CF_0-ATP synthase has 14, and the cyanobacterium Spirulina platensis enzyme apparently has 15.
a. What is the consequence of c-subunit stoichiometry for the H^+/ATP ratio?
b. What is the relationship between c-subunit stoichiometry and the magnitude of Δp (the proton-motive force)?

Answer: ATP synthase has three binding sites of ATP, corresponding to three stages of phosphorylation of ADP to ATP. One turn of the synthase is required to complete the process and the number of c-subunits determines the number of steps taken to complete one turn. Each step involves movement of a proton. As the number of c-subunits increase the ration of H^+/ATP will increase.
The proton-motive force (Δp) can be smaller with increasing numbers of c-subunits.

17. Plastoquinone oxidation by cytochrome bc_1 and cytochrome b_6f complexes apparently leads to the translocation of 4 H^+/2e^-. If $\mathscr{E}_o'$ for cytochrome f is 0.365 V (Table 19.1) and $\mathscr{E}_o'$ for PQ/PQH_2 is 0.07 V, calculate ΔG for the coupled reaction:
$$2 \text{ hv} + 4 \text{ } H^+_{in} \rightarrow 4 \text{ } H^+_{out}$$
(Assume a value of 23 kJ/mol for the free energy change (ΔG) associated with moving protons from inside to outside.)

Answer: ΔG for movement of protons from inside to outside is given as 23 kJ/mol. However, protons are moved so $\Delta G = 4 \times 23 = 92$ kJ. ΔG for reduction of plastoquinone using cytochrome f is calculated as follows:

$$\Delta G^{\circ\prime} = -n\mathcal{F}\Delta\mathcal{E}_0', \text{ where } n \text{ is the number of electrons and}$$

$$\mathcal{F} = \text{Faraday's constant} = 96.485 \frac{\text{kJ}}{\text{V}\cdot\text{mol}}$$

$$\Delta\mathcal{E}_0' = \mathcal{E}_0'(\text{acceptor}) - \mathcal{E}_0'(\text{donor})$$

$$\Delta\mathcal{E}_0' = \mathcal{E}_0'(\text{cytochrome } f) - \mathcal{E}_0'(\text{plastoquinone})$$

$$\Delta\mathcal{E}_0' = 0.365 - (0.07) = 0.295 \text{ V}$$

$$\Delta G^{\circ\prime} = -2 \times 96.485 \frac{\text{kJ}}{\text{V}\cdot\text{mol}} \times (0.295) = -56.9 \text{ kJ}$$

The ΔG for the coupled reaction is $92 - 56.9 = -35.1$ kJ.

Questions for Self-Study

1. Match an item in the first column with an item in the second.
    a. Plastid   1. Highly permeable
    b. Thylakoid vesicle   2. Stack of thylakoid vesicles
    c. Granum   3. Chloroplast
    d. Inner membrane   4. Flattened sac
    e. Outer membrane   5. Connects grana
    f. Lamella   6. Highly impermeable

2. What are the four possible fates of the energy of a quantum of light after it is absorbed by photosynthetic pigments?

3. Two experiments helped to characterize eukaryotic photosystems: (1) measurements of oxygen evolution, normalized to pigment content, as a function of the amount of incident light energy; and (2) oxygen evolution as a function of wavelength. For each of the statements below, indicate the appropriate experiment.
    a. Showed the red drop or Emerson effect
    b. Used flashes of white light
    c. Evidence for photosynthetic units
    d. Required two light flashes to get maximum oxygen evolution
    e. Evidence for the existence of two separate photosystems

4. Fill in the blanks. Eukaryotic photosystems use light energy to move electrons from _____ to _____. During this process _____ is produced as a by-product in a reaction known as _____. Also, protons are moved from the _____ of the chloroplast into the _____ _____. This movement produces a proton gradient that is subsequently used to phosphorylate ADP to produce ATP in a process known as _____. The electrons follow a path known as the _____ _____, which requires _____ quanta of light per electron to function. Light-dependent electron flow with the production of ATP can occur without by-product formation in a process known as _____ _____. This process involves only one of the photosystems, _____ _____.

5. For the reactions (a) and (b), shown below, identify the reactants and products and name the enzymatic activities.

a.

b.

6. The Calvin cycle can be thought of as consisting of two phases, a reductive phase and a non-reductive phase. What are the inputs and outputs of each phase?

7. What is the role of malate production from PEP in C4 plants ? In CAM plants?

8. Carbon dioxide fixation is regulated by what three light-induced signals?

Answers

1. a. 3; b. 4; c. 2; d. 6; e. 1; f. 5.

2. Lost as heat, lost as light (fluorescence), resonance energy transfer, energy transduction.

3. a. 2; b. 1; c. 1; d. 2; e. 2.

4. water; NADP$^+$; oxygen; photolysis; stroma; thylakoid lumen; photophosphorylation; Z scheme; 2; cyclic photophosphorylation; photosystem I (or P700).

5. a. Ribulose-1,5-bisphosphate, carbon dioxide, and water react to form two molecules of 3-phosphoglycerate. The activity is the carboxylase activity of rubisco.

b. Ribulose-1,5-bisphosphate and oxygen combine to produce 3-phosphoglycerate and phosphoglycolate. The activity is oxygenase activity of rubisco.

6. In the reductive phase, ribulose-1,5-bisphosphate, carbon dioxide, water, ATP, and reducing equivalents in the form of NADPH are used to produce glyceraldehyde-3-phosphate. In the non-reductive phase, triose phosphates are used to produce glucose and to regenerate ribulose-1,5-bisphosphate consumed in the first phase.

7. In C4 plants, malate serves as a carbon dioxide delivery system from mesophyll cells to bundle sheath cells where the Calvin cycle occurs. This allows carbon dioxide fixation to be carried out in a relatively oxygen-poor environment, lessening the possibility of photorespiration. In CAM plants, malate production allows the plants to accumulate carbon dioxide at night when loss of water is minimized.

8. Decrease in stromal pH, increase in reducing power, and Mg^{2+} efflux from thylakoid vesicles.

Additional Problems

1. Chlorophyll can be extracted from plant tissue with acetone. The acetone extract is a dark green solution. If an intense beam of visible light is directed at the solution, the solution will fluoresce with a reddish hue. However, this fluorescence is not observed for isolated chloroplasts even though the chlorophyll in chloroplasts is dissolved in a hydrophobic environment. Why does chlorophyll fluoresce in acetone but not in chloroplasts?

2. A researcher decided to demonstrate photosynthesis using isolated chloroplasts from spinach. The plan was to use an oxygen electrode to measure oxygen production as a function of light intensity. Chloroplasts were isolated by disrupting spinach leaves in a buffered solution, briefly centrifuging the sample to remove cell walls and other debris, and then centrifuging to pellet chloroplasts. The chloroplasts are resuspended in fresh buffer and repelleted by centrifugation. Finally, the chloroplasts were resuspended in a small volume of buffer to make a concentrated solution of chloroplast fragments.

    With great fanfare, the researcher loaded the chloroplasts into an oxygen electrode, illuminated the electrode with an intense source of light, and, before a packed audience of 250 excited undergraduates, found that the preparation was completely inactive. Can you offer a simple explanation?

3. In the scenario described in question 2 above, the researcher went back to the laboratory, got the photosynthesis experiment working perfectly, and scheduled another demonstration. Then, just before show time disaster struck, the oxygen electrode broke. Can you suggest an alternate method of measuring photosynthesis?

4. What do the so-called dark reactions of photosynthesis accomplish?

5. The Hatch–Slack pathway is involved in carbon dioxide fixation in C4 plants. Describe this pathway (i.e. that portion of the pathway unique to C_4 plants) and identify a similar set of enzymes in animal cells that would accomplish this same process.

6. During electron transport in chloroplasts, hydrogen ions are pumped from one side of a membrane to another. Verbally or in a diagram, describe where protons are concentrated in chloroplasts. How is this topologically analogous to proton pumping in mitochondria?

7. The metal ion in chlorophyll is magnesium. In hemoglobin and myoglobin and in the cytochromes, the metal ion is iron. In one sense, the magnesium in chlorophyll behaves much like the iron in both hemoglobin and myoglobin, yet chlorophyll itself functions like the cytochrome porphyrins. Explain.

8. The membrane-bound ferredoxins found in the electron-transport chain of photosystem I can pass electrons to either soluble ferredoxin or to cytochrome bf complex. What are the outcomes of each path?

9. What experimental evidence supports the hypothesis that pigments are organized into photosynthetic units?

Abbreviated Answers

1. Fluorescence occurs when an electron is excited to a higher energy state, makes a transition to a slightly lower energy state, and then falls back to the unexcited ground state with loss of energy as a photon of light. Isolated chlorophyll fluoresces because the excited state has a long half-life, making the transition to the slightly lower energy level more probable. In chloroplasts, the excited state is effectively quenched by resonance energy transfer so no florescence is observed.

2. For oxygen production to occur a terminal electron acceptor is necessary. Normally, NADP+ serves this role and this small molecule cofactor was probably lost during chloroplast isolation.

3. One possibility is to use a pH meter to measure light-induced proton gradient formation. Oxygen production is accompanied by movement of protons into the thylakoid lumen. In a weakly buffered solution, this will cause a drop in pH that can be measured with a pH meter.

4.   The dark reactions constitute the Calvin cycle in which CO_2 is fixed to ribulose-1,5-bisphosphate to produce 2 molecules of 3-phosphoglycerate, which are subsequently reduced by NADPH-dependent glyceraldehyde-3-phosphate dehydrogenase to glyceraldehyde-3-phosphate. Glyceraldehyde-3-phosphate is used to synthesize glucose and to resynthesize ribulose-1,5-bisphosphate.

5.   In mesophyll cells, the enzyme pyruvate-phosphate dikinase catalyzes the conversion of pyruvate to PEP. PEP carboxylase produces oxaloacetate using PEP and bicarbonate (derived from CO_2), which is converted to either malate by an NADPH-specific malate dehydrogenase or to aspartate by transamination, and these four-carbon compounds are exported to bundle-sheath cells. In the bundle-sheath cells, aspartate is converted to oxaloacetate by transamination and oxaloacetate is converted to pyruvate and CO_2 by a $NADP^+$-dependent oxidation catalyzed by malic enzyme. The CO_2 is subsequently used in the Calvin cycle, whereas the pyruvate is transported back to the mesophyll cells for recycling.

   In animal cells, the gluconeogenic enzyme pyruvate carboxylase produces oxaloacetate from pyruvate and CO_2 in the mitochondria. Oxaloacetate is converted to either malate or aspartate and exported to the cytosol. In the cytosol, malate and aspartate are converted back to oxaloacetate; however, PEP carboxykinase degrades oxaloacetate to PEP and CO_2.

6.   During electron transport in chloroplasts, protons are moved from the stroma into the thylakoid lumen. The lumen pH decreases and the stromal pH increases. In mitochondria, protons are pumped from the matrix to the intramembrane space, which is connected to the cytosol. Thus, the cytosolic pH decreases and the mitochondrial matrix pH increases. It appears that the topology is quite different: the stroma of the chloroplast and the matrix of the mitochondria increase in pH upon proton pumping, and the intramembrane space of mitochondria and the thylakoid lumen of chloroplast decrease in pH. However, the biosynthesis of thylakoids is thought to occur by an invagination of the chloroplast outer membrane. Thus, the thylakoid lumen is topologically equivalent to the cytosol.

7.   The irons in hemoglobin and myoglobin do not change oxidation state during normal physiological function and remain in the ferrous (2+) oxidation state. The magnesium ion in chlorophyll behaves in a similar manner in that it does not change its oxidation state, yet chlorophyll itself in oxidized and reduced during photosynthesis. The cytochromes are similarly oxidized and reduced during electron transport. However, the iron atom undergoes a change in oxidation state during the process.

8.   Reduction of soluble ferredoxin leads to reduction of $NADP^+$, whereas reduction of cytochrome *bf* complex leads to cyclic flow of electrons, proton-gradient formation, and ATP synthesis.

9.   By measuring O_2 evolved per flash of light at varying intensities of light flashes using the alga *Chlorella* the following data were obtained.

At saturating intensities of light, the maximum oxygen production corresponds to one oxygen evolved per 2400 chlorophylls in this organism. Thus, the chlorophylls must be acting in units of about this size.

Summary

Photosynthesis is the transformation of light energy into the chemical energy necessary to sustain life. Traditionally, synthesis of carbohydrate ($C_6H_{12}O_6$) has been viewed as the end product of the photosynthetic process, but, in reality, the primary products of photosynthesis are ATP and NADPH, the major energy sources for biosynthesis. These agents, as suppliers of phosphorylation potential and reducing potential, respectively, power many cellular processes, and therefore aptly reflect the role of photosynthesis as the ultimate and essentially universal source of biological energy.

The photosynthetic reactions are intimately associated with membranes, and in photosynthetic eukaryotes, a specialized organelle, the chloroplast, is the site of the photosynthetic process. Photosynthesis can be divided into the "light" reactions (the photochemical generation of energy) and the "dark" reactions (the utilization of chemical energy to drive biosynthesis of carbohydrate in the dark). These different reactions are localized in different chloroplast compartments: the light-dependent processes occur in membrane vesicles (the thylakoids), whereas the dark reactions occur in the stroma (the cytosol-like compartment of the chloroplast).

The transformation of light energy into chemical energy is a manifestation of the photoreactivity of chlorophyll. This π-electron-rich macrocycle readily absorbs photons (quanta of light energy), which promote π-electrons to higher energy orbitals, thereby rendering the Chl molecule a much more effective electron donor. Thus, excited-state chlorophyll (Chl*) initiates a series of electron transfer (oxidation–reduction) reactions whereby light energy is ultimately transduced into reducing power (NADPH) and phosphorylation potential (ATP).

The chlorophyll of photosynthetic organisms is organized into photosynthetic units in order to more efficiently harvest the incident light energy. Within such units, an array of several hundred Chl molecules serve as an antenna to collect photons and funnel quanta of energy to specialized Chl molecule reaction centres, where the photochemical event occurs. All Chl is in specific Chl–protein complexes which reflect the roles of Chl in the photosynthetic process: a light harvesting complex (LHC), a photosystem I (PSI) complex functioning in NADP$^+$ reduction, and a photosystem II (PSII) complex involved in oxygen evolution. These three complexes are integral components of the thylakoid membrane. PSI and PSII contain unique reaction centre chlorophylls, designated P700 in PSI and P680 in PSII.

PSII and PSI act in concert to mediate the light-driven transfer of electrons from H_2O to reduce NADP$^+$. The photoexcitation of P680 in PSII leads to the generation of a weak reductant, QH$_2$ (a reduced form of plastoquinone), and a strong oxidant, P680$^+$, which, via accepting electrons from water, leads to oxygen evolution. The reductant, QH$_2$, is coupled to PSI by an integral membrane complex containing Fe-S centres and cytochromes b_6 and f. Electrons transferred from Q via the cytochrome f complex serve to re-reduce the PSI reaction centre Chl, P700$^+$. P700 upon photoexcitation generates a strong reductant, P700*, capable of reducing Fe-S centres whose E_0' are more negative than -0.6 V. The P700$^+$ thus formed has its electron hole filled by an electron from plastocyanin, the blue copper protein serving as e^- acceptor to the cytochrome b_6–cytochrome f complex. The Fe-S centres on the reducing side of P700* provide electrons from water to reduce NADP$^+$. Their arrangement, according to the redox potential scale and their organization into the unique PSI, PSII complexes bridged by the cytochrome b_6–cytochrome f complex, gives rise to a Z-shaped pathway, the so-called "Z" scheme of photosynthesis.

The primary events in photosynthesis are light-induced electron transfers which of necessity result in a situation where oxidized donor and reduced acceptor, for example, P700$^+$ and Chl a$^-$, are in close proximity. These neighbouring, oppositely charged species invite charge recombination and consequent dissipation of the photochemical energy. To prevent this, the electron-transfer reactions following photo-excitation of reactive centres must be very rapid so that the energized electron is quickly conducted away from the oxidized form of its original donor.

ATP produced by photosynthesis arises because photosynthetic electron transfer is accompanied by transmembrane proton translocations, which establish a proton-motive force across the membrane. This electrochemical H$^+$ gradient is tapped by the chloroplast ATP synthase, CF$_1$CF$_o$–ATP synthase. Quantitative measurements indicate that 1 H$^+$ is translocated per photon entering the photosynthetic system and that the translocation of 3 H$^+$ generates the necessary electrochemical gradient to drive the synthesis of 1 ATP under conditions of non-cyclic photophosphorylation. The other photophosphorylation pattern, cyclic photophosphorylation, involves a cyclic electron transfer reaction wherein light energy incident at P700 drives an electron through a series of acceptors back to refill P700$^+$. As a consequence of the e^- transfers, proton translocations ensue that can drive ATP formation.

Carbon dioxide fixation, the synthesis of carbohydrate from CO_2, while not uniquely a photosynthetic process, is nevertheless the major investment of the chemical energy derived from photosynthesis. Carbon dioxide is fixed in organic linkage through reaction with ribulose-1,5-bisphosphate to generate 2 molecules of 3-phosphoglycerate. The enzyme catalyzing this reaction is ribulose bisphosphate carboxylase or rubisco. Rubisco also has the capacity to use O_2 in place of CO_2 in the condensation with ribulose-1,5-bisphosphate, a reaction leading to a wasteful loss of this pentose. As an oxygen-consuming, CO_2-evolving reaction, this process is aptly termed photorespiration and is viewed as a wasteful dissipation of RuBP, a crucial metabolic intermediate. The remaining reactions of Calvin cycle CO_2 fixation are similar to reactions in the pentose phosphate pathway and glycolysis. The aim of the Calvin cycle is to account for the synthesis of one hexose molecule ($C_6H_{12}O_6$) from 6 equivalents of carbon dioxide (6 CO_2). Key Calvin cycle enzymes are regulated by light-induced effects on chloroplast reducing power, pH and relative Mg^{2+} concentrations so that CO_2 fixation occurs only when light energy is available. An alternate means of CO_2 capture occurs in so-called C4 plants. These plants form

C4 compounds (instead of C3-phosphoglycerate) as the initial products of CO_2 uptake. The C4 pathway is not an alternative process to the Calvin cycle but instead is an effective means for the transport and concentration of CO_2 within cells having high potential for Calvin cycle carbon dioxide fixation. C4 plants achieve greater photosynthetic efficiency by diminishing photorespiration. Typical C4 plants include tropical grasses such as sugar cane and maize.

Chapter 21

Gluconeogenesis, Glycogen Metabolism, and the Pentose Phosphate Pathway

• •

Chapter Outline

❖ Gluconeogenesis
  ⅄ Substrates: Pyruvate, lactate, glycerol, amino acids (except Lys and Leu)
  ⅄ Active in liver and kidney: Supplies glucose to brain and muscle
  ⅄ Seven of ten glycolytic steps in reverse
  ⅄ Three steps not reversal of glycolysis for two reasons:
    • Energetics
    • Regulation
❖ Three unique gluconeogenesis steps
  ⅄ Pyruvate to PEP
    • Pyruvate carboxylase converts pyruvate to oxaloacetate
      • Biotin-dependent enzyme
      • ATP + bicarbonate to carbonyl phosphate to carboxybiotin intermediate
      • Allosteric activation by acetyl-CoA
      • Localized in mitochondria
    • Oxaloacetate to malate and back
    • PEP carboxylase converts oxaloacetate to PEP
      • Decarboxylation drives reaction
      • GTP or ATP supplies P and drives reaction
  ⅄ Fructose-1,6-bisphosphate to fructose-6-phosphate
    • Hydrolysis
    • Fructose-1,6-bisphosphatase
      • Citrate stimulates
      • Fructose-2,6-bisphosphate inhibits
      • AMP inhibits
  ⅄ Glucose-6-phosphate to glucose
    • Hydrolysis
    • Glucose-6-phosphatase
      • Releases product into ER lumen
      • Enzyme expressed in liver and kidney (not in muscle or brain)
      • High K_m for G6P: Substrate-level control
❖ Reciprocal regulation: Avoidance of substrate cycles
  ⅄ Glucose to glucose-6-phosphate and back
    • Glucokinase high K_m and not inhibited by G6P
    • Glucose-6-phosphatase high K_m
  ⅄ Fructose-6-phosphate to fructose-1,6-bisphosphate and back
    • Phosphofructokinase
      • AMP stimulates
      • Fructose-2,6-bisphosphate stimulates
      • Citrate inhibits

- Fructose-1,6-bisphosphatase
  - AMP inhibits
  - Fructose-2,6-bisphosphate inhibits
  - Citrate stimulates
- Fructose-2,6-bisphosphate levels regulated by bifunctional (tandem) enzyme
  - Phosphofructokinase 2 produces F-2,6-BP
    - c-AMP protein kinase phosphorylation inhibits PFK 2
    - F6P activates PFKase 2
  - Fructose-2,6-bisphosphatase hydrolyzes F-2,6-BP
    - c-AMP protein kinase phosphorylation activates phosphatase
    - F6P inhibits FBPase 2
- ❖ Dietary glycogen (and starch) catabolism
  - ⅄ α-amylase (saliva and pancreas) endoglycosidase
    - Hydrolyzes $\alpha(1\rightarrow4)$ amylopectin and glycogen at random: Products
      - Maltose, maltotriose, oligosaccharides
      - Limit dextrin: Branches limit
  - ⅄ Debranching enzyme: Two activities
    - Oligo ($\alpha1,4 \rightarrow \alpha1,4$) glucanotransferase: Moves three residues to new end
    - $\alpha(1 \rightarrow 6)$ glucosidase: Hydrolyzes branch
- ❖ Cellular glycogen
  - ⅄ Glycogen phosphorylase: Uses phosphate to split off glucose-1-P
  - ⅄ Debranching enzyme
- ❖ Glycogen synthesis
  - ⅄ Base: Glycogenin with glucose in acetal linkage to Tyr–OH
  - ⅄ Glycogen synthase: $\alpha(1 \rightarrow 4)$ linkage of glucose from UDP–glucose
  - ⅄ UDP–glucose: UDP–glucose pyrophosphorylase: UTP + G-1-P to UDP–glucose + PP_i
  - ⅄ Branching enzyme: Amylo($1,4 \rightarrow 1,6$) transglycosylase
    - Chain moved is 6–7 residues long and from 11-residue chain
    - Branch points: $\alpha(1\rightarrow 6)$ linkage every 8–12 residues
- ❖ Glycogen synthase regulation
  - ⅄ D-form: Less active: Dependent on G6P: Phosphorylated by protein kinase
  - ⅄ I-form: Active (independent of G6P) : No phosphate (phosphate removed by phosphoprotein phosphatase)
- ❖ Hormonal regulation
  - ⅄ Insulin: Released from β-cells islets of Langerhans of pancreas in response to high blood glucose
    - Increase uptake of glucose
    - Increase synthesis of glycolytic enzymes
    - Inhibits gluconeogenesis
  - ⅄ Glucagon α-cells islets of Langerhans of pancreas in response to low blood glucose
    - Stimulates liver to release glucose
    - Involved in long term glucose maintenance
  - ⅄ Epinephrine (adrenaline) released by adrenal glands
    - Active on liver and muscle
    - Stimulates glycogen breakdown and glycolysis
    - Inhibits gluconeogenesis
  - ⅄ Glucocorticoids: Cortisol
    - Steroid hormone active on liver, muscle, adipose tissue
    - In liver: Stimulates gluconeogenesis and glycogen synthesis
    - Catabolic: Promotes protein degradation
- ❖ Pentose phosphate pathway (hexose monophosphate shunt, phosphogluconate pathway)
  - ⅄ Supplies NADPH or ribose
  - ⅄ Two phases
    - Oxidative phase: Glucose-6-P to ribulose-5-P
    - Non-oxidative phase: Ribulose-5-P to 3-, 4-, 5-, 6-, and 7-carbons ketoses and aldoses

❖ Glucose to ribulose-5-P: Oxidative
  ⅄ Glucose-6-phosphate dehydrogenase
    • NADPH produced
    • Gluconolactone produced
    • Enzyme inhibitors
      • NADPH
      • Intermediates of fatty acid biosynthesis
  ⅄ Gluconolactonase: Gluconolactone to 6-phosphogluconate
  ⅄ 6-Phosphogluconate dehydrogenase
    • NADPH produced
    • Ribulose-5-P and carbon dioxide produced
❖ Ribulose-5-P to various sugars: Non-reductive: Enzyme types
  ⅄ Phosphopentose isomerase: Ketose to aldose conversion
  ⅄ Phosphopentose epimerase: Sugar interconversion
  ⅄ Transketolase: 2-carbon unit from keto donor to aldehyde acceptor
  ⅄ Transaldolase: Ketose and aldose formation

Chapter Objectives

Gluconeogenesis

Although gluconeogenesis is not simply the reverse of glycolysis, the two pathways share many steps and it would help to review glycolysis. Briefly, glucose is phosphorylated by hexokinase to glucose-6-phosphate, which is isomerized to fructose-6-phosphate. A second kinase reaction, catalyzed by phosphofructokinase, produces fructose-1,6-bisphosphate, which is cleaved by aldolase to produce dihydroxyacetone phosphate and glyceraldehyde-3-phosphate, two triose phosphates that are interconvertible. Glyceraldehyde-3-P is oxidized and phosphorylated to 1,3-bisphosphoglycerate, a high-energy compound used to support a substrate-level phosphorylation of ADP, leaving 3-phosphoglycerate, which is converted to 2-phosphoglycerate, dehydrated to phosphoenolpyruvate, and converted to pyruvate with accompanying ATP synthesis.

Gluconeogenesis starts with pyruvate and ends with glucose. Pyruvate can derive from lactate, amino acids, and citric acid cycle intermediates but not from acetyl-CoA units. Gluconeogenesis and glycolysis differ at three steps (see Figure 21.1), glucose to glucose-6-P, fructose-6-P to fructose-1,6-bisphosphate, and PEP to pyruvate. Understand how these three steps are bypassed and you will understand gluconeogenesis. The first two steps are catalyzed by phosphatases that hydrolyze phosphate from the substrates. The PEP to pyruvate step is a two-step process with pyruvate being converted to oxaloacetate by pyruvate carboxylase, a biotin-containing enzyme. Oxaloacetate is converted to PEP by PEP-carboxykinase, which uses ATP or GTP hydrolysis, depending on the enzyme source, to drive the reaction.

Regulation

Glycolysis and gluconeogenesis are reciprocally regulated. You should remember the following regulatory pairs: glucose-6-phosphate inhibition of hexokinase and stimulation of glucose-6-phosphatase; fructose-2,6-bisphosphate stimulation of phosphofructokinase (PFK) and inhibition of fructose-1,6-bisphosphatase (FBPase); AMP stimulation of PFK and inhibition of FBPase; and acetyl-CoA inhibition of pyruvate kinase and activation of pyruvate carboxylase. Additionally, ATP inhibits PFK and pyruvate kinase, citrate inhibits PFK, alanine inhibits pyruvate kinase, and cyclic-AMP–dependent phosphorylation inhibits pyruvate kinase. Fructose-2,6-bisphosphate can be thought of as a signal to stimulate glycolysis. This regulator is not a component of a metabolic pathway but is produced by a bifunctional enzyme regulated by cAMP-dependent phosphorylation.

Glycogen

Dietary glycogen and starch breakdown are catalyzed by α-amylase (β-amylase in plants) and debranching enzymes. Tissue glycogen is degraded by glycogen phosphorylase and synthesized by glycogen synthase. The latter is supplied with activated glucosyl residues in the form of UDP–glucose produced by UDP–glucose pyrophosphorylase. Know the role of glycogenin and branching enzymes in initiating glycogen synthesis and in introducing branches leading to multiple sites for rapid elongation or degradation of glycogen.

Regulation

Glycogen metabolism is carefully controlled by regulating glycogen phosphorylase and glycogen synthase. Glycogen phosphorylase is allosterically activated by AMP and inhibited by ATP and glucose-6-phosphate, whereas glycogen synthase is stimulated by glucose-6-phosphate. Both enzymes are subject to control by covalent modification. Glycogen phosphorylase exists in two forms, a less active *b* form and an active *a* form. Phosphorylase *a* is a phosphorylated form of phosphorylase *b*, catalyzed by a specific kinase, glycogen phosphorylase kinase which is itself under covalent regulation by cAMP-dependent protein kinase. cAMP levels are regulated hormonally by hormone binding to surface receptors, leading to release of G protein, and stimulation of adenylyl cyclase. Know this cascade. Glycogen synthase also exists in two forms that differ in both activity and the state of phosphorylation. The less active phosphorylated glycogen synthase D depends on glucose-6-phosphate for activity, whereas the active unphosphorylated glycogen synthase I is independent of glucose-6-phosphate levels.

Pentose Phosphate Pathway

Admittedly, this is an impressive pathway, but it may simplify matters to remember that it has an oxidative phase and a non-oxidative phase (see Figure 21.31). In the oxidative phase, glucose is converted to ribulose-5-phosphate and CO_2. Clearly, this must involve a phosphorylation (by hexokinase) and oxidations (by two NADP-dependent dehydrogenases). (With reflection, we might have anticipated that two oxidations are required. The CO_2 must derive from one of the alcoholic carbons of glucose via an aldehyde intermediate.)

The non-oxidative phase of the pentose phosphate pathway converts ribulose-5-phosphate into glucose-6-phosphate via 3-, 4-, 5-, 6-, and 7-carbon sugar intermediates. Some of the key enzymes involved include the following: phosphopentose isomerase catalyzes a ketose to aldose conversion (we encountered similar biochemistry in glycolysis between glucose-6-P and fructose-6-P, and between DHAP and glyceraldehyde-3-P); phosphopentose epimerase (an epimerase changes the configuration about an asymmetric carbon—we encountered one in galactose catabolism); transketolases (move two-carbon units between aldoses); and a transaldolase (with a reaction mechanism similar to the aldolase encountered in glycolysis).

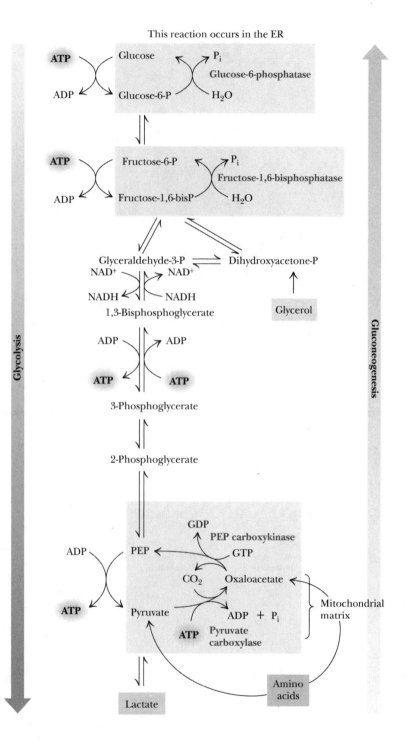

Figure 21.1   The pathways of glucogenesis and glycolysis. Species in the boxes indicate the other entry points for gluconeogenesis (in addition to pyruvate).

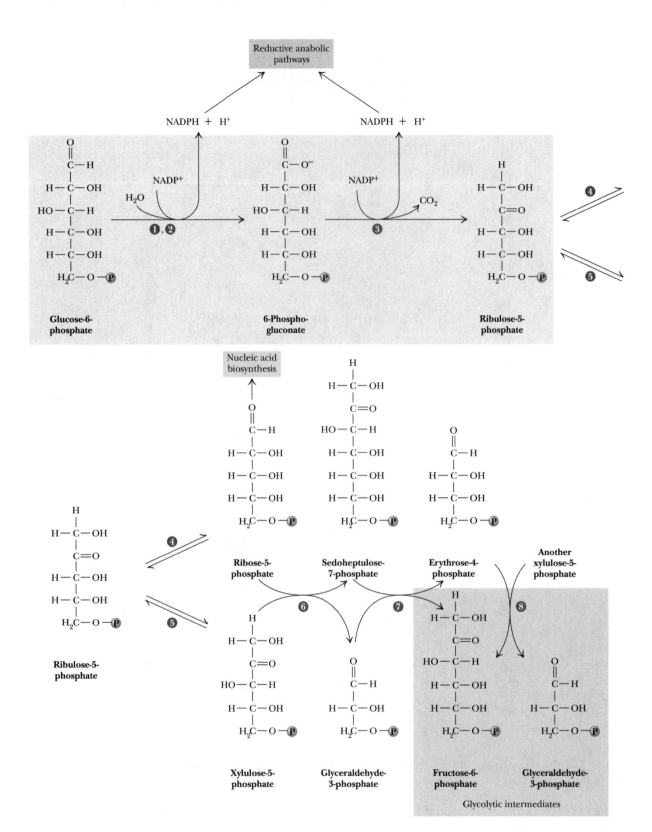

Figure 21.31   The pentose phosphate pathway. The numerals in the circles indicate the steps discussed in the core text.

Problems and Solutions

1. Consider the balanced equation for gluconeogenesis in Section 21.1. Account for each of the components of this equation and the indicated stoichiometry.

Answer: The net reaction for the synthesis of glucose from pyruvate is:

2 pyruvate + 4 ATP + 2 GTP + 2 NADH + 2 H$^+$ + 6 H$_2$O → glucose + 4 ADP + 2 GDP + 6 P$_i$ + 2 NAD$^+$

The following reactions contribute to this equation:

2 pyruvate + 2 H$^+$ + 2 H$_2$O → glucose + O$_2$
2 NADH + 2 H$^+$ + O$_2$ → NAD$^+$ + 2 H$_2$O
4 ATP + 4 H$_2$O → 4 ADP + 4 P$_i$
2 GTP + 2 H$_2$O → 2 ADP + 2 P$_i$

The six carbons of glucose derive from the 3-carbon compound pyruvate. In considering pyruvate, the keto carbon is oxidized relative to the average carbon of glucose, and hence it must be reduced to form glucose. Reduction comes at the expense of NADH. (The carboxyl carbon is also oxidized; however, the methyl carbon is reduced relative to the average carbon of glucose. An internal oxidation–reduction during gluconeogenesis changes the oxidation state of these two carbons to match that of glucose carbons.)

The hydrolysis of high-energy nucleoside triphosphates is accounted for as follows. In the first stage of gluconeogenesis, pyruvate is transformed to phosphoenolpyruvate in two steps. First, pyruvate is converted to oxaloacetate by pyruvate carboxylase, a biotin-containing enzyme. This reaction is driven by conversion of ATP to ADP and P$_i$. This is not a hydrolysis but rather a series of displacement reactions: ADP is displaced from ATP by bicarbonate; P$_i$ is displaced from bicarbonate by biotin; and biotin is displaced by pyruvate to produce oxaloacetate. Thus, hydrolysis does not occur and water is not consumed, but two ATPs produce two ADPs and two P$_i$s. Next, oxaloacetate is converted to PEP by PEP-carboxykinase, a GTP-dependent enzyme, which accounts for two GTPs and two GDPs. The two remaining ATPs are consumed when 1,3-bisphosphoglycerate and ADP are produced from 3-phosphoglycerate and ATP by phosphoglycerate kinase.

We must still account for two waters and four P$_i$s. Reduction of two moles of 1,3-bisphosphoglycerate to two moles of glyceraldehyde-3-phosphate releases two P$_i$. Finally, two hydrolysis reactions catalyzed by fructose-1,6-bisphosphatase and glucose-6-phosphatase account for two H$_2$O consumed and two P$_i$ produced.

Pyruvate derives from a number of sources including citric acid cycle intermediates, amino acids, and lactate. NADH may be supplied indirectly by the mitochondria. The inner mitochondrial membrane is impermeable to oxaloacetate, so it is converted to malate, which is transported to the cytosol. In the cytosol, malate dehydrogenase converts malate back to oxaloacetate with reduction of NAD$^+$ to NADH.

3. Use the data of Figure 21.9 to calculate the percent inhibition of fructose-1,6-bisphosphatase by 25 mM fructose-2,6-bisphosphate when fructose-1,6-bisphosphate is (a) 25 mM and (b) 100 mM.

Answer: From Figure 21.9, (a) we can estimate that at 25 mM fructose-1,6-bisphosphate, the activity of fructose-1,6-bisphosphatase in the absence of fructose-2,6-bisphosphate is approximately 15 units. In the presence of 25 mM fructose-2,6-bisphosphate, the activity is only 1 unit. The percent inhibition is given by

$$\frac{15-1}{15}\times100\% = 93.3\%$$

At 100 mM fructose-1,6-bisphosphate, the activities of fructose-1,6-bisphosphatase without and with fructose-2,6-bisphosphate are 14 and 8. The percent inhibition in this case is

$$\frac{14-8}{14}\times100\% = 42.9\%$$

5. Using the values in Table 22.1 for body glycogen content and the data in part b of the illustration for A Deeper Look (page 718), calculate the rate of energy consumption by muscles in heavy exercise (in J/sec). Use the data for fast-twitch muscle.

Answer: From Table 22.1, we are informed that a 70 kg person has about 120 g (dry weight) of glycogen, equivalent to 1920 kJ of available energy. From *A Deeper Look*, we see glycogen supplies are exhausted after approximately 60 minutes of heavy exercise. The rate of energy consumption is given by:

$$\frac{1920 \text{ kJ}}{60 \text{ min}} = 32 \frac{\text{kJ}}{\text{min}}$$

$$32 \frac{\text{kJ}}{\text{min}} = 32 \frac{\text{kJ}}{\text{min}} \times \frac{1000 \text{ J}}{\text{kJ}} \times \frac{1 \text{min}}{60 \text{sec}} = 533 \frac{\text{J}}{\text{sec}}$$

7. *(Integrates with Chapter 7) Imagine a glycogen molecule with 8000 glucose residues. If branches occur every 8 residues, how many reducing ends does the molecule have? If branches occur every 12 residues, how many reducing ends does it have? How many non-reducing ends does it have in each of these cases?*

Answer: The reducing end of a polysaccharide contains a free aldehyde or keto group. In glycogen, the linkage between glucose residues is $\alpha(1{\rightarrow}4)$ for non-branch residues and $\alpha(1{\rightarrow}6)$ for branch residues. Thus, both branch residues and non-branch residues have their anomeric carbons, C-1, in glycosidic bonds. Further, C-1 of the first glucose residue is tied up in linkage to glycogenin at the core, so there are no free reducing ends, regardless of the size of the glycogen molecule.

   The number of non-reducing ends is very much dependent on the frequency of branches. In the diagram below, n = number of residues in a branch, b = a branch residue, and e = non-reducing end.

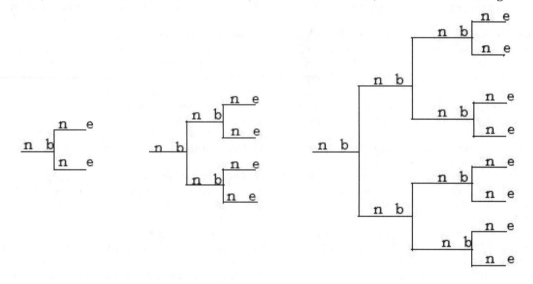

From this diagram, the following table may be constructed:

Number of Residues	Number of Branch Points (b)	Number of Ends (e)
$3n$	1	2
$7n$	3	4
$15n$	7	8
.	.	.
.	.	.
$[(2^x - 1) + 2^x]n$	$2^x - 1$	2^x

For a glycogen molecule of 8000 residues with 8 residues per branch ($n = 8$), we have:

$$[(2^x - 1) + 2^x]n = 8000 \text{ residues}$$

For $n = 8$:

$$[(2^x - 1) + 2^x] \times 8 = 8000 \text{ or}$$

$$2^x + 2^x = \frac{8000}{8} + 1$$

$$2 \times 2^x = 999$$

$$2^x = \frac{999}{2}$$

$$x = \frac{\log \dfrac{999}{2}}{\log 2} = 5.62$$

$$x = 8.964$$

The number of non-reducing ends is $2^x = 2^{8.964} = 500$

For a glycogen molecule of 8000 residues with 12 residues per branch ($n = 12$), $x = 8.381$, the number of non-reducing ends is 333, and the number of branch points is 332.

Note: 8000 residues forms $8000 \div 12 = 666$ 12-residue branches. There are 333 terminal branches and 332 internal branches.

9. (Integrates with Chapters 3 and 14) The free energy change of the glycogen phosphorylase reaction is $\Delta G^{\circ\prime} = + 3.1$ kJ/mol. If [Pi] = 1 mM, what is the concentration of glucose-1-P when this reaction is at equilibrium?

Answer: For the reaction: $glycogen_n + P_i \rightarrow glycogen_{n-1} + glucose\text{-}1\text{-}P$

$$\Delta G^{\circ\prime} = -RT \times \ln K_{eq} = -RT \times \ln \frac{[\text{glucose-1-P}][\text{glycogen}_{n-1}]}{[P_i][\text{glycogen}_n]}$$

Since $[\text{glycogen}_n] = [\text{glycogen}_{n-1}]$ this simplifies to:

$$\Delta G^{\circ\prime} = -RT \times \ln \frac{[\text{glucose-1-P}]}{[P_i]}$$

Solving for [glucose-1-P]:

$$[\text{glucose-1-P}] = [P_i] \times e^{\frac{-\Delta G^{\circ\prime}}{RT}} = [(1 \times 10^{-3}) \times e^{\frac{-3.1}{8.314 \times 10^{-3} \times 298}}$$

$$[\text{glucose-1-P}] = 0.286 \text{ mM}$$

11. The mechanistic chemistry of the acetolactate synthase and phosphoketolase reactions (shown below) is similar to that of the transketolase reaction (Figure 21.39). Write suitable mechanisms for these reactions.

Answer: The enzyme acetolactate synthase is involved in valine biosynthesis in bacteria. It is a thiamine pyrophosphate–containing enzyme. A reasonable reaction mechanism might be as follows:

Phosphoketolase is also a thiamine pyrophosphate–containing enzyme. It is used by certain bacteria to ferment glucose into lactic acid and ethanol (using xylulose-5-P in place of fructose-6-P) by the phosphoketolase pathway. (Bacteria capable of running this pathway are used to produce sauerkraut, buttermilk, and certain cheeses.) The reaction mechanism is shown below:

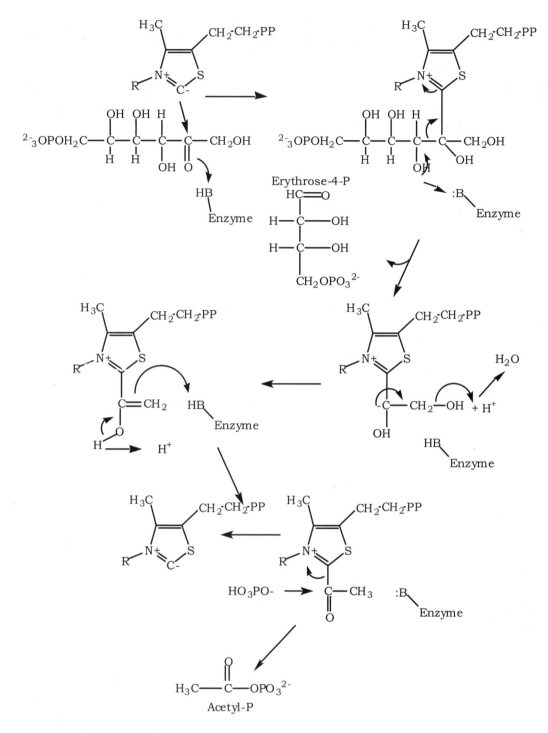

Erythrose-4-P

Acetyl-P

13. Study the structures of tolrestat and epalrestat in the Human Biochemistry box on page 725 and suggest a mechanism of action for these inhibitors of aldose reductase.

Answer: Tolrestat and epalrestat are both inhibitors of aldose reductase, an enzyme in the polyol pathway. Aldose reductase converts glucose to the sugar alcohol sorbitol and uses NADPH as a source of electrons. The structures of tolrestat and epalrestat do not seem to have any similarities to any of the substrates of the enzyme. Studies by Prendergast and co-workers (Ehrig T., Bohren K.M., Prendergast F.G., and Gabbay K.H. (1994) Mechanism of Aldose Reductase Inhibition: Binding of NADP+/NADPH and Alrestatin-like Inhibitors. *Biochemistry* 33, 7157–7165) show that these inhibitors probably bind to the enzyme–NADP+ complex at a site other than the active site or substrate-binding sites.

15. Consider the diagram you constructed in Problem 14. Which carbon atoms in ribose-5-phosphate are derived from carbon atoms in positions 1, 3, and 6 of fructose-6-phosphate?

Answer: If we started with fructose-6-phosphate labelled at carbons 1, 3, and 6 and did not allow label to move into glyceraldehyde-3-phosphate or DHAP via aldolase in glycolysis, then label would immediately show up in the aldehyde carbon of ribose from carbon 1 of fructose. This happens as a consequence of reversal of step 8 (page 726) to produce C-1 labelled xylulose. (Xylulose is converted to ribulose and then to ribose with C-1 labelled.) The other product is erythrose labelled at C-1 and C-4. See below.

| Fructose-6-P | Glyceraldehyde-3-P | Erythrose-4-P | Xylulose-5-P |

Erythrose and another fructose-6-P are converted to glyceraldehyde-3-P and sedoheptulose-7-P by reversal of step 7 (page 728). This produces glyceraldehyde with label on C-3 (from C-6 of fructose) and sedoheptulose-7-P with label on C-1, 3, 4, and 7. (Label at 1 and 3 from fructose and label at 4 and 7 from xylulose.)

| Fructose-6-P | Erythrose-4-P | Glyceraldehyde-3-P | Sedoheptulose-7-P |

Reversal of step 6 (page 726) will produce ribose labelled on C-1, 2, and 5 from sedoheptulose and xylulose labelled at carbon 1 from sedoheptulose and carbon 5 from carbon 3. When these are converted to ribose, carbons 1, 2 and 5 are labelled. See below.

| Sedoheptulose-7-P | Glyceraldehyde-3-P | Ribose-5-P | Xylulose-5-P |

17. The discussion on page 729 explains that the pentose phosphate pathway and the glycolytic pathway can be combined to provide both NADPH and ATP (as well as some NADH) without net ribose-5-phosphate synthesis. Draw a diagram to show how this may be accomplished.

Answer: NADPH production requires the oxidative stage of the pentose phosphate pathway or steps 1, 2, and 3 in Figure 21.31. To get ATP, glycolysis needs to be followed, and so fructose-6-phosphate produced by consuming ribulose-5-phosphate in the non-oxidative stage of the pathway will have to be metabolized into pyruvate in glycolysis.

19.   Glycogenin catalyzes the first reaction in the synthesis of a glycogen particle, with Tyr[194] of glycogenin (page 706) combining with a glucose unit (provided by UDP–glucose) to produce a tyrosyl glucose. Write a mechanism to show how this reaction could occur.

Answer: The mechanism proposed by Hurley and co-workers (Hurley et al. (2005) Requirements for catalysis in mammalian glycogenin. *Journal of Biological Chemistry* 280:23892–23899) is presented below.

21. (Integrates with Chapters 3 and 13) What is the structure of creatine phosphate? Write reactions to indicate how it stores and provides energy for exercise.

Answer: The structure of creatine phosphate is show below. A little reflection may help you identify this compound's structure as being very similar to the side chain of arginine. (Recall the side chain of arginine, *N*-methylate it, and attach a phosphate group in P-N linkage.) Creatine phosphate is a phosphagen, a high-energy phosphate compound used to restore ATP levels. Some organisms actually use phosphoarginine as a phosphagen. The P-N bond is highly energetic and can be used to phosphorylate ADP.

Organisms that use creatine phosphate as a phosphagen have two creatine kinases. Kinases phosphorylate substrates using the gamma phosphate of ATP as the phosphate source. Thus, creatine kinase phosphorylates creatine producing creatine phosphate in the following reaction.

creatine + ATP → creatine phosphate + ADP

One creatine kinase is located in the mitochondria where high ATP levels allow the reaction to proceed as written. This mitochondrial enzyme is used to re-charge creatine to creatine phosphate. The other creatine kinase is located in the cytoplasm, where it runs the reverse reaction when ADP levels begin to rise. This cytosolic creatine kinase recharges ADP at the expense of creatine phosphate. In effect, it catalyzes the following reaction, which is simply the reverse of the one presented above.

creatine phosphate + ADP → creatine + ATP

To link the two kinase reactions, creatine is transported into the mitochondria, while creatine phosphate is transported out of the mitochondria.

Questions for Self-Study

1. Fill in the blanks. Gluconeogenesis is the production of _____ from pyruvate and other 3-carbon and 4-carbon compounds. In animals, it occurs mainly in two organs, the _____ and _____. This pathway utilized several of the steps of glycolysis, but three key glycolytic steps are bypassed. They are the reactions catalyzed by _____, _____, and _____ _____. The conversion of pyruvate to PEP is a two-step process in which pyruvate is first converted to _____, a citric acid cycle intermediate with the addition of _____ _____. The enzyme catalyzing this step uses the vitamin _____. Production of PEP from pyruvate results in the hydrolysis of _____ high-energy phosphate bonds. The other two steps unique to gluconeogenesis are catalyzed by _____ and _____. These enzymes carry out _____ reactions.

2. The Cori cycle is an interplay of glycolysis and gluconeogenesis between two tissues. True or false:
   a. The liver is responsible for gluconeogenesis. _____
   b. Pyruvate is transported by the circulatory system. _____
   c. Production of lactate by muscle allows ATP production by fermentation. _____
   d. Glucose-6-phosphatase is localized in the endoplasmic reticulum of muscle. _____
   e. High levels of NADH in the muscle favour reduction of pyruvate. _____

3. Name three important control molecules for glycolysis and gluconeogenesis.

4. What is remarkable about phosphofructokinase-2 and fructose-2,6-bisphosphatase enzymatic activities?

5. There are two enzymes necessary to digest dietary glycogen, α-amylase and debranching enzyme. What are the functions of each?

6. Glycogen phosphorylase cleaves glucose units from tissue glycogen. This enzyme is carefully regulated by allosteric controls and by covalent modification. In the diagram presented below place the following: phosphorylase kinase, AMP, ATP, glucose-6-phosphate, glucose, phosphoprotein phosphatase 1, phosphorylase a, phosphorylase b and the active and inactive states.

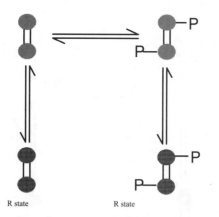

7. Describe the cascade of events from hormone stimulation to inactivation of glycogen synthase and activation of glycogen phosphorylase.

8. In the oxidative steps of the pentose phosphate pathway, glucose is converted to ribulose-5-phosphate and carbon dioxide in five steps. This short metabolic sequence serves two immediate purposes. What are they?

9. In the non-oxidative steps of the pentose phosphate pathway, 5-carbon sugars are metabolized back to glucose. The enzymes involved include an isomerase (I), an epimerase (E), transketolases (TK), and a transaldolase (TA). Which enzyme best fits each of the statements below?
   a. Thiamine pyrophosphate–dependent enzyme. _____
   b. Causes conversion of configuration about asymmetric carbon. _____
   c. Ketose–aldose conversion. _____
   d. Forms Schiff base intermediate. _____
   e. Interconverts ribulose-5-phosphate and ribose-5-phosphate. _____
   f. Forms enediolate intermediate, reduction of which may occur on either side of the carbon. _____
   g. Reduction of adduct by sodium borohydride leads to inactivation. _____
   h. Moves two carbons from a ketose to an aldose. _____

Answers

1. Glucose; liver; kidney; hexokinase (or glucokinase); phosphofructokinase; pyruvate kinase; oxaloacetate; carbon dioxide; biotin; two; fructose-1,6-bisphosphatase; glucose-6-phosphatase; hydrolysis.

2. a. T; b. F; c. T; d. F; e. T.

3. Fructose-2,6-bisphosphate, AMP, ATP, citrate, acetyl-CoA, alanine, and glucose-6-phosphate.

4. Both activities are properties of the same protein molecule, a bifunctional or tandem enzyme.

5. α-amylase is an endoglycosidase that hydrolyzes α-(1→4) linkages to produce monosaccharides, disaccharides, and short oligosaccharides in addition to limit dextrins, highly branched polysaccharides. Debranching enzyme degrades limit dextrins by removing branches.

6.

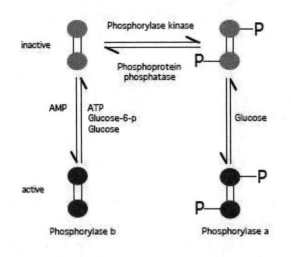

7.   Hormone binding to surface receptors leads to stimulation of adenylyl cyclase, which raises the levels of cellular cAMP. This second messenger binds to and activates protein kinase, which phosphorylates and inactivates glycogen synthase. cAMP-dependent protein kinase also phosphorylates glycogen phosphorylase kinase, leading to activation. Finally, phosphorylation of glycogen phosphorylase by glycogen phosphorylase kinase leads to activation.

8.   The oxidative steps produce 5-carbon sugars and reducing equivalents in the form of NADPH.

9.   a. TK; b. E; c. I; d. TA; e. I; f. E; g. TA; h. TK.

Additional Problems

1.   What are the three potential substrate cycles in glycolysis/gluconeogenesis and how is each regulated?

2.   Pyruvate carboxylase reacts bicarbonate and pyruvate to produce oxaloacetate. It is a vitamin-dependent enzyme. Which vitamin does it use? Describe the reaction the enzyme catalyzes.

3.   Alanine inhibits pyruvate kinase. What relationship does alanine have to this enzyme?

4.   How are glycogen phosphorylase and glycogen synthase reciprocally regulated?

5.   The oxidative phase of the pentose phosphate pathway is the following sequence:

glucose → glucose-6-phosphate → 6-phosphogluconolactone →
6-phosphogluconate → ribulose-5-phosphate

Describe the biochemistry of this sequence.

6.   Can triacylglycerol (a.k.a. fat) be used in gluconeogenesis?

Abbreviated Answers

1.   The conversion of glucose and glucose-6-phosphate catalyzed by glucokinase (in liver) and glucose-6-phosphatase is a substrate cycle confined to cells expressing glucose-6-phosphatase, such as kidney and liver cells. A substrate cycle exists between fructose-6-phosphate and fructose-1,6-bisphosphate catalyzed by phosphofructokinase and fructose-1,6-bisphosphatase. This cycle is regulated by reciprocal control of the two enzymes by fructose-2,6-bisphosphate and AMP. The conversion of PEP to pyruvate in glycolysis

and of pyruvate to oxaloacetate to PEP in gluconeogenesis is the final substrate cycle. Acetyl-CoA levels play a key role in regulating this cycle.

2.   Pyruvate carboxylase is a biotin-dependent reaction. Biotin participates in one-carbon reactions in which the carbon is fully oxidized. The enzyme catalyzes a two-step reaction. In the first step, carboxyphosphate, an activated form of CO_2, is produced by nucleophilic attack on the γ-phosphate of ATP by a bicarbonate oxygen. Carboxyphosphate is used to transfer CO_2 to biotin, which carboxylates the methyl carbon of pyruvate to produce oxaloacetate.

3.   Deamination of alanine produces pyruvate, a product of pyruvate kinase. The presence of alanine is a signal that an alternative carbon source for the production of pyruvate is present. In general, proteins are not stored to the extent that carbohydrates are, and they are therefore broken down into amino acids, which are subsequently metabolized.

4.   Glycogen phosphorylase is allosterically activated by AMP and inhibited by glucose-6-phosphate, whereas glycogen synthase is stimulated by glucose-6-phosphate. Both enzymes are also regulated by covalent modification. There are two forms of glycogen phosphorylase. The active form, phosphorylase a, differs from the less active form, phosphorylase b, by a phosphate group on Ser^{14}. Ser^{14} is phosphorylated by glycogen phosphorylase kinase, a kinase that also exists in an active, phosphorylated form and an inactive form. Phosphorylation of glycogen phosphorylase kinase is a result of cAMP-dependent protein kinase. Glycogen synthase also has two forms: an active, glucose-6-phosphate–independent form (glycogen synthase I) and a less active, glucose-6-phosphate–dependent form (glycogen synthase D). Glycogen synthase I is converted to glycogen synthase D by phosphorylation at a number of sites catalyzed by several kinases.

5.   The first step is a phosphorylation catalyzed by hexokinase. The next step is an oxidation of glucose-6-phosphate by NADP-dependent glucose-6-phosphate dehydrogenase. 6-Phosphogluconolactone is converted to phosphogluconate by hydrolysis catalyzed by gluconolactonase. Phosphogluconate is oxidatively decarboxylated to ribulose-5-phosphate and CO_2 by NADP-dependent 6-phosphogluconate dehydrogenase. So, the steps are phosphorylation, oxidation, hydrolysis, and oxidative decarboxylation.

6.   A majority of the carbons in triacylglycerol is unavailable for incorporation into glucose because they are converted into acetyl-CoA units. However, the glycerol backbone can be used as a carbon source for gluconeogenesis. (For triacylglycerols with fatty acids with an odd number of carbons, a three-carbon unit is metabolized into succinate, a citric acid cycle intermediate and therefore a substrate for gluconeogenesis.

Summary

In order to maintain normal levels of metabolic activity, cells must sustain an appropriate level of sugars, especially glucose. Glucose is synthesized from non-carbohydrate precursors by a process known as gluconeogenesis, and it can also be supplied via breakdown of glycogen (in animals) or starch (in plants or in the diet of animals). The pentose phosphate pathway is the primary source of NADPH, the reduced coenzyme essential to most reductive biosynthetic processes, including fatty acid and amino acid biosynthesis. The pentose phosphate pathway also produces ribose-5-P, an important component of ATP, $NAD(P)^+$, FAD, coenzyme A, DNA, and RNA.

Substrates for gluconeogenesis include pyruvate, lactate, most of the amino acids (except leucine and lysine), glycerol, and all the TCA cycle intermediates. Fatty acids are not substrates for gluconeogenesis, since animals cannot carry out net synthesis of sugars from acetyl-CoA. Major sites of gluconeogenesis include the liver (90%) and kidneys (10%). Glucose produced by these organs is utilized in brain, heart, muscle, and red blood cells to meet their metabolic needs. Gluconeogenesis is not merely the reverse of glycolysis. In order that the net pathway may be exergonic and that the pathway may be suitably regulated, three key enzymatic reactions replace hexokinase (glucokinase), phosphofructokinase, and pyruvate kinase from glycolysis. These reactions are catalyzed by glucose-6-phosphatase, fructose-1,6-bisphosphatase, and the pair of pyruvate carboxylase/PEP carboxykinase. The overall conversion of pyruvate to glucose is made exergonic by these substitutions, with a $\Delta G^{\circ\prime}$ of -30.5 kJ/mol.

The pyruvate carboxylase reaction, which occurs in the mitochondrial matrix, is biotin-dependent and utilizes ATP and bicarbonate as substrates. Pyruvate carboxylase is allosterically activated by acyl coenzyme A. When ATP and acetyl-CoA are high, gluconeogenesis is favoured, but when ATP and acetyl-CoA are low, acetyl-CoA is consumed by the TCA cycle for the net production of energy and ATP. Whereas pyruvate carboxylase consumes an ATP to drive a carboxylation, the PEP carboxykinase uses decarboxylation to facilitate formation of PEP. AMP inhibits fructose-1,6-bisphosphatase, and the inhibition by AMP is enhanced by fructose-2,6-bisphosphate. Glucose-6-phosphatase, the final step in gluconeogenesis, is located in the membrane of the endoplasmic reticulum. Glucose formed in liver ER by this reaction is transported to the plasma membrane and secreted directly into the bloodstream for distribution to other organs and cells.

The gluconeogenic pathway is driven by hydrolysis of ATP and GTP—the net free energy change for the pathway from pyruvate to glucose is -37.7 kJ/mol. The pathway is controlled by substrate cycles involving pairs of reactions such as phosphofructokinase (glycolysis) and fructose-1,6-bisphosphatase (gluconeogenesis). Moreover, reciprocal regulatory control ensures that glycolysis is active when gluconeogenesis is inactive and vice versa. Acetyl-CoA is a potent allosteric effector of these two pathways, inhibiting pyruvate kinase (glycolysis) and activating pyruvate carboxylase. Hydrolysis of fructose-1,6-bisphosphate by fructose-1,6-bisphosphatase is allosterically inhibited by fructose-2,6-bisphosphate, which also activates phosphofructokinase in another example of reciprocal control. Cellular levels of fructose-2,6-bisphosphate are controlled by phosphofructokinase-2 and fructose-2,6-bisphosphatase, two activities of a bifunctional enzyme, which are regulated by phosphorylation, and dephosphorylation of a single Ser residue of the 49 000 Dalton subunit.

Adult human beings typically metabolize about 160 g of carbohydrates daily, either from digestion of dietary carbohydrates or from breakdown of tissue glycogen. Dietary carbohydrates are degraded by α-amylase to produce limit dextrins, which can be further degraded by a debranching enzyme. Digestion is a highly efficient (and unregulated) process in which 100% of ingested food is absorbed and metabolized. By contrast, tissue glycogen is metabolized in a highly regulated process. Glycogen breakdown is stimulated by glucagon and epinephrine, whereas glycogen synthesis is activated by insulin. In addition to stimulating glycogen synthesis in liver and muscle, insulin also stimulates transport of glucose across cell membranes and activates several key glycolytic enzymes. Binding of glucagon to liver cell membranes activates intracellular adenylyl cyclase, producing cyclic AMP, a second messenger, which activates a protein kinase. This kinase in turn phosphorylates and activates phosphorylase kinase, which phosphorylates phosphorylase, the enzyme that catalyzes the first step in glycogen breakdown. Such kinase cascades facilitate the amplification of hormonal signals.

Glycogen synthesis involves the transfer of activated glucose units (in the form of sugar nucleotides) to a growing chain in the glycogen synthase reaction. The glycogen chain is initiated on a protein core, glycogenin, with the first glucose residue linked covalently to a Tyr–OH. Glycogen synthase catalyzes the transfer of glucosyl units from UDP–glucose to the C-4 hydroxyl groups of non-reducing ends of glycogen strands. Glycogen branching occurs by transfer of 6- or 7-residue segments from the non-reducing end of a linear chain at least 11 residues in length to the C-6 hydroxyl of a glucose residue further up the chain.

The pentose phosphate pathway converts glucose-6-phosphate in two successive oxidations and five non-oxidative reactions to a variety of carbohydrate intermediates, producing NADPH and ribose-5-phosphate as well. Oxidation of glucose-6-phosphate by glucose-6-phosphate dehydrogenase, followed by ring opening and further oxidation by 6-phosphogluconate dehydrogenase yields ribulose-5-phosphate, whereas phosphopentose epimerase produces xylulose-5-phosphate. Further rearrangement to produce other carbohydrate intermediates is carried out by transketolase and transaldolase. Transketolase is a thiamine pyrophosphate–dependent enzyme, and transaldolase functions via formation of an active site Schiff base with a lysine residue on the protein. Utilization of glucose-6-phosphate in glycolysis and the pentose phosphate pathway depends on the cell's needs for ATP, NADPH, and ribose-5-P. Depending on the cell's needs for these metabolites, three different metabolic routes produce needed NADPH or ribose-5-P, either selectively or in relatively balanced amounts. An alternative pathway yields large amounts of NADPH and ATP, with relatively small amounts of ribose-5-P.

Chapter 22

Fatty Acid Catabolism

• •

Chapter Outline

❖ Triacylglycerols: Energy storage molecules
  ⤙ Highly reduced carbon source
  ⤙ Stored without large amounts of water
  ⤙ Stored in specialized cells: Adipocytes (adipose or fat cells)
❖ Hormonal regulation
  ⤙ Adrenaline, glucagon, ACTH mobilize fatty acids from adipocytes
  ⤙ Hormone binding stimulates cAMP-dependent protein kinase
  ⤙ Triacylglycerol lipase (hormone-sensitive lipase) activated by phosphorylation
    • Triacylglycerol lipase produces fatty acid and diacylglycerol
    • Diacylglycerol lipase produces fatty acid and monoacylglycerol
    • Monoacylglycerol lipase produces fatty acid and glycerol
      • Fatty acids metabolized by β-oxidation
      • Glycerol metabolized by glycolysis
❖ Dietary triacylglycerols
  ⤙ Pancreatic lipases secreted into duodenum release fatty acids and monoacylglycerol
    • Lipase activity depends on bile salts functioning as detergents
    • Short-chain fatty acids directly absorbed
    • Long-chain fatty acids recondensed onto glycerol in epithelial cells
      • Resynthesized triacylglycerol complexed to proteins
      • Chylomicrons released into blood
❖ β-oxidation
  ⤙ Oxidation of β-carbon, cleavage of C_α–C_β bond
  ⤙ Occurs in mitochondria
  ⤙ Two-carbon acetate units split off as acetyl-CoA
❖ Fatty acid activation and transport into mitochondria
  ⤙ Short-chain fatty acids
    • Diffuse into mitochondria
    • Acyl-CoA synthetase (Acyl-CoA ligase or fatty acid thiokinase) produces acyl-CoA derivatives
    • ATP to AMP + PP_i ($PP_i \rightarrow 2P_i$) drives synthesis
  ⤙ Long-chain fatty acids: Activated in cytosol
    • Acyl-CoA synthetase produces acyl-CoA derivatives
    • Carnitine acyltransferase I produces acylcarnitine
      • Outside surface of inner mitochondrial membrane
    • Carnitine acyltransferase II reforms acyl-CoA
      • Matrix surface of inner mitochondrial membrane
❖ Enzymology of β-oxidation: Four steps
  ⤙ Acyl-CoA dehydrogenase
    • Produces C–C double bond
    • Non-covalent (but tightly bound) FAD reduced
    • $FADH_2$ passes electrons through electron transfer protein to coenzyme Q
    • Three enzymes: Chain-length specific
    • Site of inhibition of hypoglycin

- ⅄ Enoyl-CoA hydrase (crotonase)
  - • Adds water across double bond
  - • Three kinds of enzymes
    - • *Trans* double bond hydrated to L-*β*-hydroxyacyl-CoA
    - • *Cis* double bond hydrated to D-*β*-hydroxyacyl-CoA
    - • *Trans* double bond hydrated to D-*β*-hydroxyacyl-CoA
- ⅄ L-hydroxyacyl-CoA dehydrogenase
  - • Oxidizes OH
  - • NAD^+ reduced
- ⅄ Thiolase (*β*-ketothiolase)
  - • Cleaves off acetyl-CoA unit
  - • Acyl-CoA two carbons shorter
  - • Last cleavage releases
    - • Two acetyl-CoA for even carbon numbered chains
    - • One propionyl-CoA and one acetyl-CoA for odd carbon numbered chains
- ❖ Odd-chain fatty acids: In plant and marine organism triacylglycerols
  - ⅄ Propionyl-CoA converted to succinyl-CoA
    - • Propionyl-CoA also from Met, Val, Ile degradation
    - • Succinyl-CoA TCA cycle intermediate: To metabolize completely
      - • Succinyl-CoA to malate
      - • Malate to cytosol
      - • Cytosolic malate to pyruvate via malic enzyme
    - • Propionyl-CoA to succinyl-CoA: Three steps
      - • Propionyl-CoA carboxylase produces D-methylmalonyl-CoA
        - ○ Biotin-dependent reaction
        - ○ ATP hydrolysis drives reaction
      - • Methylmalonyl-CoA epimerase
        - ○ D-methylmalonyl CoA to L-methylmalonyl-CoA
        - ○ Epimerization not racemization
    - • Methylmalonyl-CoA mutase
      - • Carbonyl-CoA moiety moved from between carbons
      - • B_{12}-dependent reaction
- ❖ Unsaturated fatty acids: *β*-oxidation and additional reactions
  - ⅄ Monounsaturated fatty acids: Enoyl-CoA isomerase: *cis*-Δ^3 to *trans*-Δ^2 isomerization of double bond
  - ⅄ Polyunsaturated fatty acids: 2,4-dienoyl-CoA reductase
- ❖ Peroxisomal *β*-oxidation: Acyl-CoA oxidase: Oxygen accepts electrons: H_2O_2 produced
- ❖ *α*-oxidation: Branched-chain fatty acids: Phytol: Chlorophyll breakdown product
- ❖ *ω*-oxidation (*ω*, last letter of Greek alphabet)
  - ⅄ Dicarboxylic acid produced
  - ⅄ Cytochrome P450 requires NADPH and oxygen
  - ⅄ *ω*-carbon oxidized to carboxylic acid
- ❖ Ketone bodies: Acetoacetate, hydroxybutyrate, acetone
  - ⅄ Synthesis occurs in liver
  - ⅄ Converts acetyl units into ketone bodies
  - ⅄ Ketone bodies serve as fuel for brain, heart, muscle
- ❖ Ketogenesis: Four reactions
  - ⅄ Thiolase
    - • Reversal of last step in *β*-oxidation
    - • Acetoacetyl-CoA produced from 2 acetyl-CoA
  - ⅄ HMG-CoA synthase: *β*-hydroxy-*β*-methylglutaryl-CoA
    - • This and thiolase reaction in mitochondria lead to ketone body formation
    - • In cytosol, HMG-CoA production fuels cholesterol synthesis
  - ⅄ HMG-CoA lyase: Produces acetoacetate
  - ⅄ *β*-hydroxybutyrate dehydrogenase
    - • NADH-dependent reduction

- Acetoacetate will spontaneous decarboxylate to produce acetone
❖ Diabetes Mellitus
  ⟍ Type I: Insulin secretion deficient
  ⟍ Type II: Shortage of insulin receptors

Chapter Objectives

β-oxidation

β-oxidation is a simple series of four steps leading to degradation of fatty acyl-coenzyme A derivatives. You should know how fatty acids are supplied to β-oxidation. Lipases hydrolyze triacylglycerols. The fatty acids released are converted to acyl-CoA derivatives by synthetases that use two high-energy phosphoanhydride bonds to drive synthesis. β-oxidation is reminiscent of the steps in the citric acid cycle leading from succinate to oxaloacetate. You might recall that they included oxidation by an FAD-dependent enzyme to produce a double bond, hydration of the double bond, and reduction of the alcoholic carbon to a ketone by an NAD+-dependent enzyme. In β-oxidation (Figure 22.9), a similar series operates, but with an acyl-CoA as substrate and thiolysis of the product to release acetyl-CoA and a fatty acyl-CoA, two carbons shorter. The FAD-dependent enzyme, acyl-CoA dehydrogenase, will move electrons into the electron-transport chain at the level of coenzyme Q, and each electron pair will support production of 1.5 ATP. Odd-carbon fatty acids are metabolized by β-oxidation to yield several acetyl-CoAs and one propionyl-CoA, a three-carbon acyl-CoA. Propionyl-CoA is metabolized by a vitamin B12-dependent pathway to succinyl-CoA, a citric acid cycle intermediate.

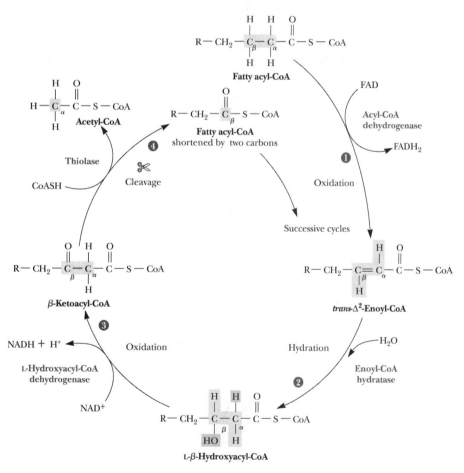

Figure 22.9 The β-oxidation of saturated fatty acids involves a cycle of four enzyme-catalyzed reactions. Each cycle produces single molecules of FADH2, NADH, and acetyl-CoA and yields a fatty acid shortened by two carbons. (The delta [Δ] symbol connotes a double bond, and its superscript indicates the lowest-numbered carbon involved.)

Oxidation of unsaturated fatty acids (Figure 22.22) requires additional enzymes. Keep this in mind by remembering that typical double bonds in fatty acids are in *cis* configuration, whereas the double bond formed during β-oxidation is *trans*. Double bonds starting at an odd-numbered carbon are simply isomerized to the *trans* configuration and moved, by one carbon, closer to the carboxyl end. Double bonds at even-numbered carbons are ultimately reduced.

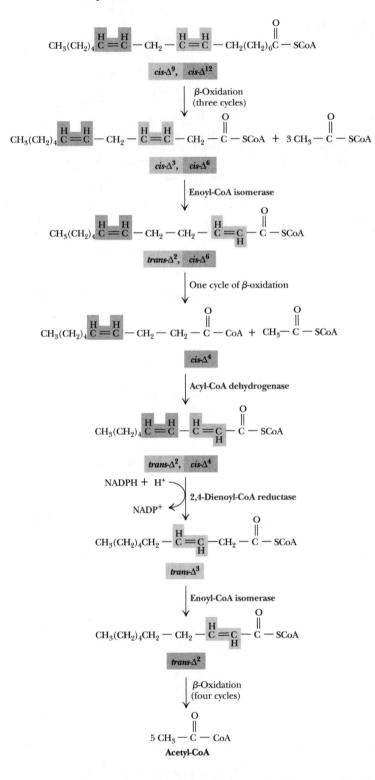

Figure 22.22 The oxidation pathway for polyunsaturated fatty acids, illustrated for linoleic acid.

Ketone Bodies

Acetyl units can be joined to form the four-carbon compound acetoacetate, which together with β-hydroxybutyrate, a reduced form of acetoacetate, are used as a source of fuel for certain organs of the body and in times of glucose shortage. You should know the metabolic sequence leading to acetoacetate production. An intermediate in the pathway, β-hydroxy-β-methylglutaryl-CoA (HMG-CoA) is an important intermediate in cholesterol synthesis.

Problems and Solutions

1. Calculate the volume of metabolic water available to a camel through fatty acid oxidation if it carries 30 lb of triacylglycerol in its hump.

Answer: If we assume that the fatty acid chains in the triacylglycerol are all palmitic acid, the fatty acid content of a triacylglycerol as a percent of the total molecular weight is calculated as follows:

$$\% \text{ Palmitic acid} = \frac{3 \times M_{r,\text{palmitic acid}}}{3 \times M_{r,\text{palmitic acid}} + M_{r,\text{glycerol}} - 3 \times M_{r,\text{water}}} \times 100\%$$

$M_{r,\text{palmitic acid}} = 256.4 \ (C_{16}H_{32}O_2)$, $M_{r,\text{glycerol}} = 92.09 \ (C_3H_8O_3)$, $M_{r,\text{water}} = 18$

$$\% \text{ Palmitic acid} = \frac{3 \times 256.4}{3 \times 256.4 + 92.09 - 3 \times 18} \times 100\% = 95\%$$

Thirty pounds of triacylglycerol corresponds to:

$$30 \text{ lb} \times \frac{453.6 \text{ g}}{\text{lb}} = 13\,608 \text{ g of triacylglycerol}$$

If 95% of this is composed of palmitic acid, we have:

$0.95 \times 13\,608 \text{ g} = 12\,928 \text{ g}$ of palmitic acid which corresponds to:

$$\frac{12\,928 \text{ g}}{256.4 \dfrac{\text{g}}{\text{mol}}} = 50.4 \text{ mol of palmitic acid}$$

β-oxidation of palmitate produces 130 moles of H_2O per mole of palmitate. Therefore, 41.2 moles of palmitate metabolized gives:

$$50.4 \text{ mol} \times 130 \frac{\text{mol water}}{\text{mol}} = 6554 \text{ mol water}$$

$$\text{At } 18 \frac{\text{g}}{\text{mol}}, \text{ this represents } 6554 \text{ mol} \times 18 \frac{\text{g}}{\text{mol}} = 117\,972 \text{ g water or } 118 \text{ litres}$$

3. Phytanic acid, the product of chlorophyll that causes problems for individuals with Refsum's disease, is 3,7,11,15-tetramethylhexadecanoic acid. Suggest a route for its oxidation that is consistent with what you have learned in this chapter. (Hint: The methyl group at C-3 effectively blocks hydroxylation and normal β-oxidation. You may wish to initiate breakdown in some other way.)

Answer: The structure of phytanic acid is:

Normally it is metabolized by α-oxidation. The enzyme phytanic acid α-oxidase hydroxylates the α-carbon to produce phytanic acid, which is decarboxylated by phytanate α-oxidase to produce pristanic acid. Pristanic acid can form a coenzyme A ester, which is metabolized by β-oxidation to yield 3 propionyl-CoA, 3 acetyl-CoA, and 2-methyl-propionyl-CoA. The reaction sequence is shown below.

5. *Human serum albumin (66.4 kD) is a soluble protein present in blood at 0.75 mM or so. Among other functions, albumin acts as the major transport vehicle for fatty acids in the circulation, carrying fatty acids from storage sites in adipose tissue to their sites of oxidation in liver and muscle. The albumin molecule has up to 11 distinct binding sites. Consult the biochemical literature to learn about the fatty acid–binding sites of albumin. Where are they located on the protein? What are their relative affinities? (Two suitable references with which to begin your study are Bhattacharya, A.A., Grüne, T., and Curry, S., 2000. Crystallographic analysis reveals common modes of binding of medium- and long-chain fatty acids in human serum albumin. Journal of Molecular Biology 303:721–732; and Simard, J.R., Zunszain, P. ., Ha, C-E., et al., 2005. Locating high-affinity fatty acid-binding sites on albumin by X-ray crystallography and NMR spectroscopy. Proceedings of the National Academy of Sciences U.S.A. 102:17958–17963.)*

Answer: In addition to the references provided, another good source of information is the following review: Hamilton, J.A., (2004) Fatty acid interactions with proteins: what X-ray crystal and NMR solution structures tell us. *Progress in Lipid Research* 43:177–199. To make sense out of any of this information, it helps to view the structure of serum albumin with fatty acids bound to it. To do this, visit the RSCB Protein Data Bank at http://www.pdb.org/pdb/home/home.do and do a search for human serum albumin. Nearly 90 hits are returned; the problem is now to decide which to focus on. This task is made easier by adding "fatty acid" to the search. The combined search returned 22 hits. The record 1e7h seemed particularly interesting because the protein structure includes 7 palmitic acids (C-16). There are structures with longer and shorter fatty acids, but palmitic acid is a very abundant fatty acid.

Serum albumin is a heart-shaped molecule. The Hamilton review indicates that it is a three-domain protein with each domain composed of two subdomains. The protein's structure is dominated by alpha helices and each domain is composed of 10 helices that divide into subdomains containing either 4 or 6 helices. There are a number of fatty acid–binding sites, and 1e7h shows seven of them that accommodate long chain fatty acids ranging from C-16 to C-18. The protein can bind a larger number of shorter fatty acids C-10 to C-14 (the 7 already mentioned plus 4 more for a total of 11).

The seven fatty acid binding sites shown in 1e7h have several common features. The carboxyl-end of the fatty acid in each case is located on the surface exposed to solvent (aqueous). The carboxyl group either forms a salt bridge with a basic amino acid or it is hydrogen-bonded to a polar amino acid. The central portion of the fatty acid is threaded though a hydrophobic pocket formed by hydrophobic faces of helices. The fatty acid in some cases lies parallel to a helix, and in others, it is sandwiched between a two-layered structure composed of alpha helices. The methyl-end of the fatty acid is located on the surface of the protein and hence exposed to solvent. The conformations of the fatty acids range from nearly straight to U-shaped.

7. *What would be the consequences of a deficiency of vitamin B₁₂ for fatty acid oxidation? What metabolic intermediates might accumulate?*

Answer: Vitamin B_{12} is a coenzyme prosthetic group for methylmalonyl-CoA mutase. This enzyme is active in metabolism of odd-chain fatty acids. The last round of β-oxidation releases acetyl-CoA and propionyl-CoA from odd-chain fatty acids. Propionyl-CoA is further metabolized by being converted to (S)-methylmalonyl-CoA by propionyl-CoA carboxylase, a biotin-containing enzyme. (S)-Methylmalonyl-CoA racemase then converts (S)-methylmalonyl-CoA to (R)-methylmalonyl-CoA, which is metabolized to succinyl CoA by methylmalonyl-CoA mutase. This enzyme is a vitamin B_{12}–dependent enzyme, and a deficiency in vitamin B_{12} will cause a build-up of (R)-methylmalonyl-CoA. Depending on the amount of odd-chain fatty acids (and propionic acid) in the diet, a deficiency of vitamin B_{12} is expected to act as a coenzyme A trap, slowly accumulating coenzyme A as methylmalonyl-CoA.

9. *How many tritium atoms are incorporated in acetate if a molecule of palmitic acid is oxidized in 100% tritiated water?*

Answer: For palmitic acid to be converted to acetate, it must pass through β-oxidation; each cycle, except the last, will result in incorporation of tritium at the α-carbon, which is destined to become carbon 2 of acetate. You might recall that the four steps of β-oxidation are dehydrogenation (oxidation), hydration, dehydrogenation (oxidation), and thiolysis. During the hydration step, the elements of water are added across a carbon–carbon double bond. In the subsequent dehydrogenation, the hydroxyacyl group, is oxidized to a keto group, with loss of two hydrogens, one of which is derived from water. The other water hydrogen remains on the α-carbon. In the thiolase reaction, a proton is abstracted to form a carbanion that is subsequently reprotonated. The proton is donated by a group on the enzyme, but it is likely to be an exchangeable proton and thus be tritiated. Thus, a C-2 carbon will have two tritium atoms, one from the hydration step and a second from the thiolase reaction.

11. **The ruby-throated hummingbird flies 800 km non-stop across the Gulf of Mexico. The flight takes 10 hours at 80 km/h. The hummingbird weighs about 4 grams at the start of the flight and about 2.7 grams at the end. Assuming that all the lost weight is fat burned for the flight, calculate the total energy required by the hummingbird in this prodigious flight. Does anything about the results of this calculation strike you as unusual?**

Answer: The hummingbird uses 4 – 2.7 = 1.3 grams of fat for the flight across the Gulf of Mexico. If we assume 37 kJ/gram of fat this amounts to

$$1.3 \text{ grams} \times 37 \ \frac{\text{kJ}}{\text{gram}} \ = \ 48.1 \text{ kJ}$$

Per kilometre, this works out to about

$$\frac{48.1 \text{ kJ}}{800 \text{ km}} = 0.06 \text{ kJ per km}$$

Let's see how this might compare against getting energy out of gasoline. That is, what kind of gas mileage might we expect from the hummingbird. Gasoline has about 45 kJ per gram. The density of gasoline is about 0.8 g per mL.

$$0.06 \ \frac{\text{kJ}}{\text{km}} \ \times \ \frac{\text{grams}}{45 \text{ kJ}} \times \frac{\text{mL}}{0.8 \text{ grams}} \times \frac{1 \text{ L}}{1000 \text{ mL}} = 1.67 \ \times \ 10^{-3} \ \frac{\text{L}}{\text{km}}$$

This sure beats the mileage my automobile gets. (The calculation assumes 100% efficiency, which is unrealistic.) Of course, the hummingbird is moving a lot less mass (4 grams) than does my car's engine.

13. **Write a reasonable mechanism for the HMG-CoA synthase reaction shown in Figure 22.26.**

Answer:

15. **Discuss the changes of the oxidation state of cobalt in the course of the methylmalonyl-CoA mutase reaction. Why do they occur as suggested in your answer to Problem 14?**

Answer: The mechanism shown above involves free-radical formation on methylmalonyl-CoA, which results in rearrangement to succinyl CoA. Free-radical formation is initiated by cleavage of the Co–C bond in cobalamin by hemolytic cleavage. Homolytic cleavage is the decomposition of a compound into 2 uncharged atoms or radicals. The electron pair in the Co–C bond is in effect split with one electron going to cobalt and the other to the methylene carbon. Cobalt is thus reduced from Co^{3+} to Co^{2+}. The methylene carbon has an unpaired electron, a free radical, that attacks the methyl carbon of methylmalonyl-CoA, abstracting a hydrogen atom (proton and electron). It thus creates a free radical on methylmalonyl-CoA. Upon rearrangement to a free-radical form of succinate, a hydrogen atom is taken from cobalamin, which allows the Co–C bond to reform. Reformation of this bond is by free-radical attack on Co^{3+}, leading to oxidation.

17. *A popular dish in the Caribbean islands consists of akee and salt fish. Unripened akee fruit (from the akee tree, native to West Africa but brought to the Caribbean by African slaves) is quite poisonous. The unripened fruit contains hypoglycin, a metabolite that serves as a substrate for acyl-CoA dehydrogenase. However, the product of this reaction irreversibly inhibits the acyl-CoA dehydrogenase by reacting covalently with FAD on the enzyme. Consumption of unripened akee fruit can lead to vomiting and, in severe cases, convulsions, coma, and death. Write a reaction scheme to show the product of the acyl-CoA dehydrogenase reaction that reacts with FAD.*

Answer: The unripened fruit of the akee tree contains a rare amino acid, hypoglycin, whose structure is shown below.

This compound is converted into a potent inhibitor of acyl-CoA dehydrogenase. Acyl-CoA dehydrogenase catalyzes the first oxidation step in β-oxidation and inhibition of this enzyme blocks fatty acid catabolism. Victims of hypoglycin poisoning become severely hypoglycemic because β-oxidation is inhibited and glucose catabolism becomes the primary source of metabolic energy.

19. *Study Figure 22.12 and comment on why nature uses FAD/FADH₂ as a cofactor in the acyl-CoA dehydrogenase reaction rather than NAD⁺/NADH.*

Answer: From Figure 22.12, we learn that the acyl-CoA dehydrogenase reaction moves two electrons from fatty acyl CoA to coenzyme Q. The electrons pass from substrate to FAD, which is reduced to $FADH_2$. Electrons are then passed one at a time through an iron–sulfur protein (ETF: UQ oxidoreductase) to coenzyme Q. Electron movement through iron–sulfur centres is a one-electron transfer. FAD and coenzyme Q are both capable of accepting one electron at a time. NAD^+ can participate on two-electron transfers only.

Questions for Self-Study

1. What is the difference between initiation of catabolism of short-chain fatty acids and long-chain fatty acids?

2. During β-oxidation, a double bond is transiently produced in the fatty acid chain. How is this double bond different than double bonds found in mono- and polyunsaturated fatty acids?

3. Fill in the blanks. Odd-carbon fatty acids are metabolized by β-oxidation until the last three carbons are released as _____. This compound is converted to _____, a citric acid cycle intermediate in a series of three steps. In the first step, a carboxyl group is added by propionyl-CoA carboxylase. This enzyme uses the water-soluble vitamin _____ during catalysis. The third reaction is catalyzed by methylmalonyl-CoA mutase, a vitamin _____-dependent enzyme.

4. Acetoacetate is an example of a ketone body. How is acetoacetate produced from acetyl-CoA? How can acetoacetate be converted to two other ketone bodies?

5. Label the compounds in the catabolic series shown below.

Answers

1. Short-chain fatty acids are transported into the mitochondria as free fatty acids where they are converted to acyl-CoA derivatives. Long-chain fatty acids are attached to carnitine and moved across the inner membrane as O-acylcarnitine. They are then transferred to coenzyme A.

2. The double bond transiently produced during fatty acid catabolism is *trans*, whereas double bonds found in naturally occurring fatty acids are usually *cis*. Also, double bonds in naturally occurring fatty acids may start at even-numbered carbons as well as odd-numbered carbons in the fatty acid chain.

3. Propionyl-CoA; succinyl-CoA; biotin; B_{12}.

4. Acetoacetate is produced in a three-step metabolic sequence from acetyl-CoA. Acetoacetyl-CoA is produced in the first step and subsequently converted to β-hydroxy-β-methylglutaryl-CoA (HMG-CoA). HMG-CoA is then metabolized to acetoacetate and acetyl-CoA. Decarboxylation of acetoacetate leads to production of acetone. Reduction of acetoacetate leads to production of β-hydroxybutyrate.

5. β-hydroxybutyrate, acetoacetate, acetoacetyl-CoA, and acetyl-CoA are across the top line. Succinyl-CoA and succinate are shown on the bottom.

Additional Problems

1. It has been suggested that conversion of gasoline-powered automobiles to ethanol will require larger fuel tanks to keep the same effective range. Can you suggest a simple reason why this is the case?

2. Production of free fatty acids from fat deposits involves three separate lipases, triacylglycerol lipase, diacylglycerol lipase, and monoacylglycerol lipase. Fatty acid production is also under hormonal regulation, but only one of the lipases is sensitive. Which lipase is hormonally controlled, how is regulation achieved, and why does it make good metabolic sense to regulate this particular lipase?

3. β-oxidation begins with conversion of a free fatty acid to an acyl-coenzyme A derivative, a reaction catalyzed by acyl-CoA synthetase. Explain why this enzyme is named synthetase.

4. Describe the chemistry involved in the four steps of β-oxidation.

5. Metabolism of fatty acids with *cis* double bonds requires one or two additional enzymes. Explain.

6. In insulin-dependent diabetes mellitus, insulin deficiency can lead to shock as a result of metabolic acidosis. A person in shock may have a detectable odour of acetone on their breath. Explain the source of acetone and the cause of acidosis.

Abbreviated Answers

1. We are informed in Table 22.1 that fat has over twice the energy content of glycogen on a per gram basis. The reason is that the average carbon in fat is less oxidized than the average carbon in glycogen, and so the amount of energy released in oxidation of carbon to CO_2 is greater. The same is true in

comparing gasoline and ethanol. Gasoline is composed primarily of hydrocarbons, whereas the average carbon in ethanol, C_2H_6O, is slightly more oxidized.

2.   Adrenaline, glucagon, and adrenocorticotropic hormone mobilize fatty acids from adipocytes by stimulation of triacylglycerol lipase or hormone-sensitive lipase. The hormones bind to surface receptors, which results in the stimulation of adenylyl cyclase and an increase in intracellular cyclic AMP levels. cAMP activates protein kinase, which in turn phosphorylates triacylglycerol lipase, leading to activation of this enzyme. Diacylglycerol lipase is active against the product of triacylglycerol lipase activity and monoacylglycerol lipase requires the product of diacylglycerol lipase activity. Thus, only the first enzyme in this series of enzymes needs to be regulated.

3.   Synthetases use cleavage of high-energy phosphoanhydride bonds to drive product formation. Acyl-CoA synthetase uses ATP to AMP + PPi conversion to produce acyl-CoA.

4.   Starting from acyl-CoA, the α- and β-carbons are reduced to form *trans*-Δ^2-enoyl-CoA and hydrated to L-β-hydroxyacyl-CoA. The β-carbon is oxidized to β-ketoacyl-CoA and cleaved to produce acetyl-CoA and an acyl-CoA two carbons shorter.

5.   For *cis* double bonds starting at an odd carbon, β-oxidation proceeds normally until the double bond is between the β and γ carbons. An enoyl-CoA isomerase is used to rearrange the *cis*-Δ^3 bond to a *trans*-Δ^2 bond, which is hydrated, oxidized, and cleaved normally. For *cis* double bonds starting at an even carbon, β-oxidation cycles eventually produce a *cis*-Δ^4 intermediate, which is converted to a *trans*-Δ^2,*cis*-Δ^4 intermediate by acyl-CoA dehydrogenase. Next, a 2,4-dienoyl-CoA reductase, in mammals, produces a *trans*-Δ^3 enoyl-CoA, which is converted to a *trans*-Δ^2 enoyl-CoA isomer by enoyl-CoA isomerase, a normal β-oxidation cycle intermediate. In *E. coli*, the double bond between carbons 4 and 5 is simply reduced by a 2,4-enoyl-CoA reductase to give *trans*-Δ^2 enoyl-CoA.

6.   Acidosis and acetone are a consequence of ketone body formation. In liver mitochondria, acetoacetate and β-hydroxybutyrate are produced and excreted into the blood to be transported to other tissues to be used as fuels. These compounds are acidic with pK_a = 3.5 and in high concentrations causes a drop in blood pH. Acetoacetate, an unstable compound, will non-enzymatically break down into acetone and CO_2.

Summary

Fatty acids represent the principal form of energy storage for many organisms. Fatty acids are advantageous forms of stored energy, since 1) the carbon in fatty acids is highly reduced (thus yielding more energy in oxidation than other forms of carbon), and 2) fatty acids are not hydrated and can pack densely in storage tissues. Fatty acids are acquired readily in the diet and can also be synthesized from carbohydrates and amino acids. Whether dietary or synthesized, triacylglycerols are a major source of fatty acids. Release of fatty acids from triacylglycerols is triggered by hormones such as adrenaline and glucagon, which bind to plasma membrane receptors and activate (via cyclic AMP) the lipases, which hydrolyze triacylglycerols to fatty acids and glycerol. A large fraction of dietary triacylglycerols is absorbed in the intestines and passes into the circulatory system as chylomicrons.

Following Knoop's discovery that fatty acids were degraded to two-carbon units, Lynen and Reichart showed that these two-carbon units were acetyl-CoA. The process of β-oxidation of fatty acids begins with the formation of an acyl-CoA derivative by acyl-CoA synthetase, but transport of the acyl chain into the mitochondrial matrix occurs via acyl-carnitine derivatives, which are converted back to acyl-CoA derivatives in the matrix. β-oxidation involves 1) formation of a C_α–C_β double bond, 2) hydration across the double bond and 3) oxidation of the β-carbon, followed by 4) a thiolase cleavage, leaving acetyl-CoA and the CoA ester of the fatty acid chain shorter by two carbons. (A metabolite of hypoglycin, found in unripened akee fruit, inhibits the first of these reactions, resulting in vomiting, convulsions, and death.) Repetition of this cycle of reactions degrades fatty acids with even numbers of carbons completely to acetyl-CoA. β-oxidation of fatty acids with odd numbers of carbon atoms yields acetyl-CoA plus a single molecule of propionyl-CoA, which is subsequently converted to succinyl-CoA in a sequence of three reactions. Complete β-oxidation of a molecule of palmitic acid generates 106 high-energy phosphate bonds, i.e., formation of 106 ATP from ADP and Pi. This massive output of energy from β-oxidation permits migratory birds to travel long distances without stopping to eat. The large amounts of water formed in β-oxidation allow certain desert and marine organisms to thrive without frequent ingestion of water.

Unsaturated fatty acids are also catabolized by β-oxidation, but two additional mitochondrial enzymes—an isomerase and a novel reductase—are required to handle the *cis*-double bonds of naturally occurring fatty acids. Degradation of polyunsaturated fatty acids also requires the activity of 2,4-dienoyl-CoA reductase. Although β-oxidation in mitochondria is the principal pathway of fatty acid catabolism, a similar pathway also exists in peroxisomes and glyoxysomes. Fatty acids with branches at odd carbons in the chain are degraded by α-oxidation. Phytol, an isoprene breakdown product of chlorophyll, is degraded via α-oxidation. Defects in this pathway lead to Refsum's disease, which is characterized by poor night vision, tremors, and neurologic disorders; it is caused by accumulation in the body of phytanic acid. ω-oxidation in the ER of eukaryotic cells leads to the synthesis of small amounts of dicarboxylic acids. This is accomplished in part by cytochrome P-450, which hydroxylates the terminal carbon atom of the fatty acid chain. Ketone bodies are a significant source of fuel and energy for certain tissues. Acetoacetate and 3-hydroxybutyrate are the preferred substrates for kidney cortex and heart muscle, and ketone bodies are a major energy source for the brain during periods of starvation. Ketone bodies represent easily transportable forms of fatty acids and move through the circulatory system without the need for complexation with serum albumin and other fatty acid binding proteins.

Chapter 23

Nitrogen Acquisition and Amino Acid Metabolism

• •

Chapter Outline

- ❖ Nitrogen cycle
  - ⅄ Nitrogen movement in the biosphere
    - N_2 in atmosphere changed to ammonium
      - Nitrogen fixation: Bacteria
    - NO_3^- (nitrate) in soil and oceans changed to ammonium
      - Nitrate assimilation: Plants, fungi, bacteria
  - ⅄ Animals need reduced dietary N and excrete N as ammonium or organic nitrogen
    - Ammonium to NO_3^- (nitrate): Nitrifying bacteria
    - NO_3^- (nitrate) to N_2: Denitrifying bacteria
- ❖ Nitrate assimilation: Two steps
  - ⅄ Nitrate reductase: $NO_3^- + 2H^+ + 2e^- \rightarrow NO_2^- + H_2O$
    - NADH source of electrons
    - SH to FAD to cyto b_{557} to MoCo
  - ⅄ Nitrite reductase: $NO_2^- + 8H^+ + 6e^- \rightarrow NH_4^+ + 2H_2O$
    - Plants
      - Light-generated reduced ferredoxin source of electrons
      - 4Fe-4S to siroheme
    - Microorganisms
      - NADPH source of electrons
      - Similar to nitrate reductase
- ❖ Nitrogen fixation: $N_2 + 10H^+ + 8e^- \rightarrow 2NH_4^+ + H_2$: Four requirements
  - ⅄ Strong reductant: Reduced ferredoxin
  - ⅄ ATP
  - ⅄ Oxygen-free environment
  - ⅄ Nitrogenase (complex)
    - Nitrogen reductase (Fe-protein)
      - 4Fe-4S cluster
      - 2ATP hydrolyzed per electron
    - Nitrogenase (MoFe protein)
      - P-cluster (8Fe-7S)
      - FeMo-cofactor (7Fe-1Mo-9S): Femoco
  - ⅄ Regulation
    - ADP inhibits
    - Ammonium represses expression of *nif* genes
    - ADP–ribosylation in some systems inactivates
- ❖ Ammonium entry into organic linkage
  - ⅄ Carbamoyl-phosphate synthetase I
    - Urea cycle
    - $NH_4^+ + HCO_3^- + 2ATP \rightarrow$ carbamoyl-phosphate $+ 2ADP + P_i$
    - N-Acetylglutamate activator

- ⅄ Glutamate dehydrogenase (GDH)
  - $NH_4^+ + \alpha\text{-ketoglutarate} + NADPH + H^+ \rightarrow \text{glutamate} + NADP^+ + 2H_2O$
    - Produces glutamate using NADPH
    - Degrades glutamate using NAD^+
  - Catabolic activity
    - ADP allosteric activator
    - GTP allosteric inhibitor
- ⅄ Glutamine synthetase (GS)
  - $Glu + NH_4^+ \rightarrow Gln$: ATP driven
- ❖ Ammonium assimilation pathways
  - ⅄ GDH and GS when ammonium high
  - ⅄ GS and GOGAT when ammonium low
    - GOGAT: Glutamate:oxo-glutarate amino transferase
      - Reductant + α-ketoglutarate + Gln → 2 Glu + oxidized reductant
      - Reductant: NADH, NADPH, reduced ferredoxin
- ❖ Glutamine synthetase regulation: Dodecameric complex
  - ⅄ Feedback inhibition
    - Gly, Ala, Ser inhibit by competing with Glu
    - AMP competes with ATP
    - His, Trp, CTP, carbamoyl-P, glucosamine-6-P inhibit
  - ⅄ Covalent modification
    - Adenylylation of Tyr inactivates
    - Degree of inactivation proportional to number of subunits adenylylated
    - Adenylyl transferase (AT): Adenylylates and deadenylylates
      - $AT \cdot P_{IIA}$ adenylylates
      - $AT \cdot P_{IID}$ deadenylylates
        - ○ Gln activates P_{IIA} inhibits P_{IID}
        - ○ α-ketoglutarate inhibits P_{IIA} activates P_{IID}
  - ⅄ Gene expression: GS subunit encoded by Gln A
    - Transcriptional enhancer: NR_I: Must be phosphorylated
    - NR_{II}: NR_I kinase
    - NR_{II}/P_{IID}-complex: NR_I-phosphatase
- ❖ Amino acid biosynthesis: Transamination of appropriate α-keto acid
  - ⅄ Essential amino acids: Required in diet
  - ⅄ Non-essential amino acids: Synthesized by organism
  - ⅄ Transamination by aminotransferases
    - Glutamate aminotransferase most common
- ❖ Carbon skeletons
  - ⅄ α-ketoglutarate family
    - Glu, Gln
    - Pro from Glu
    - Arg from Glu via ornithine
      - Ornithine's metabolic fates
        - ○ Arg precursor
        - ○ Urea cycle intermediate
        - ○ Arg breakdown product
    - Lys
  - ⅄ Aspartate family
    - Asp, Asn
    - Thr, Met, Lys
    - Ile
  - ⅄ Pyruvate family
    - Ala, Val, Leu
  - ⅄ 3-phosphoglycerate family
    - Ser, Gly, Cys

⅄ Aromatic amino acids
- Shikimate path produces chorismate
- Chorismate branch point
  - Phe, Tyr
  - Trp
- His

❖ Amino acid degradation: 20 amino acids converted to 7 metabolic intermediates
⅄ Pyruvate
- Ala, Ser, Cys, Gly, Trp (carboxyl-, α-, β-carbons), Thr

⅄ Oxaloacetate
- Asp, Asn

⅄ α-ketoglutarate
- Glu, Gln, Pro, Arg, His

⅄ Succinyl-CoA
- Val, Ile, Met

⅄ Acetoacetate
- Leu (+ acetyl-CoA)
- Lys, Trp ring
- Phe, Tyr (+ fumarate)

⅄ Acetyl-CoA
- Leu (+ fumarate)

⅄ Fumarate
- Phe, Tyr (+ acetoacetate)

Chapter Objectives

Nitrogen Acquisition

All organisms produce important compounds containing reduced nitrogens. However, the principal forms of nitrogen in the environment, N_2 (dinitrogen) and NO_3^- (nitrate), contain nitrogen in an oxidized state. Nitrogen is abstracted from the environment and converted to NH_4^+ (ammonium) by two pathways: nitrogen assimilation and nitrogen fixation. Know the basic chemistry involved and the important enzymes in these two processes.

Nitrate Assimilation

Nitrate assimilation converts nitrate to ammonium in a two-step process:

$$NO_3^- + 2\ H^+ + 2\ e^- \rightarrow NO_2^-\ (\text{nitrite}) + H_2O$$
$$NO_2^- + 8\ H^+ + 6\ e^- \rightarrow NH_4^+ + 2\ H_2O$$

The first reaction is catalyzed by nitrate reductase, a NAD(P)H-dependent enzyme that moves electrons through a protein-SH, protein-bound FAD, cytochrome b_{557}, and a molybdenum cofactor (MoCo) to reduce nitrate to nitrite. The second reaction is catalyzed by nitrite reductase. Plants utilize reduced ferredoxin, a product of photosynthesis, as a source of electrons for this reaction and direct them through a 4Fe-4S cluster to a siroheme to nitrite. Fungi and bacteria use NADPH as an electron source.

Nitrogen Fixation

Only certain prokaryotes are capable of nitrogen fixation:

$$N_2 + 8\ H^+ + 8\ e^- \rightarrow 2\ NH_3 + H_2$$

Nitrogen fixation is catalyzed by nitrogenase using reduced ferredoxin or flavodoxin as a source of electrons and ATP hydrolysis to drive the reaction. Nitrogenase is a complex of nitrogenase reductase, an O_2-sensitive enzyme that binds ATP and contains one [4F2-4S] cluster, and nitrogenase proper, an O_2-sensitive, $\alpha_2\beta_2$ heterodimer containing an iron-molybdenum cofactor (FeMoCo). Electron-pair movement through nitrogenase is driven by hydrolysis of 4 ATP, so the complete reaction consumes 16 ATP.

Ammonium Utilization

Ammonium is incorporated into organic compounds in the following ways:

1. $NH_4^+ + HCO_3^- + 2\ ATP \longrightarrow H_2N{-}\overset{\overset{\displaystyle O}{\|}}{C}{-}O{-}PO_3^{2-} + 2\ ADP + P_i + H^+$

   catalyzed by carbamoyl-phosphate synthetase I, a urea cycle enzyme.

2. $NH_4^+ + \alpha\text{-ketoglutarate} + NADPH \rightarrow \text{glutamate} + NADP^+ + H_2O$

   catalyzed by glutamate dehydrogenase.

3. $NH_4^+ + \text{glutamate} + ATP \rightarrow \text{glutamine} + ADP + P_i$

   catalyzed by glutamine synthetase.

Glutamate dehydrogenase has a higher K_m for ammonium than does glutamine synthetase and in conditions in which ammonium is not abundant, reaction 3 above predominates and glutamate is consumed. To replenish glutamate, glutamate synthase or GOGAT (glutamate:oxo-glutarate amino-transferase) catalyzes

$$NADPH + \alpha\text{-ketoglutarate} + \text{glutamine} \rightarrow 2\ \text{glutamate} + NADP^+$$

Regulation of *E. coli* Glutamine Synthetase

Regulation of this key enzyme in nitrogen metabolism is achieved by three mechanisms. The enzyme is allosterically regulated by nine inhibitors including Gly, Ala, Ser, His, Trp, CTP, AMP, carbamoyl-phosphate, and glucosamine-6-phosphate. Covalent modification of glutamine synthetase by adenylylation of a tyrosine residue leads to inactivation. Gene expression is regulated to control enzyme levels.

The level of adenylylation of glutamine synthetase is regulated by adenylyl transferase. This enzyme both adds and removes adenylyl groups but activity in general is dependent on a complex between adenylyl transferase and a regulatory protein P_{II}. P_{II} is itself a target for covalent modification by uridylyl transferase. Uridylylated P_{II} complexed with adenylyl transferase results in deadenylylation activity, deadenylylation of glutamine synthetase, and glutamine synthetase activity. Unuridylylated P_{II} complexed to adenylyl transferase stimulates deadenylylation activity leading to inhibition of glutamine synthetase. Uridylyl transferase activity is dependent on glutamine.

Amino Acid Biosynthesis

The key point to remember about amino acid biosynthesis is that an α-keto acid is first produced and then an amino group is introduced by transamination from glutamate, catalyzed by an aminotransferase. Some α-keto acids important in this regard include α-ketoglutarate, oxaloacetate, and pyruvate. α-ketoglutarate, a citric acid cycle intermediate, is used to produce glutamic acid, glutamine, proline, and ornithine, an amino acid intermediate in the urea cycle, which leads to arginine synthesis. Oxaloacetate, another citric acid cycle intermediate, is the precursor of aspartic acid, asparagine, threonine, methionine, and lysine. Four of the carbons of isoleucine derive from oxaloacetate via threonine, with two carbons coming from pyruvate. Pyruvate is used to form alanine, valine, and leucine. The glycolytic intermediate, 3-phosphoglycerate, is used to synthesize serine, glycine, and cysteine. (You might recall a relationship between serine and glycine in photorespiration.) The aromatic amino acids—phenylalanine, tyrosine, and tryptophan—all have chorismate as a common intermediate. Chorismate is produced from erythrose-4-phosphate, a pentose phosphate intermediate, and PEP via shikimate. Finally, histidine biosynthesis shares metabolic intermediates with purine synthesis. ATP and phosphoribosyl pyrophosphate are used for all of the carbons and one of the nitrogens. The remaining two nitrogens come from glutamine and glutamate.

Amino Acid Degradation

The α-amino group is removed from amino acids by transamination and excess nitrogen is excreted in one of three ways depending on the organism. It may be released as free ammonia, as urea (Figure 23.23), or as uric acid. The carbon skeletons are metabolized into seven metabolic intermediates including pyruvate, oxaloacetate, α-ketoglutarate, acetyl-CoA, fumarate, and acetoacetate. Alanine, serine, glycine, cysteine, and parts of threonine and tryptophan are converted to pyruvate. Aspartate and asparagine produce oxaloacetate; and glutamate, glutamine, proline, arginine, and histidine produce α-ketoglutarate. Valine, isoleucine, and methionine are degraded to succinyl-CoA. Leucine is converted to acetyl-CoA and acetoacetate, a ketone body. Lysine is decarboxylated twice to yield acetoacetate. Phenylalanine is converted to tyrosine by hydroxylation and tyrosine is degraded into acetoacetate and fumarate. Amino acids that can support gluconeogenesis are termed glucogenic amino acids, whereas amino acids producing only acetyl-CoA or acetoacetate are ketogenic.

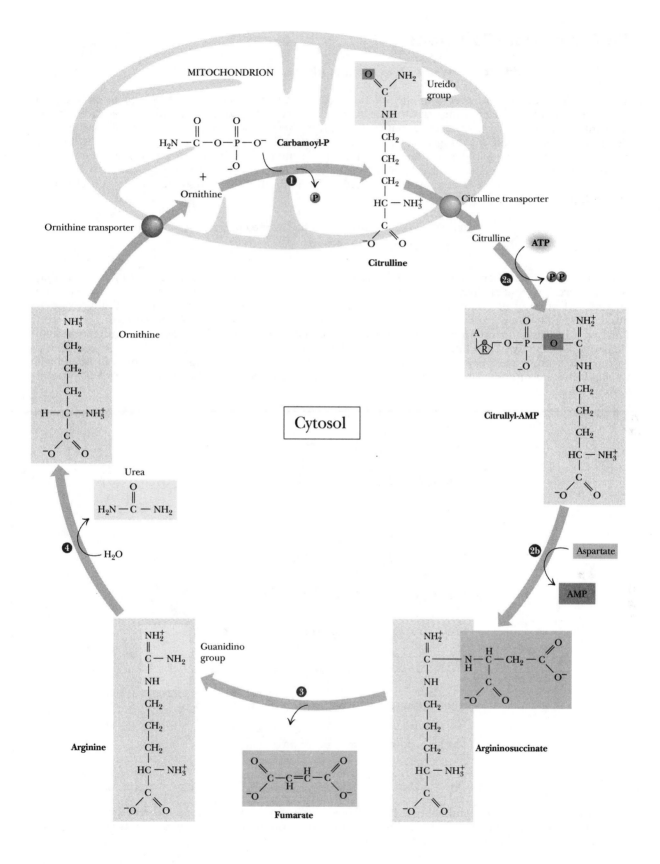

Figure 23.23 The urea cycle.

Problems and Solutions

1. What is the oxidation number of N in nitrate, nitrite, NO, N₂O, and N₂?

Answer: The oxidation number is in effect a measure of the number of electrons being shared unequally in covalent bonds. An easy compound to see this in is water. In water, each hydrogen is involved in a covalent bond with oxygen, an electronegative element. In these bonds, there is an unequal sharing of the electron pair such that the oxygen becomes partially negatively charged, whereas the hydrogens are partially positively charged. The oxidation number of a compound is equal to the formal charge of the compound, and it is the sum of the oxidation numbers of the elements of the compound. In water, for example, the formal charge is zero, which is equal to the sum of the oxidation state of oxygen plus twice the oxidation state of hydrogen.

Let X_Y = the oxidation number X of element Y.

Symbolically, $0 = X_O + 2 \times X_H$

Each hydrogen has a charge of +1, so the oxidation number of hydrogen is +1. Substituting into the above equation, we find that the oxidation number of oxygen as −2. (Oxygen has in effect gained two electrons by unequal sharing of electrons with the two hydrogens.) So, a simple rule in determining oxidation numbers is that the oxidation number of a compound is equal to the formal charge of the compound. Further, the oxidation number of the compound is equal to the sum of the oxidation numbers of the elements. Finally, hydrogen has an oxidation number of +1 because in covalent bonds it will be generous with its electron; oxygen has an oxidation number of −2 by virtue of forming strong covalent bonds with unequal sharing of electrons. With these rules in mind let us determine the oxidation state of N in the various compounds.

For nitrate, NO_3^-, whose charge is − 1, we have:

$-1 = X_N + 3 \times X_O$

Substituting $X_O = -2$, we have:

$-1 = X_N + 3 \times -2$

Solving for X_N, we find:

$X_N = +5$

For nitrite, NO_2^-, whose charge is − 1, we have:

$-1 = X_N + 2 \times X_O$

Substituting $X_O = -2$ and solving for X_N, we find:

$X_N = +3$

For NO, whose charge is 0, we have:

$0 = X_N + X_O$

Substituting $X_O = -2$ and solving for X_N, we find:

$X_N = +2$

For N₂O, whose charge is 0, we have:

$0 = 2 \times X_N + X_O$

Substituting $X_O = -2$ and solving for X_N, we find:

$X_N = +1$

For N₂, whose charge is 0, we have:

$0 = 2 \times X_N$

$X_N = 0$

For N₂, there is not an unequal sharing of electrons in the three covalent bonds formed between the two nitrogens, so the oxidation number = 0. (In calculating the oxidation numbers of elements within a group, a bond to the same element is given an oxidation number of zero.)

3. *Suppose at certain specific metabolite concentrations in vivo the cyclic cascade regulating E. coli glutamine synthetase has reached a dynamic equilibrium where the average state of GS adenylylation is poised at* n = 6. *Predict what change in* n *will occur if:*

   a. *[ATP] increases;*
   b. *P_{IIA}/ P_{IID} increases;*
   c. *[α-KG]/[Gln] increases; and*
   d. *[P_i] decreases.*

Answer: Glutamine synthetase is a key enzyme in nitrogen metabolism. In *E. coli* the enzyme is a 600-kD dodecamer that is sensitive to a number of metabolic regulators. It catalyzes the following reaction:

$$glutamate + ATP + NH_3 \rightarrow glutamine + ADP + P_i$$

The activity of the enzyme is further regulated by covalent modification; specifically the enzyme is inhibited by adenylylation catalyzed by ATP:GS:adenylyl transferase or AT. Thus, the activity of AT determines *n*, the average state of GS adenylylation. AT is itself regulated by interaction with a regulatory protein, P_{II}, which also can exist it two states, P_{IIA} and P_{IID}. Interaction with P_{IIA} results in adenylyl transferase activity, whereas interaction with P_{IID} results in deadenylylation activity. The interconversion of P_{II} between its two states is a result of uridylylation/deuridylylation catalyzed by a converter enzyme, UT. Uridylylated P_{II} is in the P_{IID} state, whereas deuridylylated P_{II} is in the P_{IIA} state. UT catalyzes both uridylylation and deuridylylation, the exact activity dependent on the ratio of [Gln]/[α-ketoglutarate]. Excess glutamine is a signal that additional glutamine is not required. Therefore, GS must be inactivated by adenylylation, a reaction itself dependent on P_{IIA}, which is formed by deuridylylation of P_{II}.

a.   An increase in [ATP] is expected to favour adenylylation of GS, causing *n* to increase, which leads to increased inhibition.

b.   An increase in P_{IIA} levels, leading to deadenylylation, will cause an increase in *n* and increase in inhibition.

c.   An increase in the ratio of [α-KG]/[Gln] is a signal that Gln is needed. Thus, GS activity is increased by deadenylylation and *n* will decrease.

d.   A decrease in [P_i], the substrate of the deadenylylation reaction, will lead to a decrease in deadenylylation, and an increase in *n*.

5.   *Why are persons on a high-protein diet (such as the Atkins diet) advised to drink lots of water?*

Answer: Humans do not store excess proteins or amino acids, and a dietary excess of either will result in degradation of amino acids and production of urea by the urea cycle. The urea cycle is carried out by liver cells, which release urea to the bloodstream to be carried to the kidney, where it is excreted in urine. Excess water will be required to meet this increase in urea synthesis and urine production.

7.   *If PEP labelled with ^{14}C in the 2-position serves as precursor to chorismate synthesis, which C atom in chorismate is radioactive?*

Answer: Chorismate, which is synthesized from PEP and erythrose-4-phosphate, is a precursor to the aromatic amino acids, tyrosine, phenylalanine, and tryptophan. Its synthesis is as follows:

9. *For each of the 20 common amino acids, give the name of the enzyme that catalyzes the reaction providing its* α-*amino group.*

Answer: For alanine, pyruvate is the α-keto acceptor for glutamate: pyruvate aminotransferase.

Arginine is synthesized from glutamate via ornithine, so its α-amino group is glutamate's α-amino group, which derives from α-ketoglutarate and ammonia by glutamate dehydrogenase.

For aspartic acid, oxaloacetate is the α-keto acceptor for glutamate:oxaloacetate aminotransferase. Aspartic acid may be converted to asparagine by asparagine synthetase.

Cysteine is derived from serine, which derives from 3-phosphoserine via glutamate:3-phosphoserine aminotransferase.

Glutamate is from glutamate dehydrogenase as discussed under arginine.

Glutamine may derive from glutamate.

Glycine derives from serine, which is also used to produce cysteine. So, its α-amino group is from glutamate:3-phosphoserine aminotransferase.

Histidine's α-amino group is introduced by l-histidinol phosphate aminotransferase, which uses glutamate as amino donor.

Isoleucine's α-amino group is from the reaction catalyzed by glutamate:α-keto-β-methylvalerate aminotransferase.

Leucine's α-amino group is from the reaction catalyzed by glutamate:α-ketoisocaproate aminotransferase.

Lysine's α-amino group comes from glutamate via N-6-(L-1,3-dicarboxypropyl)-L-Lysine: NADP⁺ oxidoreductase.

Methionine is produced from aspartate whose α-amino group comes from glutamate:oxaloacetate aminotransferase.

Phenylalanine is produced from phenylpyruvate via aminotransferase using glutamate as amino donor. The enzyme is glutamate:phenylpyruvate aminotransferase.

Proline is synthesized from glutamate, so glutamate dehydrogenase incorporates its α-amino group.

Serine was already discussed under cysteine (glutamate:3-phosphoserine aminotransferase).

Threonine is synthesized from aspartate, so glutamate:oxaloacetate aminotransferase is responsible for threonine's α-amino group.

Tryptophan's α-amino group comes from serine via glutamate:3-phosphoserine aminotransferase.

Tyrosine may derive from phenylalanine. Alternatively, it may be produced from 4-hydroxyphenyl-pyruvate by aminotransfer from glutamate by 4-hydroxyphenylalanine:glutamate aminotransferase.

Valine gets its α-amino group from glutamate:α-ketoisovalerate aminotransferase.

11. Vitamins B6, B12, and folate may be recommended for individuals with high serum levels of homocysteine (a condition called hyperhomocysteinemia). How might these vitamins ameliorate homocysteinemia?

Answer: Homocysteine comes from the compound S-adenosylmethionine (SAM). The sulfur of methionine is attached to carbon 5 of adenosine. SAM is a very important compound in the so-called one-carbon pool because it is the source of methyl groups for methyltransferases (methylase). Methyltransferases, as their name implies, transfer a methyl group from SAM to a target. (There are a large number of methyltransferases whose targets range from proteins to nucleic acids, to small molecule compounds and metabolites). When the terminal methyl group is removed from SAM, it is converted to S-adenosylhomocysteine. Two pathways are used to deal with homocysteine. S-adenosylhomocysteine itself may be methylated back to SAM, and in this pathway the methyl group comes from tetrahydrofolate, a key player in the one-carbon pool. (Tetrahydrofolate moves carbons at several oxidation states.) Tetrahydrofolate, in turn, acquires a methyl group in a vitamin B12–dependent reaction. In the other pathway, S-adenosylhomocysteine is hydrolyzed to release homocysteine, which is converted to cystathionine. This conversion involves a pyridoxal-phosphate–dependent reaction in which serine's β-carbon is attached to the sulfur of homocysteine. Metabolism of cystathionine can lead to production of cysteine or other metabolic intermediates. In any case, all of these reactions are catalyzed by pyridoxal-phosphate–dependent reactions. High blood levels of homocysteine may be corrected by vitamins.

13. People with phenylketonuria must avoid foods containing the low-calorie sweetener aspartame, also known as NutraSweet. Find the structure of aspartame in the Merck Index (or other scientific source) and state why these people must avoid this substance.

Answer: To locate the structure, use ChemBioFinder (http://chembiofinder.cambridgesoft.com/), the LIGAND database (http://www.genome.ad.jp), or NCBI's PubChem Compound database (http://www.ncbi.nlm.nih.gov/). LIGAND had aspartame, but it did not list its brand name NutraSweet. ChemBioFinder listed both, as did NCBI. The structure is shown below. Aspartame is aspartic acid linked in peptide bond to phenylalanine whose carboxyl group is methyl esterified. Phenylketonurics need to avoid this compound because they lack the enzyme phenylalanine 4-hydroxylase, which converts phenylalanine into tyrosine. The problem is not that tyrosine cannot be synthesized (phe is an essential amino acid because humans cannot synthesized it, whereas tyrosine is not because phenylalanine can normally be converted to tyrosine). Rather, the problem is that phenylalanine cannot be degraded. It is deaminated by an aminotransferase producing the α-keto acid phenylpyruvate, a phenylketone that builds up in the blood. The structures of aspartame and phenylpyruvate are shown below.

aspartame   phenylpyruvate

15. (Integrates with Chapter 17) When cells convert glucose to glycine, which carbons of glucose are represented in glycine?

Answer: Glycine is made from serine by serine hydroxymethyltransferase, which removes the β-carbon of serine to produce glycine. Serine is synthesized from 3-phosphoglycerate. So, if we can recall glycolysis, we can figure out the labelling pattern in glycine from label in glucose. In glycolysis, 3-phosphoglycerate is made by splitting fructose-1,6-bisphosphate. The phosphorylated carbons become the phosphorylated carbon of 3-phosphoglycerate. Thus, carbons 1 and 6 of glucose appear in carbon 3 of 3-phosphoglycerate, which becomes the β-carbon of serine and is lost when producing glycine. Carbon 2 of 3-phosphoglycerate derives from carbons 2 and 5 of glucose. This carbon becomes glycine's α-carbon. Finally, carbon 1 of 3-phosophoglycerate comes from carbons 3 and 4 of glucose. This carbon becomes the carboxyl carbon of 3-phosphoglycerate and the carboxyl carbon of glycine.

17. Go to www.pdf.org/ and examine the PDF file 1LM1 for glutamate synthase. Find its iron–sulfur cluster and FMN prosthetic group. Discover how this enzyme is organized into an N-terminal domain that functions in ammonia removal from glutamine (the glutaminase domain) and the α-ketoglutarate–binding site near the Fe-S and flavin prosthetic groups. Consult van den Heuvel, R.H.H., et al., 2002. Structural studies on the synchronization of catalytic centers in glutamate synthase. Journal of Biological Chemistry 277: 24579–24583, to see how these 2 sites are connected by a tunnel for passage of ammonia from glutamine to α-ketoglutarate.

Answer: Glutamate synthase catalyzes the deamination of glutamine to glutamate and couples this with conversion of α-ketoglutarate to glutamate. Thus, the overall reaction is glutamine + α-ketoglutarate = 2 glutamate. The reaction occurs in three stages. First, glutamine is deaminated by hydrolysis to glutamate and ammonia. Ammonia is then channelled through the protein to a separate domain at which α-ketoglutarate is bound. Reaction of ammonia with α-ketoglutarate produces 2-imidoglutarate, which is subsequently reduced to glutamate by an electron donor (ferredoxin or NADPH or NADH, depending on enzyme source). The protein discussed in the reference uses reduced ferredoxin as a source of electrons. The enzyme is an iron–sulfur flavoprotein. Electrons are moved from ferredoxin, which binds non-covalently to the enzyme, to a 3Fe-4S cluster to a protein bound FMN cofactor. The protein is composed of four domains that are functionally and structurally distinct regions of a 1523 amino acid residue single polypeptide chain. The N-terminal domain, residues 1–422, is responsible for deamination of glutamine with its N-terminal cysteine responsible for hydrolysis of ammonia. Electron transport from ferredoxin to FMN via the iron–sulfur cluster is located in the FMN-bonding domain, residues 787–1239. The N-terminal domain and the FMN-binding domain are connected by the central domain, residues 423–786. Finally, the C-terminal domain, which includes the region from residues 1240 to 1507, makes numerous contacts with the N-terminal domain and the FMN-binding domain, and these contacts are thought to stabilize the domains. In viewing the protein (1LM1), it should be an easy task to identify and highlight the N-terminal cysteine, which marks the deamination domain. The protein contains two heteromolecules, the iron–sulfur cluster, and FMN, and these can also be highlighted using a visualization program of your choice. (I am using iMol, but I use others as well.) In looking at the structure, the tunnel must run between these two domains and through a small portion of the central domain. (The central domain mainly contacts the outer surface of the N-terminal domain and the FMN-binding domain.) A striking feature of the C-terminal domain is a barrel like structure dominated by β-sheets.

Questions for Self-Study

1. Fill in the blanks. The two reactions below occur in the process of _____ _____. In the first step, nitrate is reduced to nitrite, while in the second step nitrite is converted to ammonium. Step (1) is catalyzed by _____ _____, and step (2) is catalyzed by _____ _____.

    $$NO_3^- + 2\ H^+ + 2\ e^- \rightarrow NO_2^- + H_2O$$
    $$NO_2^- + 8\ H^+ + 6\ e^- \rightarrow NH_4^+ + 2H_2O$$

    The enzyme, _____, is responsible for catalysis of the following reaction:

    $$N_2 + 8\ H^+ + 8\ e^- \rightarrow 2\ NH_3 + H_2$$

    in a process known as _____ _____.

2. Ammonium is incorporated into organic compounds as a result of action of which three enzymes?

3. Write a two-step reaction sequence leading from the citric acid cycle intermediate, α-ketoglutarate, to the amino acid glutamine, and name the two enzymes involved.

4. Complete the following reaction, name the general enzyme type that catalyzes this kind of reaction, and identify the products.

5. Match the non-essential amino acids with their precursor molecules.
   a. Glutamate
   b. Glutamine
   c. Aspartate
   d. Asparagine
   e. Alanine
   f. Serine
   g. Glycine
   h. Proline
   i. Tyrosine
   j. Cysteine

   1. serine and H_2S
   2. serine (one step)
   3. phenylalanine
   4. glutamate (one step)
   5. glutamate (several steps)
   6. 3-phosphoglycerate
   7. pyruvate
   8. aspartate
   9. α-ketoglutarate
   10. oxaloacetate

6. Fill in the blanks. The 20 common amino acids are degraded into 7 metabolic intermediates. These include the citric acid cycle fuel _____, four citric acid cycle intermediates _____, _____, _____, and _____, a ketone body _____, and the end product of glycolysis, _____.

7. Identify the compound drawn below. Its synthesis and degradation convert an amino acid into fumarate and produce one of the 20 common amino acids. Name the amino acid consumed and produced. This compound is part of which metabolic cycle?

8. Chorismate is a key metabolic intermediate that is derived from erythrose-4-phosphate and two PEP in the shikimate pathway. Given that the pathway does not contain oxidation steps, indicate the carbons in chorismate that derive from PEP and from erythrose-4-phosphate.

9. List four compounds that derive from chorismate.

Answers

1. Nitrate assimilation; nitrate reductase; nitrite reductase; nitrogenase; nitrogen fixation.

2. Carbamoyl-phosphate synthetase I, glutamate dehydrogenase, and glutamine synthetase.

3. Glutamate dehydrogenase: $NH_4^+ + \alpha$-ketoglutarate + NADPH → glutamate + $NADP^+$
   Glutamine synthetase: Glutamate + NH_4^+ + ATP → glutamine + ADP + P_i

4. Aminotransferases catalyze the following reaction.

5. a. 9; b. 4; c. 10; d. 8; e. 7; f. 6; g. 2; h. 5; i. 3; j. 1.

6. Acetyl-CoA; α-ketoglutarate; succinyl-CoA; fumarate; oxaloacetate; acetoacetate; pyruvate.

7. The compound is argininosuccinate, a urea cycle molecule. Its formation and degradation converts aspartate to fumarate and produces the amino acid arginine.

8. The unlabelled carbons derive from erythrose.

9. Any four of tryptophan, phenylalanine, tyrosine, vitamins E and K, Coenzyme Q, plastoquinone, and folic acid.

Additional Problems

1. Draw the structure of the citric acid cycle intermediates that can be converted to amino acids by transamination. Which amino acids do they produce?

2. The two enzymes glutamate-pyruvate aminotransferase and glutamate-oxaloacetate amino transferase were formerly used to diagnose damage to heart tissue after an infarction. By comparing the levels of these enzymes in serum drawn at various times after an incident, an estimate of the extent of heart

muscle damage could be made. Can you suggest a simple coupled assays to measure the activity of these two enzymes?

3. The polyamine spermidine is produced from two amino acids. Given the structure of spermidine, can you suggest which two amino acids are involved?

4. Describe the reaction catalyzed by glutamine synthetase, suggest a reaction mechanism, and explain why this reaction is favourable even in low concentrations of ammonium.

5. The essential amino acids in mammals include phenylalanine but not tyrosine. Draw the side chains of these two amino acids to convince yourself that tyrosine is in fact more complicated than phenylalanine in structure, and explain why phenylalanine is required but tyrosine is not.

6. What amino acids are involved in the urea cycle?

7. Excrement from birds makes an excellent fertilizer. Why?

8. Would you expect aminotransferase activity to be sensitive to sodium borohydride (NaBH₄)? Explain.

Abbreviated Answers

1. Oxaloacetate is converted to aspartate and α–ketoglutarate is converted to glutamate. The structures of the α-keto acids are shown below.

oxaloacetate α- ketoglutarate

2. Glutamate-pyruvate aminotransferase and glutamate-oxaloacetate aminotransferase catalyze the following reactions:

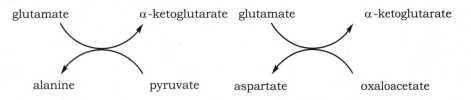

For glutamate-pyruvate aminotransferase, lactate dehydrogenase can be used to produce lactate from pyruvate with oxidation of NADH, which can be followed spectrophotometrically at 340 nm. The aminotransferase reaction can be forced toward pyruvate production by adding excess glutamate and alanine. In a similar manner, glutamate-oxaloacetate aminotransferase activity can be measured using malate dehydrogenase.

3. The butanediamine group, known as putrescine, is produced by decarboxylation of ornithine, a urea cycle intermediate. The aminopropane group derives from methionine via S-adenosylmethionine by decarboxylation and loss of 5′-methylthioadenosine.

4.   Glutamine synthetase converts glutamate and ammonium to glutamine. The name synthetase implies that the enzyme uses ATP to drive the reaction. The reaction mechanism involves nucleophilic attack of a γ-carboxylate oxyanion on the γ-phosphorus of ATP to produce γ-glutamyl-phosphate intermediate. The phosphate group is subsequently displaced by ammonium to produce glutamine.

5.   Phenylalanine can be converted to tyrosine by phenylalanine hydroxylase in an irreversible oxidation reaction involving molecular oxygen. The side chains of phenylalanine and tyrosine are:

6.   Arginine, ornithine, citrulline, and aspartate are involved in the urea cycle. Only arginine and aspartate are common amino acids found in proteins. Ornithine and citrulline are not incorporated into proteins during protein synthesis. (Citrulline was first isolated from watermelon, *Citrullus vulgaris*.)

7.   Bird droppings contain nitrogen compounds like uric acid. Birds deal with excess nitrogen by converting it into rather water-insoluble compounds that are excreted as a paste that requires minimum amounts of water.

8.   The mechanism of action of aminotransferases involves a Schiff base intermediate on pyridoxal phosphate or vitamin B_6. The incoming amino acid is deaminated with the amino group being transferred to an enzyme-bound pyridoxal phosphate. This step involves Schiff base formation, and sodium borohydride can reduce the Schiff base and inactivate the enzyme.

Summary

Nitrogen is a crucial macronutrient. In the common inorganic forms of nitrogen prevalent in the environment, nitrogen is in an oxidized state. Its assimilation into organic compounds requires reduction to the level of NH^+_4. Two metabolic pathways accomplish this end: nitrate assimilation and nitrogen fixation. Virtually all higher plants and algae and many fungi and bacteria are capable of nitrate assimilation. Nitrogen fixation is an exclusively prokaryotic process, but nitrogen-fixing bacteria do occur in symbiotic association with selected plants and animals. Animals themselves lack both of these pathways and thus are dependent on plants and microorganisms for a dietary source of reduced-N, principally in the form of protein.

The incorporation of significant quantities of ammonium into organic linkage occurs via only three enzymatic reactions, carbamoyl phosphate synthetase I, glutamate dehydrogenase (GDH), and glutamine synthetase (GS). The latter two of these three reactions are by far the most important. Two pathways of ammonium assimilation are prevalent. If $[NH^+_4]$ levels are adequate, the GDH/GS pathway operates so that one equivalent of α-ketoglutarate picks up two equivalents of NH^+_4 and glutamine is formed. If ammonium is limiting, GDH is inefficient, and thus GS becomes the only assimilating reaction. Then, glutamate synthase (GOGAT) is necessary to generate glutamate to provide the ammonium acceptor, and the assimilatory pathway is GS/GOGAT. Since the amide-N of glutamine serves as N-donor in many biosynthetic pathways, GS occupies a key position to impose regulation on nitrogen metabolism. *E. coli* GS is regulated at three levels: It is sensitive to cumulative feedback inhibition by a collection of end products of nitrogen metabolism; its activity is controlled by a bi-cyclic cascade system of covalent modification; and its synthesis is regulated at the level of gene expression.

Amino acid biosynthesis is basically a matter of synthesizing the appropriate α-keto acid carbon skeletons for the various amino acids, followed by transamination of the α-keto acid by a glutamate-dependent aminotransferase. Plants and most microorganisms can synthesize all of the 20 amino acids commonly found in proteins, but mammals lack the metabolic pathways for synthesis of 10 of these. It is a generality of nature that the longer the metabolic pathway, the more likely it is that the pathway has been lost over evolutionary time. ("Longer" here means "the greater the number of unique reactions intervening between central metabolic intermediates and the final end product"). The amino acids that mammals cannot synthesize are called "essential amino acids" to denote that it is essential for the mammal to obtain these amino acids in their diet. Amino acid biosynthetic pathways can be grouped according to shared precursors, as in the "α-ketoglutarate family of amino acids" (Glu, Gln, Pro, Arg, and in some organisms, Lys) or "the 3-phosphoglycerate family" (Ser, Gly, and Cys). The aromatic amino acids (Phe, Tyr, and Trp) are synthesized from chorismate, a metabolic intermediate central to the biosynthesis of practically all common aromatic compounds. In addition, the histidine and the aromatic amino acid biosynthetic pathways share intermediates in common with the pathways for synthesis of purine and pyrimidine nucleotides.

Chapter 24

Nucleotides and Nucleic Acids

• •

Chapter Outline

❖ Nucleic acids: DNA and RNA: Polymers of nucleoside monophosphates: Base + sugar + phosphate
❖ Heterocyclic nitrogenous aromatic bases
  ⅄ Pyrimidines: Six-member heterocyclic aromatic ring with 2 nitrogens
    • Cytosine: DNA and RNA
    • Uracil: RNA
    • Thymine: DNA
  ⅄ Purines: Five-member imidazole ring fused to six-member pyrimidine
    • Adenine: 6-Amino purine: DNA and RNA
    • Guanine: 2-Amino-6-oxy purine: DNA and RNA
  ⅄ H-bond properties
  ⅄ UV-light absorbing properties
  ⅄ Keto to enol tautomerization
❖ Sugars: 5-carbon pentose: Furanose rings: Numbering system primed
  ⅄ D-ribose: RNA
  ⅄ 2′-deoxy-D-ribose: DNA
❖ Nucleoside: N-glycosidic linkage of base to anomeric carbon of sugar
  ⅄ Anomeric carbon in β-configuration
  ⅄ Nomenclature
    • Pyrimidines: + idine: Cytidine, uridine, thymidine
    • Purines: + osine: Adenosine, guanosine
  ⅄ Two conformations
    • Syn: Base over furanose ring: Purines
    • Anti: Base not over furanose ring: Pyrimidines and purines
❖ Nucleotides: Typically 5′ nucleoside phosphate
  ⅄ Phosphate esters
    • AMP, GMP, CMP, UMP: 5′-ribonucleoside monophosphates
    • cAMP, cGMP: 3′,5′-cyclic ribonucleoside monophosphates: Regulation of cellular metabolism
  ⅄ Phosphoanhydrides
    • 5′-ribonucleoside diphosphates: ADP, GDP, CDP, UDP
      • ATP (energy currency), GTP (protein synthesis and signal transduction), CTP (lipid synthesis), UTP (carbohydrate and polysaccharide synthesis): 5′-ribonucleoside triphosphates
    • 5′-deoxyribonucleoside triphosphates : dATP, dGTP, dCTP, TTP (dTTP): DNA synthesis
❖ Nucleic acids: Nucleoside monophosphates in phosphodiester linkage 3′ to 5′
  ⅄ DNA: Genetic material: Typically double stranded
    • dsDNA: Strands antiparallel
    • Interchain H bonds form base pairs
    • Chargaff's rules: A=T, G=C, Purines = Pyrimidines
    • X-ray diffraction of Franklin and Wilkins and model building of Watson and Crick
  ⅄ RNA: Typically single stranded: Produced during transcription
    • mRNA: Carries information encoded in genes to direct protein synthesis on ribosomes
      • Derive from heterogeneous nuclear RNA (hnRNA)

- RNA processed by splicing (removal of introns and joining of exons), capping (5' end), and polyA tail addition (3' end)
  - rRNA: Components of ribosome: Protein synthesis
    - Small subunit of ribosome: Single rRNA
    - Large subunit of ribosome: Large subunit rRNA, 5S rRNA, and in eukaryotes 5.8S rRNA
  - tRNA: Carriers of activated amino acids used by ribosome for protein synthesis
  - snRNA: Small nuclear RNAs
  - siRNAs: Small interfering RNAs: Degrade mRNAs
  - miRNAs: Bind to mRNA and block translation
  - snoRNAs: Required for certain RNA modifications
- DNA versus RNA
  - Composition
    - T in DNA not U to distinguish from T formed by deamination of C
    - 2'-OH in RNA accounts for instability of RNA phosphodiester bond
  - Hydrolysis
    - RNA: Sensitive to base hydrolysis: Resistant to acid hydrolysis
    - DNA: Resistant to base hydrolysis: Depurinates by acid hydrolysis (apurinic base)
- Nucleases: Enzymes that hydrolyze nucleic acids
  - Exo-: Attack from ends
  - Endo-: Attack internally
  - *a*-side cleavage: Attacks of 3' side produces 5' phosphorylated product
  - *b*-side cleavage: Attacks of 5'' side produces 3' phosphorylated product
  - RNases: RNA specific
  - DNases: DNA specific
  - Nucleases: Cleave either DNA or RNA
  - Restriction endonucleases
    - Type I and Type III: Cleavage requires ATP
    - Type II: Cleavage site 4,6,8 base sequence with two-fold axis of symmetry

Chapter Objectives

Understand the difference between a nucleoside and a nucleotide. The nucleotides are phosphorylated derivatives of nucleosides, compounds made up of a sugar and a nitrogenous base (see Figure 24.10).

It is important to know the structures of the pyrimidines and purines. Pyrimidines are six-membered heterocyclic, conjugated rings, whereas purines have a five-membered imidazole ring fused to a six-membered ring. (The small pyrimidine has a large name whereas the large purine has a small name.) The commonly occurring pyrimidines have two nitrogens separated by a carbonyl group. In uracil and thymine, an additional carbonyl group is located adjacent to one of the nitrogens, and adjacent to it is a carbon with either a hydrogen (in uracil) or a methyl group (in thymine). Cytosine has an amino group replacing one of the carbonyl oxygens of uracil (oxidative deamination of cytosine produces uracil). In the purine double ring, the carbon separating the two nitrogens of the six-membered ring section has a hydrogen in adenine and an amino group in guanine. A carbonyl group is located adjacent to one of the nitrogens of the six-membered ring in guanosine (2-amino-6-hydroxypurine), which is substituted for an amino group in adenine (6-aminopurine).

You should be able to draw the structures of the bases and be able to identify hydrogen-bond donor and acceptor groups. Also, know the groups involved in base pairing in double-stranded DNA.

The compounds like ADP, ATP, GTP, UTP, CTP, NAD+, FAD, Coenzyme A, etc. are all either nucleotides or nucleotide derivatives of the ribonucleotides. The phosphate groups are usually attached to the 5' carbon of the ribose sugar. The dNTPs are used as precursors for DNA.

The convention for writing a nucleic acid sequence is to write, from left to right, the one-letter abbreviations of the bases from the 5'-end to the 3'-end.

Figure 24.10 The common ribonucleosides—cytidine, uridine, adenosine, and guanosine—and the less common inosine drawn in the anti conformation.

The abbreviations most commonly found are A, C, G, T, U, N (any nucleotide, base unspecified), R (purine), and Y (pyrimidine).[1]

Know what phosphodiester bonds are and that they join the 3'-hydroxyl group of a nucleotide to the 5' phosphate of an adjacent nucleotide in DNA and RNA. The single-stranded polymers thus formed have a 5'-end and a 3'-end. DNA is predominantly double-stranded, a fact reflected in Chargaff's rules.

The total DNA content of a haploid cell is its genome size. Diploid cells have two copies of DNA, while haploid cells have a single copy of DNA. The discrete molecules of cellular DNA are chromosomes. Cells may have a single chromosome or several chromosomes. Chromosomes are circular DNA molecules in some organisms and linear DNA molecules in others.

RNA molecules are much less stable than DNA molecules. RNA is sensitive to base-catalyzed cleavage because of the presence of a hydroxyl group on the 2'-ribose carbon. Cells have an abundance of RNases, which are often extremely stable, active enzymes. Finally, RNA is usually found as a single-stranded molecule, whereas DNA is usually found in a double-stranded form in which bases are protected by being sequestered in the interior of the structure.

The type II restriction endonucleases are DNA-specific DNases that recognize palindromic sequences of DNA and cut within the sequence. Understand what is meant by palindromic DNA and that after restriction endonuclease cleavage, the resulting ends may be blunt-ended, or have either 5'- or 3'-overhangs. It is a rather easy task to identify an uninterrupted palindrome by inspection. Scan the sequence of bases for adjacent, base-pair nucleotides (i.e., AT, TA, CG, GC). Once a pair is located, inspect the flanking two nucleotides; if they are also base-paired nucleotides, then they are part of a four-base palindrome. Six-base palindromes are common recognition sequences for a large number of restriction endonucleases.

The relationship between DNA, RNA, and protein is described in the central dogma outlined in Figure 24.1.

---

[1] There is an extended code, less commonly used, that covers other combinations of bases. B specifies C, G, or T (i.e., anything but A). D indicates A, G, or T (i.e., not C). H is anything but G. V refers to A, C, or G. W signifies either A or T, the weak base-pair formers. S refers to G or C, the strong base-pair formers. A or C is denoted by M, for amino, and G or T is specified by K for keto.

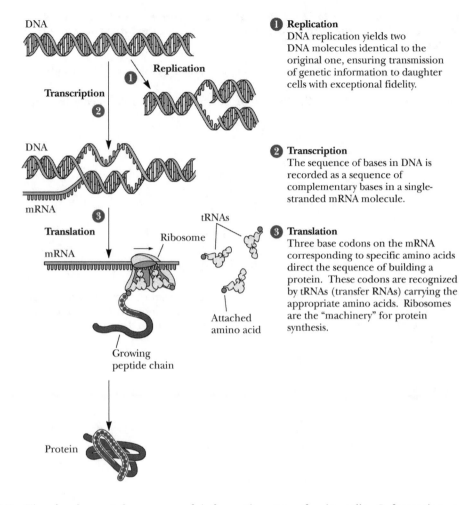

① Replication
DNA replication yields two DNA molecules identical to the original one, ensuring transmission of genetic information to daughter cells with exceptional fidelity.

② Transcription
The sequence of bases in DNA is recorded as a sequence of complementary bases in a single-stranded mRNA molecule.

③ Translation
Three base codons on the mRNA corresponding to specific amino acids direct the sequence of building a protein. These codons are recognized by tRNAs (transfer RNAs) carrying the appropriate amino acids. Ribosomes are the "machinery" for protein synthesis.

Figure 24.1 The fundamental process of information transfer in cells. Information encoded in the nucleotide sequence of DNA is transcribed through synthesis of an RNA molecule whose sequence is dictated by the DNA sequence. As the sequence of this RNA is read (as groups of three consecutive nucleotides) by the protein synthesis machinery, it is translated into the sequence of amino acids in a protein. This information transfer system is encapsulated in the dogma: DNA→RNA→protein.

Problems and Solutions

1. *Draw the principal ionic species for 5'-GMP occurring at pH 2.*

Answer:

3. Chargaff's results (Table 24.1) for ox DNA yielded a molar ratio of 1.29 for A to G, 1.43 for T to C, 1.04 for A to T, and 1.00 for G to C. Given these values, what are the mole fractions of A, C, G, and T in ox DNA?

Answer: For ox DNA: A/G = 1.29; T/C = 1.43; A/T =1.04, G/C = 1.00; (A + G)/(T + C) = 1.1

What are the mole fractions of A, C, G, T? Before starting, we should recognize that the data are inconsistent. For example,

$$\frac{T}{C} \times \frac{A}{T} = \frac{A}{C} \text{ and}$$

$$\frac{A}{G} \times \frac{G}{C} = \frac{A}{C} \text{ so}$$

$$\text{Does } \frac{T}{C} \times \frac{A}{T} = \frac{A}{G} \times \frac{G}{C}?$$

$$\frac{T}{C} \times \frac{A}{T} = 1.43 \times 1.04 = 1.487$$

$$\frac{A}{G} \times \frac{G}{C} = 1.29 \times 1.00 = 1.290$$

Clearly, there are problems with the data. It is likely that the original data were concentrations of A, G, T, and C, and if we had these data, it would be trivial to calculate the mole fractions of each. Using the data given, we could get several different answers depending on which of the ratios we used. Here is one possible answer. Let,

$$f_A + f_G + f_C + f_T = 1.0$$

where the terms are the mole fraction of each nucleotide.

$f_A + f_G + f_T + f_C = 1.0$

But $f_A = 1.04 \; f_T$ and $f_G = 1.0 \; f_C$

Thus:

$1.04 \; f_T + 1.0 \; f_C + f_T + f_C = 1.0$, or

$2.04 \; f_T + 2.0 \; f_C = 1.0$

By substituting $f_T = 1.43 \; f_C$, we find:

$2.04 \times 1.43 \; f_C + 2f_C = 1.0$, and

$f_C = 0.20$

And since $\frac{G}{C} = 1.0$, $f_G = 0.20$

$f_A = 1.29 f_G = 1.29 \times 0.20$

$f_A = 0.26$

And, finally since

$\frac{f_T}{f_C} = 1.43$,

$f_T = 1.43 \times f_C = 1.43 \times 0.02 = 0.29$

The final answer is:

$f_A = 0.26$, $f_C = 0.20$, $f_G = 0.20$, $f_T = 0.29$

These are consistent with some of the data but not all of it. Below are other solutions you might come up with that are consistent with some of the data but not all of it.

A	C	G	T
0.30	0.23	0.23	0.33
0.29	0.20	0.20	0.28
0.29	0.20	0.20	0.28

By treating the data as several equations in A, G, T, and C, you can come up with a solution that best fits all the data. Using A/G = 1.29, here is an example of one such equation:

$$A - 1.29G + 0*C + 0*T = 0$$

The others are (from T/C = 1.43, A/T = 1.04, A/G = 1, A+G/C+T = 1.1, and A + T + C + G = 1):

$$0*A + 0*G - 1.43C + T = 0$$
$$A + 0*G + 0*C + 1.04T = 0$$
$$A - G + 0*C + 0*T = 0$$
$$A + G - 1.1C - 1.1T = 0$$
$$A + G + C + T = 1.0$$

We have six equations. What we want to do is find the best solutions for A, G, C, and T so that when substituted into these equations, they are as consistent as possible. To do this, we need to rearrange them such that they all are functions that equal zero. (The first five are already in this form. The fifth would be A + G + C + T − 1 = 0.

We then square each, sum them, and then find solutions for A, G, C, and T that minimize the sum of the squares. (In effect, this is a form of a least squares solution.) (The solution can be obtained using matrix algebra.) The answer is A = .295, G = .223, C = .201, and T = .280.

As an overkill, it must be that since the input data were A, G, T, and C, some of the relationships presented in Table 24.1 are not truly independent. For example, the ratio of purines to pyrimidines must have been calculated with A, G, C, and T as input. If we eliminate this relationship from the analysis, the answer is A = .289, T = .286, G = .218, and C = .206.

5. Adhering to the convention of writing nucleotide sequences in the 5′→3′ direction, what is the nucleotide sequence of the DNA strand that is complementary to D-ATCGCAACTGTCACTA?

Answer: 5′-TAGTGACAGTTGCGAT-3′

Note: The complementary sequence written 5′ to 3′ is sometimes referred to as the reverse complementary sequence. (As an example, consider the sequence GAGGCTT. Its reverse is TTCGGAG— i.e., the sequence literally written in reverse. For the reverse sequence: by exchanging each base for its complementary base [i.e., A for T and G for C] we have AAGCCTC, which is the strand that is complementary to GAGGCTT but written 5′ to 3′. When the reverse complementary sequence is so defined, the complementary sequence is defined literally. Thus, the complementary sequence of GAGGCTT is CTCCGAA.)

7. The DNA strand that is complementary to the template strand copied by RNA polymerase during transcription has a nucleotide sequence identical to that of the RNA being synthesized (except T residues are found in the DNA strand at sites where U residues occur in the RNA). An RNA transcribed from this non-template DNA stand would be complementary to the mRNA synthesized by RNA polymerase. Such an RNA is called antisense RNA because its base sequence is complementary to the "sense" mRNA. One strategy to thwart the deleterious effects of genes activated in disease states (such as cancer) is to generate antisense RNAs in affected cells. These antisense RNAs would form double-stranded hybrids with mRNAs transcribed from the activated genes and prevent their translation into protein. Suppose transcription of a cancer-activated gene yielded an mRNA whose sequence included the segment 5′-UACGGUCUAAGCUGA. What is the corresponding nucleotide sequence (5′→3′) of the template strand in a DNA duplex that might be introduced into these cells so that an antisense RNA could be transcribed from it?

Answer: For an mRNA 5′-UACGGUCUAAGCUGA-3′, what is the corresponding sequence of a template strand in DNA that might make antisense RNA? Antisense RNA has a sequence complementary to the mRNA shown above. It would have to be transcribed from DNA with a sequence complementary to itself. Thus, the DNA must have a template sequence identical (except T for U) to the original mRNA: 5′-TACGGTCTAAGCTGA-3′

In the spring of 1998, Phase III clinical trials for an antisense drug for the treatment of cytomegalovirus retinitis in AIDS patients were completed and a new drug application for this antisense drug was filed with the U.S. FDA.

9. Based on the information in Table 24.2, describe 2 different 20-base nucleotide sequences that have restriction sites for BamHI, PstI, SalI, and SmaI. Give the sequences of the SmaI cleavage products of each.

Answer: Table 10.2 lists type II restriction endonucleases, their recognition sequence, where in the sequence the enzyme cuts, in addition to other information. *Bam*HI *Pst*I, *Sal*I, and *Sma*I all recognize six-base restriction sites. Since we are asked to produce a 20-base sequence, we will have to have restriction sites overlap. We are not asked to order the sites, so this leaves us free to try several combinations.

Enzyme	Recognition Sequence
*Bam*HI	GGATCC
*Pst*I	CTGCAG
*Sal*I	GTCGAC
*Sma*I	CCCGGG

Looking at the recognition sequences, it is clear that having *Bam*HI and *Sma*I adjacent to each other will allow a two-base overlap (of G's or C's, depending on order). So we could start out with either of these two:

1. GGATCCCGGG or 2. CCCGGGATCC

To (1), we could add *Pst*I and *Sal*I sites with single-base overhangs as follows:

CTGCAGGATCCCGGGTCGAC

Digestion of this oligonucleotide with *Sma*I would produce:

CTGCAGGATCCC and GGGTCGAC

To (2), we could add *Pst*I and *Sal*I sites with single-base overhangs as follows:

GTCGACCCGGGATCCTGCAG

Digestion of this oligonucleotide with *Sma*I would produce:

GTCGACCC and GGGATCCTGCAG

Alternatively, we could have started with the *Bam*HI/*Sma*I-overlapped DNA on an end, and then added in the other sites.

For (1), we would get:

GGATCCCGGGTCGACTGCAG

Digestion of this oligonucleotide with *Sma*I would produce:

GGATCCC and GGGTCGACTGCAG

For (2), we would get:

CTGCAGTCGACCCGGGATCC

Digestion of this oligonucleotide with *Sma*I would produce:

CTGCAGTCGACCC and GGGATCC

11. Gene expression is controlled through the interaction of proteins with specific nucleotide sequences in double-stranded DNA.
   a. List the kinds of non-covalent interactions that might take place between a protein and DNA.
   b. How do you suppose a particular protein might specifically interact with a particular nucleotide sequence in DNA? That is, how might proteins recognize specific base sequences within the double helix?

Answer: a.   The weak forces are hydrophobic interaction, van der Waals interactions, hydrogen bonds, and ionic bonds. Of these, we might not expect excessive hydrophobic interactions to occur between a protein and dsDNA because dsDNA presents very little in the way of hydrophobic surfaces to the solvent. The bases themselves are hydrophobic, but they are stacked in dsDNA. One might expect hydrogen bonding to occur between a protein and bases in a DNA sequence. One might also expect ionic bonding between the negatively charged sugar–phosphate backbone of DNA and positively charged amino acid residues from arginine and lysine.

b.   Without unwinding dsDNA, a protein would have to make base-specific interactions via either the major groove or minor groove. There is more information regarding the identity of base pairs in the major groove. In addition, the dimensions of an α-helix are compatible with the space in the major groove. Thus, one might expect proteins to bind via the major groove.

13.   **A carbohydrate is an integral part of a nucleoside.**
   a.   **What advantage does the carbohydrate provide? Polynucleotides are formed through formation of a sugar–phosphate backbone.**
   b.   **Why might ribose be preferable for this backbone instead of glucose?**
   c.   **Why might 2-deoxyribose be preferable to ribose in some situations?**

Answer: a.   A nucleoside is a base in glycosidic linkage to a sugar. Bases are poorly water-soluble and attachment to a sugar will improve their water solubility. Sugars present numerous hydroxyl groups that contribute to water solubility and provide attachment points for other molecules.

b. and c.   Moving from hexose to ribose to deoxyribose, there is a decrease in the number of hydroxyl groups. DNA is much more stable to alkaline hydrolysis than RNA because it lacks a 2' hydroxyl, which in RNA can attack nearby phosphodiester linkages. One could imagine hexoses being even worse in this regard. The use of a hexose in place of a ribose might make packaging of DNA more difficult. The presence of additional hydroxyl groups would require more exposure to water molecules. Further, there would be an increased likelihood that unwanted side reactions involving hydroxyl groups would occur.

15.   **The RNAs acting in RNAi are about 21 nucleotides long. To judge whether it is possible to uniquely target a particular gene with an RNA of this size, consider the following calculation: What is the expected frequency of occurrence of a specific 21-nucleotide sequence?**

Answer: The probability of finding a specific 21-nucleotide sequence is simply $(1/4)^{21}$ or 2.27×10^{-12}, assuming that we are working with nucleic acid with roughly equal amounts of A, G, C, and T. The frequency of occurrence of this sequence is $1/2.27 \times 10^{-12}$ or one in 4.40×10^{12} nucleotides. The general formula used is $(1/4)^n$, where n is the number of bases and $(1/4)$ is the probability or frequency of a particular base.

17. **Snake venom phosphodiesterase is an a-specific exonuclease (Figure 24.28) that acts equally well on single-stranded RNA or DNA. Design a protocol based on snake venom phosphodiesterase that would allow you to determine the base sequence of an oligonucleotide. (Hint: Adapt the strategy for protein sequencing by Edman degradation, as described on page 113.)**

Answer: One approach might be to simply partially digest the oligonucleotide for varying lengths of time, and then analyze the products by mass spectrometry, specifically MALDI-TOF (Matrix-assisted laser desorption ionization–time of flight). Complete digestion will only produce individual nucleotides, but partial digestion will produce a collection of nucleotides with ragged ends and whose molecular weights differ by loss of a particular nucleotide.

Questions for Self-Study

1.   Fill in the blanks. The two basic kinds of nucleic acids are _____ and _____. They are composed of building blocks termed _____; however, the building blocks are not identical for the two kinds of nucleic acids. One contains the five-carbon sugar _____, whereas the other has a modified form of this sugar or _____. The building blocks all contain nitrogenous bases attached to the sugar by _____ bonds. The nitrogenous bases are either derivatives of the 6-membered heterocyclic ring compound _____ or of purines, a compound composed of a 6-membered heterocyclic ring with a 5-membered

_____ ring fused to it. The two common purines are _____ and _____. The 6-membered heterocyclic ring compounds include _____, _____, and _____. A ring compound attached to a sugar is termed a _____.

2. True or false:
   a. ATP is an example of a deoxynucleoside triphosphate. _____
   b. cAMP is a 3'–5' cyclic form of AMP. _____
   c. The α-phosphate of GTP is the phosphate closest to the sugar moiety. _____
   d. The only biological function of dCTP is as a building block in synthesis of DNA. _____
   e. The only biological function of CTP is as a building block in synthesis of RNA. _____
   f. The most common ribonucleoside triphosphates have phosphate attached to the 5' carbon of the sugar moiety. _____

3. Chargaff's rules provided an important clue to solve the structure of double-stranded DNA. What are Chargaff's rules?

4. True or false:
   a. An AT base pair and a CG base pair have about the same physical dimensions. _____
   b. If GGGGCCCC represents the sequence of bases in one strand of a double-stranded DNA then the complementary strand must have the sequence CCCCGGGG. _____
   c. mRNA is single-stranded. _____
   d. Heterogeneous nuclear RNA or hnRNA are RNA molecules made in the nucleus and processed into mRNA. _____
   e. rRNA and tRNA are devoid of unmodified nucleosides _____

5. DNA and RNA react differently to acid and base conditions. Explain.

6. Of the following statements, which are true for type II restriction enzymes?
   a. They are usually exonucleases.
   b. Their recognition sequences are palindromic.
   c. Cleavage is by hydrolysis of both strands.
   d. Cleavage produces 3'-phosphates and 5' hydroxyl groups.
   e. A single restriction enzyme can produce blunt ends or protruding ends depending on the salt conditions.

Answers

1. DNA; RNA; nucleotides (or nucleoside monophosphates); ribose; deoxyribose; glycosidic; pyrimidine; imidazole; adenine; guanine; cytosine; uracil; thymine; nucleoside.

2. a. F; b. T; c. T; d. T; e. F; f. T.

3. [A] = [T]; [G] = [C]; [pyrimidines] = [purines]

4. a. T; b. F (sequences are always written 5' to 3'); c. T; d. T; e. F.
5. RNA is relatively resistant to dilute acid, whereas DNA undergoes hydrolysis of glycosidic bonds to purines. DNA is not susceptible to alkaline hydrolysis, whereas RNA is readily hydrolyzed to nucleotides in alkaline solution.

6. b and c.

Additional Problems

1. The nucleotides are an important class of biomolecules used as components of the nucleic acids, DNA, and RNA. Describe the structure of the nucleoside monophosphates found in DNA and RNA. In your description, be sure to describe the three chemical groups that make up a nucleotide and be certain to indicate any difference between deoxyribonucleotides and ribonucleotides.

2. Draw a base pair involving either G and C, or A and T.

3. DNA methylation is known to most commonly occur at position 6 in A and position 5 in C. However, the formation of 5-methylcytosine can create so-called mutational hot-spots. Cytosine can undergo oxidative deamination at position 4. In the unmethylated form, this deamination can be corrected, because it is easily recognized. Deamination of 5-methylcytosine, however, can create problems. Explain.

4 In the following sequence of DNA, underline a 4-base palindrome, a 6-base palindrome, and a purine-rich sequence.

GAGAAATATAGATCAGAGTTAACTC

5. In the following compounds, the order of solubility is adenine < deoxyadenosine < adenosine < adenosine triphosphate. Explain what each is (i.e., base, nucleoside, or nucleotide), how they differ, and why they show this relative solubility.

6. When a solution of double-stranded DNA is heated, a sharp transition is observed in the ultraviolet absorption properties of the solution. The solution begins to absorb greater amounts of light at high temperatures, corresponding to the process of denaturation. What physical changes in the double-stranded DNA molecules occur during this process of denaturation?

7. The restriction endonuclease *Bam*HI recognizes the sequence GGATCC and cleaves between the G's. The enzyme *Bgl* II ("Bagel two") recognizes AGATCT and cuts between AG. What kind of overhangs are generated (i.e., 5′ or 3′)? Are the overhangs complementary to one another? If the cleavage products are joined together (i.e., a *Bam*HI fragment joined to a *Bgl* II fragment), is the hybrid molecule cleavable by either endonuclease?

Abbreviated Answers

1. The nucleoside monophosphates found in DNA and RNA are composed of a phosphate group, a sugar moiety, and a nitrogenous base. The sugar is a 5-carbon compound, deoxyribose for DNA and ribose for RNA. The phosphate group is attached to the 5′-carbon of the sugar. Attached to the 1′-carbon is a nitrogenous base. Bases are either purines, adenine or guanine; or pyrimidines, cytosine in DNA and RNA, or thymine in DNA only or uracil in RNA only. (Thymine is 5-methyluracil.)

2.

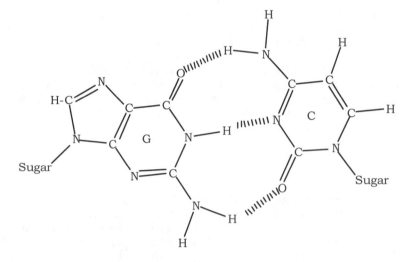

3. Oxidative deamination of cytosine produces uracil, a base not commonly found in DNA. Cells have a repair system that scans DNA for uracils and removes them. The presence of 5-methylcytosine causes problems for this repair process. Oxidative deamination of 5-methylcytosine produces 5-methyluracil, also known as thymine. Thymine is a natural component of DNA.

4.

4-base
palindromes

GAGAAATATAGATCAGAG<u>TTAACTC</u>

purine rich

6-base
palindrome

5. Adenine is a base. In general, the bases are poorly soluble in aqueous solution. Deoxyadenosine is a nucleoside composed of adenine and the 5-carbon sugar deoxyribose. Adenosine is a ribonucleoside containing the 5-carbon ribose sugar. Both deoxyadenosine and adenosine are more soluble than adenine by virtue of the hydroxyl groups on their sugar moieties. Adenosine triphosphate is ATP, a ribonucleoside triphosphate. The presence of the triphosphate group greatly increases solubility.

6. The forces holding double-stranded DNA together include hydrogen bonds and base-stacking. Denaturation of double-stranded DNA results in strand-separation and unstacking of bases. Base stacking occurs by an interaction of π-electrons located above and below the base-planes. One of the consequences of base-stacking is a decrease in the molar extinction coefficient. Stacked bases have a lower extinction coefficient than unstacked bases. Thus, denaturation is accompanied by an increase in

ultraviolet light absorption, a phenomenon known as the hyperchromic effect. The ultraviolet absorbance of denatured DNA is approximately 40% higher than that of native DNA.

7.   *Bam*HI produces 5′-overhangs as shown below:

Bgl II also produces 5′-overhangs as shown below:

The overhangs are compatible, but the hybrid site formed by joining a *Bam*HI half site with a *Bgl*II half site is not recognized by either. The junction is no longer a 6-base palindrome.

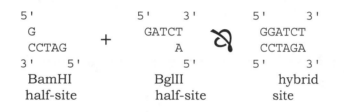

Summary

The nucleic acids, ribonucleic acid (RNA) and deoxyribonucleic acid (DNA), are important biopolymers of nucleotides, compounds containing nitrogenous bases, a 5-carbon sugar (ribose or deoxyribose) and phosphate. This chapter describes the basic biochemistry of nucleic acids and nucleotides. The nitrogenous bases come in two types, pyrimidines and purines. Pyrimidines are 6-membered, heterocyclic, aromatic ring structures containing two nitrogens. There are three principal pyrimidines: cytosine, uracil, and 5-methyluracil or thymine. Cytosine is found in both DNA and RNA, whereas uracil is in RNA and thymine in DNA. The general structure of a purine is a 5-membered imidazole ring fused to a pyrimidine ring. In DNA and RNA, there are two common purines, namely adenine and guanine. Both purines and pyrimidines contain numerous groups that can participate in hydrogen bonds as donors or acceptors or both. In fact, complementary groups exist on adenine and uracil (or thymine) and on guanine and cytosine such that they can form hydrogen-bonded pairs. This base-pairing is the foundation for the structure of double-stranded DNA.

Because the bases have extensive, conjugated double bonds, they absorb light strongly in the UV range. The conjugated bond system allows delocalization of π-electrons, forming electron clouds above and below the base-plane. Delocalized π-electrons can interact by base-stacking, another force stabilizing double-stranded DNA. Base-stacking also affects the efficiency of electronic transitions of π-electrons, such that stacked bases absorb less UV light than unstacked bases. The transition from an ordered nucleic acid structure stabilized by hydrogen bonds and base-stacking to an unordered structure is accompanied by an increase in UV absorbance. This transition is known as denaturation, and it results in a hyperchromic shift in UV absorption.

Purines and pyrimidines have low water solubility which improves when they are attached to either ribose or deoxyribose sugars through N-glycosidic bonds. The resulting compounds are known as nucleosides. The common nucleosides are cytidine, uridine, thymidine, adenosine, and guanosine. Phosphorylated derivatives of nucleosides are known as nucleotides, with phosphoric acid esterified normally to the 5′-carbon of the sugar. DNA and RNA are polymers of deoxyribonucleoside monophosphates and ribonucleoside monophosphates, respectively. But nucleoside monophosphates are not used directly to biosynthesize DNA and RNA. Rather, triphosphate derivatives serve this purpose. The nucleotides used to biosynthesize DNA are deoxyadenosine 5′-triphosphate (dATP); deoxyguanosine 5′-triphosphate (dGTP); deoxycytosine 5′-triphosphate (dCTP); and deoxy thymidine 5′-triphosphate (TTP or dTTP). The corresponding nucleoside triphosphates for RNA are adenosine 5′-triphosphate (ATP); guanosine 5′-triphosphate (GTP); cytosine 5′-triphosphate (CTP); and uridine 5′-triphosphate (UTP).

The deoxyribonucleoside triphosphates are used exclusively as building blocks for DNA. However, the ribonucleoside triphosphates, in addition to serving as the building blocks for RNA, have additional uses. ATP is the major energy currency of the cell, in addition to being a component of coenzymes such as NAD^+ and FAD. GTP is used during protein synthesis and in cell signalling; CTP is involved in phospholipid synthesis; and UTP is involved in various aspects of carbohydrate metabolism.

Nucleic acids are linear polymers of nucleoside monophosphates linked by phosphodiester bonds between the 3′-hydroxyl of one nucleotide and the 5′-phosphate of another. Because of this, nucleic acids are vectorial molecules, with two distinct ends, the 5′-end and the 3′-end. By convention, the sequence of nucleotides in a nucleic acid is represented by the one-letter abbreviations of the bases starting from the 5′-end and continuing toward the 3′-end.

The only biological role of DNA is as genetic material, and the vast majority of organisms use double-stranded DNA for this purpose. In double-stranded DNA (dsDNA), two strands of deoxyribonucleoside monophosphate polymers are joined together in an antiparallel fashion by hydrogen bonds. The hydrogen bonds occur between pairs of complementary bases: A and T; and G and C. Compositional analysis of dsDNA reveals: [A] = [T]; [C] = [G]; and [purine] = [pyrimidine]. These relationships are known as Chargaff's rules. Depending on the organism, genomic DNA may be a single DNA molecule (or chromosome) or may be divided into several discrete DNA molecules (chromosomes).

RNA serves a number of biological roles including informational, catalytic, and structural. As an informational molecule, messenger RNA functions to bring genetic information, encoded in a sequence of bases in DNA, to the ribosome, the site of cellular protein synthesis. This information is used to direct the sequence of amino acids to be joined to form a protein. mRNA production begins with transcription, in which an RNA copy of a sequence of bases along one strand of DNA is made. In eukaryotic organisms, RNA transcription is localized to the nucleus. The primary transcripts, the initial products of transcription also known as heterogeneous nuclear RNA (hnRNA), are processed into mRNA in a series of reactions. Processing includes: (1) Addition of a G residue to the 5′-end of the primary transcript and methylation of this residue and nearby ribose sugars and bases, in a process known as capping; (2) cleavage of the primary transcripts to produce a shortened 3′-end at which adenylic acid residues are added to form polyA tails; and (3) removal of various internal sequences (introns or intervening sequences) by cleavage and subsequent ligation (of exons).

The process of protein synthesis reveals structural and catalytic aspects of RNAs. Ribosomes are ribonucleoprotein complexes of ribosomal proteins and unique RNA molecules known as ribosomal RNA (rRNA). All ribosomes are composed of two parts or subunits, the small subunit and the large subunit. The structure and function of subunits during protein synthesis is determined in large part by rRNAs. The small subunit contains a single rRNA (approximately 1500 bases in prokaryotic rRNA and 1800 bases in eukaryotic rRNA). The large subunit has at least two rRNAs: a 120 bases rRNA known as the 5S rRNA; and a larger rRNA (approximately 3000 bases in prokaryotes and 5000 bases in eukaryotes). (Eukaryotes often have a so-called 5.8S rRNA, which corresponds in sequence to the 5′-end of the large subunit rRNA of prokaryotes.)

The amino acids used by the ribosome during protein synthesis are attached to the 3′-end of small RNA molecules known as transfer RNAs (tRNA). Transfer RNAs are used to decode a sequence of three adjacent nucleotides (a codon) in terms of a unique amino acid. In this process, tRNAs form hydrogen bonds between codons on mRNA and a three-base sequence, the anticodon, on tRNA. In addition to tRNAs, cells contain other relatively small, stable RNA molecules. In particular, a class of RNA molecules known as small nuclear RNAs or snRNAs are responsible for mRNA processing in the nucleus of eukaryotic cells.

Apart from the number of strands, there are only minor differences between DNA and RNA: deoxyribose versus ribose sugars, and thymine versus uracil. The absence of a 2′-OH group in deoxyribose makes DNA stable against base-catalyzed hydrolysis. In fact, DNA is a very stable molecule ideally suited as genetic material. The choice between thymine and uracil arises as a result of the tendency of cytosine to deaminate to uracil. Since thymine is found in DNA, any uracil in DNA must result from deamination of cytosine. Cells have enzymes to remove uracil in DNA, replacing it with thymine and thus preventing mutations.

There is a large number of enzymes, termed nucleases, that catalyze cleavage of phosphodiesterase bonds by hydrolysis. These include DNA-specific enzymes (DNases), RNA-specific enzymes (RNases), or non-specific nucleases that attack either internal phosphodiester bonds (endonucleases) or phosphodiester bonds on the end of a polymer (5′-exonucleases or 3′-exonucleases). Further, the phosphodiester bond may be attacked on the *a*-side, producing a 5′-phosphate, or on the *b*-side, producing a 3′-phosphate. Restriction endonucleases are DNA-specific endonucleases. There are three types (I, II, and III) of restriction endonucleases. Type I cleaves DNA without regard to sequence; type II recognizes specific sequences, often palindromic, and cleaves within the sequence; and type III recognizes a specific DNA sequence and cleaves nearby. Type II restriction endonucleases are important tools in genetic engineering and molecular biology.

Chapter 25

Structure of Nucleic Acids

• •

Chapter Outline

❖ DNA sequencing
  ⅄ Chain termination (dideoxynucleotide): Sanger
    • Enzymatic synthesis of DNA using DNA polymerase
    • Primer extended using dNTPs but terminated using specific ddNTPs (lack 3′ hydroxyl)
    • ddNTPs labelled with fluorescent dyes of different colour
    • Analyze products by electrophoresis
❖ Double-stranded DNA: Strands antiparallel: Base pairs AT and GC
  ⅄ B-form DNA: Right-handed helix
    • Parameters: 0.34 nm/base pair, 10 bp/turn, P = 3.4 nm
    • H-bonded base pairs AT and GC inside
    • Base pairs perpendicular and stacked
    • Negative charged phosphate and sugar outside
    • Major and minor groove
  ⅄ A-form DNA: Right-handed helix
    • Parameter: 0.224 nm/base pair, 11 bp/turn, P = 2.46 nm
    • Base pairs tilted
    • dsRNA and DNA/RNA hybrids
  ⅄ Z-form DNA: Left-handed helix
    • Dinucleotide repeat: Pyrimidine–purine
    • Conformation: Purine –syn, pyrimidine –anti
    • Zigzag pattern of sugar-phosphate backbone
    • 5-methylC and supercoils stabilize
❖ Intercalating agents: Planar, hydrophobic molecules that insert between stacked base pairs: Ethidium bromide, acridine orange, actinomycin D
❖ Alternative hydrogen-bonded structures
  ⅄ Cruciforms: Inverted repeats form stems and loops
  ⅄ Hoogsteen pairs:
    • Alternatives to AT and GC pairing that does not interfere with canonical pairs
    • H-DNA: Triple helix formed by Hoogsteen base pairing
    • Quadruplex DNA: Four-stranded DNA in G-rich dsDNA
❖ DNA denaturation: Strand separation and loss of base stacking
  ⅄ Temperature, pH, ionic strength: Disrupt H bonds
  ⅄ Hyperchromic shift of UV absorbance upon denaturation
  ⅄ T_m: Midpoint of transition, $T_m = 69.3 + 0.42(\%G+C)$ in 0.2 M Na^+
❖ Renaturation
  ⅄ Reannealling of single stranded nucleic acids
  ⅄ For genomic DNA: Rate reflects complexity of DNA
  ⅄ Nucleic acid hybridization
    • Measure evolutionary relationships
    • Identify specific gene
❖ DNA molecules
  ⅄ Linear: Chromosomes of eukaryotes
  ⅄ Circular: Bacterial chromosomes, plasmids, some viruses

- ❖ Supercoils: Release of tortional stress due to underwinding or overwinding of DNA
  - ⅄ Negative supercoils: Underwound DNA
  - ⅄ Positive supercoils: Overwound DNA
  - ⅄ $L = T + W$
    - ⸰ L = linking number
    - ⸰ T = twist: Number of helical turns
    - ⸰ W = writhe: Number of supercoils ($W = 0$ for relaxed DNA)
  - ⅄ Superhelical density, $\sigma = (L - L_0)/L_0$
  - ⅄ Natural DNA negatively supercoiled as a result of topoisomerase activity
    - ⸰ Type I topoisomerases: Cut one strand
    - ⸰ Type II topoisomerases: Cut two strands
- ❖ Eukaryote chromosomes
  - ⅄ Nucleoprotein complexes called chromatin
  - ⅄ Nucleosomes: Histone H2A, H2B, H3, H4 octamers with 146 bp of dsB-DNA wrapped in left-handed coil making about 1.65 turns
  - ⅄ Histones: Basic: Arginine- and lysine-rich proteins
  - ⅄ Histone H1: Link consecutive nucleosomes together
  - ⅄ Solenoid: 30 nm filaments: 6 nucleosomes/turn
  - ⅄ Nonhistone proteins
    - ⸰ SMC proteins: ATPases involved in chromosome dynamics
      - • Multiple domains: DNA-binding, ATP-binding, hinge, dimerization domain
- ❖ Chemical synthesis of DNA
  - ⅄ Solid phase synthesis using "gene machine"
  - ⅄ Phosphoramidite chemistry
  - ⅄ 3′ to 5′ direction
- ❖ RNA structure: Typically single-stranded molecules: Intrastrand H bonding produces secondary structures
  - ⅄ Stems: A-form dsRNA ± internal bulges
  - ⅄ Loops
    - ⸰ U-turns
    - ⸰ Tetraloops
  - ⅄ Junctions
    - ⸰ Region where several stem-loops meet
  - ⅄ Others
    - ⸰ Coaxial stacking of two stems
    - ⸰ Pseudoknots
      - • Pairing of bases in loop of stem and loop
      - • Pseudo because pairing is less than a full turn of the helix
    - ⸰ Ribose zippers
- ❖ RNA classes
  - ⅄ tRNA: Small (73 to 94 nucleotides) RNA charged with amino acids
    - ⸰ Aminoacylated tRNA: Substrate for protein synthesis and decoding function
    - ⸰ Cloverleaf secondary structure
      - • Acceptor stem: CCA 3′: End at which amino acid is attached
      - • D loop: Modified base
      - • Anticodon stem and loop: Three-base anticodon: Decodes mRNA
      - • TψG loop: Modified base
  - ⅄ rRNA: Component of ribosome: Protein synthetic machinery
    - ⸰ Small subunit: Single rRNA: 16S (1500 nt) or 18S (1800 nt)
    - ⸰ Large subunit: Two or three rRNAs
      - • Large subunit rRNA: 23S (2900 nt) or 28S (5000 nt)
      - • 5S rRNA: 120 nt
      - • 5.8S rRNA: 160 nt (eukaryotic cytoplasmic ribosomes)

Chapter Objectives

Sequencing Nucleic Acids

It is important to know how DNA is sequenced. The chain termination or dideoxy method was developed by F. Sanger. DNA is produced enzymatically using a template and a primer that defines the 5′-end of the DNA that is produced. As the primer is being extended, base-specific chain-termination events produce a nested set of extension products. The sequence of the synthesized strand is determined by separating the products according to size using electrophoresis. The sequence of the synthesized strand is read from the gel or from an autoradiograph of the gel starting from short products and moving toward long products, reading 5′ to 3′.

DNA Secondary Structure

Understand the structure of B-form double-stranded DNA. The two strands are antiparallel and are held together by complementary base pairs. The strands wrap around each other forming a right-handed helix with 10 base pairs per helix turn, 3.4 nm per turn, and 0.34 nm between base pairs along the helix axis. The helix axis runs perpendicular to the planar base pairs. Because the helix axis is centred within the base pairs, the helix has a major and a minor groove. Compared to B-form DNA, A-form DNA has 11 base pairs per helical turn, and as a consequence the helix is broader, the base pairs are tilted with respect to the helix axis, and they are closer together. Double-stranded RNA and DNA–RNA hybrids assume the A-form conformation. Z-DNA is a left-handed structure requiring regions of alternating pyrimidine–purine sequence to form.

Solution Properties of DNA

Many techniques in genetic engineering and molecular biology exploit the properties of double-stranded DNA. For example, DNA solutions can be freed of protein by extraction with organic solvents such as liquid phenol or chloroform because DNA is a highly charged, polar molecule. It is not soluble and will therefore not partition into these immiscible organic solvents. To precipitate DNA, an alcohol like ethanol or propanol is added to an aqueous DNA solution. However, a counter ion (Na^+ or NH_4^+) must be present in order for the negatively charged DNA to form a salt and precipitate. Many techniques require single-stranded DNA. DNA can be denatured by high temperatures or by treatment with urea or formamide to disrupt hydrogen bonds. Additionally, pH values in excess of 11.5 will disrupt hydrogen bonds.

Intracellular DNA

In general, cellular DNAs are extremely large molecules and, in order to fit inside a cell, DNA must be compacted. Prokaryotic organisms accomplish this, in part, by having circular DNAs that are supercoiled. Eukaryotic organisms take a different approach: DNA is associated with specific proteins, termed histones, in complexes known as nucleosomes. Nucleosomes are octamers of two each of histones H2A, H2B, H3, and H4 around which double-stranded DNA is wrapped to give the appearance of "beads-on-a-string." The nucleosomes are further organized into solenoids having six nucleosomes per turn to produce 30-nm filaments. The filaments are further organized to form miniband units of the chromosome. The structures actually seen by light microscopy during mitosis or meiosis are even more highly condensed.

RNA

RNAs are typically single-stranded molecules. However, they may have complementary regions that interact by base pairing to form short stretches of A-form helix. An example of this is the cloverleaf secondary structure model of tRNAs. Know the general structure of a tRNA and be able to identify important regions such as the D loop, anticodon, variable loop, TψC loop, and acceptor stem. Like proteins, RNAs have tertiary structure, and in tRNA, the interactions responsible for tertiary structure are made between residues far removed from each other in the sequence. In phylogenetic sequence comparisons, these residues have been identified as highly conserved positions and are virtually identical in all tRNAs. Phylogenetic comparisons have been made with small subunit-ribosomal RNAs and with large-subunit RNAs. These large, stable RNA molecules play a key role in protein synthesis, a fundamental cellular reaction.

Problems and Solutions

1. The oligonucleotide d-AGATGCCTGACT was subjected to sequencing by Sanger's dideoxy method, using fluorescent-tagged dideoxy-nucleotides and capillary electrophoresis, essentially as shown in Figure 25.3. Draw a diagram of the gel-banding pattern within the capillary.

Answer: In order to sequence the oligonucleotide d-AGATGCCTGACT by the Sanger dideoxy method, a reaction is set up such that the oligonucleotide serves as a template for primer extension using a DNA polymerase. As the primer is extended, sequence-specific terminations occur, producing a set of extended primer products that differ in length on their 3'-ends. The sequence actually read in Sanger sequencing is the sequence of the extended primer strand (which is complementary to the template strand).

The sequence-specific stops are generated by chain termination during polymerization. The polymerase is supplied with deoxynucleotide triphosphates—dATP, dGTP, dCTP, and dTTP—plus small amounts of fluorescently labelled dideoxynucleotides—ddATP, ddGTP, ddCTP, and ddTTP. When the polymerase begins a round of elongation, it fills its nucleotide elongation site with a nucleotide complementary to the template. The solution, however, is a mixture of regular deoxynucleotide and dideoxynucleotide, and so either a normal deoxynucleotide or a dideoxynucleotide is selected. If a normal deoxynucleotide is used, the polymerase simply extends the nascent single-stranded DNA molecule by one nucleoside monophosphate. If a dideoxynucleotide is used, the nascent chain has this nucleotide attached to its 3'-end. Since elongation depends on a 3'-hydroxyl group, the chain terminates with addition of the dideoxynucleoside. Additionally, the chain is now modified with a fluorescent dye. When the mixture is subject to capillary electrophoresis, fragments will separate by size with smaller fragments migrating faster. The electrophoresis unit is equipped with a laser fluorescent spectroscope that scans at a fixed position in the capillary. As DNA molecules migrate past the laser, they are excited and fluoresce. The wavelength and magnitude of the fluorescence is recorded to identify the dideoxynucleotide. Figure 25.3 shows a snapshot of capillary electrophoresis with bands at different locations in the capillary system, each showing a colour dependent on the dideoxynucleotide on its 3'-end.

To get an idea of what the gel might look like, let's assume a 20-base sequencing primer was used. The following set of products would be produced with their 3'-ends labelled with different fluorescent dyes attached to each of the dideoxynucleotides.

G	A	T	C
22	21	23	24
26	25	30	28
27	29	32	31
36	36	36	36

(Included in each column were limiting values (i.e., 36) to simply show the top of the gel.) Reading from bottom to top gives the sequence of the extended primer 5' to 3'. The sequence is: 5' AGTCAGGCATCT 3'. This corresponds to a template sequence: 5' AGATGCCTGACT 3'.

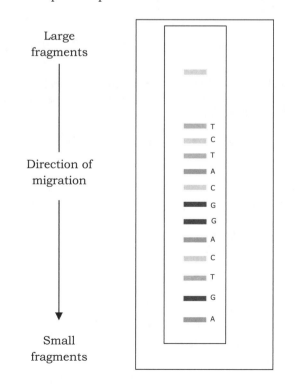

Large fragments

Direction of migration

Small fragments

3. X-ray diffraction studies indicate the existence of a novel double-stranded DNA helical conformation in which ΔZ (the rise per base pair) = 0.32 nm and P (the pitch) = 3.36 nm. What are the other parameters of this novel helix: (a) the number of base pairs per turn, (b) Δφ (the mean rotation per base pair), and (c) c (the true repeat)?

Answer: For dsDNA with $\Delta Z = 0.32$ nm/base pair, $P = 3.36$ nm/turn

a.   The number of base pairs per turn is

$$\frac{3.36\,\dfrac{\text{nm}}{\text{turn}}}{0.32\,\dfrac{\text{nm}}{\text{base pair}}} = 10.5 \text{ per turn}$$

b.   The mean rotation per base is

$$\frac{360\,\dfrac{\text{deg}}{\text{turn}}}{10.5\,\dfrac{\text{base pairs}}{\text{turn}}} = 34.3° \text{per base pair}$$

c.   To determine the true repeat, first find what values of X and Y satisfy the following equation:

$$X \text{ turns} \times 10.5\,\frac{\text{base pairs}}{\text{turn}} = Y \text{ base pair}$$

After 21 base pairs, and two turns, the helix repeats itself. The true repeat is

$$2 \text{ turns} \times 3.36\,\frac{\text{nm}}{\text{turn}} = 6.72 \text{ nm}$$

5. If 80% of the base pairs in a duplex DNA molecule (12.5 kbp) are in the B-conformation and 20% are in the Z-conformation, what is the long dimension of the molecule?

Answer: Z-DNA contains 12 base pairs per turn, 0.36 to 0.38 nm rise per base pair, and a pitch of 4.86 nm. If 20% of a 12.5 kbp DNA molecule is in Z-conformation and the rest is B-conformation, this represents 2.5 kbp in Z-DNA and 10.0 kbp in B-DNA. The overall length is:

$$2.5 \text{ kbp} \times 0.37\,\frac{\text{nm}}{\text{bp}} + 10.0 \text{ kbp} \times 0.34\,\frac{\text{nm}}{\text{bp}} = 4325 \text{ nm} = 4.33\,\mu\text{m}$$

7. Suppose 1 double-helical turn of a superhelical DNA molecule changes conformation from B-form to Z-form. What are the changes in L, W, and T? Why do you suppose the transition of DNA from B-form to Z-form is favoured by negative supercoiling?

Answer: Z-DNA has 12 bp/turn and B-DNA has 10 bp/turn. For 1 turn of B-form helix:

$$L_\text{B} = 1.0 + W_\text{B}$$

Now, this turn includes 10 bp, which in Z-DNA makes only $(10/12)$th of a turn; thus:

$$L_\text{Z} = \frac{10}{12} + W_\text{Z} = 0.83 + W_\text{Z}$$

For a transition from B to Z, strands are not broken, so:

$$L_\text{B} = L_\text{Z} \text{ or}$$
$$1.0 + W_\text{B} = 0.83 + W_\text{Z} \text{ or}$$
$$W_\text{Z} - W_\text{B} = 0.167$$

That is, in going from B- to Z-DNA, there is a positive change in superhelicity. Given some number of negative supercoils in B-DNA, this number will be reduced in Z-DNA. Thus, negative supercoils favour Z-DNA.

9.   The characteristic secondary structures of tRNA and rRNA molecules are achieved through intrastrand hydrogen bonding. Even for the small tRNAs, remote regions of the primary sequence interact via H bonding when the molecule adopts the cloverleaf pattern. Using Figure 25.33 as a guide, draw the primary structure of tRNA and label the positions of its various self-complementary regions.

Answer:

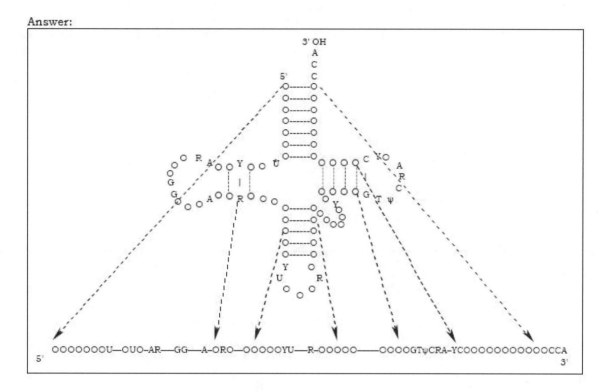

11.   At 0.2 M Na⁺, the melting temperature of double-stranded DNA is given by the formula T_m = 69.3 + 0.41(%G + C). The DNAs from mice and rats have (G + C) contents of 44% and 40%, respectively. Calculate the T_ms for these DNAs in 0.2 M NaCl. If samples of these DNAs were inadvertently mixed, how might they be repurified from one another?

Answer: The T_m in 0.2 M Na is given by:

$$T_m = 69.3 + 0.41 \times \%(G+C)$$

$$T_{m(mouse)} = 69.3 + 0.41 \times 44 = 87.3°C$$

$$T_{m(rat)} = 69.3 + 0.41 \times 40 = 85.7°C$$

The density of DNA is dependent on base composition and so isopycnic centrifugation in CsCl could be attempted. (However, it might prove far easier to just start out with new rats and mice.)

13.   (Integrates with Chapter 24) Pseudouridine (ψ) is an invariant base in the TψC loop of tRNA; ψ is also found in strategic places in rRNA. (Figure 24.23 shows the structure of pseudouridine.) Draw the structure of base pair that ψ might form with G.

Answer: Uridine and pseudouridine are drawn below. In pseudouridine, because the base is attached to a carbon (and not a nitrogen as in uridine), pseudouridine has an additional hydrogen-bond donor. To form a pair with guanine, we must match up H-bond donors and acceptors.

Uridine, U   Pseudouridine, ψ

In the figure below, a canonical G:C base pair is drawn along with a G:U pair and two possible pairings of G and Ψ. G pairs with U but the U has to be positioned in a slightly different location relative to the C of a GC pair. The G:U pair is an example of a wobble interaction. One of the two G:Ψ pairs below looks like a G:U pair, whereas the other has the ribose in a very different location.

15. Listed below are 5 DNA sequences. Which one contains a type-II restriction endonuclease ("6-cutter") hexanucleotide site? Which one is likely to form a cruciform structure? Which one is likely to be found in Z-DNA? Which one represents the 5'-end of a tRNA gene? Which one is most likely to be found in a triplex DNA structure?

 a. CGCGCGCCGCGCACGCGCTCGCGCGCCGC
 b. GAACGTCGTATTCCCGTACGACGTTC
 c. CAGGTCTCTCTCTCTCTCTCTC
 d. TGGTGCGAATTCTGTGGAT
 e. ATCGGAATTCATCG

Answer: The 6-cutter is sequence (e). Type-II restriction endonucleases typically digest sequences that are palindromic, meaning the sequence of the top strand is the same as the complementary strand when read 5' to 3'. While some type-II enzymes recognize interrupted palindromes, most have uninterrupted palindromic sequences as targets. An easy way to search by eye for a uninterrupted palindromic sequence is to look for two adjacent bases that are complementary like AT or TA or GC or GC. These are in fact 2-base uninterrupted palindromes. To see if the 2-base palindrome happens to be part of a larger palindrome, we need to look at the flanking bases to see if they are complementary. If they are, then the sequence is a 4-base palindrome. There is actually a 6-base palindrome in sequence (a) (CGCGCG) right at the 5'-end, and this sequence repeats itself further down the sequence. There are, however, no enzymes that recognize this sequence. The palindrome GCGCGC, which is recognized by the restriction endonuclease *Bss*HII, is also found twice in sequence (a). But this sequence also has many CG (pyrimidine–purine) repeats characteristic of Z-DNA. Sequence (b) has CGTACG near its 3′-end, which is recognized by *Bsw*WI. Sequence (c) also has a 6-base sequence recognized by *Bsa*I, which recognizes GGTCTC and cuts downstream of this sequence. Sequences (d) and (e) both have GAATTC, which is the recognition site for *Eco*RI. So they all have "6-cutter" sites, but sequence (e) only matches to the first question and not any of the others.

After I was done visually inspecting the sequences as explained above, I ran the sequences through NEB cutter (http://tools.neb.com/NEBcutter2/index.php). This is a very useful site for analysis of DNA for restriction endonuclease recognition sites. After submitting a sequence, I selected "Custom digest" from the "Main options" menu and selected "Enzymes with a particular site length" and restricted this to 6-base recognition sites.

Cruciform structure is (b). Cruciform structures require inverted repeats. These are sequences that show two-fold symmetry: the sequence 5′ to 3′ is identical in both strands. Palindromes are inverted repeats, but they have problems folding into cruciforms because the terminal loops are too tight. Sequences that form cruciforms are interrupted palindromes. In sequence (a), we decided that there were two 6-base recognition sites for the enzyme *Bss*HII, and they are separated by several bases and might form a cruciform. Sequence (b) has a 10-base inverted repeat. The first 10 bases on the strand shown are duplicated on the bottom strand, so sequence (b) could form a cruciform with a 10-base pair stem and a 6-base loop. One way to look for palindromes is to do a dot plot of the sequence versus its reverse complement or inverse complement. The reverse complement is simply the complement written 5′ to 3′. Generating reverse complements by hand is easy enough for short sequences, but the following URL has a program to do this: http://www.bioinformatics.org/sms/index.html. A simple dot plot program can be found at http://www.vivo.colostate.edu/molkit/dnadot/index.html. This same site also has a sequence manipulation program that will generate inverse complements. Inverted repeats show up along the diagonal in a dot plot ,and the only sequence to give a strong diagonal is (b).

Z-DNA is formed in regions containing pyrimidine–purine repeats, and sequence (a) fits the bill.

The 3′-end of tRNAs end in 5′...CCA-3′, and so we need to look for a sequence complementary to this, namely 5′ TGG...3′, and sequence (d) works.

The only sequence we haven't used is (c), which can form a triplex DNA. Sequence requirements for triple-stranded DNA formation include two pyrimidine-rich strands and a third purine-rich strand. Sequence (c) and its complement are pyrimidine-rich and purine-rich, respectively.

17. Online resources provide ready access to detailed information about human genome. Go the National Center for Biotechnology Information (NCBI) genome database at http://www.ncbi.nlm.nih.gov/genome/ and click on Homo sapiens in the Map Viewer genome annotation updates list to access the chromosome map and organization of the human genome. Next, go to http://www.ncbi.nlm.nih.gov/genome/ In the "Search For" box, type in the following diseases to discover the chromosomal location of the affected gene and, by exploring links highlighted by the search results, to discover the name of the protein affected by the disease:
   a. Sickle-cell anemia
   b. Tay–Sachs disease

Answer: a. For some reason a search for "sickle-cell anemia" at Map Viewer failed to yield results, but "sickle-cell" did return one hit near the tip of the short arm of chromosome 11. The human genome view on which the hit is highlighted shows the 22 human autosomes, X and Y chromosomes, and the mitochondria. The autosomes are arranged (and named) from biggest to smallest with short arm on top. In addition, the search result returned hits to different assemblies. Human sickle-cell anemia is caused by a mutation in the beta-globin gene. Activating the link below chromosome 11 will return a more detailed map. On the left-hand side is an Ideogram showing the location of the hit referenced against chromosome-banding patterns. You should see that the beta-globin gene is located between band 11p15 and the telomere. You can use the "Maps & Options" button to change maps. One of the more useful maps to use is the Gene map, which includes links to OMIM (On line Mendelian Inheritance in Man), a database dedicated to diseases. Be sure to make the gene map the master map in order to see links to other databases from it.
b. Tay–Sachs disease yielded hits on chromosome 15 (when only "Tay-Sachs" was searched for). A link to OMIM is shown when chromosome 15 is activated and the gene map viewed on the returned page. By using the link to OMIM we learn that Tay–Sachs disease is an autosomal, progressive neurodegenerative disorder that is fatal at an early age and involves the gene for the protein hexosaminidase A. Using the protein link (pr) (you only see this link and others when the gene map is the master map), which eventually leads to NP_000511, we find a summary of hexosaminidase A, where we learn that this protein is a subunit of the lysosomal enzyme beta–hexosaminidase. This enzyme is responsible for degradation of ganglioside GM2 and other N-acetyl hexosamines.

Questions for Self-Study

1. For DNA sequencing using the chain termination or dideoxy technique, which of the following are true and which are false?
   a. The 5′-ends of synthesized DNAs have dideoxynucleotides on them.
   b. The 5′-ends of synthesized DNAs are determined by the sequence of the primer.
   c. The sequence read is the sequence of the template strand.
   d. The DNA polymerase moves along the template strand 3′ to 5′.
   e. In automatic sequencing, the 3′-ends of products are labelled with fluorescent agents.
   f. The 3′-ends of extension products are all the same.
   g. Only double-stranded DNA can be sequenced using this technique.

2. Double stranded DNA is composed of canonical base pairs.
   a. What are they?
   b. What is the orientation between the two strands of dsDNA?
   c. What is the consequence of the two glycosidic bonds holding the bases in each base pair not being directly opposite one another?

3. Answer the following questions with A (A-form DNA), B (B-form DNA) or Z (Z-DNA).
   a. The double-helical form adopted by double stranded RNA _____
   b. Left-handed helix _____
   c. Approximately 10 base pairs per turn _____
   d. Plane of base pair perpendicular to helix axis _____
   e. Accommodates syn glycosyl bond conformation _____
   f. Is stabilized by cytosine methylation and by supercoiling _____
   g. Formation is sequence dependent _____
   h. Approximately 11 base pairs per turn _____
   i. Helix axis runs through the base pairs _____
   j. Helix axis runs through the major groove _____

4. Fill in the blanks. The transition from dsDNA to single-strand DNA is called _____. This process occurs when DNA is subjected to conditions such as _____ or _____ that disrupt _____ bonds. The transition is accompanied by an _____ in the UV absorbance, or a _____ shift, caused by _____ of bases. The temperature at which one-half of the dsDNA has converted to ssDNA is termed the _____ temperature. This temperature is dependent on the solution conditions. For example, as salt concentration increases, the transition temperature _____. High values of pH and high concentrations of urea will _____ the transition temperature. The reverse process, namely the transition from ssDNA to dsDNA, is termed _____. The rate of this transition is dependent on the complexity of the DNA such that highly repetitive DNA will produce dsDNA at a _____ rate, whereas single-copy, complex DNA will produce dsDNA at a _____ rate.

5. Order the following terms: miniband, chromosome, histone HI, nucleosome, solenoid, base pair, histone octamer.

6. On the diagram of the secondary structure of tRNA shown below indicate the location of the following features:

   a. Anticodon
   b. Acceptor stem
   c. CCA
   d. D loop
   e. Variable loop
   f. Location of highly conserved bases involved in tertiary interactions
   g. Anticodon stem
   h. 5′ end
   I. 3′ end

Answers

1. a. F; b. T; c. F; d. T; e. T; f. F; g. F

2. a. AT and GC; b. The two strands are antiparallel; c. The helix has a major groove and a minor groove.

3. a. A; b. Z; c. B; d. B; e. Z; f. Z; g. Z; h. A; I. B; j. A

4. denaturation (or melting); pH; temperature (or changes in ionic strength, urea concentration, formamide concentration); hydrogen; increase; hyperchromic; unstacking; melting (or transition or T_m); increases; decrease; renaturation (or reannealling); fast; slow.

5. base pair < histone HI < histone octamer < nucleosome < solenoid < miniband < chromosome.

6.

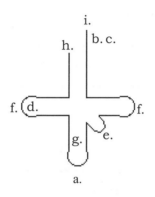

Additional Problems

1. Phylogenetic sequence comparisons have played a key role in determining the secondary structure of ribosomal RNAs. Helical regions are first identified as complementary regions within an RNA sequence from a particular organism. However, the existence of complementary bases does not prove that a helix forms between two regions. Evidence in support of a secondary structure is gained by comparing the same regions from other organisms. The object of this comparison is to find examples of compensatory base-changes for each complementary pair suspected of being part of a helix. Compensatory base-changes identify conserved base-pairs as opposed to conserved sequences that happen to be complementary. The sequences presented below are a small portion of the small-subunit rRNA from three different organisms. Each can form hairpin structures.

    a. Identify the complementary regions involved in hairpin formation. (In addition to the canonical base pairs, G:U pairs are found in RNA helices.)
    b. Locate compensatory base-changes within the helical regions of the hairpin.

Organism	Sequence
Halobacterium cutirbrum	UAGCCGUAGGGGAAUCUGCGGCUG
Homo sapiens	UUUCCGUAGGUGAACCUGCGGAAG
Homo sapiens (mitochondria)	UAAGUGUACUGGAAAGUGCACUUG

2. A common technique used to isolate plasmid DNA from bacterial cells is to lyse cells in a solution containing SDS and sodium hydroxide, neutralize the lysate using potassium acetate, and centrifuge the neutralized lysate to remove chromosomal DNA and cellular debris. Explain why this technique separates chromosomal DNA from plasmid DNA.

3. Ethidium bromide is an intercalating agent used to stain DNA. It can be removed from DNA solutions by extraction with butanol. How does ethidium bromide interact with DNA and how does butanol extraction overcome this interaction?

4. There is currently a great deal of interest in repetitive DNA as markers to identify an individual's DNA. Sketch a $c_o t$ curve for a DNA sample composed of 40% repetitive DNA and 60% non-repetitive DNA. Suggest a possible technique for isolating repetitive DNA.

5. During synthesis of an oligonucleotide using phosphoramidite chemistry, a failure occurred at the very last coupling cycle such that only half of the oligonucleotides got extended to full length. The oligonucleotide was to be used for two purposes: as a primer in dideoxynucleotide sequencing, and as a mutagenic primer in site-specific mutagenesis. (In oligonucleotide-directed, site-specific mutagenesis, an oligonucleotide, with a single-base difference from a wild-type sequence, is used as a primer to synthesize a mutant copy of a template DNA.) Would it be wise for the researcher to use the synthesized oligonucleotide without purifying the full-length oligonucleotide product?

Abbreviated Answers

1. The primary and secondary structures are drawn below with compensatory base-changes indicated by arrows.

Primary Structure	Secondary Structure
Halobacterium cutirbrum 5'　　　　　　　　　　3' UAGCCGUAGGGGAAUCUGCGGCUG	5'　　　　　　　G UAGCCGUAGG　　G ‖‖‖‖‖‖‖‖‖‖　　A GUCGGCGUCU　A 3' ⇑　　　　⇑ A
Homo sapiens 5'　　　　　　　　　　3' UUUCCGUAGGUGAACCUGCGGAAG	5'　　　　　　　U UUUCCGUAGG　　G ‖‖‖‖‖‖‖‖‖‖　　A GAAGGCGUCC　A 3'⇑⇑　　　⇑
Homo sapiens (mitochondria) 5'　　　　　　　　　　3' UAAGUGUACUGGAAAGUGCACUUG	5'　　　　　　　G UAAGUGUACU　　G ‖‖‖‖‖‖‖‖‖‖　　A GUUCACGUGA　A 3' ⇑⇑⇑　⇑⇑

2. The combination of SDS and sodium hydroxide will lyse cells. SDS is a strong protein denaturant that will remove protein from DNA. Sodium hydroxide will denature DNA. Closed-circular, plasmid DNA is resistant to denaturation because as base pairs are broken and DNA is unwound, supercoils are introduced in plasmid DNA. Supercoiling prevents complete denaturation from occurring. Upon addition of potassium acetate, the basic sodium hydroxide is rapidly neutralized. Plasmid DNA renatures, whereas chromosomal DNA forms a tangled mass of partially single-stranded and partially double-stranded DNA. Further, a potassium-SDS salt forms that is insoluble and precipitates. This precipitate together with cellular debris, denatured protein, and tangled, chromosomal DNA are all removed from solution upon centrifugation leaving behind plasmid DNA. (Because RNA is sensitive to base-catalyzed cleavage, some of the cellular RNA is destroyed as well.)

3. The structure of ethidium bromide is shown below.

This planar molecule will intercalate between stacked base pairs and interact via π-bonding. (In this state or when dissolved in organic solvents, ethidium will fluoresce when excited with ultraviolet light. Ethidium fluorescence is commonly used to detect DNA in agarose or acrylamide gels.) The presence of delocalized π-electrons makes ethidium very soluble in organic solvents. During extraction of DNA/ethidium solutions with butanol, the ethidium will partition into the organic phase.

4. It may be possible to isolate repetitive DNA using isopycnic centrifugation provided the density of the repetitive DNA is different than the average density of the non-repetitive DNA.

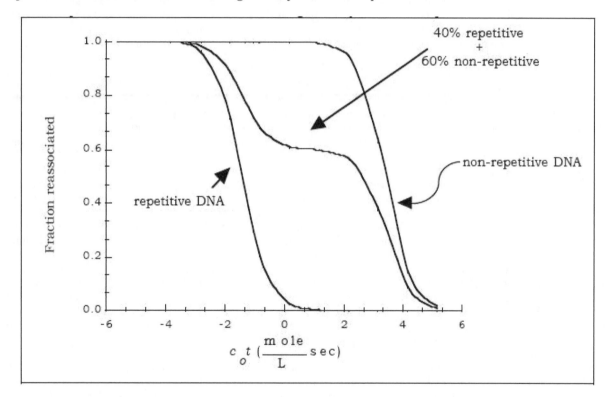

5. Provided a capping step is carried out during each cycle of oligonucleotide synthesis, a failure at any one step will produce an oligonucleotide of length equal to the cycle number at which the failure occurred. Thus, failure at the last step produces a polymer one nucleotide shorter than the full-length oligonucleotide. The full-length product and the failure product have the same 3′-ends but differ by one base on their 5′-ends. Using a mixture of the two as primers for sequencing will produce two sets of sequence products that differ at each band by a single base, giving the sequencing gel the appearance of having "shadow bands."

The mixture of products should pose no problems in oligonucleotide-directed, site-specific mutagenesis.

Summary

In the chain termination method of DNA sequencing, a DNA strand of unknown sequence is enzymatically copied using DNA polymerase, dATP, dGTP, dCTP, and dTTP, plus four dideoxynucleoside triphosphate analogs uniquely labelled with fluorescent dyes. Incorporation of a dideoxynucleotide into the growing chain terminates subsequent extension of the chain. Represented among the products is a "ladder" of DNA strands, each one residue longer than the next. The sequence is revealed by considering which dideoxy-NTP analog specifically ended the strand. The 3'-ends of DNA are labelled with dideoxynucleotides carrying different fluorescent dyes to distinguish products from one another.

The double helix is the dominant secondary structure of DNA. Two DNA strands of opposite polarity and complementary base sequence are paired through formation of interchain hydrogen bonds. Exclusive pairing of A only with T and G only with C creates spatially equivalent units, the canonical, or "Watson-Crick", A:T and G:C base pairs. The double helix is stabilized not only by these hydrogen bonds between base pairs, but also by π,π interactions as the flat hydrophobic faces of the aromatic base pairs stack upon one another down the helix centre. Hydrogen bonds between the polar sugar-phosphates of the two strands and the surrounding water contribute to helix stability. The negatively charged phosphates along the backbone are localized to the exterior of the helix where they can enter into stabilizing ionic interactions with cations in solution. The prevalent double-helical form of DNA in solution is the B-conformation, in which the base pairs are arranged virtually at right angles to the helix axis, and each base pair circumscribes an angle of 36° around the helix. Thus there are about 10 base pairs per helix turn. Each base pair contributes 0.34 nm to the length of the helix, whose pitch then is 3.4 nm. Because the N-glycosidic bonds of the paired bases are not directly across the helix diameter from one another, the sugar-PO_4 backbones are not spaced symmetrically about the helix circumference and the helix has a major and a minor groove.

DNA can adopt double-helical forms other than the B-conformation. An alternative right-handed form is A-DNA, a "shorter, squatter" helix formed upon slight dehydration of B-DNA. A-DNA has 11 base pairs per turn. DNA:RNA hybrids and double-stranded regions of RNA chains are typically of the A-conformation. Z-DNA is a left-handed double helix. Typically, Z-DNA or regions of DNA in the Z-conformation have an alternating purine–pyrimidine nucleotide sequence, as in dCpGpCpGpCpG. Along either strand, the GpC dinucleotide is conformationally different than the CpG next in line. GpC dinucleotides circumscribe an angle of −45° about the helix axis, but CpGs cover only −15°. Thus, the GpCs are the "horizontal" zigs and the CpGs are the "vertical" zags of this "zigzag" or Z-DNA. Z-DNA has 12 base pairs per turn and a single narrow groove.

The double helix in solution is a dynamic, flexible structure, best described in terms of tertiary structure as a semi-rigid random coil. Even its short-range structure is not truly represented as a smooth, featureless barberpole-like molecule. Bases differ sufficiently in structural character that a short sequence of them lends a structural "signature" to its localized segment of DNA, generating the possibility for sequence-specific recognition by DNA-binding proteins.

Bases are capable of pairing in a variety of ways to form novel DNA structures like cruciforms, triplexes, and quadruplexes. Cruciform DNA arises from canonical (AT, TA, GC, GC) pairing of inverted repeats within the same strand of DNA. Triplexes and quadruplexes depend on Hoogsteen pairing between T and A and protonated C and G. Hoogsteen pairs do not interfere with canonical base pairing and so both can occur leading to H-DNA, which is triplex DNA. Quadruplex structures are formed with G-rich regions interacting in parallel via Hoogsteen bonding.

Environmental extremes of temperature, pH, or ionic strength can disrupt the hydrogen bonds between the base pairs, leading to separation of the DNA strands, so-called "denaturation" or "melting" of DNA. The strands will "reanneal" if appropriate conditions for H-bond formation are restored. The rate of renaturation depends on the relative concentrations of complementary strands in the DNA solution, and thus is a measure of the sequence complexity of a DNA.

Supercoils represent yet another structural complexity in DNA. They form within dsDNA that in effect has no free ends and arise because of underwinding or overwinding of the DNA helix. Both positive and negative supercoils render the DNA more compact in structure, as compared to "relaxed" DNA, which lacks supercoils. All naturally occurring circular DNA molecules are negatively supercoiled. Negative supercoiling stabilizes Z-DNA.

Chromosomes are nucleoprotein complexes, consisting principally of DNA and a set of basic proteins known as histones. The histones are organized into nucleosomes, octameric units composed of four pairs of the histones H2A, H2B, H3, and H4, around which the DNA is wound. Nucleosomes are then wound into solenoids to form a 30 nm filament, a fundamental structural motif in chromosome structure. This 30 nm filament is believed to arrange into loops of DNA perhaps a million base pairs long. A cytologically distinct structure in chromosomes, called the mini-band, may consist of 18 loops ordered around the circumference of the chromosome axis. Chromosomes contain hundreds of mini-bands.

DNA can be chemically synthesized in the laboratory using phosphoramidite derivatives of the nucleotides and solid-phase techniques of polymerization. Genes greater than 1000 base pairs in length have been assembled from oligonucleotide precursors made in this fashion, opening possibilities for the controlled manipulation of the nucleotide sequence of a gene and a facile analysis of the effects brought about by such changes.

RNA molecules are usually single-stranded. Nevertheless, RNA species have ornate, highly conserved secondary structures derived from extensive intrachain sequence complementarity in the strands. The single strands of tRNA, upon alignment of intrastrand complementary regions, form a cloverleaf secondary structure consisting of three H-bonded loops and an H-bonded stem. Hydrogen-bonding interactions between the loops then create a "bent" or L-shaped tertiary structure. Ribosomal RNA molecules also possess a high degree of intrastrand sequence complementarity, yielding a complex secondary structure on alignment. The folding patterns observed in the various rRNA species appear to have been highly conserved across the phylogenetic spectrum from archaea and bacteria to higher eukaryotes, suggesting a common design and purpose for these molecules that has persisted over evolutionary time. mRNA displays secondary structural properties as well, but little is known about the details of such structures in these rather labile RNAs.

Chapter 26

Synthesis and Degradation of Nucleotides

• •

Chapter Outline

- ❖ Nucleotides
    - ⅄ NTPs: RNA biosynthesis
        - ◆ ATP: Energy currency
        - ◆ UTP: Carbohydrate metabolism
        - ◆ CTP: Phospholipid metabolism
        - ◆ GTP: Protein synthesis, signal transduction
    - ⅄ dNTPs: DNA biosynthesis
- ❖ Formation: Two options
    - ⅄ *De novo* synthesis
    - ⅄ Salvage pathway
- ❖ One-carbon pool
    - ⅄ Biotin: Used to move carboxylate carbons
    - ⅄ Folate: Used to move carbons at other oxidation states
        - ◆ Active form tetrahydrofolate (THF): Produced by dihydrofolate reductase
        - ◆ Carbon attached to N^5, N^{10} or both
        - ◆ Carbon enters via serine hydroxymethyltransferase reaction
- ❖ Purine biosynthesis: IMP biosynthesis
    - ⅄ Synthesized on ribose-5-P
    - ⅄ Ribose-5-phosphate pyrophosphokinase reaction rate limiting: PRPP formed
        - ◆ ADP, GDP inhibitors
    - ⅄ Glutamine phosphoribosyl pyrophosphate amidotransferase
        - ◆ Committed step
        - ◆ GMP, GDP, GTP inhibitory site
        - ◆ AMP, ADP, ATP inhibitory site
        - ◆ Azaserine inhibition: Antitumour agent
    - ⅄ GAR synthetase: Condensation of glycine via carboxyl group
    - ⅄ GAR transformylase: Uses formyl-THF
        - ◆ Methotrexate inhibits
    - ⅄ FGAR amidotransferase (FGAM synthetase)
    - ⅄ AIR synthetase
        - ◆ Formation of imidazole ring
        - ◆ Activation of formyl group for second ring closure
    - ⅄ AIR carboxylase
    - ⅄ SAICAR synthetase
        - ◆ This and previous enzyme on bifunctional polypeptide
    - ⅄ Adenylosuccinase (adenylosuccinate lyase) produces AICAR
        - ◆ AICAR: Histidine biosynthesis
    - ⅄ AICAR transformylase: Uses formyl-THF: Produces FAICAR
        - ◆ Methotrexate inhibits
    - ⅄ IMP cyclohydrolase: Dehydration and ring closure
        - ◆ This and AICAR transformylase on bifunctional polypeptide

- ❖ IMP precursor of AMP and GMP
  - ⅄ AMP production
    - · Adenylosuccinate synthetase: GTP-dependent reaction
    - · Adenylosuccinase: AMP and fumarate
  - ⅄ GMP production
    - · IMP dehydrogenase
    - · GMP synthetase: ATP-dependent reaction
- ❖ NTP production
  - ⅄ Adenylate kinase: (d)AMP + ATP → (d)ADP + ADP
  - ⅄ Guanylate kinase: (d)GMP + ATP → (d)GDP + ADP
  - ⅄ Nucleoside diphosphate kinase: (d)NDP + ATP → (d)NTP + ADP
- ❖ Purine salvage
  - ⅄ Adenosine phosphoribosyltransferase: APRT
  - ⅄ Hypoxanthine-guanine phosphoribosyltransferase: HGPRT
    - · Lesch–Nyhan syndrome defect
- ❖ Purine nucleotide degradation
  - ⅄ Dietary nucleotides
    - · Nucleotidases and phosphatases produce nucleosides
    - · Nucleosidases or nucleoside phosphorylases produce bases
  - ⅄ Intracellular nucleotides
    - · Nucleotidase produces nucleosides
    - · A and dA to inosine by adenosine deaminase
    - · Purine nucleoside phosphorylase releases base as hypoxanthine
    - · Hypoxanthine to xanthine by xanthine oxidase
    - · Xanthine
      - • Hypoxanthine (from inosine) to xanthine by xanthine oxidase
      - • Guanine to xanthine by guanine deaminase
- ❖ Anaplerotic cycle: Fumarate production
  - ⅄ AMP to IMP via adenosine deaminase: Degradation
  - ⅄ IMP to AMP via adenylosuccinate synthetase and adenylosuccinase: Fumarate produced
- ❖ Uric acid: Metabolism/excretion
  - ⅄ Primates: End product (but urea production accounts for nitrogen excretion also)
    - · Excess levels leads to crystallization and gout
    - · Allopurinol blocks xanthine oxidase
  - ⅄ Birds, terrestrial reptiles, insects: Uric acid only pathway of nitrogen excretion
  - ⅄ Mollusks and other mammals: Uric acid to allantoin by urate oxidase
  - ⅄ Bony fish: Allantoin to allantoic acid by allantoinase
  - ⅄ Sharks, rays, amphibians: Allantoic acid to glyoxylic acid and urea by allantoicase
  - ⅄ Marine invertebrates: Convert urea to ammonia and carbon dioxide
- ❖ Pyrimidine biosynthesis: Precursors are carbamoyl-P and aspartate
  - ⅄ Carbamoyl-P synthetase II
    - · CPS-II and following two enzymes on multifunctional polyprotein: In mammals
    - · UDP/UTP inhibitory; PRPP and ATP stimulatory
  - ⅄ ATCase: Carbamoyl-P condensed with aspartate
    - · Regulation
      - • *E. coli* enzyme inhibited by CTP, activated by ATP
  - ⅄ Dihydroorotase: Ring closure
  - ⅄ Dihydroorotate dehydrogenase
    - · NAD$^+$-linked in bacteria
    - · Quinone-linked in eukaryotes
  - ⅄ Orotate phosphoribosyltransferase
    - · Transferase and decarboxylase (below) on UMP synthase: In mammals single polypeptide
  - ⅄ OMP decarboxylase to form UMP
- ❖ UTP and CTP formation
  - ⅄ Nucleoside monophosphate kinase: UMP + ATP → UDP + ADP

⊥ Nucleoside diphosphate kinase: UDP + ATP → UTP + ADP

⊥ CTP synthase: Animation of UTP to give CTP

❖ Pyrimidine degradation

⊥ U and C: β-Alanine, ammonium, carbon dioxide

⊥ T: β-Aminoisobutyric acid

❖ Deoxyribonucleotide biosynthesis

⊥ Ribonucleotide reductase

• $(R1)_2(R2)_2$ subunit structure

• R1: Two regulatory sites

○ Overall activity site: ATP activates, dATP inhibits

○ Substrate specificity site

▪ Bound ATP specifies UDP or CDP

▪ Bound dTTP specifies GDP

▪ Bound dGTP specifies ADP

• NADPH source of electrons

• Electrons moved to thioredoxin by thioredoxin reductase

❖ Thymine nucleotides

⊥ dUDP to dUTP to dUMP: dUTPase catalyzes last step; Or dCMP to dUMP by dCMP deaminase

⊥ dUMP to dTMP by thymidylate synthase

• 5-fluorouracil converted to inhibitor or thymidylate synthase

Chapter Objectives

Purine Biosynthesis

Purine biosynthesis starts with 5-phosphoribosyl pyrophosphate, and the complete pathway involves formation of nucleotide derivatives. N-9 is the first component of the purine ring to be added from the side chain amino group of glutamine. The five-membered, imidazole ring components include N-9 and a formylglycine residue introduced by amide linkage of glycine to N-9 followed by formylation. Before imidazole ring formation is completed, N-3 is incorporated from glutamine. Imidazole ring formation produces an amino derivative of imidazole ribotide or AIR. To complete synthesis of the purine inosine monophosphate, the precursor of ATP and GTP, two carbons and one nitrogen are needed. The first carbon is introduced as a carboxyl group, the remaining nitrogen derives from the α-amino group of aspartic acid. Aspartic acid is attached by an amide linkage to carboxylated AIR and the carbon skeleton is eliminated as fumarate. (A similar reaction occurs in the urea cycle.) Formylation of N-3, incorporated prior to imidazole-ring closure, and subsequent ring closure produces inosine monophosphate. Amination of IMP using the α-amino group of aspartate, and releasing the carbon skeleton of aspartate as fumarate produces AMP. GMP is produced by oxidation of C-2 followed by amination using the side chain nitrogen of glutamine.

Purine Degradation

The common pathway for purine degradation is to produce free bases that are metabolized to xanthine, then uric acid, and depending on the organism, allantoin, allantoic acid, urea, or CO_2, H_2O, and ammonia.

Purine Points to Consider

Know why methotrexate inhibits purine formation and why the sulfonamides (structural analogs of p-aminobenzoic acid [PABA, an ingredient in sunscreen]) function as folic acid antagonists. Understand the role of phosphoribosyltransferases in purine salvage pathways and the consequence of HGPRT deficiency (Lesch–Nyhan syndrome). Gout is a consequence of excess uric acid production. Know why allopurinol is used to treat gout.

Pyrimidine Biosynthesis

In contrast to purine synthesis, pyrimidine ring formation is completed before being attached to ribose. Synthesis starts with production of carbamoyl-phosphate from bicarbonate and the side chain amino group of glutamine. (We encountered carbamoyl-phosphate synthesis in the urea cycle where it was produced in the mitochondria. Carbamoyl-P synthesis leading to pyrimidine biosynthesis is catalyzed by a second synthetase located in the cytosol.) The nitrogen and carbon of carbamoyl-phosphate account for two of the ring components of the six-membered pyrimidine ring. The remaining components derive from aspartate. Aspartic acid is carbamoylated by amide linkage of a carbamoyl group to the α-amino group of aspartic acid. This is followed by ring closure and oxidation to produce orotate (uracil-6-carboxylic acid, with the carboxyl group from the α-carboxyl group of aspartic acid). Orotate is attached to a phosphoribosyl group and decarboxylated to form UMP.

Deoxyribonucleotide Biosynthesis

Ribonucleotide reductase catalyzes the conversion of NDP to dNDP without regard to base (see Problem 6 for details on regulation of this important enzyme). The reducing power derives from thioredoxin, a small protein with reactive sulfhydryl groups that undergo oxidation–reduction cycles. The reducing power of thioredoxin is replenished by NADPH-dependent thioredoxin reductase. Thymine nucleotides are synthesized from dUMP by methylation with methylene-tetrahydrofolate as methyl-group donor.

Problems and Solutions

1. Draw the purine and pyrimidine ring structures, indicate the metabolic source of each atom in the rings.

Answer: For purine biosynthesis:

For pyrimidine biosynthesis:

3. Illustrate the key points of regulation in (a) the biosynthesis of IMP, AMP, and GMP; (b) E. coli pyrimidine biosynthesis; and (c) mammalian pyrimidine biosynthesis.

Answer: a. IMP is the precursor of both AMP and GMP, and its production is regulated by both purine nucleotides. Regulation occurs in the first two steps catalyzed by ribose-5-phosphate pyrophosphorylase and glutamine phosphoribosyl-pyrophosphate amidotransferase. Ribose-5-phosphate pyrophosphorylase is inhibited by both ADP and GDP. Glutamine phosphoribosyl-pyrophosphate amidotransferase regulation is similar, but more complex. This enzyme is sensitive to inhibition by AMP, ADP, and ATP at one site, and inhibition by GMP, GDP, and GTP at another site, and the enzyme is activated by PRPP. IMP is a branch point to either AMP or GMP. AMP production from IMP initiates with adenylosuccinate synthetase, an enzyme that is inhibited by AMP, the final product of the branch. In an analogous fashion, GMP production from IMP initiates with IMP dehydrogenase subject to GMP inhibition.

b. The first step in pyrimidine biosynthesis is the formation of carbamoyl phosphate in a reaction catalyzed by aspartate transcarbamoylase. In *E. coli*, ATCase is feedback inhibited by CTP and activated by ATP.

c. In contrast, regulation of pyrimidine biosynthesis in mammals occurs at the level of carbamoyl phosphate synthesis. Both UTP and CTP inhibit carbamoyl phosphate synthetase II, whereas PRPP and ATP are allosteric activators.

5. Since dUTP is not a normal component of DNA, why do you suppose ribonucleotide reductase has the capacity to convert UDP to dUDP?

Answer: Thymidine, a component of DNA, is produced by methylation of dUMP by the enzyme thymidylate synthase. dUMP is derived from dUTP through the action of dUTP diphosphohydrolase in the following reaction: dUTP + H_2O → dUMP + PP_i.

Thus, to produce dUMP, a source of dUTP is required. Ribonucleotide reductase converts NDP to dNDP without regard to base. Thus, dUDP is produced and can be phosphorylated to dUTP. Ultimately, UDP is the precursor to dTTP, which is one of the deoxyribonucleotide triphosphates required for DNA synthesis.

7. (Integrates with Chapters 17–19 and 21) By what pathway(s) does the ribose released upon nucleotide degradation enter intermediary metabolism and become converted to cellular energy? How many ATP equivalents can be recovered from 1 equivalent of ribose?

Answer: Ribose is metabolized in the pentose phosphate pathway, glycolysis, and the citric acid cycle. To enter the pentose phosphate pathway, ribose is phosphorylated at the expense of ATP and converted to ribulose-5-phosphate, which is metabolized as follows. Ribulose-5-phosphate is used to produce triose phosphate equivalents that are fed through glycolysis into the citric acid cycle. Thus, 3 ribose units follow this route and will produce 5 triose phosphates. Starting with 3 ribose (or a total of 15 carbons), the non-oxidative phase of the pentose phosphate pathway is used to produce a total of 5 triose phosphates. For example, using ribulose-5-phosphate isomerase, ribulose-5-phosphate epimerase, transketolase, and transaldolase, 3 ribose-5-phosphates are converted to 2 fructose-6-phosphate and glyceraldehyde-3-phosphate. To convert fructose-6-phosphate to glyceraldehyde-3-phosphate, ATP is consumed. Thus, to this stage, a total of 5 ATP are consumed; 3 to phosphorylate ribose initially* and 2 additional ATP to metabolize fructose-6-phosphate. Net to this stage: −5 ATP.

The 5 glyceraldehyde-3-phosphates are metabolized to pyruvate with production of 5 NADH, equivalent to 15 ATP, and 10 ATP directly, for a total of 25 ATP. Pyruvate metabolism accounts for 1 NADH to form acetyl-CoA, and 1 GTP, 3 NADH, and 1 $FADH_2$ in the citric acid cycle for a total of 15 ATP per pyruvate. So, 5 pyruvates yield 75 ATP.

The total is −5 + 25 + 75 = 95 ATP per 3 ribose or 31.7 ATP per ribose.

* If we started with ribose-1-phosphate, the net would be −2 ATP instead of −5 ATP. The extra expense of 3 ATP is avoided by rearranging ribose-1-phosphate to ribose-5-phosphate.

9. Write reasonable chemical mechanisms for steps 6, 8, and 9 in purine biosynthesis (see Figure 26.3).

Answer:

Step 6: AIR synthetase

Phosphorylated intermediate

AIR

11. Write a balanced equation for the oxidation of uric acid to glycolic acid, CO₂, and NH₃, showing each step in the process and naming all of the enzymes involved.

Answer: The conversion of uric acid to glycolic acid and ammonia is shown in Figure 26.12. Uric acid is converted to allantoin, which is converted to allantoic acid. Allantoic acid is then converted to glyoxylic acid and urea, which is broken down to carbon dioxide and water. The sequence is shown below.

uric acid + 2 H₂O + O₂ → ~~allantoin~~ + C₂O + ~~H₂O₂~~ (Urate oxidase)
~~allantoin~~ + H₂O → ~~allantoic acid~~ (Allantoinase)
~~allantoic acid~~ + H₂O → glyoxylic acid + ~~2 Urea~~ (Allantoicase)
~~2 urea~~ + 2 H₂O → 2 CO₂ + 4 NH₃ (Urease)

To get rid of hydrogen peroxide, we will use hydrogen peroxide oxidoreductase, which reacts two moles of hydrogen peroxide to produce water and oxygen as shown below.

~~H₂O₂~~ → H₂O + ¹/₂ O₂ (Hydrogen peroxidase oxidoreductase)
Net: uric acid + 5 H₂O + ¹/₂ O₂ → 3 CO₂ + 4 NH₃ + glyoxylic acid

By counting elements on both sides of the reaction, you will see that the equation is balanced. The structures of uric acid and glyoxylic acid are shown below.

13. *(Integrates with Chapter 14) Unlike its allosteric counterpart glycogen phosphorylase (an α_2 enzyme), E. coli ATCase has a heteromeric ($\alpha_6\beta_6$) organization. The α-subunits bind aspartate and are considered catalytic subunits, whereas the β-subunits bind CTP or ATP and are considered regulatory subunits. How would you describe the subunit organization of ATCase from a functional point of view?*

Answer: Since each catalytic subunit should be associated with a regulatory subunit, we could consider ATCase as a hexamer of $\alpha\beta$ heterodimers or $(\alpha\beta)_6$. When we discussed hemoglobin, its structure suggests it is a dimer of heterodimers or $(\alpha\beta)_2$.

15. *Write a balanced equation for the synthesis of dTMP from UMP and N^5,N^{10}-methylene-THF. Thymidylate synthase has 4 active-site arginine residues (Arg^{23}, $Arg^{178'}$, $Arg^{179'}$, and Arg^{218}) involved in substrate binding. Postulate a role for the side chains of these Arg residues.*

Answer: UMP is first converted to UDP by nucleoside monophosphate kinase. UDP then serves as substrate for ribonucleotide reductase, which converts UDP to dUDP. To produce dTMP, dUDP is phosphorylated to dUTP, dUTP converted to dUMP by pyrophosphorylase, and finally, dUMP to dTMP by thymidylate synthase, which uses N^5,N^{10}-methylene-THF. The reactions are shown below:

$$\text{UMP} + \text{ATP} \rightarrow \text{UDP} + \text{ADP}$$
$$\text{UDP} + \text{NADPH} + \text{H}^+ \rightarrow \text{dUDP} + \text{NADP}^+ + \text{H}_2\text{O}$$
$$\text{dUDP} + \text{ATP} \rightarrow \text{dUTP} + \text{ADP}$$
$$\text{dUTP} + \text{H}_2\text{O} \rightarrow \text{dUMP} + \text{PP}_i$$
$$\text{PP}_i + \text{H}_2\text{O} \rightarrow 2\ \text{P}_i$$
$$\text{dUMP} + N^5,N^{10}\text{-methylene-THF} \rightarrow \text{dTMP} + \text{DHF}$$

Net: UMP + 2 ATP + H_2O + NADPH + H^+ + N^5,N^{10}-methylene-THF $\rightarrow$ dTMP + 2 ADP + 2 P_i + $NADP^+$ + DHF

17. *The crystal structure of E. coli dihydrofolate reductase (DFR) with $NADP^+$ and folate bound can be found in the Protein Data Bank (www.rcsb.org/pdb) as file 7DFR. Go to this website, enter "7DFR" in the search line, and click on "View in Jmol" when the 7DFR page comes up. Explore the graphic of the DFR structure to visualize how its substrates are bound. (If you hold down the left button on your mouse and move the cursor over the image, you can rotate the structure to view it from different perspectives.) Note in particular the spatial relationship between the nicotinamide ring of $NADP^+$ and the pterin ring of folate. Do you now have a better appreciation for how this enzyme works? Note also the location of polar groups on the 2 substrates in relation to the DFR structure.*

Answer: The binding sites for dihydrofolate is a hydrophobic pocket whose bottom is formed by a parallel pleated sheet. The protein's overall structure is dominated by a seven-stranded sheet structure, with the last two strands being antiparallel and the rest parallel. In the region forming the dihydrofolate-binding pocket, the parallel beta sheet strands are joined by crossover structures with helices and random coils that form an opening to the pocket. Dihydrofolate is buried in this pocket with its glutamic acid residue on the surface of the protein and exposed to solvent. The binding site for $NADP^+$ is located below the sheet, and an opening between two strands of the sheet allows access by the nicotinamide ring of $NADP^+$ to the hydrophobic interior of the dihydrofolate-binding pocket. The rest of the $NADP^+$ (essentially ADP) is bound on the surface of the enzyme on the side opposite of the glutamic acid residue of dihydrofolate. The nicotinamide ring is in close proximity to dihydrofolate's two fused 6-membered rings, and this places the hydride donor of the nicotinamide ring close to the 7-position of folate, which is the hydride acceptor.

Questions for Self-Study

1. The *de novo* synthesis of AMP and GMP start with IMP.
    a. Synthesis of IMP starts with _____.
    b. Two of the carbons of the purine ring of IMP are supplied by the one-carbon pool as formyl groups attached to _____.
    c. Two of the nitrogens derive from the side chain of _____, a common amino acid.
    d. One carbon derives from _____ _____ in a reaction that interestingly does not require biotin (nor ATP hydrolysis).
    e. The amino acid _____ is completely consumed during IMP synthesis accounting for two carbons and one nitrogen.
    f. One nitrogen derives from _____, an amino acid whose carbon skeleton is released as fumarate.

2. The intermediate 5-phosphoribosyl-α-pyrophosphate plays key roles in both *de novo* purine biosynthesis and in purine salvage pathways. Explain.

3. Match the disease or clinical condition with its appropriate enzyme.
    a. Lesch-Nyhan Syndrome
    b. Severe Combined Immunodeficiency Syndrome (SCID)
    c. Gout

    1. Xanthine oxidase
    2. Hypoxanthine-guanine phosphoribosyltransferase (HGPRT)
    3. Adenosine deaminase

4. In mammals, there are two enzymes that synthesize carbamoyl phosphate. The enzymes are localized in different compartments of the cell and participate in different metabolic pathways. Draw the structure of carbamoyl phosphate. Name the two enzymes that synthesize this compound, identify their cellular locations, and state in which metabolic pathways they function.

5. Fill in the blanks. The enzyme _____ _____ produces deoxyribonucleotide diphosphates from ribonucleotide diphosphates. The reducing equivalents for this reaction come from NADPH but are supplied to the enzyme through _____, a small protein with two cysteine residues that undergo reversible oxidation–reduction cycles between cysteine sulfhydryls and _____ disulfide.

Answers

1. a. ribose-5-phosphate; b. tetrahydrofolate; c. glutamine; d. carbon dioxide; e. glycine; f. aspartate.

2. The purine ring of IMP is synthesized on a ribose moiety and the first reaction involves 5-phosphoribosyl-α-pyrophosphate. This derivatized sugar is used as a substrate for adenine phosphoribosyltransferase and hypoxanthine-guanine phosphoribosyltransferase to salvage free bases.

3. a. 2; b. 3; c. 1.

4. Carbamoyl phosphate synthetase II is a cytosolic enzyme involved in pyrimidine biosynthesis. Carbamoyl phosphate synthetase I is a mitochondrial enzyme of the urea cycle (and arginine biosynthesis). The structure of carbamoyl phosphate is shown.

$$H_2N-\overset{\overset{\displaystyle O}{\|}}{C}-O-\overset{\overset{\displaystyle O}{\|}}{\underset{\underset{\displaystyle O^-}{|}}{P}}-O^-$$

5. Ribonucleotide reductase; thioredoxin; cystine.

Additional Problems

1. Why are the sulfonamides effective against bacterial but not animal cells?

2. Describe the anaplerotic pathway involving AMP deaminase, adenylosuccinate synthetase, and adenylosuccinase.

3. Some patients with gout suffer from a defect in PRPP amidotransferase. What reactions does this enzyme catalyze? Can you suggest a defect in the enzyme that might lead to gout?

4. How does purine biosynthesis differ fundamentally from pyrimidine biosynthesis?

Abbreviated Answers

1. Sulfonamides are structural analogs of p-aminobenzoic acid, a component of folate. Animals do not synthesize folate. However, bacteria synthesize it *de novo* or using precursors including p-aminobenzoic acid. Thus, sulfonamides will compete with p-aminobenzoic acid, leading to inhibition of folic acid biosynthesis.

2. AMP deaminase converts AMP to IMP. Adenylosuccinate synthetase attaches aspartate to IMP to form adenylosuccinate, which is degraded into AMP and fumarate, a citric acid cycle intermediate.

3. PRPP amido transferase produces 5-phosphoribosylamine from 5-phosphoribosyl pyrophosphate and glutamine. It is the first step in purine biosynthesis. The defect in this enzyme cannot lead to enzyme inactivation, as this would have the effect of lowering uric acid levels (and perhaps being lethal). The enzyme is subject to feedback inhibition by guanine nucleotides and adenine nucleotides. A defect in allosteric inhibitor binding might lead to a loss of feedback inhibition of purine production, further leading to increased uric acid production and gout.

4. Purines are synthesized as nucleotide derivatives, whereas pyrimidines are produced as the free base orotate, which is subsequently converted to a nucleotide.

Summary

Nearly all organisms have the ability to synthesize purine and pyrimidine nucleotides *de novo*. Since these nucleotides are the direct precursors for RNA and DNA synthesis, their formation is a particularly active process in rapidly proliferating cells, as seen in bacterial infections or cancerous malignancies. Consequently, enzymes of nucleotide biosynthesis are often the targets of drugs designed to halt uncontrolled cell division.

The nine atoms of the purine ring are contributed by five separate precursors: CO_2; the amino acids glycine, aspartate, and glutamine; and one-carbon units contributed by THF derivatives. The purine ring is constructed on a ribose-5-phosphate scaffold. PRPP, the "active form" of ribose-5-P, is the limiting substance in purine biosynthesis. The *de novo* purine synthetic pathway has as its first purine product, IMP. IMP synthesis is regulated at the first two steps: 1) Ribose-5-P pyrophosphokinase is allosterically inhibited by ADP and GDP; 2) glutamine-PRPP amidotransferase is subject to cumulative feedback inhibition by adenine and guanine nucleotides. This latter enzyme has two sites for allosteric inhibition, one where AMP, ADP, and ATP act; and a second where GMP, GDP, and GTP act. The two prominent purines, AMP and GMP, are formed from IMP via a bifurcated pathway with two reactions in each branch. The first enzyme in the AMP branch, adenylosuccinate synthetase, has GTP as a substrate and is feedback inhibited by AMP. The initial step in the GMP branch, IMP dehydrogenase, is feedback inhibited by GMP, while the second step, GMP synthetase, uses ATP as its energy source. This product inhibition and reciprocity in energy donor provides an effective regulatory mechanism for balancing the formation of AMP and GMP to meet cellular needs.

Purine salvage pathways furnish a means to recover free purine bases and nucleosides released as a consequence of nucleic acid degradation and turnover. Though these salvage enzymes seem peripheral to the major utilization, deficiencies in them, as in the absence of HGPRT (hypoxanthine-guanine phosphoribosyltransferase) in Lesch–Nyhan Syndrome, have tragic consequences. Further, aberrations in purine catabolism, as in ADA (adenosine deaminase) deficiency, the underlying cause of Severe Combined

Immunodeficiency Syndrome or "SCID," can also be devastating. The end product of purine catabolism is uric acid. An excess accumulation of uric acid leads to the clinical disorder known as gout. Allopurinol, an analog of hypoxanthine, is an effective treatment. Allopurinol binds tightly to xanthine oxidase, inhibiting its activity and preventing uric acid build-up. Purine metabolism even fulfills an anaplerotic role. In skeletal muscle, a cyclic series of purine transformations known as the purine nucleoside cycle has the net effect of converting aspartate to fumarate to replenish the level of citric acid cycle intermediates.

De novo pyrimidine biosynthesis first yields the six-membered pyrimidine ring; only then is the ribose-5-moiety added to create a nucleotide. Just two precursors, carbamoyl-P and aspartate, provide the requisite six atoms of the pyrimidine. In *E. coli*, pyrimidine synthesis is regulated at aspartate transcarbamoylase (ATCase), the step where carbamoyl-P and aspartate condense to form carbamoyl-aspartate. ATCase is the paradigm of allosteric enzymes (Chapter 12); it is feedback inhibited by the ultimate ribonucleotide end product of the pyrimidine pathway, CTP, and is activated by ATP. In animals, carbamoyl phosphate synthetase II (CPS-II) is the committed step in pyrimidine biosynthesis. Animal CPS-II is feedback inhibited by UDP and UTP, while ATP and PRPP are allosteric activators. Pyrimidine synthesis in mammals provides an example of "metabolic channelling." The first three reactions are catalyzed by a multifunctional polypeptide that contains the active sites for CPS-II, ATCase, and DHOase. A second multifunctional polypeptide carries both OPRTase and OMP decarboxylase activities (reactions 5 and 6 of the pathway). Such multifunctional proteins achieve metabolic channelling: the direct transfer of substrate from one active site to the next, avoiding dissociation from the protein followed by diffusion (and dilution) in free solution to the next enzyme.

Deoxyribonucleotides have only one metabolic purpose—to serve as building blocks in DNA synthesis. Ribonucleoside diphosphates (NDPs) are the substrates for deoxyribonucleotide formation; NDP reduction at the 2′-position forms the corresponding dNDP. The enzyme mediating this reaction is ribonucleotide reductase, and NADPH is the ultimate source of reducing power for dNDP synthesis. Ribonucleotide reductase has two distinct allosteric sites in addition to its active site, and its activity is regulated by an elegant feedback control circuit that balances the supply of dNTPs. One of the active sites determines the overall active of the enzyme depending on whether ATP or dATP is bound. ATP activates; dATP inhibits. The second allosteric site is the substrate specificity site. Occupation of this site by its effectors, ATP, dTTP, dGTP, or dATP, determines which NDP substrate (CDP, UDP, GDP, or ADP) is bound and reduced in the active site.

Synthesis of thymine deoxynucleotides begins with the deoxyribonucleotides, dUDP and dCDP, both of which can lead to dUMP: dUDP→dUTP→dUMP or dCDP→dCMP→dUMP. The conversion of dCDP to dUMP is catalyzed by dCMP deaminase, an allosteric enzyme that provides a control point for regulation of dTTP formation. Thymidylate synthase catalyzes the synthesis of dTMP from dUMP and N^5,N^{10}-methylene-THF. Because of its pivotal role in the pathway of dTTP formation, thymidylate synthase has become an attractive target for chemotherapeutic agents designed to selectively inhibit cell division through denial of adequate amounts of DNA precursors.

Chapter 27

Recombinant DNA: Cloning and Creation of Chimeric Genes

• •

Chapter Outline

❖ Genetic engineering: Application of recombinant DNA technology
❖ Cloning vectors: Requirements
⅄ Origin of replication
⅄ Selectable marker: Typically antibiotic resistance
⅄ Cloning site: Polylinker in region not required for vector function
❖ Vector Types: dsDNAs
⅄ Plasmids: Circular elements that can accept up to 10 kbp of foreign DNA
⅄ Bacteriophage λ: Linear element used to clone 20 kbp inserts
⅄ Cosmids: λ cohesive ends separated by 40 kbp insert DNA
⅄ Shuttle vector: Origins of replication active in two different organisms
⅄ Expression vector: Polylinker downstream of promoter
⅄ Yeast artificial chromosomes (YACs): Linear DNA with autonomously replicating sequence (ori), telomeres, and centromere
❖ Chimeric or recombinant plasmids
⅄ Linearized vector and compatible foreign insert DNA
⅄ DNA ligase joins DNA
⅄ Transformation incorporates DNA into host cell
❖ DNA libraries: A collection of recombinant plasmids with insert DNA from particular organism
⅄ $N = [\ln(1 - P)/\ln(1 - f)]$
• P = probability that library of size N has DNA fragment of interest
• f = (insert size)/(genome size)
❖ cDNA libraries
⅄ cDNA: mRNA directed synthesis of DNA
• PolyA mRNA isolated using oligo(dT)
• Reverse transcriptase produces DNA from mRNA
❖ Library screening
⅄ Southern analysis: DNA
• Replica plate onto nitrocellulose
• Lyse and denature using alkaline pH
• Probe with complementary nucleic acid probe
⅄ Northern analysis: RNA: Used to identify RNAs
⅄ Probes
• Degenerate oligonucleotides
• Heterologous probe: DNA fragment from gene in related organism
❖ Microarrays: Gene chips: DNA sequence arrays used to detect large numbers of nucleic acids
❖ Expression vectors
⅄ RNA expression: Transcription of cloned gene driven by RNA polymerase promoter
⅄ Protein expression of cloned DNA

- Bacterial vectors and host
    - DNA must lack introns
    - Vector must contain bacterial promoter and ribosome-binding site
    - Promoters: Strong and regulatable
  - Eukaryotic vector elements
    - Viral promoters
- ❖ Fusion proteins: cDNA cloned in frame with protein coding region on vector
- ❖ Screening of expression libraries: Antibodies to detect specific protein or fusion protein
- ❖ Reporter gene: Used to clone promoters: Easily detected protein product like GFP
- ❖ Yeast two-hybrid system: Identify protein–protein interactions
    - Bait: DNA-binding domain of GAL 4 fused to characterized protein
    - Target (prey): Library of GAL 4 transcriptional activation domain-target protein fusions
- ❖ PCR: Polymerase chain reaction: *In vitro* amplification of DNA
- ❖ Site-specific *in vitro* mutagenesis: Specific alteration of DNA sequence by in vitro technique
- ❖ RNA interference: dsRNA that causes inactivation of specific mRNA: Gene knockdown
    - dsRNA with one strand complementary to mRNA target expressed in cells
    - Dicer processes dsRNA to produce small interfering RNA (siRNA)
    - siRNA binds to RNA-induced silencing complex
        - siRNA unwound
        - Strand complementary to mRNA paired
        - dsRNA cleaved

Chapter Objectives

Cloning Vectors

Understand the purpose of vectors in recombinant DNA technology. They are the vehicles by which foreign DNA is incorporated into cells in a form that will be amplified by the cell. Some important vectors include the following:

1. Plasmids: small, circular, double-stranded DNA elements containing a selectable marker, typically a gene conferring resistance to an antibiotic.
2. Bacteriophage λ: a linear double-stranded DNA-containing virus used to clone large (up to 16 kbp) DNA fragments.
3. Cosmid: a hybrid cloning vector, containing a plasmid origin of replication and a λ *cos* site, capable of carrying DNA inserts up to 40 kbp.
4. M13: a filamentous, single-stranded, circular DNA-containing virus whose life cycle includes a double-stranded circular DNA that can be manipulated much like a plasmid. Recombinant M13s are used as templates for chain-termination sequencing.
5. YACs: yeast artificial chromosomes, the "jumbo jets" of genetic engineering, are used to clone extremely large DNA fragments (100s of kbp).

Formation of Recombinants

Generally, vectors contain multiple restriction endonuclease recognition sites in a single region known as the polylinker. To produce a recombinant or chimeric vector, the vector is digested with a restriction enzyme that recognizes a site in the polylinker, and the DNA to be inserted is digested with an enzyme that will produce ends compatible to the vector-digest. The DNAs are combined using DNA ligase and the recombinants are introduced into cells by transformation. Transformation may be accomplished chemically (a cell capable of being transformed is said to be competent). Alternatively, a brief, intense, electrical shock may be used to transiently produce holes in cells through which DNA can diffuse into the cell. This process is known as electroporation. Vectors that are infectious, such as λ or M13, enter cells by a process known as transfection.

Detecting Recombinants

Producing recombinants is an easy task, but finding the correct recombinant in a library of recombinants is often difficult. Know the techniques available for this purpose including Southern analysis, selecting for expression, screening for expression, and production of hybrid proteins for antibody screening. Reporter gene constructs are used to clone DNA elements involved in regulation of gene expression.

PCR

PCR is a powerful technique for amplifying DNA *in vitro*. Understand the principles behind this technique. You should be able to show that as a function of cycle-number, the full length product defined by flanking oligonucleotide primers, is amplified exponentially.

Problems and Solutions

*1. A DNA fragment isolated from an **EcoRI** digest of genomic DNA was combined with a plasmid vector linearized by **EcoRI** digestion so sticky ends could anneal. Phage T4 DNA ligase was then added to the mixture. List all possible products of the ligation reaction.*

Answer: The ligation products will include linear and circular DNA molecules made with either the genomic fragment or the vector DNA or a combination of both. Because both DNAs have the same "sticky ends," they may join in any orientation. (Depending on the ratio of genomic fragment DNA to vector DNA, recombinants between the two DNAs may be favoured.) Only ligation products with vector DNA will successfully transform cells. Further, ligated DNA products with more than one copy of vector DNA are typically unstable in cells.

*3. A vector has a polylinker containing restriction sites in the following order: **HindIII, SacI, XhoI, BglII, XbaI,** and **ClaI**.*
*   a. Give a possible nucleotide sequence for the polylinker.*
*   b. The vector is digested with **HindIII** and **ClaI**. A DNA segment contains a **HindIII** restriction site fragment 650 bases upstream from a **ClaI** site. This DNA fragment is digested with **HindIII** and **ClaI**, and the resulting **HindIII–ClaI** fragment is directionally cloned into the **HindIII–ClaI** digested vector. Give the nucleotide sequence at each end of the vector and the insert, and show that the insert can be cloned into the vector in only 1 orientation.*

Answer: The sequence of a polylinker with sites for *Hind*III, *Sac*I, *Xho*I, *Bgl*II, *Xba*I, and *Cla*I will have the following 6-base recognition sites:

Site	Enzyme
AAGCTT	*Hind*III
GAGCTC	*Sac*I
CTCGAG	*Xho*I
AGATCT	*Bgl*II
TCTAGA	*Xba*I
ATCGAT	*Cla*I

Combining these, we find:

```
AAGCTTGAGCTCGAGATCTAGATCGAT
AAGCTT    CTCGAG TCTAGA
HindIII    XhoI   XbaI
       GAGCTC AGATCT  ATCGAT
        SacI   BglII   ClaI
```

Note: The following pairs overlap: *Sac*I and *Xho*I; *Xho*I and *Bgl*II; *Bgl*II and *Xba*I; and, *Xba*I and *Cla*I.

b.   *Cla*I recognizes ATCGAT and cuts after the first T. *Hind*III recognizes AAGCTT and cuts after the first A. Assuming the vector is circular, the polylinker is shown below with the location of cut sites (in bold) for both enzymes on both strands.

```
-AAGCTTGAGCTCGAGATCTAGATCGAT-
-TTCGAACTCGAGCTCTAGATCTAGCTA-
```

Digestion will produce:

```
-A        AGCTTGAGCTCGAGATCTAGAT        CGAT-
-TTCGA        ACTCGAGCTCTAGATCTAGC        TA-
```

Note: The top and bottom strands are shown and the dashes indicate continuation of the sequence of the vector. Two fragments are produced by digestion of the vector with *Cla*I and *Hind*III. The polylinker is cut out of the vector. One end of the polylinker and one end of the vector have a 4-base 5′-overhang of AGCT. The other ends of both contain a 2-base 5′-overhang of CG. (Keeping track of 5′- and 3′-ends can be a bit tricky. The reference sequence is the top sequence, which starts AAGCT.... It is written conventionally

5' left to 3' right. Its complementary sequence, the bottom strand, is shown 3' to 5'. Left ends of top strands are 5' and right ends are 3'. The reverse is true for bottom strands.)

We are informed that a DNA fragment that contains a *Hind*III site 650 bases upstream of a *Cla*I site was also digested with both enzymes. The original DNA looks like this:

```
-AAGCTT---650---ATCGAT-
-TTCGAA---650---TAGCTA-
```

And, when digested, it gives the following products:

```
-A          AGCTT---650---AT      CGAT-
-TTCGA          A---650---TAGC       TA-
```

The 650-base pair fragment has ends identical to the digested polylinker shown in the first digest, and so it could replace it in a ligation reaction. It could not, however, be cloned in the reverse orientation because the ends would no longer be compatible. (The 2-base 5'-overhang is not compatible with the 4-base 5'-overhang.) So the fragment can clone in only one direction.

5. **The South American lungfish has a genome size of 10.2×10^{10} bp. If a genomic library of lungfish DNA was constructed in a vector capable of carrying inserts averaging 45 kbp in size, how many individual clones would have to be screened to have a 99% probability of finding a particular DNA fragment?**

Answer:

$$N = \frac{\ln(1-P)}{\ln(1-f)} \text{ where } P = 0.99 \text{ and } f = \frac{45 \text{ kbp}}{1.02 \times 10^{11}} = \frac{45 \times 10^3}{1.02 \times 10^{11}} = 4.41 \times 10^{-7}$$

$$N = \frac{\ln(1-0.99)}{\ln(1-4.41 \times 10^{-7})} = 1.04 \times 10^7 = 10.4 \text{ million}$$

7. **Figure 27.3 shows a polylinker that falls within the β-galactosidase coding region of the lacZ gene. This polylinker serves as a cloning site in a fusion protein expression vector where the cloned insert is expressed as a β-galactosidase fusion protein. Assume the vector polylinker was cleaved with BamHI and then ligated with an insert whose sequence reads**
GATCCATTTATCCACCGGAGAGCTGGTATCCCCAAAAGACGGCC...
What is the amino acid sequence of the fusion protein? Where is the junction between β-galactosidase and the sequence encoded by the insert? (Consult the genetic code table on the inside front cover of the textbook to decipher the amino acid sequence.)

Answer: *Bam*HI recognizes GGATCC and cuts after the first G giving
```
G          GATCC
CCTAG          G
```

Once ligated with insert, the sequence becomes

GGATCCATTTATCCACCGGAGAGCTGGTATCCCCAAAAGACGGCC....

What is the amino acid sequence of the fusion protein? To answer this we must know the reading frame at the *Bam*HI site. This is shown in Figure 27.3. The reading frame is such that GAT in the *Bam*HI site is in frame. This gives:

```
G|GAT|CCA|TTT|ATC|CAC|CGG|AGA|GCT|GGT|ATC|CCC|AAA|AGA|CGG|CC...
  Asp Pro Phe Ile His Arg Arg Ala Gly Ile Pro Lys Arg Arg Pro
```

9. **Combinatorial chemistry can be used to synthesize polymers such as oligopeptides or oligonucleotides. The number of sequence possibilities for a polymer is given by x^y, where x is the number of different monomer types (for example, 20 different amino acids in a protein or 4 different nucleotides in a nucleic acid) and y is the number of monomers in the oligomers.**
    a. **Calculate the number of sequence possibilities for RNA oligomers 15 nucleotides long.**
    b. **Calculate the number of amino acid sequence possibilities for pentapeptides.**

Answer: For RNA oligomers, the total number of sequences is given by $4^{15} = 1\,073\,741\,824$ or about a billion different 15-mers. For a pentapeptide, the total number of sequences is given by $20^5 = 3\,200\,000$ or about 3 million.

11. Describe an experimental protocol for the preparation of 2 cDNA libraries, one from anaerobically grown yeast cells and the second from aerobically grown yeast cells.

Answer: mRNA is isolated from total RNA of both aerobically and anaerobically grown yeast. The mRNA is used as template with reverse transcriptase and oligo dT to produce ssDNA, which is then converted to dsDNA and cloned into a vector. To insure that full-length mRNA is being used to produce the cDNA library, there are protocols that exploit the 5′-cap of full-length mRNAs.

13. You have an antibody against yeast hexokinase A (hexokinase is the first enzyme in the glycolytic pathway). Describe an experimental protocol using the cDNA libraries prepared in Problem 11 that would allow you to identify and isolate cDNA for hexokinase. Consulting Chapter 5 for protein analysis protocols, describe an experimental protocol to verify that the protein you have identified is hexokinase A.

Answer: The cDNA library would have to be cloned into an expression vector. That is, the cDNA library would have to be cloned behind a promoter, so that the sequence information is used to produce a protein. Libraries of clones would then be screened for production of an antigen recognized by the hexokinase A antibody. The antibody could be coupled to a matrix to be used to isolate the gene product. The gene product could then be subjected to trypsin digestion and mass spectrometry to identify the protein. Alternatively, the cloned gene could be sequenced.

Biochemistry on the Web

15. Search the National Center for Biotechnology Information (NCBI) website at http://www.ncbi .nlm.nih.gov/sites/genome/ to discover the number of organisms whose genome sequences have been completed. Explore the rich depository of sequence information available here by selecting 1 organism from the list and browsing through the contents available.

Answer: Go to the NCBI home page at http://www.ncbi.nlm.nih.gov/. In the Resource List, click on Genomes and Maps to go to the Entrez Genome site at http://www.ncbi.nlm.nih.gov/genome.

Questions for Self-Study

1. What three common features are shared by all cloning vectors?

2. How is the enzyme T4 DNA ligase used to produce chimeric plasmids?

3. Match the terms in the columns below:
   a. Bacteriophage λ   1. A plasmid capable of propagation in two different organisms
   b. Cosmid   2. Cellular uptake of exogenous DNA
   c. M13   3. Vector used to clone extremely large DNA molecules
   d. Shuttle Vector   4. A filamentous, ssDNA phage
   e. Transformation   5. A transformation technique
   f. YAC   6. A bacterial virus used as a cloning vector
   g. Electroporation   7. A hybrid vector containing *cos* sites

4. Which of the following apply to Southern analysis?
   a. Can be used to detect specific recombinants
   b. Is useful in chromosome walking
   c. Uses antibodies to detect gene expression
   d. Used labelled RNA or DNA as a probe
   e. Is used to identify RNA

5. What is the difference between fusion protein expression and reporter gene expression in genetic engineering?

6. Polymerase chain reaction or PCR is an *in vitro* technique used to amplify specific sequences of DNA. It consists of repeated cycles of a three-step process. What are the three steps that constitute a cycle and what happens during each step?

Answers

1. An origin or replication, a selectable marker, a cloning site.

2. T4 DNA ligase is used to covalently join foreign DNA into a cloning site on a plasmid.

3. a. 6; b. 7; c. 4; d. 1; e. 2; f. 3; g. 5

4. a., b., d.

5. In fusion gene expression, a protein-coding region under study is cloned into an expression vector to produce a recombinant sequence that is expressed as a hybrid or fusion protein. In this case, the experimenter is interested in studying the expressed protein. Reporter genes are used to identify transcriptional regulatory elements like promoters and enhancers.

6. Denaturation: dsDNA template is converted to ssDNA by high temperature. Annealing: Temperature is lowered to allow DNA primers to bind to template DNA. Polymerization (extension): Primer extension occurs at the temperature optimum for thermostable DNA polymerase.

Additional Problems

1. An experimenter decided to use PCR to isolate a particular gene from an exotic organism. The gene under study had previously been characterized in several different organisms. The experimenter was able to locate two conserved regions within the gene, to make oligonucleotides complementary to these two regions, and to set up a PCR amplification. The experimenter programmed the thermocycler and left for the weekend. After two cycles, a power failure occurred, erasing the memory in the thermocycler. A colleague, realizing the importance of the experiment, decided to restart the thermocycler. However, the colleague knew nothing about PCR, and so the person asked you what to do.
    a. Describe a typical PCR cycle and explain the purpose of each step in the cycle.
    b. The person takes your advice and is in fact so excited by your description of PCR that the person runs a gel. No products were found. Desperate for results, the person decides to change one of the temperatures in the cycle and performs a second PCR run. Which temperature, which direction, and why?
    c. The adjustment results in production of only one faint band, not an impressive yield for such a marvelous procedure. The person decides to make one more attempt and triples the total number of cycles. This time several bands are produced. Can the results be trusted? Explain.

2. One of the constraints of standard PCR is having to know the sequence of two separate regions of a gene. Can you suggest a method that eliminates the necessity of having to know two separated sequences within a gene?

3. In Problem 5 above, you were asked to calculate the genome library size of lungfish DNA necessary to have a 99% probability of finding a particular DNA fragment. The answer came out to 10 million. If the library is plated onto Petri dishes, with approximately 1000 colonies per plate, calculate the number of plates required, the total surface area, and the height if the plates were stacked on top of each other. (A typical Petri dish is 100 × 15 mm.)

4. a. A biochemist is attempting to clone a eukaryotic gene and, using Southern analysis of an *Eco*RI digest of total genomic DNA, learns that the gene is located on a 2.5 kbp *Eco*RI fragment. Further, it was discovered that the *Eco*RI fragment lacks *Bam*HI restriction sites. Suggest an appropriate vector to use in this case.
    b. The strategy the biochemist decides to take is to digest total genomic DNA with *Eco*RI, separate the fragments by agarose gel electrophoresis, cut out of the gel the 2.5 kbp fragment, elute the DNA from the gel slice, and ligate the DNA into a suitable vector. "Piece of cake!" the biochemist

exclaims, "This will be a one-step cloning and we'll have our gene without having to screen our recombinants by Southern analysis." This is an optimistic statement. Can you explain why?

5. Vectors based on λ are available to simplify chromosome walking. They contain two different bacteriophage RNA polymerase promoters (from SP6, T3, or T7 phage) flanking a cloning site. Further, the RNA polymerase promoters are on opposite strands and they are oriented such that expression from these promoters produces RNAs complementary to the insert ends. Explain how these vectors facilitate chromosome walking.

6. In one version of oligonucleotide-directed, site-specific mutagenesis, a recombinant M13 is used as a template for second-strand synthesis using a mutagenic oligonucleotide. The mutagenic oligonucleotide is complementary to several bases on both sides of the target base but at the target base it produces a single-base mismatch. The oligonucleotide is used *in vitro* to synthesize a complementary strand whose ends are ligated together by DNA ligase. Thus, a single-stranded M13 is converted to a double-stranded, closed, circular form (often referred to as the RF or replicative form). Suggest a simple assay to check for second-strand synthesis and for DNA ligase activity.

Abbreviated Answers

1. a.   In a typical PCR reaction, double-stranded template DNA and two primers, complementary to two sequences flanking the region to be amplified, are mixed with a thermostable DNA polymerase and dNTPs. The mixture is first heated to 90–95°C to denature the template DNA. Then, the temperature is lowered to between 40°C and 60°C to allow primer binding to the template. Finally, the temperature is adjusted to the temperature optimum for the DNA polymerase to allow primer extension to occur (72–75°C). The process of heating to denature, cooling to allow primer binding, and heating to extend primer represents a cycle that is repeated a number of times, the result of which is an exponential amplification of the DNA between the two primers.

b.   Failure to amplify may be a result of inefficient primer binding to the template because the temperature of the second stage of the cycle, namely primer binding, exceeds the T_m of the primer. One possibility is to lower the primer-binding temperature.

c.   The production of only a faint band may be parent nature's way of telling you that something is not quite right with the reaction. It may be the case that the primers are inappropriate for the template DNA. Typically, PCR reactions are set up to produce a generous amplification after a specified number of cycles. Increasing substantially the cycle number may allow for amplification of DNA contaminating the template DNA. In addition, increasing the cycle-number provides additional opportunities for random mispriming to occur and to be subsequently amplified.

2.   In a process known as inverse-PCR, DNA can be amplified from a region of known sequence outward in both directions. Template DNA is digested with a restriction enzyme known to cut outside of the region of interest. (Southern analysis can be used to screen for an appropriate enzyme.) The fragmented DNA is circularized by ligation and then linearized by digestion with an enzyme that cuts at a single location within the DNA. The enzyme used in this case must cut within the region of known sequence producing a linear DNA whose ends contain the previously characterized sequence. Primers whose sequences are derived from the characterized region of DNA are now used to amplify as shown below.

In anchored-PCR, template DNA is fragmented by restriction digestion and the ends ligated to a primer whose sequence is known. Amplification occurs between this primer and an internal, previously characterized sequence within the gene. This is shown below.

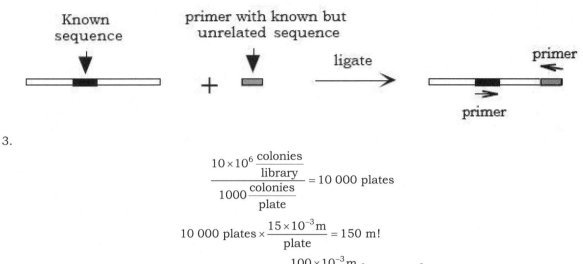

3.

$$\frac{10 \times 10^6 \frac{colonies}{library}}{1000 \frac{colonies}{plate}} = 10\ 000\ plates$$

$$10\ 000\ plates \times \frac{15 \times 10^{-3}\,m}{plate} = 150\ m!$$

$$10\ 000\ plates \times \pi \times (\frac{100 \times 10^{-3}\,m}{2})^2 = 78.5\ m^2$$

4.   a.   The 2.5 kbp fragment is a small fragment that could be cloned in a plasmid. Cosmids, λ, and YACs are all more appropriate for much larger fragments.

b.   The cloning strategy is sound; however, the biochemist may be a bit optimistic in thinking that the 2.5 kbp fragment identified by Southern analysis is a unique fragment. Eukaryotic genomes are large, greater than 10×10^6 bp for yeast, a simple eukaryote, and a digest with a restriction enzyme with a 6-base recognition sequence is expected to generate a very large number of fragments. For example, the probability of finding a particular 6-base sequence is $(1/4)^6 = (1/4096)$. For a genome of 10×10^6 bp one might expect to have around $10 \times 10^6 \times (1/4096) = 2441$ sites. Therefore, an enzyme with a 6-base recognition sequence is expected to generate thousands of bands that will form essentially a continuum upon electrophoresis. The fact that Southern analysis highlights a single band only means that, of all of the bands in the continuum at that particular size, there is one (or possibly more) with the sequence of interest. The biochemist will have to screen the products of the cloning procedure.

5.   In chromosome walking, the ends of a cloned fragment are used as probes to search for other clones in the library containing overlapping segments of the DNA. The vectors described are ideally suited for the purpose of producing RNAs from DNA at the ends of the cloned fragment. The RNA can be labelled and used in Southern analysis to search for overlapping clones.

6.   One easy assay is to examine the products by agarose gel electrophoresis. Single-stranded template M13 has a faster electrophoretic mobility than double-stranded M13. Therefore, second-strand synthesis will be accompanied by a gel shift of the M13 template to a slower migrating form. If second-strand synthesis is successful, a double-stranded, nicked circle is produced. Successful ligation will convert the nicked circle to a covalently closed double-stranded molecule. Electrophoresis in the presence of ethidium bromide is capable of distinguishing between these two. Ethidium bromide binding to covalently closed, double-stranded DNA will induce positive supercoils. Thus, the mobility of the ligated product will be slightly faster than relaxed circles in the presence of ethidium.

Summary

Plasmids are circular, extrachromosomal DNA molecules. Plasmids have the ability to self-replicate and often carry genes for novel metabolic capacities (such as antibiotic resistance) that allow host cells to grow under otherwise adverse conditions. These facts make plasmids ideal vehicles for the amplification of foreign DNA segments. The discovery of restriction endonucleases provided an essential tool for generating big DNA fragments with predictable features, such as defined ends. In particular, restriction endonucleases that create 5'- and 3'-overhangs, "sticky ends," ease the task of assembling chimeric plasmids *in vitro*. The circular plasmid is opened, or "linearized," by restriction endonuclease digestion, a foreign DNA segment is annealed to it via hybridization of its ends with the complementary "sticky ends" of the plasmid, and the two DNA sequences are covalently ligated using DNA ligase, a process that recloses the plasmid circle. Using these techniques and related developments, essentially any DNA sequence can be cloned.

Since the size of foreign DNA inserts in plasmids is inherently limited to 10 kbp, other vector systems for the propagation of larger DNA segments have emerged, such as bacteriophage λ–based cosmid cloning systems and even the creation of artificial yeast chromosomes (YACs) for cloning purposes.

The overriding aim of most cloning work is the isolation and characterization of specific genes. Since any given gene represents only a tiny fraction of an organism's genome or total DNA content, the challenge is to find the particular DNA sequence that represents the gene among a large population of extraneous DNA segments. Genomic libraries are prepared by partially digesting the organism's DNA and cloning the fragments into a suitable vector. The library is then screened for the gene of interest, using probes designed to uniquely identify the gene. Typically, a probe is a single-stranded DNA molecule whose nucleotide sequence is complementary to some region of the target gene. Genes can also be cloned by identifying a clone derived from a gene on the same chromosome and using this clone as a probe to find clones of neighbouring DNA segments, then repeating the process, progressively moving along the chromosome. This tactic is called "chromosome walking." Libraries can also be constructed by copying the mRNA population isolated from a selected cell type into DNA using reverse transcriptase. The product, cDNA, is converted to duplex DNA and cloned into an appropriate vector. cDNA libraries cloned into expression vectors where the DNA inserts are both transcribed and translated in recipient cells can be screened for protein products of the gene using immunological techniques and other methods. The properties of gene regulatory sequences can be investigated by cloning them into sites adjacent to genes encoding easily assayed protein products, so-called reporter genes. Expression of the reporter gene serves as an index of the transcriptional efficiency of the cloned regulatory sequence.

The major problem with cloning is identifying a particular clone of interest and this is often accomplished by nucleic acid hybridization. Complementary single-stranded DNA or RNA can be used to identify cloned DNA. In Southern hybridization, denatured DNA is transferred to a solid filter and the filter then probed with DNA with a sequence of interest to the experimenter. The transferred DNA could be from a plate of bacterial colonies each harboring recombinant plasmids or DNA could be from an agarose or polyacrylamide gel. DNA microarrays rely on hybridization to detect expression of many genes under a variety of conditions. The "gene chips" are solid supports decorated with many single-strand DNA probes derived from genomic information. One can use gene chips to detect differential expression of genes under particular environmental conditions. This is accomplished by isolating mRNA under particular conditions, converting it to cDNA and then, in effect, determining how efficiently cDNA hybridizes to the gene chips.

Polymerase chain reaction (PCR) is a technique for greatly amplifying the amount of any DNA segment in a genome, provided sequence information is available about regions flanking the desired segment. This information is used in synthesizing pairs of complementary oligonucleotides that anneal next to the segment (one oligonucleotide at each 3'-end). These oligonucleotides serve to prime synthesis of the region by DNA polymerase. The resultant duplex DNA is melted by heating to 95°C, and the solution is cooled to initiate another cycle of synthesis. Repeating this thermal cycle and synthesis regime for 25 cycles leads to a million-fold amplification in the concentration of the original DNA sequence. PCR has been automated through the invention of thermal cyclers that carry out the entire process in less than 4 hours. PCR is thus an automated, cell-free amplification procedure for generation of specific DNA sequences.

With cloned genes in hand, alteration of the nucleotide sequences of these genes in order to observe the consequences of these "mutations" on the biological function of the gene or gene product became feasible. *In vitro* mutagenesis has been used to change the nucleotide sequence in a systematic way so that the effects of specific amino acid substitutions within a protein can be tested. Such manipulations have proved very valuable for elucidating the role of individual amino acids in the structure and function of proteins.

Chapter 28

DNA Metabolism: Replication, Recombination, and Repair

• •

Chapter Outline

- ❖ Characteristics of DNA replication
    - ⅄ Semiconservative
        - • Meselson and Stahl (1958)
            - • Cells grown in 15-N: Shifted to 14-N
            - • DNA analyzed by CsCl gradient centrifugation after 1 or 2 generations
    - ⅄ Semidiscontinuous
        - • Leading strand: Continuous
        - • Lagging strand: Discontinuous: Okazaki fragments
- ❖ Enzymology of DNA replication
    - ⅄ Major DNA polymerases in *E. coli*
        - • DNA polymerase I: First characterized by Kornberg (1959): Repair and removal of primers
            - • 5′ Polymerase activity
                - ○ Low processivity
            - • 3′ Exonuclease
                - ○ Proofreading
                - ○ Exonuclease and polymerase on large (Klenow fragment)
            - • 5′ Exonuclease: Nick translation
        - • Polymerase III: Replication
            - • Core enzyme: Three subunits
                - ○ α = polymerase
                - ○ ε = 3′ exonuclease: Proofreading
                - ○ θ
            - • DNA polymerase III*
                - ○ Two cores
                - ○ γ = Clamp loader
            - • DNA polymerase III holoenzyme
                - ○ Two β dimers (one dimer per core): Sliding DNA clamp
    - ⅄ Primase: Adds RNA primers
    - ⅄ DNA ligase: Joins 3′ hydroxyl with 5′ phosphate
- ❖ Initiation at oriC
    - ⅄ DnaA binds to 245 bp region composed of four 9 bp repeats
    - ⅄ Strands separate at three AT-rich repeats on 5′ end of oriC
    - ⅄ DnaB binds to oriC forming prepriming complex: Helicase activity
    - ⅄ Addition of primase completes primosome
- ❖ Elongation
    - ⅄ DnaB helicase on leading template
    - ⅄ PriA helicase on lagging strand template

- ❖ Termination
  - ⼈ *Ter* locus contains oppositely oriented *Ter* sequences
  - ⼈ Tus protein: Contrahelicase
  - ⼈ Catenated DNA disengaged by topoisomerase II (DNA gyrase)
- ❖ Eukaryotic DNA replication
  - ⼈ Multiple replicators (ori's)
  - ⼈ Prereplication complex
    - • ORC (origin recognition complex) binds replicators
    - • Cdc6p binds to ORC
    - • RLFs (replication licensing factors) bind to DNA: Two required
      - • RLF-B: Confined to cytosol: Binds when nuclear envelop is lost
      - • RLF-M: MCM protein complex
  - ⼈ Pre-RC substrate for two protein kinases
    - • Cyclin-dependent protein kinase/cyclin B complex: Cyclin B-CDK
      - • Phosphorylates ORC, Cdc6p, MCM, Cdc7p-Dbf4p
    - • Cdc7p-Dbf4p kinase activated by cyclin B-CDK
      - • Activity serves as replication switch
- ❖ Eukaryotic DNA polymerases
  - ⼈ DNA polymerase α: Initiator of nuclear DNA replication
  - ⼈ DNA polymerase δ: Principal enzyme
    - • Forms complex with PCNA (DNA clamp)
    - • High processivity
  - ⼈ DNA polymerase ε: Role in replication
  - ⼈ DNA polymerase β: DNA repair
  - ⼈ DNA polymerase γ: Mitochondrial enzyme
- ❖ DNA ends: Telomeres
  - ⼈ Tandem repeats of G-rich 5 to 8 bp segments
  - ⼈ Telomerase maintains telomeres
    - • RNA-dependent DNA polymerase
    - • Ribonucleoprotein particle where RNA serves as template for telomere
- ❖ Reverse transcriptase: Three activities
  - ⼈ RNA-dependent DNA polymerase
  - ⼈ RNase H: Removes RNA of RNA/DNA hybrid
  - ⼈ DNA-directed DNA polymerase
- ❖ General (homologous) recombination
  - ⼈ Meselson and Weigle: Recombination in λ
    - • Density label two strains: Recombinants had intermediate density
  - ⼈ Holliday model
    - • Chromosomes pair (synapse)
    - • DNA unwinds
    - • Strand invasion
    - • Holliday junction
    - • Branch migration
    - • Resolution of junctions
      - • Patch recombination
      - • Splice recombination
- ❖ Enzymology of recombination
  - ⼈ RecBCD
    - • Helicase and nuclease activities
    - • Chi site: GCTGGTGG: Induces RecBCD nuclease activity
    - • Product is ssDNA tail with chi site at 3′-end
  - ⼈ ssDNA-binding protein: Coats DNA as RecBCD helicase unwinds dsDNA
  - ⼈ RecA
    - • ATP-dependent DNA strand exchange
    - • Binds ssDNA and dsDNA: Forms extended filaments

- High-affinity primary DNA-binding site binds ssDNA
- Second dsDNA binds at secondary DNA-binding site
- When homologous DNA encountered dsDNA converted to ssDNA
- Strand exchange occurs
- RuvA, RuvB, RuvC proteins
  - RuvA and RuvB: Holliday-junction–specific helicase: Catalyzes branch migration
  - RuvC endonuclease that resolves Holliday junctions
- ❖ Transposons
  - McClintock identified activator gene in maize in 1950 (Nobel prize for work in 1983): Mobile genetic element
  - Insertion sequences: Simplest transposon
- ❖ DNA repair
  - Mismatch repair: Methyl-directed pathway determines template strand
  - Photoreaction of pyrimidine dimers: Photolyases use light energy to reverse pyrimidine dimers
  - Excision repair
    - Base excision: Removal of single altered base
      - DNA glycosidase removes damaged base
      - AP endonuclease cleaves at AP site
      - Exonuclease removes AP site
    - Nucleotide excision: Removes damaged base by removing short ssDNA fragment
- ❖ Molecular nature of mutations
  - Point mutations: Base substitutions
    - Transitions: Purine to purine or pyrimidine to pyrimidine
    - Transversions: Purine to pyrimidine or pyrimidine to purine
  - Insertions or deletions
    - Cause frame shifting
    - Produced by intercalating agents
  - Base analog mutations
    - 5-bromouracil: Thymine analog whose tautomeric form pairs with G (not A)
    - 2-aminopurine: Incorporates as A but pairs with C
  - Chemical mutagens
    - Nitrous acid: Deamination of bases: C changed to U gives G to A mutation
    - Hydroxylamine: Modifies C: Modified C pairs with A not G
    - Alkylating agents: Modified bases mispair
- ❖ RNA as genetic material
  - ssRNA most common
  - Retrovirus: ssRNA genome replicated to dsDNA that inserts into host genome
- ❖ Immunoglobulin genes
  - Antibodies: Immunoglobulin proteins: Immune response agents that bind foreign substances called antigens
  - IgG: Major class of circulating antibodies
    - H_2L_2 heterotetramer: H = heavy chain, L = light chain
      - L chain: 214 amino acids
        - V_L: Residues 1–108 variable
          - Hypervariable regions (complementarity-determining regions)
        - C_L: Residues 109–214 constant
      - H chain: 446 amino acids
        - V_H: Residues 1–108 variable
          - Hypervariable regions
        - C_H: Residues 109–446 constant
          - C_H1, C_H2, C_H3
      - Structure: Immunoglobulin fold
  - Immunoglobulin genes
    - DNA rearrangement during B lymphocyte formation produces novel genes
    - L-chain genes

- Kappa genes and Lambda genes
- Each has V and J (**j**oining) regions
  - Multiple J regions
  - Multiple V regions
  - V and J joined in different combinations
- H-chain genes
  - Multiple V regions
  - Multiple D genes (diversity)
  - Multiple J genes
  - Multiple C genes
  - V, D, and J joined in different combinations
- V-J and V-D-J joining
  - In germ line cells, V and D genes followed by CACAGTGN$_{23}$ACAAAAACC
  - In germ line cells, D and J genes preceded by GGTTTTTGTN$_{12}$CACTGTG
  - Sequences are complementary to each other: Recombination recognition signals
  - RAG1 and RAG2 bind sequences: V(D)J recombinase

Chapter Objectives

DNA Replication

Review the structure of DNA before starting this chapter. You should already know that dsDNA is composed of two strands that run antiparallel to each other and that a single stand of DNA has a 5′-end and a 3′-end. Each strand is a polymer of deoxyribonucleoside monophosphates held together in phosphodiester linkage between the 5′-carbon of one nucleotide and the 3′-carbon of the next nucleotide. The strands are held to each other by complementary hydrogen bonds between pairs of bases AT, TA, GC, and CG.

DNA is replicated semiconservatively. Understand what this means and how the experiments of Meselson and Stahl proved it. These experiments employed the stable heavy isotope of nitrogen ^{15}N to grow a culture of *E. coli* to contain dense DNA. The culture was then shifted to ^{14}N-containing media, grown for a number of generations, and after each generation sampled to determine the density of DNA.

Replication initiates at specific locations termed origins of replication or ori. Typically, replication from an ori proceeds in both directions.

Enzymology

All DNA polymerases require a ssDNA template to direct the synthesis of a complementary strand. The complementary strand is produced by addition of deoxyribonucleoside monophosphate groups derived from dNTPs to the 3′-end of the growing complementary strand. Thus, the polymerase moves 3′→5′ along the template and extends the newly synthesized strand 5′→3′.

The Kornberg polymerase DNA pol I, a 109 kD, single-chain polypeptide, was the first DNA polymerase to be characterized. It plays a role in replication and repair. You should know the various activities exhibited by this DNA-dependent DNA polymerase, including polymerase, 3′ exonuclease, and 5′ exonuclease. The 3′ exonuclease functions in proofreading, whereas the 5′ exonuclease, acting concurrently with polymerase activity, can cause nick translation or movement of a DNA gap by removing DNA (or RNA) on the 5′-end of the gap and adding DNA to the 3′-end of the gap. DNA polymerase I can cause strand displacement and has low processivity.

The principal polymerase in DNA replication in *E. coli* is DNA polymerase III, a complex of several proteins with separate functions. The α subunit has polymerase activity, the ε subunit has 3′→5′ exonuclease activity or proofreading, and several other protein components are active in assembly of polymerase III, binding of polymerase III to template DNA, and high processivity. The ssDNA used as template by DNA polymerase III is supplied by a combination of actions by DNA gyrase and DNA helicase. DNA gyrase introduces negative supercoils into dsDNA in an ATP-dependent process. Negative supercoils overcome torsional stress caused by helicase-catalyzed unwinding of dsDNA, a process also driven by ATP hydrolysis. This action at an origin of replication leads to a replication bubble consisting of two replication forks. At each fork, there is leading strand synthesis and lagging strand synthesis. Leading strand synthesis occurs in the direction of replication fork movement, whereas lagging strand replication is away from the replication fork. At a replication fork, DNA is replicated semidiscontinuously. Synthesis is primed on both strands at a replication fork by primase, a DNA-dependent RNA polymerase. As the replication fork moves to expose unreplicated DNA, the lagging strand is periodically reprimed. Later, the

RNA primers are removed by RNase H, an RNase specific for RNA:DNA hybrids, and by nick translation by DNA polymerase I. Any gaps are filled in leaving nicks that are sealed by DNA ligase.

RNA-dependent DNA polymerase or reverse transcriptase can convert an RNA template into DNA. Reverse transcriptases have, in addition to DNA polymerase activity, RNase H activity and DNA-dependent DNA polymerase activity.

DNA Repair

Mismatch repair removes mispaired bases on DNA by scanning duplex DNA for mispairs, excising the incorrect member of the pair, and replacing it with the correct base. Mispairs in newly synthesized DNA are corrected because the template DNA is methylated, while the nascent DNA strand is unmethylated. UV-induced pyrimidine dimers are corrected by a light-dependent cleavage catalyzed by photolyase. Excision repair is active against several kinds of damaged DNA, including apurinic and apyrimidinic sites created by base removal. The general approach to excision repair is to create flanking single-strand breaks on the same stand in order to remove the damaged DNA.

Recombination

General recombination involves exchange of DNA between two molecules that have similar sequences. DNAs with similar sequences that are derived from a common sequence are homologous. Thus, the process is known as homologous recombination. In homologous recombination, the two DNAs pair, single-stranded nicks are produced, and the ssDNAs displace each other and ligate to form a branched structure. The branch migrates, causing strand exchange, and is finally resolved by strand cleavage into either patch recombinants or splice recombinants (see answer to Problem 6). The enzymology of general recombination is best understood in *E. coli* in which Rec A protein, RecBCD protein complex, and ssDNA-binding protein or SSB play key roles. The RecBCD protein complex initiates recombination by attaching to the end of DNA and unwinding it. As DNA is unwound, it begins to rewind but at a slower rate, giving rise to a bubble of ssDNA. When a specific sequence (GCTGGTGG) known as a Chi site is encountered, RecBCD causes a single strand nick, producing a ssDNA tail that is coated with SSB. RecA binds to SSB-coated ssDNA to form a nucleoprotein filament that binds to dsDNA and causes strand displacement. Ligation leads to branch formation, branch migration, and resolution of the Holliday junction.

Alteration in DNA Sequence

DNA sequences can be altered by mutation, recombination, and transposon insertion. Mutations include insertions and deletions of one or more base pairs and changes in a single base (point mutations) leading to either a transition (a purine–purine change or a pyrimidine–pyrimidine change) or a transversion (purine–pyrimidine or vice versa). Small insertions and deletions can be produced by intercalating agents such as acridine orange, whereas large deletions and insertions can be produced by recombination or by transposon mutagenesis. Transposons, first described by McClintock, are genetic elements that can change their location within DNA.

Immunoglobulin Genes

Understand how somatic recombination leads to cells with unique immunoglobulin genes. Recombination involves joining, in combinatorial fashion, segments of genetic information to produce a virtually unique recombinant.

Problems and Solutions

1.   (a) If ^{15}N-labelled E. coli DNA has a density of 1.724 g/mL, ^{14}N-labelled DNA has a density of 1.710 g/mL, and E. coli cells grown for many generations on ^{14}NH$_4^+$ as nitrogen source are transferred to media containing ^{15}NH$_4^+$ as sole N-source, what will be the density of the DNA after one generation, assuming replication is semiconservative? (b) Supposing replication took place by a dispersive mechanism, what would be the density of DNA after one generation? (c) Design an experiment to distinguish between semiconservative and dispersive modes of replication.

Answer: After one generation for both semiconservative and dispersive modes of replication, DNA of an intermediate density $(1.724 + 1.710)/2 = 1.717$ g/mL) is expected. In order to distinguish between the two models, DNA is denatured into single-stranded DNA and subsequently analyzed by CsCl density gradient centrifugation to determine the density of the single strands. For the dispersive model, single-stranded DNA of only a single density is expected, whereas for the semiconservative model, two DNA populations with slightly different densities will be observed.

3. *Assuming DNA replication proceeds at a rate of 750 base pairs per second, calculate how long it will take to replicate the entire E. coli genome. Under optimal conditions, E. coli cells divide every 20 minutes. What is the minimal number of replication forks per E. coli chromosome in order to sustain such a rate of cell division?*

Answer: The *E. coli* genome is 4.64×10^6 bp. Assuming that DNA replication proceeds at a rate of 750 base pairs per second, the time required to replicate this amount of DNA assuming bidirectional replication (i.e., two replication forks starting at a single origin of replication and moving in opposite directions) is given by:

$$\frac{4.64 \times 10^6 \text{bp}}{2 \times 750 \dfrac{\text{bp}}{\text{sec}}} = 3093 \text{ sec} = 51.6 \text{ min} = 0.86 \text{ hr}$$

For the genome to be replicated within 20 minutes, the cell must be replicating DNA at the rate of:

$$\frac{4.64 \times 10^6 \text{bp}}{20 \text{ min}} = 2.32 \times 10^5 \frac{\text{bp}}{\text{min}}$$

At a replication bubble, DNA is being synthesized at the rate of

$$2 \times 750 \frac{\text{bp}}{\text{sec}} = 1500 \frac{\text{bp}}{\text{sec}} = 90\,000 \frac{\text{bp}}{\text{min}}$$

There are $\dfrac{2.32 \times 10^5 \dfrac{\text{bp}}{\text{min}}}{90\,000 \dfrac{\text{bp}}{\text{min}}} = 2.58$ replication bubbles or 5.16 replication forks

5. *It is estimated that there are ten molecules of DNA polymerase III per E. coli cell. Is it likely that E. coli growth rate is limited by DNA polymerase III availability?*

Answer: For maximum growth rate, approximately 5 replication forks are active. (See Problem 3.) If each replication fork has two copies of DNA polymerase III, then 10 molecules of the enzyme should be sufficient to support maximum growth.

7. *How do DNA gyrases and helicases differ in their respective functions and modes of action?*

Answer: DNA gyrases introduce negative supercoils into DNA. These enzymes act by binding to DNA at crossover configurations caused by positive supercoils, catalyzing phosphodiester bond breakage of one of the duplex DNAs at the crossover, passing the uncleaved DNA through the gap, and reforming of the phosphodiester bonds, which results in conversion of positive supercoil to negative supercoil. The process is driven by a conformational change in gyrase and ATP hydrolysis is required to re-establish the original conformation. Gyrases move ahead of replication forks, introducing negative supercoils and thus facilitating strand unwinding at the replication fork.

Helicases are enzymes that separate DNA strands by unwinding DNA using ATP hydrolysis. Helicases bind to regions of double-stranded DNA, move along a single strand, and disrupt base pairs. Translocation and strand unwinding are coupled to ATP hydrolysis.

9. *From the information in Figure 28.17, diagram the recombinational event leading to the formation of a heteroduplex DNA region within a bacteriophage chromosome.*

Answer: Assume that the dsDNA illustrated below represents the same gene from two bacteriophages. The genes are not identical but are homologous. To make heteroduplex DNA: single-strand nicking, followed by strand invasion, ligation, branch migration, and resolution of the Holliday junction produce two heteroduplex molecules. Subsequent DNA mismatch repair or replication will produce recombinant bacteriophage.

11. *If RecA protein unwinds duplex DNA so that there are about 18.6 bp per turn, what is the change in* $\Delta\phi$, *the helical twist of DNA, compared to its value in B-DNA?*

Answer: B-DNA has 10 bp per turn. The $\Delta\phi$ is calculated as follows:

$$\Delta\phi = \frac{360°}{10 \text{ bp}} = 36° \text{ per bp}$$

For RecA-unwound DNA, $\Delta\phi$ is:

$$\Delta\phi = \frac{360°}{18.6 \text{ bp}} = 19.4° \text{ per bp}$$

The change in $\Delta\phi = 36° - 19.4° = 16.6°$

13. *Show the nucleotide sequence changes that might arise in a dsDNA (coding strand segment GCTA) upon mutagenesis with (a) HNO₂, (b) bromouracil, and (c) 2-aminopurine.*

Answer: (a) Nitrous acid (HNO₂) converts cytosine to uracil and adenine to hypoxanthine by deamination. Uracil base pairs with adenine, which subsequently pairs with thymine. Thus, cytosine to uracil results in C to T transitions. For the sequence GCTA, C to T transitions on the top strand will produce:

GTTA

Modification of C on the complementary strand (complementary to GCTA) will produce:

ACTA

It is possible, although much less probably, to get double-mutations:

ATTA

Hypoxanthine, produced by deamination of adenine, can pair with cytosine, which in turn pairs with G. The net result is A to G transitions caused by deamination of A. The sequence GCTA may be converted to:

GCTG

Modification of A on the complementary strand (complementary to GCTA) will produce:

GCCA

It is possible, although much less probably, to get double-mutations:

GC**C**G

We considered only mutations to C's or A's separately. It is possible to have simultaneous mutations to C's and A's, which would generate combinations of the sequences shown above.

b. Bromouracil is a base analog of uracil with a bromine atom at carbon 5. It resembles thymine and can be incorporated into DNA in place of T. However, the presence of the electronegative Br influences the keto to enol tautomerization. In the enol tautomer, 5-bromouracil pairs with guanine. Thus, incorporation of 5-bromouracil for T produces T to C transitions or A to G transitions. In addition, the enol tautomer may be incorporated into DNA in place of C, resulting in C to T transitions and G to A transitions, but this might be expected to occur less often.

The sequence GCTA and its complement, TAGC, (both written 5' to 3') would each be synthesized in the presence of bromouracil and during synthesis of each strand, the T's could be replaced by bromoU (U_{Br}). Thus, GCTA would be GCU$_{Br}$A and TAGC would be U$_{Br}$AGC. Mutations would occur when these U$_{Br}$-containing DNAs were replicated and mispaired with G. GCU$_{Br}$A would produce TGGC (written 5' to 3'), the complement of which is **GCCA**. Thus, GCTA is mutated to GCCA. U$_{Br}$AGC would product GCTG (written 5' to 3'). Thus, GCTA is mutated to **GCTG**. GCCG would only occur if the mutagen were present during a second round of DNA synthesis.

Bromouracil could substitute for C during DNA synthesis if it were in its enol form and paired with a G. The sequence GCTA and its complement, TAGC, (both written 5' to 3') would each be synthesized in the presence of bromouracil, and during synthesis of each strand, the C's could be replaced by bromoU (U_{Br}). Thus, GCTA would be GU$_{Br}$TA and TAGC would be TAGU$_{Br}$. Mutations would occur when these U$_{Br}$-containing DNAs were replicated and mispaired with G. GU$_{Br}$TA would produce TAAC (written 5' to 3') the complement of which is **GTTA**. Thus, GCTA is mutated to GTTA. TAGU$_{Br}$ would product ACTA (written 5' to 3'). Thus, GCTA is mutated to **ACTA**. ATTA would only occur if the mutagen were present during a second round of DNA synthesis.

c. 2-aminopurine (A_2) is an adenine analog that substitutes for A but can pair with cytosine. The sequence GCTA and its complement TAGC (both written 5' to 3') serve as templates during which A_2 is incorporated in place of A. Thus, GCTA produces TA$_2$GC and when this is replicated it produces **GCCA**. TAGC produces GCTA$_2$, and when this is replicated, it produces CAGC, the complement of which is **GCTG**. GCCG would be produced very rarely.

15. *Give a plausible explanation for the genetic and infectious properties of PrP^sc.*

Answer: Prion diseases are neurodegenerative diseases caused by proteinaceous infectious particles or prions. To date, there in no convincing evidence that the infectious agent of prion diseases carries genetic material of any kind. Rather, the disease can be transmitted by an aberrant form of the prion protein PrP. PrP is a normal cellular protein found in uninfected individuals. (Using knockout mice, it has been shown that PrP is a non-essential gene but its presence is required for prion disease development.) Normal (or cellular) PrP has a different conformation than PrP^sc (**sc**rapies is a prion disease first identified in sheep): cellular PrP is largely alpha helical, whereas scrapies PrP contains beta strands. It has been postulated that scrapies PrP causes disease by inducing cellular PrP to undergo a conformational change to the beta-structure–dominated form.

17. *Asako Furukohri, Myron F. Goodman, and Hisaji Maki wanted to discover how the translesion DNA polymerase IV takes over from DNA polymerase III at a stalled replication fork (see Furukohri, A., Goodman, M.F., et al., 2008. A dynamic polymerase exchange with Escherichia coli DNA polymerase IV replacing DNA polymerase III on the sliding clamp. Journal of Biological Chemistry 283:11260–11269). They showed that DNA polymerase IV could displace DNA polymerase III from a stalled replication fork formed in an in vitro system containing DNA, DNA polymerase III, the β-clamp, and SSB. Devise your own experiment to show how such displacement might be demonstrated. (Hint: Assume that you have protein identification tools that allow you to distinguish easily between DNA polymerase III and DNA polymerase IV.)*

Answer: It would be useful to conduct an experiment that could identify proteins that are released from replication forks and those that are bound to them. Identification could be made using monoclonal antibodies specific for DNA polymerase III and antibodies specific for DNA polymerase IV. A stalled replication fork is a large macromolecular complex that should be separable from the DNA polymerase complexes using a technique like centrifugation—perhaps gradient centrifugation. Stalled replication fork complexes could be treated with increasing amounts of DNA polymerase IV and then separated by centrifugation. Fractions across a sucrose gradient, for example, could then be quantitated with respect to DNA polymerase III and IV. One would expect less DNA polymerase III associated with replication forks as the concentration of competing DNA polymerase IV is increased.

Questions for Self-Study

1. The experiments of Meselson and Stahl showed that DNA is replicated semiconservatively. The experiments ruled out conservative and dispersive models. Describe the experiments and explain how they favoured semiconservative replication over the other two models.

2. DNA polymerase I and DNA polymerase III in *E. coli* play key roles in DNA replication. Determine which polymerase best fits each of the statements below.
   a. Proofreading on a separate subunit
   b. Highly processive enzyme
   c. Used to generate Klenow fragment
   d. Multi-subunit enzyme
   e. Active in DNA repair
   f. Repairs gaps left after RNA primers removed
   g. Single polypeptide chain
   h. Functions at a replication fork
   i. Moderately processive enzyme
   j. Carries out nick translation

3. Match the columns.
   a. DNA gyrase
   b. Helicase
   c. Leading strand
   d. Lagging strand
   e. Primase
   f. RNase H
   g. DNA ligase
   h. SSB
   i. Localizes helicase to replication fork
   j. β-subunit of DNA pol III

   1. Rep protein
   2. Joins 3′ hydroxyl to 5′ phosphate
   3. ATP-dependent dsDNA unwinder
   4. RNA polymerase
   5. Okazaki fragments
   6. Attaches holoenzyme to DNA
   7. 3′-end toward replication fork
   8. Type II topoisomerase
   9. Blocks DNA 2° structure formation
   10. Removes primers from Okazaki fragments

4. What are the three enzymatic activities of reverse transcriptase?

5. If an error occurs during replication resulting in a mismatched base pair, how does the repair mechanism distinguish between the correct, template base and the incorrect base?

6. UV-damaged DNA can be repaired by excision repair or by dimer reversal. Explain.

7. To acquire new genes, cells can be transformed by plasmids. In this case, the plasmid has the necessary genetic elements to direct its replication and segregation into daughter cells, thus insuring that it is stably maintained. However, cells can also be transformed by DNA devoid of such elements (origins of replication). For example, in the classic experiments of F. Griffith, cells were transformed using sheared, chromosomal DNA. How can linear DNA (lacking an origin of replication) get incorporated stably into cells?

8. General recombination in *E. coli* depends on at least three proteins, RecA protein, RecBCD protein complex, and single-stranded DNA-binding protein (SSB). For each of the statements below, indicate which protein fits best.
   a. Promotes RecA binding to ssDNA
   b. Forms nucleoprotein filaments that unwind DNA to 18.6 bp per turn
   c. Recognizes the sequence GCTGGTGG (Chi site)
   d. Catalyzes DNA strand exchange
   e. Binds to single-stranded DNA only
   f. Unwinds DNA in an ATP-dependent reaction
   g. Binds to the ends of a DNA duplex

9. In 1983, Barbara McClintock was awarded the Nobel Prize in physiology or medicine for discoveries she made in the 1950s. What important class of genetic elements did McClintock discover?

10. Briefly explain how antibody diversity is accomplished.

11. Match the columns.
   a. Deletion
   b. Insertion
   c. Transversion
   d. Transition

   1. GGGACCC → GGGGCCC
   2. GGGGCCC → GGGCCCC
   3. GGGACCC → GGGAACCC
   4. GGGACCC → GGGCCC

12. The base analog 5-bromouracil (5-BU) is a thymine analog that causes transitions because it tautomerizes readily from the keto form to the enol form. In the keto form, 5-BU pairs with A, but in the enol form it pairs with G. The structure of 5-BU in the keto form is shown below. Draw the enol form and show how this form pairs with G and how the keto form pairs with A.

5-BU   Adenine   Guanine

Answers

1. *E. coli* was grown in ^{15}N for several generations to uniformly label DNA with this heavy nitrogen isotope. Cells were then shifted to ^{14}N for a few generations and DNA was isolated after each generation. The densities of DNA were then compared by density centrifugation. It was found that after one generation DNA of a density intermediate to that of ^{15}N-labelled DNA and ^{14}N-labelled DNA was produced. Subsequent generations produced two bands of density, one corresponding to the band after one generation and a second corresponding to ^{14}N-labelled DNA. The intermediate density DNA, produced after one generation, was further analyzed under denaturing conditions and it was found to be composed of single-stranded ^{15}N DNA and single-stranded ^{14}N DNA.

2. a. III; b. III; c. I; d. III; e. I; f. I; g. I; h. III; i. I; j. I.

3. a. 8; b. 3; c. 7; d. 5; e. 4; f. 10; g. 2; h. 9; i. 1; j. 6.

4. RNA-directed DNA polymerase, RNase H (degrades RNA of RNA/DNA duplex), and DNA-directed DNA polymerase.

5. The DNA is scanned for methyl groups located on the parent, template strand.

6. In excision repair, the damaged base is removed along with a few residues flanking the damage site. This action leaves a gap that is subsequently filled. In dimer reversal, photolyase binds to the dimer and using the energy of visible light, disconnects the bases from each other.

7. The DNA must be incorporated into genomic DNA by either site-specific or general recombination. (Hfr crosses and general transduction also depend on recombination.)

8. a. SSB; b. RecA; c. RecBCD; d. RecA; e. SSB; f. RecBCD; g. RecBCD.

9. Mobile elements (transposable elements or transposons).

10. Genetic rearrangements produce an intact gene by combining several separate elements. Each element derives from a set of similar elements. Further, imprecise joining of elements adds to genetic diversity.

11. a. 4; b. 3; c. 2; d. 1.

12.

5-BU (enol)   Guanine   5-BU (keto)   Adenine

Additional Problems

1. The enzyme uracil-N-glycosylase is part of a DNA repair system that removes deoxyuracil from DNA. The enzyme scans DNA for uracil and hydrolyzes the glycosidic bond between sugar and base to leave an apyrimidinic site. How is this apyrimidinic site dealt with subsequently?

2. Suggest two mechanisms by which deoxyuracil gets into DNA. (Hint: One has to do with deoxynucleotide biosynthesis; the other has to do with instability of a certain base.)

3. Suggest a method of incorporating labelled dNTPs into DNA using DNA polymerase I.

4. Okazaki fragments arise from lagging-strand synthesis. Yet in wild-type cells, no long fragments are initially observed. Can you explain why both long and short fragments are expected at early stages of replication? Bonus: Can you explain why long fragments are not observed in wild-type cells but are observed in *ung*⁻ cells (*ung*⁻ codes for uracil-N-glycosylase).

5. The genetic locus of DNA Q mutations was first identified as one of a number of so-called *mut* (mutator) loci. What function of DNA metabolism might this locus be responsible for?

6. How was bidirectional replication first shown?

7. Explain why the base analog 5-bromouracil can give rise to T-A to C-G transitions.

8. The chemical mutagens and base analogs described in this chapter are very effective at inducing transitions. Transversions occur less frequently. Provide an explanation.

9. Based on your knowledge of enzymes that have been encountered in your studies on intermediary metabolism, can you correctly restate the "one-gene, one-enzyme hypothesis"?

Abbreviated Answers

1. An apurinic endonuclease recognizes the site and causes strand cleavage to remove the deoxyribose and several flanking positions, creating a gap that is repaired by DNA polymerase and ligase.

2. Deoxynucleotide biosynthesis involves formation of dNDPs from NDP without regard to base. Thus, dUDP is formed and converted to dUTP. Normally, dUTPase hydrolyzes dUTP to dUMP and PPᵢ but with less-than-perfect efficiency. Occasionally, dUTP is incorporated into DNA in place of dTTP. The second mechanism for formation of uracil in DNA is by non-enzymatic oxidative deamination of Cs.

3. DNA can be labelled by taking advantage of the nick translation activity of DNA polymerase I. DNA is first nicked with limited digestion by DNase I, which creates randomly positioned single-strand breaks.

These breaks or nicks are positions at which DNA polymerase I will initiate nick translation. If radioactively labelled dNTPs are employed, the newly synthesized stand will be appropriately labelled.

4. Because the lagging strand is periodically reprimed, it is synthesized as short DNA fragments or Okazaki fragments. With time, Okazaki fragments are converted into long DNA fragments by removal of the RNA primers and ligation. The leading strand is synthesized continuously because its elongation is in the same direction as replication fork migration. No long fragments are observed in wild-type cells because of the uracil repair mechanism. Uracil is randomly incorporated into both the leading and lagging strands. Removal of the base followed by chain cleavage excises the uracil residues, leaving gaps to be repaired. The leading strand, although produced continuously, is fragmented by this repair system. Mutant *ung⁻* cells do not repair uracil-containing DNA and produce long and short fragments.

5. DNA Q codes for the proofreading subunit of DNA polymerase III. Certain mutations at this locus cause cells to undergo frequent mutagenesis because of error-prone DNA replication.

6. Cells were grown for a number of generations in low amounts ³H-thymidine to uniformly label DNA with a small amount of radioactivity. Cells were then shifted for a brief period of time to high levels of ³H-thymidine. Cells were subsequently fixed and autoradiographed to determine the location of heavily labelled DNA.

7. The base analog 5-bromouracil will more readily undergo keto–enol tautomerization because of the influence of the bromine group. In the enol tautomeric form, 5-bromouracil will pair with G. Thus, a T-A pair will be converted to a 5-bromouracil-G pair then to a C-G pair.

8. Mutagens are effective only because the damage they cause is not efficiently repaired by DNA repair mechanisms. To produce a transition requires a purine–pyrimidine mismatch during mutagenesis, and these are less likely to be repaired than purine–purine or pyrimidine–pyrimidine mismatches produced during transversion mutagenesis.

9. On several occasions we have encountered single polypeptide chains that have two enzymatic activities. For example, phosphofructokinase 2 and fructose bisphosphatase 2 activities, responsible for fructose-2,6-bisphosphate metabolism, are found on a single protein. A more correct statement would be "one-gene, one-polypeptide."

Summary

The maintenance of the genetic information encoded in the sequence of bases in DNA is accomplished via replication; the expression of this information is achieved through transcription. DNA replication is semiconservative: The two strands of the DNA double helix separate and each serves as a template for the synthesis of a new complementary strand. Thus, two daughter DNA double helices identical in every respect are reproduced from a single parental double helix. Each daughter double helix consists of one parental strand and one new strand. Using the techniques of ^{15}N-density labelling of DNA and CsCl density gradient ultracentrifugation, Meselson and Stahl provided the experimental proof establishing the semiconservative mechanism of replication.

In 1957, Arthur Kornberg and his colleagues reported the discovery of an enzyme from *E. coli* capable of DNA synthesis. This enzyme, DNA polymerase I, catalyzed the incorporation of the deoxynucleoside 5'-triphosphates dATP, dGTP, dCTP, and dTTP into DNA in the presence of a template strand to copy and a primer strand that provided a free 3'-OH end for nucleotide addition. Successive addition of nucleotides at the 3'-end of the primer drove chain elongation in the 5'→3' direction. *E. coli* DNA pol I is a 109 kD polypeptide of 928 amino acid residues possessing three catalytic sites: one responsible for the 5'→3' DNA polymerase activity and two others that catalyzed distinct exonuclease reactions, one in the 3'→5' direction (the "3'-exonuclease") and one in the 5'→3' direction (the "5'-exonuclease"). The 3'-exonuclease activity improves the fidelity of replication by checking the accuracy of base-pairing between the base just incorporated and its complementary base in the template. If this pairing is inappropriate, the 3'-exonuclease excises the offending base, giving the polymerase another chance to insert the correct base. The 5'-exonuclease activity acts only on dsDNA and serves a repair function: It "edits out" sections of damaged DNA or any ribonucleotides incorporated during the initiation of DNA replication (see below).

All DNA polymerases discovered thus far catalyze chain growth in the 5'→3' direction, adding each new base as specified by a template DNA strand according to the A:T/G:C base-pairing rules of Watson and Crick. The template is read in the antiparallel 3′→5′ direction and the incoming nucleotide is added to the 3′-end of a primer chain. It turns out that DNA pol III, not DNA pol I, is the principal DNA-replicating enzyme of *E. coli*. DNA pol III consists of a 165 kD "core" polymerase of α, ε and θ subunits, where the 120 kD α subunit provides the polymerase active site and the 27.5 kD ε subunit contributes the proofreading 3′-exonuclease function. In vivo, this "core" polymerase is part of an 800 kD complex, the DNA polymerase holoenzyme. The processivity of DNA polymerase III holoenzyme exceeds 5000; that is, it can associate with a template strand and read along it to synthesize a complementary DNA strand greater than 5000 nucleotides long without once dissociating.

DNA replication is a complex process. First, the DNA helix must be unwound to expose single-stranded template regions. Unwinding can impose torsional stress, and ATP-dependent DNA gyrases act to introduce negative supercoils to counteract this stress. ATP-dependent helicases catalyze the actual disruption of the double helix, breaking the H bonds between the base pairs as they move along a strand of the DNA duplex. Replication is bidirectional: It begins at unique sites on chromosomes ("origins of replication"). The strands are separated here to form a "bubble," and so-called "replication forks" proceed away from the origin in both directions along the parental dsDNA, growing two daughter DNA duplexes in their wake. Replication is semidiscontinuous because DNA polymerases only work in the 5′→3′ direction, reading a template in the 3′→5′ sense. This polarity means that DNA polymerases can continuously copy the emerging 3′→5′ strand, but the 5′→3′ parental strand must be copied discontinuously: Only when a single-stranded stretch of this 5′→3′ strand has been exposed can the DNA polymerase move long it in the 3′→5′ direction to synthesize its complement. Reiji Okazaki provided the experimental verification for this semidiscontinuous mode of replication when he discovered that the radioactivity immediately incorporated into newly synthesized DNA occurred in short fragments, 1000–2000 nucleotides in length. With time, this radioactivity was associated with progressively longer DNA strands as the Okazaki fragments were ligated together to form a covalently contiguous DNA chain. DNA ligase catalyzes this reaction. The continuously synthesized DNA strand is called the "leading strand"; the discontinuously synthesized strand is called the "lagging strand." The primers for DNA synthesis in vivo are RNA oligonucleotides complementary to the DNA template. These RNA primers are synthesized by primase, an RNA polymerase. No RNA is found in mature DNA duplexes because DNA pol I binds at the 3′-OH nicks of Okazaki fragments. Its 5′→3′ exonuclease then cuts out the RNA and the gaps this creates are filled in with DNA by the 5′→3′ polymerase activity. DNA ligase then seals the junctions.

In *E. coli*, DNA replication begins at a unique 245 bp site, *oriC*, and proceeds bidirectionally. *DnaA protein* first binds at four 9 bp repeats within *oriC* and then additional *DnaA protein* binds to create a nucleosome-like assembly. *DnaA protein* then mediates the opening of the duplex at three A:T-rich tandem repeats at the 5′-side of *oriC*. Other proteins bind to form a "pre-priming complex" and the helix is further unwound. Primase then joins the pre-priming complex to yield the primosome. Two primosomes are formed at *oriC*, one for each replication fork. At each replication fork, two DNA polymerase III holoenzymes are present; one catalyzes leading-strand synthesis and the other, lagging-strand synthesis.

In eukaryotes, DNA replication occurs during the S phase of the cell cycle. A number of multimeric DNA polymerases are found in eukaryotic cells. DNA polymerase α and DNA polymerase δ are believed to constitute an "asymmetric dimer" replicase located at each replication fork, with DNA polymerase δ synthesizing the leading strand and DNA polymerase α forming the lagging strand.

RNA-directed synthesis of DNA occurs in certain RNA viruses known as retroviruses. The enzyme responsible is reverse transcriptase. Like all DNA polymerases, it incorporates nucleotides in the 5′→3′ direction, reading its template in the 3′→5′ direction. A tRNA H-bonded to the RNA template serves as primer. Reverse transcriptases display two other enzymatic activities in addition to their RNA-dependent DNA polymerase activity: an RNase H activity and a DNA-dependent DNA polymerase activity. RNase H degrades RNA chains in RNA/DNA hybrid duplexes. Its role in retroviral replication is to digest the genomic RNA chain so that the DNA-dependent DNA polymerase activity of reverse transcriptase can then copy the just-made DNA strand to give a duplex DNA. This DNA duplex then either mediates the subsequent course of the viral infection or becomes inserted into the host genome where it can lie dormant for many years. The reverse transcriptase of human immunodeficiency virus, the etiological agent in AIDS, is inhibited by the triphosphate derivative of AZT.

Genetic recombination involves the breakage and reunion of DNA strands, so that a physical exchange of parts takes place. The Holliday model for general recombination postulates a sequence of events, including alignment of homologous sequences on two different duplex DNA molecules, introduction of single-strand nicks at analogous sites on both DNAs, invasion of each of the single strands into the other DNA duplex (strand invasion), and ligation of the free ends from different duplexes to create a cross-stranded intermediate, the Holliday junction. This junction can migrate along the DNA molecules so that considerable lengths of nucleotide sequence from one duplex become associated via base pairing with the other DNA duplex. If strands of the duplexes become nicked and then religated with strands of the other, recombinant duplexes can be formed. The enzymology of general recombination is understood, at least in outline. The *Rec*BCD complex attaches to the end of a DNA duplex and progresses along it, unwinding the helix in an ATP-dependent reaction. *Rec*BCD enzyme also nicks the duplex at Chi "hotspots" of recombination to produce an ssDNA tail, a necessary prelude to the entry of *Rec*A protein into the process. The protein *Rec*A catalyzes the DNA strand exchange reaction, the reaction by which one strand of a duplex is displaced and replaced by an invading single strand from another duplex in an ATP-driven process. SSB (single-stranded DNA-binding protein) facilitates the action of RecA by binding to ssDNA and keeping it from assuming any secondary structure that might impede strand exchange. The Holliday junction ensuing from RecBCD, RecA action upon two adjacent and homologous DNA duplexes is resolved in *E. coli* by the *ruv*C endonuclease/resolvase into one of the two isomeric recombinant forms, patch or splice. Cleavage of exchanged strands yields patch recombinants; cleavage of parental strands gives splice recombinants.

The immunoglobulin genes represent a system that has evolved for generating a large repertoire of protein diversity from a finite amount of genetic information. DNA rearrangement (gene reorganization) is the biological mechanism that allows a variety of protein isoforms from a limited number of genes. DNA rearrangement occurs only among genes encoding proteins of the immune response, like the immunoglobulin genes. IgG is an $\alpha_2\beta_2$ tetramer composed of 2 light (L) chains and 2 heavy (H) chains. The L and H polypeptide chains are remarkable in that the amino acid sequence over the first 108 residues of both is highly variable. It is the variable region of the immunoglobulin polypeptide chains that is ultimately responsible for antigen recognition and binding. Sequence diversity in these regions endows these proteins with the unparalleled repertoires of structure recognition essential to the immune response. The unusual organization of the immunoglobulin genes accounts for this amino acid sequence diversity: the genetic information for an immunoglobulin chain is scattered among multiple gene segments in germline cells. During vertebrate development, these segments are assembled by DNA rearrangement into complete genes. The mechanism for light-chain and heavy-chain gene assembly is based on secondary structures formed between consensus heptamer and nonamer sequences separated by 12-bp and 23-bp spacers. These heptamer/nonamer, 12-23-bp spacers are located adjacent to the rearranging genes and act to bring the genes into juxtaposition for the recombination events that underlie L-chain and H-chain gene assembly. Imprecise joining (the joining of these genes within codes) creates even greater amino acid sequence diversity in the variable regions of κ chains.

Mutations change the nucleotide sequence of DNA, either by substituting one base pair for another, or by inserting or deleting one or more base pairs. Point mutations are those mutations due to the substitution of one base pair for another. They may be either transitions (where a purine replaces a purine, or a pyrimidine, a pyrimidine) or transversions (where a purine replaces a pyrimidine, or vice versa). Point mutations arise from a number of causes. Some are due to mistakes in base pairing between the usual bases of DNA, others appear via the incorporation of base analogs with aberrant base-pairing properties into DNA during replication, and still others are a result of chemical modifications altering pairing of bases already present in the DNA. Intercalation of flat aromatic molecules like acridine orange creates insertion/deletion mutations through distortion of the DNA double helix that leads to a misreading during replication. Transposons are discrete DNA segments, about 10 kb in length, which promote their own movement into and out of DNA. Transposons are thus a natural source of insertion mutations.

Chapter 29

Transcription and the Regulation of Gene Expression

• •

Chapter Outline

- ❖ Central Dogma: Crick: DNA → RNA → protein
    - ⅄ Transcription: DNA to RNA
    - ⅄ Translation: RNA to protein
- ❖ Transcription
    - ⅄ Enzymology (*E. coli*)
        - • DNA-dependent RNA polymerase (RNA polymerase)
            - • 3′ polymerase activity
            - • NTPs as substrates
        - • Subunit structure
            - • $\alpha\beta'\beta$: Core enzyme: Elongation
            - • $\alpha\beta'\beta\sigma$: Holoenzyme: Initiation
            - • β' = DNA-binding subunit
            - • β = NTP-binding sites
            - • σ = promoter recognition
    - ⅄ Initiation
        - • Closed promoter complex
            - • σ of holoenzyme binds to promoter
            - • Promoter: Two conserved sequences
                - o Pribnow box (−10): TATAAT
                - o −35: TTGAGA
                - o Separation between elements: 17 bp
        - • Open promoter complex
            - • dsDNA unwound
            - • RNA polymerase at start of initiation (+1)
                - o Negative numbers: Upstream of start site
                - o Positive numbers: Downstream of start site
        - • Several phosphodiester bonds made
            - • Initiation site binds ATP or GTP (complementary to template start site)
            - • Elongation site binds NTP complementary to template
            - • Phosphodiester bond formation
            - • After 5 to 9 bonds formed σ dissociates
                - o Rifamycin: Blocks initiation site NTP binding
                - o Rifampicin: Blocks translocation
                - o Cordycepin: Adds to 3′-end of RNA but lacks 3′OH: Chain termination
    - ⅄ Termination: Two types
        - • Rho-independent termination: Three terminator elements
            - • G:C-rich inverted repeat forms stem
            - • Non-repeated sequence separates inverted repeats forms loop
            - • 6 to 8 U's on end
            - • RNA polymerase pauses and terminates after element is transcribed

- Rho-dependent termination
    - Rho: ATP-dependent helicase
    - Rho binding site: C-rich regions of transcript
- ❖ Transcriptional regulation in prokaryotes
    - ⅄ Gene organization
        - Genes coding for enzymes with common goals often transcribed together
        - Genes organized into operon
        - Transcription produces polycistronic message
        - Operator near operon promoter regulates initiation of transcription
            - Induction: Increased synthesis in response to specific substrate
                - ○ Inducer: Small molecule binds to protein
                - ○ Gratuitous inducer: Not metabolized (e.g., *lac* operon's IPTG)
            - Repression: Decreased synthesis in response to specific metabolite
            - Constitutive expression: Expression not regulated
    - ⅄ *lac* operon: Jacob and Monod: Operon hypothesis
        - Genes for lactose metabolism expressed when lactose present and glucose absent
        - Operator: Palindromic sequence near promoter recognized by *lac* repressor protein
        - *Lac* repressor protein: *lacI* gene product
            - In absence of inducer, *lac* repressor binds to operator and blocks promoter
            - Inducer binding to *lac* repressor causes release of repressor from operator: Promoter available
        - CAP: Positive regulator
            - Catabolite activator protein: Binds near promoter increases promoter strength
                - ○ Binding is cAMP dependent
                - ○ cAMP levels determined by adenylyl cyclase levels
                - ○ Glucose leads to low cAMP levels
    - ⅄ *araBAD* operon: Positive and negative control by *AraC*
        - CAP protein: Catabolite repression
        - *araC* gene product: Induction via arabinose
            - *AraC* gene product binds to operator: Blocks transcription
            - Arabinose binding relocates *araC* gene product on operator and binds CRP–cAMP: Activation
    - ⅄ *trp* Operon
        - Trp repressor: *trpR* gene product
            - When complexed to tryptophan: Binds to operator and blocks transcription
            - Low tryptophan cause *trp* repressor to release from operator
            - Trp repressor regulates two other operons
                - ○ *aroH*: Aromatic amino acid synthesis: Related metabolism
                - ○ *trpR*: Example of autogenous regulation (autoregulation)
        - Attenuation: Any regulatory mechanism that manipulates transcription termination or transcription pausing to regulate gene transcription downstream
            - Leader peptide mRNA properties
                - ○ Two tryptophan codons (High percentage of tryptophan in 14 amino acid polypeptide)
                - ○ Three secondary structures:
                    - ▪ Pause structure and terminator: Compatible
                    - ▪ Antiterminator: Incompatible with pause and terminator
                - ○ Low *trp*
                    - ▪ Slow progression of ribosome
                    - ▪ Formation of antiterminator
                - ○ High *trp*
                    - ▪ Rapid progression of ribosome
                    - ▪ Formation of pause–terminator structure

- ❖ Eukaryotic transcription: Three RNA polymerases: Require transcription factors to bind to promoter
  - ⅄ RNA polymerase I
    - ⋅ Transcribes rRNA genes
    - ⋅ α-αmanitin resistant
  - ⅄ RNA polymerase II
    - ⋅ Transcribes mRNA genes
    - ⋅ α-αmanitin sensitive
  - ⅄ RNA polymerase III
    - ⋅ Transcribes tRNA and 5S rRNA genes
    - ⋅ α-αmanitin sensitive but less than RNA polymerase II
- ❖ RNA polymerase II
  - ⅄ Multiple subunits (12 in yeast)
    - ⋅ RPB1: DNA binding (β-like)
      - • C-terminal domain (CDT): PTSPSYS repeats
        - ○ Unphosphorylated CDT: Initiation competent
        - ○ Phosphorylated CDT: Elongation competent
    - ⋅ RPB2: NTP binding (β-like)
    - ⋅ RPB3 (α-like), RPB4 (σ-like)
  - ⅄ Promoters: General transcription factors bind to common promoter elements
    - ⋅ TATA box at -25
    - ⋅ Initiator element (Inr) at start site
    - ⋅ DPE at $+30$
    - ⋅ Proximal elements
      - • CAAT box: Around -80: Strong promoter
      - • GC box: Housekeeping genes
    - ⋅ Enhancers (upstream activation sequences)
      - • Distance and orientation insensitive
    - ⋅ Response elements: Promoter modules that make genes responsible to common regulation
  - ⅄ Initiation: Core promoter bound by basal apparatus: Components
    - ⋅ RNA polymerase II
    - ⋅ General transcription factors: TFIIB, TFIID, TFIIE, TFIIF, TFIIH
      - • TFIID
        - ○ TATA-binding protein
        - ○ TAFs: TBP-associated factors
    - ⋅ Mediator: Connects enhancers to general transcription factors
- ❖ Transcriptional regulation in eukaryotes
  - ⅄ Nucleosome structure
    - ⋅ Swi–Snf complex disrupts nucleosomal arrays in ATP-dependent manner
    - ⋅ Histone Modifications
      - • Histone acetyltransferse (HAT): Acetylate lysine to remove charge
      - • Phosphorylation of ser, methylation of lys, sumoylation of lys
      - • Histone deacetylases complex (HDAC): Remove acetyl groups
      - • Histone code: Patterns of modifications recruit specific proteins
- ❖ DNA-binding motifs
  - ⅄ Helix-turn-helix
    - ⋅ C-terminal helix recognition helix
      - • Binds to major groove
  - ⅄ Zinc finger motifs
    - ⋅ C_2H_2 class: Zn coordinated by 2 C and 2 H
    - ⋅ C_x class: Zn coordinated by cysteine
  - ⅄ bZIP motif: Basic region with leucine zipper
    - ⋅ Leucine zipper: Protein dimerization domain: Coiled-coils formed between two zippers
    - ⋅ Basic region: Rich in basic amino acids: DNA-binding domain

❖ Post-transcriptional processing in eukaryotes
⅄ Capping: 5′-end activity
· Guanylyl transferase adds guanylyl in 5′-5′ linkage
· 7 Position of G methylated
⅄ Polyadenylation: 3′-end activity
· Consensus AAUAAA in mRNA signal for endonuclease and poly(A) polymerase activity
• mRNA cut 10 to 30 nt downstream
• 100 to 200 adenine residues added to 3′-end
⅄ Splicing
· hnRNA (heterogeneous nuclear RNA) converted into mRNA
· Introns removed
• 5′ splice site
• 3′ splice site
• Branch site: Lariat formed
· Exons joined
· Process catalyzed by spliceosome
• Small nuclear ribonucleoprotein particles (snRNPs)
• Constitutive splicing: Formation of single mRNA
• Alternative splicing: Formation of a variety of RNAs

Chapter Objectives

This chapter covers several important topics including RNA production or transcription, RNA processing, regulation of transcription and gene expression, and DNA-binding proteins.

RNA

RNAs are linear polymers of ribonucleotide monophosphates held together by phosphodiester bonds between the 5′-carbon of one nucleotide and the 3′-carbon of another nucleotide. The polymers have two distinct ends, a 5′-end and a 3′-end. Single-stranded RNAs often can form intrachain hydrogen-bonded structures by complementary base pairing. There are three general classes of RNAs: mRNAs, the agents of gene expression that bring genetic information from DNA to the ribosome to direct assembly of proteins; ribosomal RNAs (rRNA), structural and functional components of ribosomes; and, small stable RNAs like tRNAs, adaptor molecules that participate in protein synthesis.

RNA Polymerase

The principal RNA polymerase in *E. coli* is RNA polymerase I, a DNA-dependent RNA polymerase with $\alpha_2\beta\beta'$ subunit composition. In order to initiate transcription, the core polymerase requires the sigma factor σ which functions to identify specific DNA sequences termed promoters. A typical *E. coli* promoter is composed of a −35 region, with a consensus sequence of TCTTGACAT and a −10 region or Pribnow box with consensus sequence TATAAT. Initiation begins with the RNA polymerase holoenzyme, $\alpha_2\beta\beta'\sigma$, binding to the −35 region and migrating to the −10 region, where strand separation is initiated to expose the start-of-transcription site. Initiation of transcription usually begins with ATP or GTP in part because the initiation site, a nucleotide-binding site on the RNA polymerase, preferentially binds these nucleotides. Nucleotide binding at this site, located on the β-subunit, can be blocked by rifamycin B. (A related compound rifampicin allows the first phosphodiester bond to form but blocks subsequent RNA polymerase movement.) After a short oligonucleotide has been synthesized, the σ factor dissociates from the RNA polymerase, leaving the core complex to the task of elongation. Elongation continues until termination signals are encountered of which there are two types, rho-independent and rho-dependent. In rho-independent termination, the 3′-end of the RNA is synthesized to include the termination signal, a sequence that forms a short G:C-rich stem and small loop with a run of unpaired U's. Termination sequence folding causes RNA polymerase to pause and terminate transcription. Rho-dependent termination, a less common mechanism, involves ρ factor, an ATP-dependent helicase that unwinds RNA:DNA duplexes in response to C-rich regions of the mRNA unoccupied by ribosomes.

Eukaryotes contain three classes of nuclear RNA polymerases: RNA polymerase I responsible for rRNA transcription, RNA polymerase II which transcribes protein-encoding genes, and RNA polymerase III responsible for 5S rRNA, tRNA, and other small stable RNAs. The three classes of RNA polymerases are distinguishable by their sensitivity to α-amanitin, a mushroom poison. RNA polymerase I is resistant to the compound, RNA polymerase II is sensitive to inhibition of chain elongation by α-amanitin, and RNA polymerase III is less sensitive. All three classes of RNA polymerases interact with specific promoter sequences with the aid of transcription factors.

RNA polymerase II promoters commonly have sequence elements near the start of transcription; examples include the TATA box and an initiator element. The TATA box has a TATAAA consensus sequence and is located 25 bases upstream of the start of transcription. The transcription start site is located within the initiator element.

Regulation of Transcription

Lactose is metabolized by a set of gene products encoded by the *lac* operon. Transcription of the *lac* operon results in a polycistronic mRNA, a mRNA with coding regions for three separate proteins. Regulation of the *lac* operon is achieved by repression and activation. RNA polymerase requires an additional protein to transcribe the *lac* operon because the promoter is a rather weak, inefficient promoter. The catabolite activator protein (CAP) acts as a positive regulator in this regard by binding to the *lac* promoter. However, binding occurs only in the presence of cAMP, which binds to CAP. *E. coli* prefers glucose and will metabolize it in preference to lactose when both sugars are present. Glucose preference results because glucose inhibits cAMP production, leading to loss of promoter binding by CAP. Repression of the *lac* operon is achieved by *lac* repressor protein binding to an element termed the operator, located near the promoter. Repressor binding blocks RNA polymerase from gaining access to the transcription start site. Release of repression occurs when lactose is present. Lactose is converted to allolactose, which functions as an inducer by binding to the *lac* repressor protein, causing it to dissociate from the operon. Derivatives of lactose that are non-metabolizable yet function as inducers are termed gratuitous inducers. The *lac* operon is under both positive and negative control and is both inducible and repressible.

The arabinose operon is also regulated by repression and induction. Repression is caused by the *araC* gene product binding as a dimer to two sites, one of which is located near the promoter and the other some distance away to produce a DNA loop. Arabinose binding to *araC* protein causes it to vacate the distant site, remain attached to the promoter site and bind to an additional site in the promoter. In this conformation, the *araC* dimer binds two CAP–cAMP, causing the promoter to turn on.

The *trp* operon is regulated by repression and by transcription attenuation. Repression is achieved by *trp* repressor protein binding to the promoter in a *trp*-dependent manner. The ability to transcribe and translate concurrently makes attenuation possible. The attenuator is a short region near the end of the first gene in the *trp* operon. The attenuator is remarkable in having two tandem Trp codons in a region that can form two different secondary structures. When Trp is plentiful, translation is tightly coupled to transcription, and one of the two secondary structures, the terminator secondary structure, is favoured. When Trp is low, the ribosome pauses at the tandem Trp codons, allowing the attenuator to assume an antiterminator secondary structure.

Transcription in eukaryotes is regulated at initiation by promoter strength, by enhancers or upstream activation sequences (UAS), and by responsive elements. The function of enhancers is independent of proximity to the promoter and orientation of the enhancer with respect to the promoter. Responsive elements are located near the transcription start site and are recognized by specific proteins that bind to the responsive element.

DNA-Binding Motifs

There are three prominent classes of DNA-binding motifs, helix-turn-helix, zinc finger, and leucine zippers. The helix-turn-helix motif is typically 20 residues arranged into a 7-residue helix, a small β-turn, and a second helix of about 7 residues that functions as the recognition helix. The recognition helix interacts with a specific DNA sequence via the major groove. The zinc finger motif contains a zinc-binding site defined by either two cysteines and two histidines (C_2H_2) or by several cysteines (C_x). The domain is at the base of a small loop that interacts with DNA via the major groove. The leucine zipper motif is a periodic repetition of leucine zippers along a helix such that leucines line one face of the helix. Proteins containing leucine zippers do not actually bind DNA via the leucine zipper. Rather DNA binding is a property of a sequence of predominantly basic amino acids N-terminal to the leucine zipper. The zipper functions as a protein-dimerization site.

Post-Transcriptional Processing

In eukaryotes, transcription produces a class of primary transcripts in the nucleus known as heterogeneous nuclear RNA. This RNA is processed in three ways to produce mature mRNA. The primary transcripts are modified on the 5′-end by a cap structure, on the 3′-end by a polyA tail, and internally by splicing. The 5′ cap consists of a guanine residue joined in 5′-5′ phosphodiester linkage that is methylated at position N-7 on the base and may contain additional ribose methylations on the first and second nucleotide of the primary transcript. 3'-polyadenylation occurs after transcription of a poly(A) processing signal (consensus sequence AAUAAA) has been transcribed in the primary transcript. Transcripts are cleaved downstream of this signal and 100 to 200 adenine residues are attached to the end. Splicing (Figure 29.43) removes introns or intervening sequences from the primary transcript and joins the remaining exons to produce mRNA. Nucleoprotein complexes in the nucleus carry out splicing. The process involves recognition of the two ends of an intron, cleavage and removal of the intron, and ligation of the exon. The splicing reaction passes through an intermediate structure known as a lariat structure or RNA branch with the 5'-end of the intron joined to a specific base within the intron in 5'-2' phosphodiester linkage.

Problems and Solutions

1. The 5'-end of an mRNA has the sequence
...AGAUCCGUAUGGCGAUCUCGACGAAGACUCCUAGGGAAUCC...
What is the nucleotide sequence of the DNA template strand from which it was transcribed? If this mRNA is translated beginning with the first AUG codon in its sequence, what is the N-terminal amino acid sequence of the protein it encodes? (See Table 30.1 for the genetic code.)

Answer: The nucleotide sequence of the DNA sense strand has the following sequence, written 5' to 3':

...GGATTCCCTAGGAGTCTTCGTCGAGATCGCCATACGGATCT...

The first AUG codon, underlined, is shown below:

...AGAUCCGU<u>AUG</u>GCGAUCUCGACGAAGACUCCUAGGGAAUCC...

The sequence of the protein from the N-terminal amino acid to the C-terminal amino acid is

```
...AGAUCCGUAUG GCG AUC UCG ACG AAG ACU CCU AGG GAA UCC...
            Met Ala Ile Ser Thr Lys Thr Pro Arg Glu Ser...
```

3. RNA polymerase has 2 binding sites for ribonucleoside triphosphates: the initiation site and the elongation site. The initiation site has a greater K_m for NTPs than the elongation site. Suggest what possible significance this fact might have for the control of transcription in cells.

Answer: The initiation site has a preference for purine ribonucleoside triphosphates in addition to having a greater K_m for NTPs than the elongation site. This means that at a given concentration of NTPs, the initiation site will fill only if the concentration of NTPs is high enough to also fill the elongation site. Thus, initiation occurs only where there are sufficient NTPs to support elongation. Having a preference for ATP or GTP ties initiation of polymerization intimately to energy levels in cells.

5. DNA-binding proteins may recognize specific DNA regions either by reading the base sequence or by "indirect readout." How do these 2 modes of protein DNA recognition differ?

Answer: When the base sequence is used for recognition, a DNA-binding protein typically binds to dsDNA through the major groove. In the major groove, each base pair displays a characteristic pattern of hydrogen-bond donors and acceptors. There is similar information in the minor groove but not as diverse as that presented in the major groove.

Indirect readout refers to conformational variations in the dsDNA helix formed as a consequence of the sequence. Base pairs have slightly different sizes. In addition, neighbouring base pairs influence stacking interactions. Thus, the exact shape of a region of dsDNA is influenced by the sequences of bases.

7. Describe why the ability of bZIP proteins to form heterodimers increases the repertoire of genes whose transcription might be responsive to regulation by these proteins.

Answer: *bZIP* polypeptides form dimers by interacting through leucine zippers, amphipathic α-helices containing a periodic repetition of leucine residues spaced every 7 residues such that they line up on one side of the helix. These proteins are DNA-binding proteins as well, interacting with DNA through a short stretch of basic residues located N-terminal to the leucine zipper motif. The specificity of DNA binding is determined by the sequence of basic residues. Because *bZIP* proteins function as dimers, two sequence elements on DNA are recognized. In the case of homodimer formation, the sequence elements form a dyad. However, heterodimers can bind to DNA lacking dyad symmetry. In fact, the *bZIP*-binding site may be composed of two distinct regions, each recognized separately by different *bZIP* proteins that function together as a heterodimer. The ability to form heterodimers allows for composite *bZIP*-binding sites, lacking dyad symmetry, to be recognized by *bZIP* proteins.

9. *Figure 29.31 illustrates some of the various covalent modifications that occur on histone tails. How might each of these modifications influence DNA:histone interactions?*

Answer: The modifications mentioned in Figure 29.31 include acetylation and methylation of lysine and phosphorylation of serine in addition to methylation of arginine. Acetylation of the ε-amino group of lysine will effectively remove lysine's positive charge. The acetyl group is attached via amide linkage (in effect, a peptide bond). The lone pairs on the nitrogen are lost to electron delocalization due to the carbonyl group. Thus, acetylation will remove lysine's positive charge. Methylation of lysine will add a more bulky group to lysine's ε-amino group, and while this is not expected to change charge, it might be expected to interfere with ionic interactions. (The pK_a values of methyl amine and dimethyl amine are essentially the same. Thus, we should not expect a major change in pK_a when lysine's ε-amino group, a primary amine, is methylated and converted to a secondary amine.)

Phosphorylation of serine will convert a neutral polar group to a negatively charged phosphate group with 2− charge. This modification allows for additional ionic interactions. Methylation of arginine is not expected to change arginine's charge, but it may interfere with ionic interactions.

Histones interact with DNA through ionic bonding and the large number of basic amino acids, such as arginine and lysine, are ideal for this purpose. Acetylation of lysine is expected to effectively remove lysine's positive charge, thereby reducing ionic interactions between histones and DNA. Phosphorylation of serine will produce a strong negative charge on an otherwise neutral amino acid. This modification is expected to allow certain regions of histones to be repelled by DNA.

Modification by methylation will influence ionic-bonding capabilities by adding a bulkier group on a primary nitrogen.

11. *What might be the advantages of capping, methylation, and polyadenylylation of eukaryotic mRNAs?*

Answer: Capping and polyadenylation effectively protect the 5′- and 3′-ends of RNA from exonucleolytic degradation. There is evidence that the cap and polyA tail interact and that this interaction is important for mRNA recognition. This insures that only full-length, completely processed mRNAs are translated. A specialized structure on the 5′-end helps in mRNA recognition during initiation of translation. Cap formation occurs shortly after the 5′-end of a primary transcript is produced, and the cap is bound by factors required for further processing of the primary transcript. Finally, export of a processed primary transcript is dependent on polyadenylation of the 3′-end. This insures that no RNA is released before its time.

13. *(Integrates with Chapter 25.) The SWI/SNF chromatin-remodelling complex peels about 50 bp from the nucleosome. Assuming B-form DNA, how long is this DNA segment? In forming nucleosomes, DNA is wrapped in turns about the histone core octamer. What fraction of a DNA turn around the core octamer does 50 bp of DNA comprise? How does 50 bp of DNA compare to the typical size of eukaryotic promoter modules and response elements?*

Answer: B-form DNA has 3.4 nm per turn and 10 base pairs per turn or 0.34 nm per base pair. Thus, a 50-base pair segment of B-form DNA is (50 bp × 0.34 nm/bp =) 17 nm. Approximately 147 bp of DNA are wrapped around a nucleosome core, making 1.65 turns. Thus, 50 bp represents (50 bp × 1.65 turns/146 bp =) 0.565 turn. Promoter and response elements are around 20 to 25 bp; thus, the 50 bp peeled off from a nucleosome by the SWI/SNF complex could easily expose one of these elements.

15. *(Integrates with Chapters 6 and 25) The α-helices in HTH (helix-turn-helix motif) DNA-binding proteins are formed from 7− or 8–amino acid residues. What is the overall length of these α-helices? How does their length compare with the diameter of B-form DNA?*

Answer: The Δz for an α-helix is 0.15 nm per amino acid residue. For a helix 7 to 8 residues long, its length ranges from (0.15 nm × [7 or 8] =) 1.05 nm to 1.2 nm. The diameter of B-form DNA is about 2 nm, but the distance across a base pair is approximately 1.1 nm (between 1'-carbons). The major groove is approximately 1.2 nm wide and 0.8 nm deep. This would easily accommodate an α-helix (whose diameter is around 0.6 nm, ignoring side chains). The 1.2 nm of length would cover about 3 base pairs (1.2 nm ÷ 0.34 nm/bp).

17. RNA polymerase II is inhibited by α-amanitin. This mushroom-derived toxin has no effect on the enzyme's affinity for NTP substrates, but it dramatically slows polymerase translocation along the DNA. Go to www.pdb.org/ to view pdb file 1K83, which is the structure of RNA polymerase II with bound α-amanitin. Locate α-amanitin within this structure and discuss why its position is consistent with its mode of inhibition.

Answer: Download the file as outlined in the answer to Problem 16. To get a quick picture of the situation, display the protein as a ribbon and colour the ribbons using the chain-colouring option. This colours each polypeptide chain a different colour. Next, locate α-amanitin and display it as a space-filled molecule. You should discover that the inhibitor is located at the bottom of a cleft formed between the two largest subunits of RNA polymerase II, chains A and B (Rpb1 and Rbp2 subunits). The bottom of the cleft is formed by two long α-helices from chain A that are antiparallel to each other. While the cleft is formed by chains A and B, the residues that form the α-amanitin–binding site come from chain A. The α-amanitin–binding site is located at the bottom of the cleft bounded by three helices from the chain A, each at right angles to each other. They include one of the two helices that form the bottom of the cleft, the "bridge" helix that extends from the main part of chain A across the cleft and another short helix. The bridge helix is closest to the α-amanitin–binding site and makes the majority of contact with the inhibitor.

The α-amanitin–binding site is approximately 20 Å from a manganese ion that is located at the active site, the nucleotide-binding site, and the site of phosphodiester bond formation. Thus, α-amanitin is not expected to interfere with either nucleotide binding or bond formation. The inhibitor interferes with DNA translocation and thus elongation is blocked.

Questions for Self-Study

1. Describe the events leading up to initiation of transcription by *E. coli* RNA polymerase. Be sure to include in your discussion the importance of promoter elements in a typical promoter.

2. Name the two types of transcriptional termination mechanisms found in bacteria.

3. The last two columns of the table shown below are incorrect. Correct them.

RNA Polymerase Type	Genes Transcribed	α-Amanitin Sensitivity
RNA polymerase I	protein-encoding genes	intermediate sensitivity
RNA polymerase II	tRNAs, 5S rRNA, and others	resistant
RNA polymerase II	ribosomal RNA genes	very sensitive

4. Eukaryotic RNA polymerase II requires what additional class of proteins to function?

5. The *lac* operon is under both positive and negative control. Explain how both the presence of lactose and the absence of glucose are required for initiation of transcription of the *lac* operon.

6. How does the availability of tryptophan regulate gene expression in the *trp* operon?

7. Eukaryotic genes: Match the terms.
   a. A common element found in many promoters
   b. A promoter element found in "housekeeping " genes
   c. Orientation- and distance-independent regulatory sequences
   d. Responsive elements

   1. GC box
   2. Subject promoters to regulation by some common signal
   3. TATA box
   4. Enhancers (or upstream activation sequences)

8. What are the three major classes of DNA-binding motifs?

9. How are the 5'- and 3'-ends of eukaryotic transcripts typically modified?

10. The primary transcript of an eukaryotic gene is typically longer than its mRNA. Explain.

Answers

1. Initiation of transcription begins when RNA polymerase holoenzyme, through its σ subunit, binds to the −35 region of a promoter to form a closed complex. The polymerase moves along the promoter until it reaches the −10 region or Pribnow box, where it unwinds about 12 base pairs of DNA to expose the transcription start site. This arrangement is known as the open promoter complex. Initiation begins with a nucleoside triphosphate, usually ATP or GTP, binding to the initiation site on RNA polymerase. The elongation site binds the next nucleotide, and phosphodiester bond formation occurs. The holoenzyme produces a short oligonucleotide chain before its σ factor dissociates, leaving the core complex to complete elongation.

2. ρ-dependent (rho-dependent) and ρ-independent.

3.

RNA Polymerase Type	Genes Transcribed	α-Amanitin Sensitivity
RNA polymerase I	ribosomal RNA genes	resistant
RNA polymerase II	protein-encoding genes	very sensitive
RNA polymerase II	tRNAs, 5S rRNA, and others	intermediate sensitivity

4. RNA polymerase II requires general transcription factors.

5. Initiation of transcription is blocked by *lac* repressor protein binding to an element in the promoter of the *lac* operon known as the operator. Repressor protein binding occurs only in the absence of an inducer, a galactose derivative. The *lac* promoter is a weak promoter and requires an additional factor for transcription. This factor is a complex of catabolite activator protein (CAP) and cyclic AMP (cAMP). This complex binds to a region upstream of the RNA polymerase–binding site in the promoter. cAMP is necessary for CAP binding and the levels of cAMP are sensitive to glucose such that glucose decreases cAMP levels. Thus, in the absence of glucose, cAMP levels are high enough to support CAP binding to the promoter.

6. There are two mechanisms. Initiation of transcription is blocked by the Trp repressor protein. This protein binds tryptophan and associates with the promoter, at a site termed the operator, to block initiation of transcription. The operon is also controlled by transcriptional attenuation. The operon codes for a small leader peptide. The rate at which this leader sequence is translated affects transcriptional termination.

7. a. 3; b. 1; c. 4; d. 2.

8. Helix-turn-helix, zinc finger, and leucine zipper.

9. The 5'-end of a transcript is capped by a 7-methylguanylyl residue in 5' to 5' linkage. The 3' end contains a poly(A) tail 100 to 200 adenine residues in length.

10. The primary transcript contains exons and introns. The exons are sequences destined to be present in the mature mRNA but they are not contiguous in the primary transcript. Rather, they are separated by introns. The process of splicing removes introns and joins exons to form the mature mRNA.

Additional Problems

1. What characteristics are associated with the −10 region (Pribnow box) of RNA polymerase promoters in *E. coli*?

2. What is a consensus sequence?

3. Describe the differences and similarities between RNA polymerase I and DNA polymerase I in *E. coli*.

4. Describe the structure of a rho-independent transcriptional terminator.

5. The operator of the *lac* operon was first identified by *cis–trans* complementation tests. In these tests, a partial diploid is produced from two cell lines showing defects in lactose metabolism. The idea behind *cis–trans* complementation is to determine if the defects in lactose metabolism are due to mutations in the same gene or in different genes. If mutations are in different genes, then a partial diploid will be capable of metabolizing lactose. For example, the *lac* operon contains two genes necessary for lactose metabolism that code for β-galactosidase and lactose permease. A partial diploid between a cell defective in β-galactosidase but containing a normal permease and a cell defective in permease but containing a normal β-galactosidase will result in a diploid capable of lactose metabolism. How might operator mutations behave in *cis–trans* complementation tests?

6. Why does IPTG cause induction of the *lac* operon? How does induction by IPTG differ from induction by lactose via allolactose?

7. How might splicing increase the versatility of eukaryotic genes?

8. How might the fact that mature mRNAs have 3′-poly(A) tails be used to isolate mature mRNAs from eukaryotic cells?

9. Modified nucleosides can be identified by reverse phase HPLC. How might you expect ribose-methylated and unmethylated nucleosides to differ on reverse phase HPLC? What about 7-methyl G *versus* unmodified G?

Abbreviated Answers

1. The −10 region or Pribnow box is an A:T−rich sequence of about 6 bases located approximately 10 bases upstream of the start of transcription. The high A-T content allows this region to "melt" so that the strands separate. The RNA polymerase–promoter complex shifts from the closed form to the open form at the −10 region.

2. A consensus sequence is a sequence representing the most commonly found base in each position within a DNA element.

3. Both enzymes utilize nucleotide triphosphates to produce nucleic acid polymers, both require a template, read the template 3′→5′ direction, and produce the nucleic acid is the 5′→3′ direction. RNA polymerase is capable of initiating RNA synthesis by incorporating the very first 5′ nucleotide, whereas DNA polymerase requires a primer to function. RNA polymerase does not proofread nor does it have exonuclease activity. DNA polymerase has 3′- and 5′-exonuclease activity for proofreading and nick translation.

4. Rho-dependent terminators are DNA elements that when transcribed produce a short sequence of mRNA capable of forming a G:C-rich stem and loop followed by a stretch of U's.

5. Operator mutations may give rise to constitutive expression of the *lac* operon if, for example, the *lac* repressor protein–binding site is altered. The phenotype is constitutive expression of the *lac* operon even in a partial diploid. Operator mutations are examples of *cis* acting mutations because they affect or influence genes only on the same DNA.

6. IPTG (isopropylthiogalactoside) is a galactose derivative capable of binding to the *lac* repressor protein, thereby altering its ability to bind to the operator of the *lac* promoter. Induction by allolactose is transient because allolactose is converted to lactose, which is metabolized to galactose and glucose by β-galactosidase. IPTG is not degraded by β-galactosidase and induction is long-lasting.

7. For certain genes, alternative splicing patterns give rise to different gene products that code for proteins with different properties.

8. A polyT derivatized matrix can be used to separate poly(A) mRNA from total cellular RNA.

9. In reverse phase HPLC, hydrophobic interactions are responsible for adsorption. Therefore, ribose-methylated nucleosides are expected to bind with higher affinity and require higher concentrations of organic solvent to be removed from the reverse phase matrix. The same is true for modified bases, with the exception of 7-methyl modification of G (and A). This modification gives rise to a positive charge on N-7 leading to a decrease in hydrophobicity. 7-Methyl G will elute from a matrix at lower concentrations of organic solvent than unmodified G.

Summary

Transcription is the process whereby RNA chains are synthesized according to a DNA template. The enzymes responsible are DNA-dependent RNA polymerases. Prokaryotes have a single RNA polymerase, which synthesizes rRNA and tRNA as well as mRNA. RNA polymerases, like DNA polymerases, polymerize nucleotides in the $5' \rightarrow 3'$ direction, reading along templates in the $3' \rightarrow 5'$ direction. In contrast to DNA polymerases, RNA polymerases can catalyze the *de novo* synthesis of nucleotide chains.

E. coli RNA polymerase consists of a catalytic "core" of subunit composition $\alpha_2\beta\beta'$. This core requires a σ subunit in order to recognize promoter sequences, which signal the sites where genes begin. Addition of a σ subunit to the "core" RNA polymerase yields the RNA polymerase holoenzyme. This holoenzyme binds at promoter sites that are characterized by two features: the Pribnow box, a TATAAT sequence element located at position −10, and a 9 bp consensus sequence TCTTGACAT near position −35. RNA polymerase holoenzyme then "melts" the DNA at the A:T–rich Pribnow box to form an "open complex" adjacent to the +1 site where transcription is initiated. Chain elongation proceeds at the rate of 20 to 50 nucleotides per second, moving slower in G:C–rich regions where DNA strand separation is more difficult. Chain termination occurs when a G:C–rich inverted repeat sequence near the end of the transcript forms a stable stem-loop structure which halts further translocation of the RNA polymerase. This stem-loop is followed by a series of A residues in the template, which are transcribed, into U's in the RNA. The hydrogen bonds holding these A:U base pairs are exchanged for A:T pairs between the "sense" and "antisense" DNA strands to re-anneal the DNA duplex and release the nascent transcript.

Eukaryotes have three classes of DNA-dependent RNA polymerases; all are found in the nucleus. RNA pol I transcribes the major rRNA genes, RNA pol II transcribes the protein-encoding genes and thus leads to mRNA synthesis, and RNA pol III transcribes tRNA genes as well as those genes encoding a number of other small cellular RNAs. All three RNA polymerases are large complex multimeric proteins. Each class of RNA polymerase recognizes a distinct set of promoter elements appropriate to the genes it transcribes. Distinct sets of DNA-binding proteins called transcription factors mediate these interactions, much as the σ subunit of the *E. coli* RNA polymerase directs it to its proper "transcription start sites."

Many genes in bacteria are organized into clusters known as operons. Expression of these genes to produce a single polycistronic mRNA is under the control of promoter and operator regulatory elements lying upstream. Transcription is controlled by induction and repression, processes in which the interaction of regulatory proteins with small metabolites determines whether these regulatory proteins will bind to DNA and facilitate or limit transcription. For example, the *lac* operon is expressed provided the regulatory protein, *lac* repressor, is not bound at the operator site. The presence of the *lac* repressor on the operator blocks transcription, an example of negative control. β-galactosides induce expression of the *lac* operon by binding to *lac* repressor and promoting its dissociation from the operator. The affinity of *lac* repressor binding to operator DNA binding is 3 orders of magnitude greater than the affinity of the inducer(IPTG):*lac* repressor complex for operator DNA.

The *lac* operon is also under positive control by CAP, the catabolite activator protein. In the presence of cAMP, CAP binds near the *lac* promoter and assists transcription initiation by RNA polymerase. When [cAMP] is low, free CAP cannot associate with RNA polymerase and promote transcription, so the *lac* operon is not expressed. The availability of glucose, *E. coli*'s preferred carbon and energy source, leads to lower cAMP levels and repression of the *lac* operon as well as other operons involved in the metabolism of alternative carbon and energy sources. This phenomenon is called catabolite repression.

The *araBAD* operon, another of the catabolite repressible operons, is also controlled both positively and negatively by the regulatory protein *AraC*. In the absence of arabinose, *AraC* binds to three regulatory sites (*araO₁*, *araO₂*, and *araI*) in the *araBAD* operon and prevents transcription. However, when arabinose binds to *AraC*, this protein releases from one of the sites and joins with CAP-(cAMP)$_2$ to activate transcription of the *araBAD* operon.

Operon expression may also be regulated after transcription has begun through a mechanism known as attenuation. Attenuation is determined by the availability of charged aminoacyl-tRNAs. Operons encoding enzymes of amino acid biosynthesis often have multiple codons for that particular amino acid early in their polycistronic message. If the particular aminoacyl-tRNA is low in concentration, the ribosome translating these codons stalls, awaiting arrival of the aminoacyl-tRNA. This pausing by the ribosome allows a secondary structure called the antiterminator to form downstream in the mRNA. RNA polymerase perceives this antiterminator and continues transcription of the entire operon. However, if the relevant aminoacyl-tRNA is present in abundance, the ribosome translates these codons quickly and an alternative secondary structure appears further downstream in the mRNA, the terminator. RNA polymerase perceives the terminator and terminates transcription early in the operon, so the operon's genes are not expressed. The antiterminator and terminator are mutually exclusive secondary structures since one of the RNA segments they use is the same.

Transcriptional regulation in eukaryotes is more complicated. The promoters of eukaryotic genes are defined by modules of short conserved sequences, such as the TATA, CAAT, and GC boxes, which bind transcription factors essential to RNA polymerase II function. In addition to these promoter elements, eukaryotic genes have enhancers, sequence elements whose presence is necessary for full expression of the gene. Enhancers may be located in either orientation with respect to the gene and may lie either upstream or downstream from it. Enhancers act non-specifically to enhance transcription from any nearby promoter, but enhancer function is dependent on binding a specific transcription factor. Many genes respond to a common regulation and are characterized by the presence of common sequence elements in their promoters known as response elements. The heat shock element (HSE) and glucocorticoid response element (GRE) are examples. These response elements are recognized by specific transcription factors that coordinate expression of all genes containing the particular response element. DNA looping provides a mechanism for convening a variety of specific regulatory proteins at the transcription initiation site.

Certain structural motifs recur in DNA-binding proteins. In particular, DNA-binding proteins often employ an α-helix as their DNA recognition element. The diameter of an α-helix matches closely the width of the major groove in B-form DNA, and these recognition helices fit within the major groove, identifying specific nucleotide sequences through a variety of atomic interactions, including hydrogen-bonding patterns with the edges of the bases, ionic and H-bonding with the sugar-phosphate backbone, as well as van der Waals fits and hydrophobic interactions with projecting non-polar —CH$_3$ groups on thymine residues. DNA-binding proteins erect a variety of structural scaffolds serving to deliver the α-helix or other recognition elements to the DNA site, and it is really these scaffolds that have lent their names to the structural motifs: the helix-turn-helix, the Zn-finger, and the leucine zipper. The great majority of DNA-binding proteins possess one of these three basic motifs.

Chapter 30

Protein Synthesis

• •

Chapter Outline

- ❖ Code characteristics
    - ⅄ Triplet code: Three bases decoded as one amino acid
        - • All 64 triplets used: 61 amino acid codons: 3 stop codons
    - ⅄ Non-overlapping, no commas, unambiguous, universal (or nearly so)
    - ⅄ Degenerate: Synonymous codons decode same amino acid
        - • Third base degenerate (except in two cases)
        - • Second base
            - • Pyrimidines code for hydrophobic amino acids
            - • Purines code for polar or charged amino acids
    - ⅄ Aminoacyl-tRNA synthesis: At least 20 enzymes charge tRNAs that decode 61 codons
        - • Cognate tRNAs: All tRNAs charged by particular synthetase
        - • Reaction mechanism: Two-step process
            - • Activation of amino acid by formation of aminoacyl adenylate
            - • Transfer of amino acid to 3′OH of tRNA
        - • Recognition
            - • Amino acid binding site
            - • tRNA-binding site: Determinants on tRNA
                - ○ At least one of anticodon bases
                - ○ One or more of three base pairs in acceptor stem
                - ○ Discriminator base N of NCCA at 3′-end
            - • Two classes of synthetases
                - ○ Class I
                    - ▪ Typically monomeric
                    - ▪ Adds amino acid to 2′OH (but it moves to 3′OH)
                    - ▪ Nucleotide-binding site is Rossman fold
                        - • HIGH sequence
                        - • KMSKS sequence
                    - ▪ Binds tRNA acceptor stem from minor groove
                - ○ Class II
                    - ▪ Typically oligomeric
                    - ▪ Adds amino acid to 3′OH
                    - ▪ Three motifs
                        - • Motif 1: Dimerization motif
                        - • Motifs 2 and 3: Active site
- ❖ Wobble Rules: tRNA interactions with mRNA: Explains degeneracy of code
- ❖ Codon Usage: Certain codons preferred over others
- ❖ Nonsense suppression: Mutant tRNA that recognizes stop codons (UAA, UAG, UGA)
- ❖ Ribosomes: Cellular translational machinery
    - ⅄ Prokaryotic ribosomes (*E. coli*): 70S particle: Two subunits
        - • Small subunit: 30S
            - • 21 proteins: S-proteins
            - • 16S rRNA: 1542 nt

- Large subunit: 50S
  - 31 distinct proteins: L-proteins
  - 23S rRNA: 2904 nt
  - 5S rRNA: 120 nt
  - rRNAs derive from one precursor transcript
- Eukaryotic cytoplasmic ribosomes: 80S particle: Two subunits
  - Small subunit: 40S
    - 33 proteins
    - 18S rRNA: Around 1800 nt
  - Large subunit: 60S
    - 49 proteins
    - 28S rRNA: Around 4700 nt
    - 5S rRNA: 120 nt
    - 5.8S rRNA: 160 nt: Homologous to 5′-end of prokaryotic 23S rRNA
- ❖ Stages of protein synthesis in prokaryotes
  - Initiation: Formylmet-tRNA, mRNA, small subunit, large subunit
    - Formylmet-tRNA: Initiator tRNA
      - 5′-base not paired
      - CCU sequence in D-loop
      - Three G:C bp in anticodon stem
      - Formyl group added to charged tRNA by methionyl-tRNA formyl transferase
    - mRNA
      - Ribosome-binding site (Shine–Dalgano sequence) near 5′-end interacts with 16S rRNA
      - Complementary sequence on 16S rRNA near 3′-end interacts with ribosome-binding site
    - Initiation factors
      - IF-1, IF-3: Dissociate 30S subunits
      - IF-2: Binds GTP and fmet-tRNA and deposits fmet-tRNA into P site
        - GTP hydrolysis accompanied by IF release and 50S binding
        - 70S initiation complex formed
  - Elongation
    - Elongation factor Tu (EF-Tu)
      - Binds GTP and charged-tRNA
      - Deposits charged-tRNA into A-site
      - GTP hydrolysis releases EF-Tu·GDP
        - GDP exchanged for GTP by EF-Ts (Guanylyl exchange protein)
    - Peptide bond formation: Peptidyl transferase: 50S activity: 23S rRNA activity
    - Translocation
      - Deacylated tRNA removed from P site
      - Peptidyl-tRNA moved to P site
      - mRNA moved so that new codon in A site
      - EF-G: GTPase catalyzes translocation
  - Termination: Stop codon in A site
    - RF-1 recognizes UAA and UAG
    - RF-2 recognizes UAA and UAG
    - RF-3: GTPase
    - Ribosome recycling factor: Disassembles ribosome
- ❖ Eukaryotic protein synthesis
  - Eukaryotic initiator tRNA$_i$: Charged with Met: Not formylated
  - Three stages of initiation
    - 43S preinitiation complex formation: eIF2, eIF4A, eIF3, and Met-tRNA$_i$
    - mRNA binding to 43S preinitiation complex
      - eIF4E: mRNA cap-binding protein

- • 80S initiation complex formed upon large subunit binding
- ⋏ Elongation
    - • EF-1: Two components
        - • EF1A: EF-Tu counterpart
        - • EF1B: EF-Ts counterpart
- ⋏ Termination: Single RF recognizes all stop codons
- ⋏ Regulation of translation: Phosphorylation
    - • S6 phosphorylation stimulated by growth factors
    - • eIF2α phosphorylated by variety of kinases leading to inactivation
- ❖ Inhibitors of protein synthesis
    - ⋏ Streptomycin: Low concentrations cause misreading
    - ⋏ Macrolide antibiotics: Plugs exit tunnel for peptide chain

Chapter Objectives

Ribosomes

The site of cellular protein synthesis is the ribosome, a two-subunit ribonucleoprotein complex. You should be familiar with the ribosome vocabulary, including the following terms: 16S rRNA, 18S rRNA, 23S rRNA, 28S rRNA, 5S rRNA, 5.8S rRNA, small subunit, 30S subunit, 40S subunit, large subunit, 50S subunit, 60S subunit, 70S ribosome, 80S ribosome, S-proteins, and L-proteins. The rRNAs derive from operons containing structural genes for the small- and large-subunit rRNAs and depending on cell type, the 5S rRNA. A primary transcript is processed by nucleolytic cleavage and post-transcriptional modifications, typically methylations, to produce the mature rRNAs. Even before processing occurs, certain ribosomal proteins begin to bind to the rRNA. This binding is followed by binding of other ribosomal proteins, leading to an ordered assembly of the ribonucleoprotein complex.

Protein Synthesis

Although the ribosome plays the leading role in protein synthesis, it is assisted at each stage by non-ribosomal protein factors specific for stages of protein synthesis, including initiation, elongation, and termination. Initiation is a property of the small subunit and various initiation factors. A special tRNA charged with Met is used in initiation of protein synthesis. (In prokaryotes, it is termed f-Met-tRNA$_f$Met where f indicates that Met is formylated. In eukaryotes, Met-tRNA$_i$Met is used.) Initiation begins when a ribosome, aided by initiation factors, dissociates into subunits in order to produce free small subunits. The small subunit binds mRNA and a complex of f-Met-tRNA$_f$Met and another initiation factor to form a preinitiation complex that is joined by the large subunit to form the initiation complex. Initiation complex formation is accompanied by GTP hydrolysis and release of ribosome-bound initiation factors. The outcome of initiation is an aminoacylated-tRNA bound in the so-called P site on the ribosome. In peptide chain elongation, a second aminoacyl-tRNA–binding site, the A site, is filled, in an elongation factor-dependent manner, with an aminoacylated-tRNA appropriate for the codon on the mRNA. In *E. coli*, the elongation factor EF-Tu binds to aminoacyl-tRNA and GTP to form a complex. This complex binds to the A site on the ribosome and deposits the charged tRNA at that location with subsequent hydrolysis of GDP and release of P$_i$ and EF-Tu:GDP complex. For EF-Tu to participate in another round of elongation, it must be recharged by binding to another elongation factor, EF-Ts, which causes GDP to be released in forming a EF-Tu:EF-Ts complex that is resolved to EF-Tu:GTP and EF-Ts by GTP binding. Peptide bond formation is a property of the ribosome alone. The large subunit catalyzes the transpeptidation or peptidyl transfer of the P-site amino acid to the A-site aminoacylated-tRNA. The uncharged tRNA in the P site is released and the A-site tRNA, now carrying a dipeptide and hence called a peptidyl-tRNA, is translocated along with the mRNA from the A site to the P site. Translocation is dependent of elongation factors EF-G in the case of *E. coli*. The vacated A site is now free to accept another aminoacylated tRNA to continue elongation. In the event that a stop codon enters the A site, chain termination ensues. Protein release factors bind to the A site and cause hydrolysis of the peptide from peptidyl-tRNA.

Inhibitors of Protein Synthesis

Protein synthesis is an important target for antibiotics. You should be familiar with the kinds of inhibition caused by various antibiotics including inhibition of initiation, of A-site binding, of peptidyl transferase activity, and of translocation. Puromycin causes premature release of peptides. Diphtheria toxin inhibits EF-2 in eukaryotes by covalent ADP-ribosylation. Ricin causes chain cleavage of the large subunit rRNA, and Colicin E-3 cleaves prokaryotic small subunit ribosomes.

Post-Translational Processing

The most common form of protein modification is proteolytic cleavage to activate a protein, or to release mature protein products from a larger primary translational product. Proteins are also targeted to specific locations within the cell or are destined for transport out of the cell. In prokaryotes, a signal sequence, located on the N-terminus of a protein, or at a more internal location, may direct the protein to be exported from the cell or to become a membrane-bound protein. Signal recognition particles play a role in halting protein synthesis shortly after a signal peptide is produced and, in conjunction with docking protein, directing the nascent protein to the endoplasmic reticulum membrane where protein synthesis resumes.

Problems and Solutions

1. (Integrates with Chapter 27) The following sequence represents part of the nucleotide sequence of a cloned cDNA:

> **. . . CAATACGAAGCAATCCCGCGACTAGACCTTAAC. . .**

Can you reach an unambiguous conclusion from these data about the partial amino acid sequence of the protein encoded by this cDNA?

Answer: We are faced with the problem of deciding on a reading frame. Assuming that we have the non-coding strand sequence, we can inspect it for stop codons, UGA, UAG, UAA. (It makes no sense to look for AUG start codons because the sequence might have come from any location within the cDNA.) By inspection, we find two stop codons as shown below.

> . . . CAATACGAAGCAATCCCGCGAC**TAG**ACCT**TAA**C. . .

These two stop codons are not in the same reading frame (because they are not separated by an integral multiple of three nucleotides). Therefore, either of the two different reading frames that include TAG and TAA may represent the region coding for the C-terminal portion of the protein. The third possible reading frame (the one that starts with CAA) does not contain a stop codon. More information is required in order to decide which is the correct reading frame. One possibility is to compare codon usage in the three frames with codon usage in other genes from the same organism. Alternatively, we might turn to amino acid composition analysis. The amino acid sequence of the third reading frame is:

> Gln-Tyr-Glu-Ala-Ile-Pro-Arg-Leu-Asp-Leu-Asn

Certain amino acids are often found in low frequencies in proteins, as for example, Met (AUG), Trp (UGG), His (CAU/C), Cys (UGU/C), Tyr (UAU/C), and Phe (UUU/C). However, of these relatively rarely used amino acids, we find only the tyrosine codon shown below.

> . . . CAA**TAC**GAAGCAATCCCGCGACTAGACCTTAAC. . .

It may be possible to check the protein for chymotrypsin cleavage (chymotrypsin cleaves after tyrosine) and this may help us decide if the tyrosine codon is in the appropriate reading frame.

A similar analysis may be applied to the complementary strand whose sequence, written 5′ to 3′, is:

> GTTAAGGTCTAGTCGCGGGATTGCTTCGTATTG

This sequence has two stop codons in different reading frames as shown below.

> GT**TAA**GGTC**TAG**TCGCGGGATTGCTTCGTATTG

The third reading frame, shown below, may be an open reading frame.

> G **TTA A**GG TC**T AG**T CGC GGG ATT GCT TCG TAT TG

If translated it would produce the following amino acid sequence:

> Leu-Arg-Ser-Ser-Arg-Gly-Ile-Ala-Ser-Tyr-

3. Review the evidence establishing that aminoacyl-tRNA synthetases bridge the information gap between amino acids and codons. Indicate the various levels of specificity possessed by aminoacyl-tRNA synthetases that are essential for high-fidelity translation of messenger RNA molecules.

Answer: Information flow in biological systems is described in the central dogma first postulated by Francis Crick. Genetic information is stored and transmitted from generation to generation in the form of a sequence of bases in nucleic acids. Nucleic acids are faithfully copied in the process of replication, which is directed by base-pair interactions involving complementary hydrogen bonds. The information content of a nucleic acid is its sequence of bases. A portion of this sequence is used to direct the synthesis of proteins, linear chains of amino acids, in a process known as gene expression. For most genes, gene expression involves at least two steps, transcription and translation. In transcription, an mRNA is produced by a base-pair–directed polymerization. In translation, mRNAs are used to direct the synthesis of proteins by ribosomes. Even in this process, complementary base-pair interactions between mRNAs and tRNAs are paramount in importance. Yet, translation results in the production of linear chains of amino acids. Thus, during gene expression, a change in information content from nucleotide sequences to amino acid sequences occurs. The point at which this information gap is bridged is the production of aminoacyl-tRNAs by aminoacyl-tRNA synthetases. These enzymes must speak two languages, one based on nucleotides, the other based on amino acids.

In order for translation to occur with high fidelity, aminoacyl-tRNA synthetases must accurately charge tRNAs. This is accomplished by a two-step reaction. As the name implies, synthetases produce aminoacylated-tRNAs at the expense of ATP hydrolysis. In the first step in catalysis, an amino acid is adenylated to form an aminoacyl-adenylate that is tightly bound to the enzyme. This reaction is accompanied by elimination of PP_i, which is subsequently hydrolyzed by pyrophosphatases rendering the reaction irreversible. In the second stage of catalysis, the amino acid is transferred to either the 2'-OH or the 3'-OH of a tRNA.

Specificity exists at each of these two stages. The aminoacyl adenylation reaction depends on the amino acid specificity of the amino acid binding site. This specificity is not absolute and activation of inappropriate amino acids occurs with low frequency. This may lead to misacylation. Aminoacyl-tRNA synthetases carefully edit this step to insure that misacylated tRNAs are not released. Misacylated tRNAs trigger a deacylase that hydrolyzes inappropriate

5. Point out why Crick's wobble hypothesis would allow fewer than 61 anticodons to be used to translate the 61 sense codons. How does "wobble" tend to accelerate the rate of translation?

Answer: The wobble hypothesis allows base pairs to form between the 5' anticodon position and the 3' codon position according to the following rules:

5' Anticodon	3' Codon
C	G (canonical pair)
A	U (canonical pair)
U	A (canonical pair) or G
G	C (canonical pair) or U
I	U, C, or A

To decode a set of four codons that differ only in their 3' base, a minimum of two anticodons is necessary. For example, to decode the four codons of threonine, ACU, ACC, ACA, and ACG, the anticodons IGU and CGU (written 5' to 3') are sufficient. Because inosine (I) can base pair with U, C, or A, the IGU anticodon will decode AGU, AGC, and AGA. The anticodon CGU decodes ACG only. In this example, we can see that four codons can be decoded by only two anticodons.

The wobble rules explain the degeneracy of the genetic code. In all cases the codons NNU/C (or NNY) are always degenerate. To decode NNU requires a 5' anticodon base that pairs with U; the choices are A, G, or I. However, A is normally converted to I whenever it occurs in the 5' anticodon position. Therefore, only G or I are possible, both of which base pair with C as well. If G is used, then the anticodon will recognize both NNU and NNC. If I is used, this anticodon will recognize NNU, NNC, and NNA.

The codons NNA/G (NNR) are often degenerate because the 5' position of anticodons may contain U that is capable of pairing with both A or G. Anticodons with C for 5' base will only decode a single codon and in fact there are two instances where this occurs in the genetic code. Both methionine and tryptophan are coded for by a single codon each, AUG and UGG, respectively. Their anticodons must be CAU and CCA.

Wobble allows non-canonical base pairs to form. This makes codon–anticodon interactions less stable, allowing for an increase in the rate of translation. Wobble also allows decoding of the 61 sense codons with far fewer tRNAs. A bit of reflection will show that the minimum number of tRNAs is 32. The standard genetic code can be represented by 16 blocks of 4 codons with codons in a particular block differing only in their 3′ nucleotide. Each block will require a minimum of 2 tRNAs, except the block containing TAT, TAC, TAA, and TAG. The first two code for tyrosine, whereas the last two are stop codons. So this block requires only one tRNA to decode TAT and TAC. The rest of the blocks require two tRNAs each and this sums to 31 tRNAs. Initiation of protein synthesis, however, requires an additional initiator tRNA that is charged with methionine giving a total of 32 tRNAs in a minimal set. (Additional tRNAs would be required to decode selenocysteine and pyrrolysine.)

7. Nonsense suppression occurs when a suppressor mutant arises that reads a nonsense codon and inserts an amino acid, as if the nonsense codon was actually a sense codon. Which amino acids do you think are most likely to be incorporated by nonsense suppressor mutants?

Answer: The most likely candidates for nonsense suppressors are tRNAs that decode codons that differ from stop codons by one base. For UAA and UAG termination codons, tRNAs that decode the following amino acid codons are candidates: Leu, Ser, Tyr, Trp, Gln, Lys, and Glu. For the UGA termination codon, tRNAs that decode Trp, Cys, Arg, Gly, Ser, and Leu are candidates. However, there are certain constraints on nonsense suppression. The tRNA gene to be mutated must not be an essential gene to the cell. Ideally, a tRNA gene whose function is covered by another tRNA is best suited to become a nonsense suppressor. In the above list, Leu, Ser, and Arg tRNAs are good candidates because each of these amino acids have six codons. An amino acid coded by four codons, such as glycine, is also a good candidate. The remaining amino acids are coded by only one codon (e.g., Trp) or two codons each. These are the least likely candidates to serve as suppressors. The tRNA that decodes the UGG Trp codon would have to be first duplicated to provide an additional gene copy to mutate to a nonsense suppressor.

9. If the tunnel through the large ribosomal subunit is 10 nm long, how many amino acid residues might be contained within it? (Assume that the growing polypeptide chain is in an extended β-sheet–like conformation.)

Answer: For a peptide in extended β-sheet conformation, the distance between residues is 0.35 nm. For a length of 10 nm, this represents (10 nm ÷ 0.35 nm/residue) 28.6 residues.

11. What ideas can you suggest to explain why ribosomes invariably exist as two-subunit structures, instead of a larger, single-subunit entity?

Answer: Ribosomes catalyze peptide bond formation using two aminoacyl-tRNAs as substrates that bind to two distinct tRNA-binding sites on the ribosome known as the P site and the A site. During each round of elongation, the P site is transiently occupied by a peptidyl-tRNA containing the newly synthesizes N-terminal portion of the polypeptide attached via aminoacyl linkage to the 3′-end of a tRNA. The A site is filled with an aminoacyl-tRNA appropriate to the codon displayed at the A site. The ribosome catalyzes peptide bond formation by nucleophilic attack by the amino group of the aminoacyl-tRNA in the A site on the carbonyl carbon of the acyl bond on the peptidyl-tRNA in the P site. The result is polypeptide chain transfer from the P site to the A site. As a result, the P site is now occupied by an uncharged tRNA, whereas the A site contains a peptidyl-tRNA one amino acid longer. In order for elongation to continue, the P site must be vacated, the peptidyl-tRNA, now in the A site, must be moved into the P site, and the A site must be refilled. This process, known as translocation, occurs in at least two steps or stages. In the first step, during peptide bond formation, the acceptor end of the A-site aminoacyl-tRNA moves into the P site to form the peptide bond. The result of this movement is formation of a hybrid tRNA-binding site: the 3′-end of the A-site tRNA is now in the P site, a P/A hybrid state. What is the fate of the now deacylated tRNA? Interestingly, this tRNA is not immediately released from the ribosome. Rather, it is transferred to a third tRNA-binding site, the E site or exit site. However, the transfer is accomplished in two steps. As the 3′-end of the A-site tRNA moves into the P site and peptide bond formation occurs, the 3′-end of the now deacylated tRNA moves into the E site, forming an E/P hybrid state. To occupy these two hybrid tRNA-binding states, E/P and P/A, the tRNAs must move relative to the large subunit, an event that may be accomplished by movement of the small subunit. In order for elongation to continue, the A site must be vacated. This is accomplished by resolving the P/A hybrid state into P-site binding and the E/P hybrid state into E-site binding. The A site is now free to bind a new aminoacyl-tRNA, which initially interacts with the ribosome through a third hybrid binding site, the T/A. The transition of aminoacyl-tRNAs from T/A binding to the A site may be a proofreading step, and this transition may be influenced by E-site binding such that A-site binding results in release of an uncharged tRNA from the E-site.

The tRNA-binding sites involve aspects of both the large and the small subunits. To produce hybrid sites, the subunits may be required to move relative to each other. The functional significance of this movement may be responsible for the high fidelity of protein synthesis.

13. *What is the Shine–Dalgarno sequence? What does it do? The efficiency of protein synthesis initiation may vary by as much as 100-fold for different mRNAs. How might the Shine–Dalgarno sequence be responsible for this difference?*

Answer: The Shine–Dalgarno sequence is a purine-rich sequence of 4 to 8 nucleotides located on prokaryotic mRNAs around 10 nucleotides upstream of an AUG codon used as an initiation codon. The Shine–Dalgarno sequence is often called the ribosome-binding site because mRNAs interact with ribosomes by interacting with a complementary, pyrimidine-rich sequence located near the 3′-end of the small subunit rRNA. This rRNA sequence is fixed for a given prokaryote; there is only one population of ribosomes. Shine–Dalgarno sequences on mRNAs show a range of variability from gene to gene. The degree to which a Shine–Dalgarno sequence is complementary to the pyrimidine-rich sequence on rRNA determines the efficiency with which a particular mRNA is used in initiation complex formation. mRNAs showing a high degree of complementarity are capable of interacting strongly with ribosomal small subunits and are therefore initiated frequently.

15. *(Integrates with Chapter 14) Why might you suspect that the elongation factors EF-Tu and EF-Ts are evolutionarily related to the G proteins of membrane signal transduction pathways described in Chapter 14?*

Answer: EF-Tu functions during elongation as a ternary complex with GTP and an aminoacyl-tRNA. This ternary complex delivers charged tRNAs to an empty A site on a ribosome. Upon binding to the ribosome, GTP hydrolysis occurs, resulting in deposition of the aminoacyl-tRNA into the A site and release of an EF-Tu:GDP complex and inorganic phosphate. EF-Tu functions catalytically and in order to participate in another round of elongation, GDP must be exchanged for GTP. This is accomplished indirectly by action of EF-Ts. (Ts and Tu refer to the temperature stability of these two proteins. EF-Ts activity is stable to high temperatures, whereas EF-Tu activity is unstable.) EF-Ts binds to the EF-Tu:GDP complex, displaces GDP, and forms a heterodimeric EF-Tu:EF-Ts protein complex. This complex dissociates upon GTP binding to EF-Tu, resulting in free EF-Ts and EF-Tu:GTP.

Many signal transduction pathways involve G proteins, GTP-binding proteins capable of stimulating or inhibiting another protein. G proteins are capable of these activities only when they have bound GTP, and these activities are transient because G proteins have intrinsic GTPase activity, which is responsible for hydrolyzing GTP to inactivate the protein. G proteins consist of three subunits α, β, and γ. The α subunit is a guanine nucleotide-binding protein that binds either GTP or GDP and exhibits GTPase activity. There are two types of α subunits, α_s and α_i that stimulate or inhibit respectively. Following GTP hydrolysis, the α subunit contains bound GDP, which must be replaced with GTP. This is accomplished by the α subunit associating with the β and γ subunits to form a membrane-bound complex. This complex is capable of interacting with membrane-bound receptor proteins but only when the receptor protein is activated by hormone-binding. This interaction of G protein complex and hormone-loaded receptor protein results in dissociation of GDP, binding of GTP, and dissociation of an α:GTP complex that can now act on adenylate cyclase. Thus, G proteins participate in a GTP–GDP cycle reminiscent of EF-Tu:EF-Ts, and it comes as no great surprise that the proteins are related.

17. *Go to www.pdb.org and bring up PDB file 1GIX, which shows the 30S ribosomal subunit, the 3 tRNAs, and mRNA. In the box on the right titled "Biological Assembly," click "View in Jmol." By holding the right mouse button down and moving your cursor over the image, you can rotate it to view it from any perspective.*
   a. How are the ribosomal proteins represented in the image?
   b. How is the 16S rRNA portrayed?
   c. Rotate the image to see how the tRNAs stick out from the structure. Which end of the tRNA is sticking out?
   d. Where will these ends of the tRNAs lie when the 50S subunit binds to this complex?

Answer: The More Images option only shows static views of the molecule. In fact, it shows either the asymmetric unit or the biological molecule, which happen to be the same for this file. You can toggle between both views by using the box with arrows just below the heading Images and Visualization. To manipulate the model, you must use one of the viewing programs like Jmol. If you use Jmol, it should launch right in your web browser and you should see that the proteins are depicted as ribbons of different color to make protein identification easy. The rRNA is a single-stranded ribbon or line. The tRNA is shown as a line for the sugar/phosphate backbone and ring structures for the bases. The aminoacylated 3′-ends of the tRNAs are sticking out away from the 30S subunit. When the 50S joins the small subunit to form the ribosome, these tRNA ends will be located in the peptidyl transferase centre of the large subunit.

MBT Protein Workshop and QuickPDB View open the file showing proteins as lines coloured rainbow (N-terminus blue to C-terminus red). The tRNAs are stick figures.

Questions for Self-Study

1. Match:

a.	30S	1.	Large subunit rRNA of eukaryotic ribosome
b.	50S	2.	Small rRNA in large subunit of eukaryotes only
c.	70S	3.	Eukaryotic ribosome
d.	40S	4.	Small subunit rRNA of prokaryotic ribosome
e.	60S	5.	Small subunit rRNA of eukaryotic ribosome
f.	80S	6.	Small subunit of prokaryotic ribosome
g.	23S	7.	Large subunit rRNA of prokaryotic ribosome
h.	16S	8.	Large subunit rRNA in both prokaryotes and eukaryotes
i.	28S	9.	Prokaryotic ribosome
j.	18S	10.	Large subunit of eukaryotic ribosome
k.	5S	11.	Large subunit of prokaryotic ribosome
l.	5.8S	12.	Small subunit of eukaryotic ribosome

2. Translation can be divided into three phases. What are they? During each phase, two tRNA-binding sites on the ribosome, the A site and the P site, are occupied by various modified tRNAs or release factors. For each phase of protein synthesis, state the occupancy of the A site and the P site.

3. What is the role of the Shine–Dalgarno sequence (ribosome-binding site), a purine-rich region of prokaryotic mRNAs located upstream of the initiator codon?

4. Identify the following as associated with initiation (I), elongation (E), or termination (T) of translation.
   a. IF-2
   b. EF-Tu
   c. Cap-binding protein
   d. EF-Ts
   e. EF-G
   f. RF-1
   g. IF-3
   h. 40S preinitiation complex
   i. eIF-2
   j. polysomes

5. Match a protein synthesis inhibitor with its mode of action.

Inhibitor		Mode of Action
a.	Streptomycin	1. Causes release of peptide in covalent linkage with antibiotic
b.	Puromycin	2. ADP-ribosylated eEF-2
c.	Diptheria toxin	3. Blocks peptidyl transferase activity of 50S subunit
d.	Ricin	4. Cleaves prokaryotic small subunit rRNA
e.	Colicin E3	5. Inactivates eukaryotic large subunit rRNA by base removal
f.	Chloramphenicol	6. Codon misreading

Answers

1. a. 6; b. 11; c. 9; d. 12; e. 10; f. 3; g. 7; h. 4; i. 1; j. 5; k. 8; l. 2.

2. During initiation of protein synthesis the P site is occupied by charged initiator tRNA and the A site is occupied by an aminoacyl-tRNA. During elongation, the P site is occupied by a peptidyl tRNA or transiently by an uncharged tRNA. The A site is occupied by an aminoacyl-tRNA and transiently by a peptidyl tRNA. During termination, the P site is occupied by a peptidyl-tRNA and the A site is recognized by a release factor.

3. The ribosome-binding site interacts with a pyrimidine rich region near the 3'-end of the small subunit ribosome to properly align the translational start site on the ribosome.

4. a. I; b. E; c. I; d. E; e. E; f. T; g. I; h. I; i. I; j. E.

5. a. 6; b. 1; c. 2; d. 5; e. 4; f. 3.

Additional Problems

1. In addition to ribosomes, *in vitro* protein synthesis systems from *E. coli* require a high-speed supernatant that supplies protein factors required for all of the side reactions necessary for protein synthesis. The reaction must be supplied with ATP, GTP, amino acids and a compound known as citrovorum. Citrovorum is an old name for folinic acid, formyl tetrahydropteroyl-glutamic acid. Explain why ATP, GTP, and citrovorum are added. What role do they play in protein synthesis?

2. How are the 5S rRNA and 5.8S rRNA related? How is the 5.8S rRNA related to the large subunit rRNA?

3. The substrates for protein synthesis are not free amino acids but aminoacylated tRNAs. Explain what an aminoacyl-tRNA is and how is it formed.

4. During the elongation phase of protein synthesis, two tRNA-binding sites orchestrate the elongation of a protein. Describe this process.

5. The small subunit of the ribosome is responsible for initiation of protein synthesis. It interacts with several proteins and various RNAs to form a preinitiation complex. Later, the preinitiation complex is joined by the large subunit to form the initiation complex, a complete ribosome lacking an aminoacyl-tRNA at the A site. Describe how a preinitiation complex forms.

6. In eukaryotic ribosomes, initiation of protein synthesis is regulated by phosphorylation of eIF-2. Explain.

7. The elongation factor EF-Tu is a GTPase required for binding of aminoacylated tRNA to the A site. This protein is recycled during protein synthesis by interacting with another protein, EF-Ts. Describe this interaction.

8. In terms of codon recognition, how is termination fundamentally different than elongation in protein synthesis?

Abbreviated Answers

1. ATP is required for aminoacylation of tRNAs by aminoacyl-tRNA synthetases. Hydrolysis of GTP is used at various stages of protein synthesis to drive reactions. Formyl-tetrahydropteroly-glutamic acid serves as a formyl-group donor for methionyl-tRNA$_f^{Met}$ formyl transferase to formylate the charged initiator tRNA.

2. The 5S rRNA and the 5.8S rRNA are both components of the large subunit of the ribosome. The 5.8S is specific for eukaryotic cytoplasmic ribosomes, whereas the 5S rRNA is found in eukaryotes and prokaryotes. The 5.8S rRNA of eukaryotes has a sequence similar to the 5'-end of the large subunit rRNA of prokaryotes.

3. Aminoacyl-tRNAs represent activated forms of amino acids used by the ribosome as substrates for peptide bond formation during protein synthesis. Aminoacyl-tRNAs are formed by aminoacyl-tRNA synthetases in a two-step reaction driven by hydrolysis of ATP.

4. During a cycle of elongation, the P site is occupied by a peptidyl-tRNA produced by preceding rounds of elongation and the A site is occupied by an aminoacyl-tRNA appropriate for the codon in the A site. Peptide bond formation occurs by nucleophilic attack of the amino group of the A-site aminoacyl-tRNA on the carbonyl carbon of the ester bond in the peptidyl-tRNA, resulting in peptide bond formation, deacylation of the P-site tRNA, and formation of a peptidyl-tRNA in the A site. The P-site tRNA is released and the peptidyl-tRNA in the A site is translocated to the P site in a factor-dependent manner. Translocation of the tRNA is accompanied by movement of the mRNA as well, to bring a new codon into the A site. The A site is filled with the appropriate aminoacylated tRNA by a factor-dependent process.

5. A ribosome is dissociated by initiation factors into a large subunit and a small subunit. The small subunit binds mRNA and a complex of a specific initiation factor (IF-2 in prokaryotes), GTP, and charged initiator-tRNA to form a preinitiation complex. The complex is joined by the large subunit with release of initiation factors to produce the initiation complex.

6. In eukaryotes, initiation of protein synthesis begins with formation of a ternary complex with eIF-2, GTP, and Met-tRNA$_i^{Met}$. The complex associates with a small subunit to produce a 40S preinitiation complex. The α-subunit of eIF-2 can be phosphorylated by a specific kinase. Phosphorylated eIF-2 binds eIF-2B tightly and effectively eliminates eIF-2B-dependent recycling of eIF-2.

7. EF-Tu forms a complex with GTP and an aminoacyl-tRNA before binding to the ribosome. Ribosome binding stimulates GTPase activity resulting in release of P$_i$, A-site binding of the aminoacyl-tRNA, and release of EF-Tu:GDP complex. EF-Ts binds to this complex and displaces GDP to produce an EF-Tu:EF-Ts complex. GTP can dissociate EF-Ts from this complex, thus allowing EF-Tu to participate in another round of elongation.

8. For termination codons, codon recognition is achieved by protein release factors instead of tRNAs.

Summary

Translation is the process whereby genetic information is expressed through synthesis of a protein. Ribosomes are the agents of protein synthesis. Ribosomes are self-assembling ribonucleoprotein particles ubiquitous to all cells, invariably consisting of two unequal subunits, each containing more than 20 different proteins and at least one characteristic ribosomal RNA (rRNA) molecule.

All the peptide bonds in the protein, from the first to the last, are formed in the elongation phase. Elongation proceeds via the codon-directed association of aminoacyl-tRNAs with the ribosome:mRNA complex, as the ribosome moves along the mRNA and encounters successive codons. The ribosome:mRNA complex has two aminoacyl-tRNA binding sites: the A site where an incoming aminoacyl-tRNA binds, and the P site where peptidyl-tRNA (the tRNA carrying the growing polypeptide chain) is held. Peptide bond formation is achieved when the α-carboxyl end of the polypeptide chain is transferred from its tRNA to the free α-NH$_2$ group of the aminoacyl-tRNA in the A site. The deacylated tRNA (the tRNA left after transfer of the polypeptide) leaves the P site. The tRNA in the A site now bears the polypeptidyl chain and it is translocated from the A site to the P site as the ribosome moves one codon further along the mRNA. This codon now directs the binding of the next incoming aminoacyl-tRNA in the A site, and the process repeats itself until all the codons have been translated. Termination of polypeptide synthesis is triggered by the appearance of a nonsense codon (UAA, UAG, or UGA) in the A site. Release factor proteins bind at the A site, transforming the peptidyl transferase activity of the ribosome into a peptidyl hydrolase, and the free polypeptide is released. The ribosome:mRNA complex then dissociates.

The reactions of peptide chain initiation, elongation, and termination are orchestrated at each step by specific soluble proteins—initiation factors, elongation factors, and release factors. GTP hydrolysis provides the energy to drive conformational changes in the protein-synthesizing apparatus. These conformational changes represent the workings of the protein synthesis machinery in its cycle of successive amino acid addition to the growing peptidyl chain. Two GTPs are expended for each amino acid added to the chain: one in aminoacyl-tRNA binding at the A site, and one in the coupled movement of the ribosome along the mRNA that translocates the peptidyl-tRNA from the A site to the P site. Ribosomal subunits cycle rapidly through protein synthesis. Polysomes, consisting of an mRNA molecule with several ribosomes simultaneously translating it, serve as the active protein-synthesizing units.

While the translation is similar in prokaryotes and eukaryotes, both the process and the accompanying apparatus are considerably more complex in eukaryotes. Protein synthesis inhibitors have been very useful in probing the mechanism of protein synthesis; some have clinical value as antibiotics.

Chapter 31

Post-transcriptional Regulation of Gene Expression: mRNA Turnover and Micro-RNA

• •

Chapter Outline

❖ mRNA turnover
 ⚔ Stability and decay (half-life)
  • *cis*-acting elements
   • AU-rich elements
   • Premature termination codons
  • *trans*-acting elements
   • RNA-binding proteins
   • microRNAs
❖ mRNA life cycle
 ⚔ *cis*- and *trans*-acting element-mediated export and translation regulation
  • Processing bodies
   • Dcp 1/2, Dhh1p/RCK/p54, XRN1p (mRNA degradation enzymes)
   • GW182, Ago2 (microRNA-mediated regulation in P-bodies)
❖ mRNA decay
 ⚔ Deadenylation-dependent
  • Deadenylation
   • PABP and eIF4G interaction leading to mRNA circularization
   • Deadenylases (serve to shorten the poly(A) tail)
    o PAN2-PAN3, CCR4-NOT, and PARN
    o Critical length, loss of PABP, loss of mRNA circularization
  • Decapping
   • Dcp 1/2, Dhh1p/RCK/p54
  • Degradation
   • 5′ to 3′
    o XRN1p
   • 3′ to 5′
    o Exosome
 ⚔ Deadenylation-independent
  • Endoribonucleases
   • PMR1, IRE1, G3BP, and RNase MRP
   • microRNAs
❖ AU-rich-mediated decay
 ⚔ AU-rich elements (also GU-rich elements)
  • Located mainly in the 3′UTR of mRNA
  • Inherent instability in the mRNA
 ⚔ ARE-binding proteins
  • Stabilizing
   • HuR
  • Destabilizing
   • KSRP, AUF-1/hnRNP D, and tristetraprolin (TTP)

Chapter Objectives

mRNA Turnover

mRNA turnover encompasses all of the cellular processes involved in regulating mRNA stability and decay. These processes vary from typical, baseline mRNA degradation to specific degradation aimed at modifying production of a particular protein through subsequent translation or removing aberrant transcripts that may lead to toxic protein products. Protein players involved in general mRNA decay include deadenylases (PAN2-PAN3, CCR4-NOT, and PARN), decapping enzymes (Dcp 1/2, Dhh1p/RCK/p54), and exoribonucleases (XRN1p, exosome). *cis*- and *trans*-elements that influence the half-life of mRNAs, or their rate of turnover, include microRNAs, RNA-binding proteins, AU-rich elements, and premature termination codons.

General Degradation

In general, mRNAs are degraded either in deadenylation-dependent or -independent manners. In the case of deadenlyation dependence, mRNAs first undergo an extensive shortening of their poly(A) tail via the action of deadenylases. The shortening of the poly(A) tail causes removal of PABP–mRNA interactions at the level of the poly(A) tail, which in turn prevents PABP–eIF4G interactions required for mRNA circularization. Once in an open conformation, the mRNA becomes greatly accessible for decapping enzymes and degradation enzymes (exoribonucleases). In the case of deadenylation independence, the mRNA is first cleaved by endoribonucleases at internal sites, followed by degradation via exoribonucleases acting at the exposed ends of the mRNA. This method of mRNA degradation can be seen in microRNA–mediated mRNA degradation, where the PIWI domain of Ago proteins acts as a slicer, cleaving the mRNA.

AU-rich Mediated Decay

Most oncoprotein mRNAs contain a 3′-untranslated region (3′UTR) that harbours segments rich in adenosine (A) and uridine (U) (known as AU-rich elements or AREs) that cause them to be highly unstable unless circumstances call for their corresponding protein to be expressed. As such, the main function of AU-rich mediated decay is to limit the lifetime of short-lived mRNAs and therefore tightly regulate the expression of these proto-oncogenes. Although there are several classes of AREs, the AUUUA motif is most commonly found in AREs, and most AREs are located in the 3′UTR of mRNAs. The common feature of ARE-binding proteins (AUBPs) is their ability to interact with AREs of target mRNAs. In general, AUBPs can be subdivided into two broad categories: destabilizing and stabilizing AUBPs. Examples of destabilizing AUBPs include KSRP, AUF-1/hnRNP D, and tristetraprolin. On the other hand, the most notable example of a stabilizing AUBP is HuR, known for increasing the half-lives of pro-survival and growth transcripts.

mRNA Surveillance Systems

In order to maintain RNA integrity, several cellular processes act to degrade aberrant RNA transcripts, such as nonsense-mediated decay and non-stop decay. Nonsense-mediated decay makes use of up-frameshift (UPF) proteins, as well as exon–exon junctions in order to distinguish between normal stop codons and premature termination codons. Non-stop decay serves to eliminate mRNAs lacking a stop codon.

microRNA-mediated Degradation

microRNAs are 21–25 nucleotide(nt)-long single-stranded RNAs that serve to promote mRNA turnover through mRNA decay, as well as promoting mRNA translational repression. microRNA biogenesis involves initial transcription of the microRNA by RNA Pol II, followed by initial cleavage by Drosha, a nuclear ribonuclease, giving rise to hairpin structure for the immature microRNA. Subsequently, the microRNA is exported and cleaved by another ribonuclease, Dicer, yielding the mature microRNA, which can be loaded into the RISC (RNA-induced silencing complex) for downstream mRNA silencing (through decay or repression). The RISC is mRNP complex composed of Ago proteins, which perform the mRNA and microRNA binding, as well as the slicer activity of the complex that leads to mRNA cleavage and subsequent degradation.

Problems and Solutions

1. The stability of 1 mRNA is typically stated by giving its half-life. What types of mRNAs do you expect would have short half-lives? What types of mRNAs do you expect to have longer half-lives?

Answer: mRNA half-life is defined as the length of time for which an mRNA is stable inside the cell. As such, highly regulated genes, such as proto-oncogenes and cytokine genes, typically have very short half-lives, allowing for tight control over the availability of these transcripts to translation machinery. On the other hand, common housekeeping genes, such as genes related to the cell cytoskeleton (actin/tubulin), tend to have longer half-lives, as their protein products are virtually always essential for cell function.

3. If the poly(A) tail of a mRNA is too short, why is the message no longer translated?

Answer: Once the poly(A) tail is shortened beyond the critical length, PABP can no longer bind to the mRNA poly(A) tail. Since mRNA is maintained in a circularized state through interaction between PABP molecules at the poly(A) tail and eIF4G at the mRNA 5'-cap, the loss of PABP causes opening of the mRNA, greatly reducing the efficiency of mRNA translation. Subsequent mRNA decapping would result in loss of binding to eIF4E, preventing the mRNA from being loaded into the ribosome.

5. Fill in the blanks: A mature mRNA typically contains a _____ of roughly 150–200 nucleotides at its 3'-end. This part of the mRNA is typically bound by several _____ molecules, which in turn, interact with _____ at the level of the mRNA 5'-GTP cap to render the mRNA circularized. A group of enzymes known as _____ serve to shorten the 3'-end of the mRNA to about 20–25 nucleotides, known as the _____ length, leading to downstream mRNA decay.

Answer: poly(A) tail, PABP, eIF4G, deadenylases, critical.

7. Name two cis-elements that influence mRNA stability. Do these elements enhance or inhibit mRNA turnover?

Answer: The AU-rich element enhances mRNA turnover by rendering the transcript less stable, potentially recruiting the exosome and other *trans*-acting mRNA degradation factors. A premature termination codon within a transcript also serves to enhance mRNA turnover through the action of nonsense-mediated decay.

9. Three transcripts exhibit the following RNA sequences:
Transcript A: AGCGAUGGCACCCUGGUAGCCAGUGCUAGAAAUGCCCUGU
Transcript B: AGUCGAUCGAUCGAUCGAUGAUUUAGUCGAUGCCGUAGCU
Transcript C: AGUACGUAGUUAUUUAUAGCUGAUUUAUUUAUUUAGCUAG

Which transcript will likely have the smallest half-life? The largest half-life? How might over-expression of a stabilizing AUBP affect each of these transcripts (in terms of half-life)?

Answer: Transcript C, which contains the most AREs, is likely to have the shortest half-life, while Transcript A, which does not contain any AREs, is likely to have the longest half-life. In addition, Transcript A's half-life will not likely be affected by a stabilizing AUBP, while Transcripts B and C will likely become more stable (longer half-lives) as a result of over-expression of a stabilizing AUBP, due to the presence of AREs in their 3′UTRs.

11. *What type of error in a messenger RNA triggers nonsense-mediated decay (NMD)?*

Answer: A premature termination codon.

13. *Where in the cell does NMD occur?*

Answer: NMD occurs in the cytoplasm; specifically, it is believed to take place in Processing Bodies.

15. *miRNAs are 21–25 nt long. How is it possible that 1 miRNA can bind and affect multiple mRNAs?*

Answer: Perfect complementarity is only required at the level of the seed element within a miRNA. As such, multiple mRNAs, despite having different sequences upstream or downstream of the seed element, may both contain the same seed element, allowing for binding of the same miRNA.

17. *If a miRNA binds to the mRNA of ZAZI with perfect complimentarity, would you expect to see a decrease in ZAZI protein, ZAZI mRNA, or both?*

Answer: Both. Perfect complimentarity allows for cleavage of the target mRNA via Ago protein slicer activity and subsequent mRNA degradation. Since the decrease in mRNA levels would result in a decrease in translation, a decrease in ZAZI protein levels would also result.

Summary

mRNA turnover represents the balance between the rates of stabilization and decay of an mRNA. The length of time for which an mRNA is stable is known as its half-life, and can be increased or decreased in the presence of specific RNA-binding proteins. When a transcript is no longer needed, or its translation must be terminated, it is targeted to cytoplasmic foci known as P-bodies which represent accumulations of translationally repressed mRNAs as well as mRNA degradation enzymes.

General mRNA decay begins with shortening of the poly(A) tail by deadenylases. When the poly(A) tail is shortened to 25 nucleotides, it can no longer interact with PABP, leading to opening of the circularized mRNA. Further deadenylation can lead to 3′ to 5′ degradation by exonucleases such as the exosome, or decapping by DCP1/2 can lead to 5′ to 3′ degradation by Xrn1 exonuclease. Alternative methods of mRNA decay exist, such as deadenylation-independent mRNA decay, which directly recruits decapping enzymes, and endonuclease-mediated decay. *Cis-* and *trans-* elements involved in mRNA stability or decay serve to accelerate or slow down the recruitment of deadenylases and decapping enzymes.

One of the best studied mRNA *cis*-elements is the AU-rich element (ARE). AREs are present in 5 to 8 percent of human mRNAs, including many oncogenes. ARE-containing messages are very unstable, as the AREs serve as binding sites for destabilizing RBPs that recruit mRNA degradation factors and the exosome. AREs can also, however, recruit stabilizing RBPs that act to increase the limited half-life of the target mRNA. Interactions between RBPs and target mRNAs can be identified using biochemical techniques such as RNA-EMSA or RIP-Chip. In addition to AREs, other *cis*-elements such as GU-rich elements have been shown to contribute to mRNA instability and decay.

Genomic mutations can lead to transcripts harbouring premature stop codons as a result of frameshifts or deletions. These transcripts can give rise to truncated proteins, which can be dysfunctional or may have toxic dominant-negative effects. As such, the cell contains a mechanism for eliminating aberrant mRNA, known as nonsense-mediated decay (NMD). NMD involves a number of factors including UPF1-3 and the Ski proteins, as well as the exon–junction complex (EJC). The EJC is deposited on the mRNA during splicing, and plays a major role is triggering NMD upon discovery of a premature stop codon. NMD is subjected to two positional rules: the EJC is always placed 20–24 nucleotides upstream of the exon–exon junction post-splicing, and NMD is not triggered if the premature stop codon is within

55 nucleotides of the junction. Finally, for removal of aberrant transcripts lacking any stop codon, the cell uses its non-stop decay pathway.

miRNA-mediated gene regulation involves the action of short, *trans*-acting, 22 nucleotide, single-stranded RNA molecules. These molecules are originally transcribed as hairpin-structured double-stranded RNA, which is then processed by the nuclear endoribonuclease Drosha and the cytoplasmic endoribonuclease Dicer to give rise to the mature miRNA. The mature miRNA then interacts with Argonaute proteins as part of a larger complex known as the RISC, which carries out the gene silencing activity. miRNAs are capable of triggering both translational repression of target mRNAs as well as mRNA degradation by binding to specific target mRNAs at regions known as seed elements.

Finally, in analyzing regulation of mRNAs from their introduction at the level of transcription to their degradation, we can propose a unified theory of gene expression, where the different steps of the mRNA life cycle, from transcription to processing, export to translation and decay, are interconnected and co-regulated. This concept is supported by observations in the field of ribonomics, where functionally related mRNAs are co-regulated as RNA operons or regulons through the action of RNA-binding proteins. Finally, taking into account all of the notions in this chapter, we can see how RNA-based therapies can potentially serve to treat a number of human diseases.

Chapter 32

Completing the Protein Life Cycle: Folding, Processing, and Degradation

• •

Chapter Outline

❖ Protein folding: Chaperones
  ⋏ TF (Trigger factor in *E. coli*), NAC (in eukaryotes) bind to nascent chain on ribosome
  ⋏ Hsp70 (DnaK): Binds to nascent polypeptide chain at hydrophobic residues to prevent folding
  ⋏ DnaJ (Hsp40): Binds to unfolded proteins and passes them to Hsp70 (DnaK)
  ⋏ GrpE: ADP/ATP exchange on DnaK
  ⋏ Hsp60: Chaperonins
    • Group I in eubacteria
      • GroES-GroEL
    • Group II in archaea and eukaryotes
      • CCT (triC) a GroEL analog
      • Prefoldin (GimC)
  ⋏ Hsp90: Eukaryotic foldosome that folds signal transduction molecules
❖ Post-translational processing
  ⋏ Post-translational modifications like phosphorylation, acetylation, methylation, etc.
  ⋏ Proteolytic cleavage of pro-enzymes
    • Introduce diversity of protein products
    • Activation of preproprotein
    • Targeting of proteins in protein translocation
  ⋏ Protein translocation
    • Characteristics of translocation systems
      • Proteins made as preproteins with signal peptides
      • Specific protein receptors exist on target membrane
      • Movement catalyzed by complex structures: Translocons: ATP (or GTP) driven
      • Proteins generally maintained in loosely folded conformations for translocation competence
  ⋏ Prokaryotic translocation
    • N-terminal leader sequence
      • N-terminus of leader sequence: Basic amino acids
      • Central domain hydrophobic
      • C-terminus: Nonhelical structure
    • Leader peptidase: Removes leader sequence
  ⋏ Eukaryotic translocation and protein sorting
    • Secreted and membrane proteins synthesized on ER-localized ribosomes
      • Cytoplasmic ribosome initiates translation
      • N-terminal signal sequence detected by signal recognition particle (SRP)
      • SRP–ribosome complex binds to docking protein: ER membrane protein
      • Ribosome delivers peptide to translocon
      • Signal peptidase cleaves leader sequence
      • Membrane proteins carry 20-residue stop transfer sequence

- Retrograde transport : Sec61p: Moves protein from ER back to cytosol
- Mitochondrial protein import
  - N-terminal sequence 10 to 70 residues long
    - Form amphiphilic α-helix
    - Binds to TOM (mitochondria outer membrane translocase)
  - Outer membrane protein
    - TOM passes protein to SAM (sorting and assembly complex)
  - Inner membrane protein
    - TOM to TIM22
  - Matrix protein
    - TOM to TIM23
- Chloroplasts
  - TOCs and TICs

❖ Protein degradation: Ubiquitination most common pathway in eukaryotes
  - Ubiquitin: Conserved 76-residue protein
    - E1: Ubiquitin-activation protein: Attaches to C-terminal Gly of ubiquitin
    - E2: Ubiquitin-carrier protein: Accepts ubiquitin from activator protein: Carried on cysteine residue
    - E3: Ubiquitin-protein ligase: Binds target protein: Protein ubiquitinated on amino groups
  - Proteins with acidic N-termini
    - N-termini altered by Arg-tRNA
  - PEST sequences: Target proteins for degradation
  - Proteasomes
    - 20S proteasomes
    - 26S proteasomes
  - HtrA protease: DegP in *E. coli*
    - Functions as chaperone at low temperature (20°C)
    - Switch from chaperone to protease function as temperature increases

❖ Sumoylation: Addition of small ubiquintin-like modifiers
  - Reaction requires three-enzyme conjugation system
  - Consequences of SUMO addition
    - Blocking protein binding site: Inhibition of protein–protein interaction
    - Creation of binding site for interacting partner protein
    - Induction of protein conformational change

Chapter Objectives

Protein Folding

Protein folding starts before the polypeptide is released from the ribosome. In many cases, folding is assisted by molecular chaperones. Be familiar with the names, order of action, and mechanism of a few of them: TF, NAC, HSP70, HSP60, GroES–GroEL, CCT (or TriC), and Hsp90. Chaperones act via cycles of binding and hydrolysis of ATP. If hydrophobic patches are exposed and not buried within the protein structure on their surface, they have the potential for incorrect associations with other like patches, ultimately leading to precipitation. Hsp70s recognize these exposed hydrophobic regions as signals that the protein is not folded correctly, and bind to them, thereby blocking damaging associations. Both GroES–GroEL and CCT are large structures into which proteins are sequestered for ATP-dependent folding. Hsp90s are chaperones that act in concert with Hsp70 to assist in the folding of proteins operating in signal transduction pathways.

Post-Translational Processing

The most common form of protein modification is proteolytic cleavage to activate a protein, or to release mature protein products from a larger primary translational product. Proteins are also targeted to specific locations within the cell or are destined for transport out of the cell. In prokaryotes, a signal sequence, located on the N-terminus of a protein, or at a more internal location, may direct the protein to be exported from the cell or to become a membrane-bound protein. Signal recognition particles play a role in halting protein synthesis shortly after a signal peptide is produced and, in conjunction with docking protein, direct the nascent protein to the endoplasmic reticulum membrane where protein synthesis resumes. Proteins cross into the endoplasmic reticulum lumen, or become integrated into the membrane, via an aqueous tunnel called a translocon. The translocon is aligned with the exit tunnel from the 50S ribosomal subunit, and together they form a continuous channel from the ribosome through the membrane. Once the N-terminus reaches the endoplasmic reticulum lumen, the signal sequence is proteolytically removed by leader peptidase.

Most mitochondrial proteins are encoded in the nucleus and are post-translationally imported from the cytoplasm. Proteins are directed to the mitochondria by N-terminal targeting presequences that have the ability to form amphipathic α-helices. Proteins enter the mitochondria through the TOM and TIM translocons, located in the outer and inner mitochondrial membranes, respectively.

Protein Degradation

Ubiquitin plays a role in degradation of proteins in eukaryotes. This pathway is specific and efficient in removing defective proteins from the cell by attaching multiple copies of ubiquitin to the protein to be degraded, which in turn targets the protein for destruction in the proteosome. Proteins having Arg, Lys, His, Phe, Tyr, Trp, Leu, Asn, Gln, Asp, or Glu at their N-termini are particularly susceptible to ubiquitination and proteosome-mediated degradation. These proteins have half-lives of between 2 and 30 minutes. In contrast, proteins with Met, Ser, Ala, Thr, Val, Gly, or Cys at their N-termini are resistant to ubiquitin-mediated degradation.

Proteins marked for destruction are degraded by one of two related proteosomes, differentiated on the basis of their size. These are large oligomeric structures enclosing a central cavity wherein degradation takes place. HtrA proteases have a dual function in prokaryotic cells. At low temperatures, HtrA acts as a chaperone, preventing aggregation and promoting folding. At high temperatures, however, HtrA develops protease activity, and instead of correcting a misfolded protein, destroys it.

Problems and Solutions

1. **(Integrates with Chapter 30) Human rhodanese (33kD) consists of 296 amino acid residues. Approximately how many ATP equivalents are consumed in the synthesis of the rhodanese polypeptide chain from its constituent amino acids and the folding of this chain into an active tertiary structure?**

Answer: The energetics of protein synthesis requires at least 4 ATP equivalents per amino acid residue incorporated into protein. During elongation, the A-site is filled at the expense of GTP that occurs during recycling of EF-1, a eukaryotic elongation factor. A second GTP hydrolysis drives translocation catalyzed by EF-2, the eukaryotic translocation factor. Peptide bond formation is driven by the high-energy aminoacyl bond on the aminoacyl-tRNA substrate. Formation of aminoacyl-tRNAs is catalyzed by aminoacyl-tRNA synthetases, enzymes that consume ATP and produce AMP and PP$_i$. Pyrophosphatase hydrolysis of PP$_i$ accounts for an additional high-energy phosphate bond. For synthesis of human rhodanese with 296 amino acid residues, the A-site will have to be filled 295 times, accounting for (295 × 4 =) 1180 ATP equivalents. Met-tRNA$_i$ formation consumes 2 ATPs. Initiation requires 2 ATP equivalents, 1 in the form of GTP during eIF-2 mediated Met-tRNA$_i$ binding to form the 40S pre-initiation complex, and 1 in the form of ATP during 40S initiation complex formation. Peptide chain termination in eukaryotes requires GTP hydrolysis, thus accounting for an additional ATP equivalent. Thus, 1,180 + 4 + 1 = 1185 ATP equivalents are consumed to synthesize rhodanese. In order to properly fold the polypeptide chain, an additional 130 equivalents of ATP are consumed during the folding cycle catalyzed by molecular chaperones. Active rhodanese production requires approximately 1315 equivalents of ATP.

3. **Protein molecules, like all molecules, can be characterized in terms of general properties such as size, shape, charge, and solubility/hydrophobicity. Consider the influence of each of these general features on the likelihood of whether folding of a particular protein will require chaperone assistance or not. Be specific regarding just Hsp70 chaperones or both Hsp70 chaperones and Hsp60 chaperonins.**

Answer: Hsp70 binds to exposed hydrophobic portions of target polypeptides via an 18 kDa domain residing in the central portion of its sequence. Since hydrophobic patches are not exposed in proteins that have attained their final conformation, Hsp70s interact only with polypeptides that have not yet folded. It would be expected that since the occurrence of charged residues within a sequence decreases its overall hydrophobicity, charge would negatively impact the binding of the chaperones. Size, on the other hand, would not be expected to play a role in Hsp70 binding, as multiple chaperones could bind to larger polypeptides, or to multiple hydrophobic regions on a single polypeptide.

For Hsp 60 and HSP 70, the Hsp60 chaperonin acts in concert with Hsp70 to achieve the final folded conformation of certain proteins. Unlike the Hsp70, however, Hsp60 action requires that the polypeptide fit inside the chaperonin cavity. This sets an upper limit on the size of the polypeptide that can be folded by Hsp60. Since the cavity has a diameter of 5 nm, we can calculate the molecular weight of a protein that can be folded as follows: The volume of a protein with a radius of 2.5 nm is

$$V = \frac{4}{3}\pi r^3 = \frac{4}{3}\pi(2.5)^3 = 65.4 \text{ nm}^3$$

Using 1.25 g/mL as the density of a typical protein, we calculate the molecular weight of a protein with a radius of 2.5 nm:

$$M_r \text{ (kD)} = V \text{ (nm}^3) \times \frac{1.25\dfrac{g}{cm^3 \cdot molec} \times 6.02 \times 10^{23}\dfrac{molec}{mol} \times 0.001\dfrac{kD}{g\big/mol}}{10^{21}\dfrac{nm^3}{cm^3}}$$

$$= V \text{ (nm}^3) \times 0.7525\frac{kD}{nm^3} = 65.4 \text{ nm}^3 \times 0.7525\frac{kD}{nm^3} = 49.2 \text{ kD}$$

Thus, a protein larger than approximately 50 kDa will be too large to fit into the Hsp60 cavity and cannot be folded by this chaperonin.

5.   The GroEL ring has a 5-nm central cavity. Calculate the maximum molecular weight for a spherical protein that can just fit into this cavity, assuming the density of the protein is 1.25 g/mL.

Answer: This calculation was made for Problem 3 above. In that problem, the following relationship was developed between the volume of a spherical protein and its molecular weight:

$$M_r \text{ (kD)} = V \text{ (nm}^3) \times 0.7525\frac{kD}{nm^3}$$

This can be further modified to give the relationship between molecular weight and a protein's radius:

$$M_r \text{ (kD)} = V \text{ (nm}^3) \times 0.7525\frac{kD}{nm^3}$$

$$= \frac{4}{3}\pi r^3 \times 0.7525\frac{kD}{nm^3} = 3.15\frac{kD}{nm^3} \times r^3$$

Accordingly, a spherical protein with a radius of 2.5 nm has a molecular weight of approximately 50 kDa.

7.   (Integrates with Chapter 30) In what ways are the mechanisms of action of EF-Tu/EF-Ts and DnaK/GrpE similar? What mechanistic functions do the ribosome A-site and DnaJ have in common?

Answer: GrpE and EF-Ts are nucleotide exchange factors working on DnaK and EF-Tu, respectively. Their reaction mechanisms can be summarized as follows: GrpE catalyzes replacement of ADP with ATP on DnaK → DnaK converted to form having low affinity for substrate → Causes release of substrate → DnaK changes conformation to a form having a high affinity for a DnaJ/unfolded protein substrate → DnaJ stimulates ATPase activity of DnaK → DnaK:ATP is converted to DnaK:ADP, and the reaction cycle starts again.

EF-Ts catalyzes replacement of GDP with GTP in EF-Tu → EF-Tu converted to a form having high affinity for aminoacyl-t-RNA → Binding of aminoacyl-t-RNA:EF-Tu to the A site of the ribosome stimulates ET-Tu GTPase activity → EF-Tu:GTP is converted to EF-Tu:GDP → aminoacyl-t-RNA:EF-Tu adjusts conformationally to the A site, allowing codon:anticodon recognition, and the reaction cycle starts again.

DnaJ and the A-site of the ribosome have similar functions in that they both stimulate the NTP hydrolysis activity of their respective partner NTPases, thereby causing in them stabilizing conformational changes.

9.   The Sec61p translocon complex is not only essential for translocation of proteins into the ER lumen, it also mediates the incorporation of integral membrane proteins into the ER membrane. The mechanism for integration is triggered by stop-transfer signals that cause a pause in translocation. Figure 32.5 shows the translocon as a closed cylinder spanning the membrane. Suggest a mechanism for lateral transfer of an integral membrane protein from the protein-conducting channel of the translocon into the hydrophobic phase of the ER membrane.

Answer: Translocation of the nascent polypeptide continues through the Sec61p translocon until a transmembrane-spanning region of hydrophobic amino acids is encountered. This stop-transfer sequence causes translocation to pause and a conformational change takes place within the translocon that opens the channel to the core of the membrane bilayer. The transmembrane region then slips laterally out of the translocon into the membrane, and translation at the ribosome continues.

11. (Integrates with Chapters 6, 10, and 30) During co-translational translocation, the peptide tunnel running from the peptidyl transferase centre of the large ribosomal subunit and the protein-conducting channel are aligned. If the tunnel through the ribosomal subunit is 10 nm and the translocon channel has the same length as the thickness of a phospholipid bilayer, what is the minimum number of amino acid residues sequestered in this common conduit?

Answer: The thickness of a bilayer is approximately 5 nm, so the combined channel through the Sec61p translocon and the ribosome is 15 nm. In the most extended β-sheet-like conformation, each residue spans a distance of 0.347 nm. In this conformation, the overall channel would contain:

$$\frac{15\,\text{nm}}{0.347\,\text{nm}\big/\text{residue}} \approx 43\;\text{residues}$$

By using the distance values for the most extended β-sheet-like conformation, this represents the minimum number of residues that can be sequestered in the ribosome/translocon channel. In fact, the experimentally determined number is 70 residues, indicating that the nascent polypeptide is in a less extended conformation with an average distance per residue of approximately 0.21 nm.

13. Assign the 20 amino acids to either of 2 groups based on their susceptibility to ubiquitin ligation by E₃ ubiquitin protein ligase. Can you discern any common attributes among the amino acids in the less susceptible versus the more susceptible group?

Answer: E₃ ubiquitin protein ligase selects proteins by the nature of the N-terminal amino acid. Since susceptible proteins must have a free α-amino terminus to be susceptible to degradation, proteins with Pro at their N-terminus are not degraded through the ubiquitin pathway. Proteins with Met, Ser, Ala, Thr, Val, Gly, or Cys at the amino terminus are resistant to selection by E₃ ubiquitin protein ligase, whereas those having Arg, Lys, His, Phe, Tyr, Trp, Leu, Ile, Asn, Gln, Asp, or Glu at their N-terminus are susceptible.

   It is difficult to recognize common chemical attributes that apply to all amino acids residing in one group or another. For instance, while the charged amino acids are in the susceptible group, other hydrophilic amino acids (i.e., Ser and Thr) are resistant. Similarly, both groups contain hydrophobic amino acids.

15. HtrA proteases are dual-function chaperone-protease protein quality control systems. The protease activity of HtrA proteases depends on a proper spatial relationship between the Asp-His-Ser catalytic triad. Propose a mechanism for the temperature-induced switch of HtrA proteases from chaperone function to protease function.

Answer: A temperature-induced change in protein function implies that the protein undergoes a change from one conformation at low temperature to another conformation at the higher temperature. In the case of HtrA, it is likely that the high-temperature conformation brings the Asp-His-Ser triad into a spatial configuration that allows them to act catalytically.

17. *Fluorescence resonance energy transfer (FRET) is a spectroscopic technique that can be used to provide certain details of the conformation of biomolecules. Look up FRET on the Web or in an introductory text on FRET uses in biochemistry, and explain how FRET could be used to observe conformational changes in proteins bound to chaperonins such as GroEL. A good article on FRET in protein folding and dynamics can be found here: Haas, E., 2005. The study of protein folding and dynamics by determination of intramolecular distance distributions and their fluctuations using ensemble and single-molecule FRET measurements.* **ChemPhysChem 6:858–870.** *Studies of GroEL using FRET analysis include the following: Sharma, S., et al., 2008. Monitoring protein conformation along the pathway of chaperonin-assisted folding.* **Cell 133:142–153;** *and Lin, Z., et al., 2008. GroEL stimulates protein folding through forced unfolding.* **Nature Structural and Molecular Biology 15:303–311.**

Answer: Fluorescence resonance energy transfer or FRET is a process by which energy is transferred from one fluorescent molecule to another. This process can be used to measure distance between fluorescent molecules in the range of 1 nm to 10 nm, dimensions useful in studying proteins and other macromolecules. The energy transfer is between two fluorescent dyes. For transfer to occur, the emission spectrum of the so-called donor dye must overlap with the absorption (or excitation) spectrum of the acceptor dye. Furthermore, the distance between the two dyes must be within approximately 10 nm or less. Measurements of efficiency of energy transfer are used to measure the distance between two dyes. Techniques employing FRET are widely used in biochemistry and molecular biology. In the particular experimental problem under consideration, protein folding, the protein under study must be covalently modified with two fluorescent dyes on specific amino acid residues. Considering two such dyes on a polypeptide chain, the efficiency with which FRET occurs between them will depend on the distance separating them. This distance will obviously depend on the separation distance along the polypeptide chain. That is, dyes located on different ends will transfer energy less efficiently than dyes located on amino acids close together on the chain. But proteins do not remain as extended polypeptide chains. Rather, they fold up into a conformation dictated by the protein's amino acid sequence and solvent conditions. As a polypeptide folds, regions along the chain that are far apart in primary structure may be close together in the final conformation. The folding process follows a pathway or a series of pathways that start off with local hydrophobic interactions. GroEL participates in protein folding by preventing protein aggregation (among protein molecules) during the folding process by sequestering the protein. GroEL also presents the folding protein with a changing environment ranging from hydrophobic to hydrophilic. In the hydrophobic environment, proteins relinquish their local hydrophobic interactions in favour of interaction with GroEL. As the environment changes, proteins move though conformations that are stabilized by a hydrophobic core characteristic of many globular proteins.

Questions for Self-Study

1. What is the dominant driving force for protein folding?

2. How does an Hsp70 chaperone recognize a protein as unfolded?

3. True or false:
   a. All chaperones bind and release from their target proteins via cycles of ATP binding and hydrolysis. _____
   b. All chaperons contain central cavities in which proteins are sequestered to allow them to fold. _____
   c. All proteins follow the same pathway through the various chaperones during their folding. _____
   d. Hsp90 and Hsp70 act in conjunction to fold proteins involved in signal transduction. _____
   e. Chaperones operate independently and never use "helper" proteins or "co-chaperones" to mediate protein folding. _____

4. Fill in the blanks. The endoplasmic reticulum is an internal compartment typically composed of two regions, the smooth ER and the _____ _____ _____. The later region is so named because _____ stud its surface. These macromolecular complexes are translating proteins destined to be processed in the endoplasmic reticulum. Translation of these proteins actually starts in the cytosol. When a short N-terminal sequence of the nascent polypeptide, termed the _____ _____, emerges from the ribosome, it is recognized by the _____ _____ _____. This ribonucleoprotein complex binds to the ribosome and blocks further protein synthesis until the ribosome is escorted to the cytosolic surface of the endoplasmic reticulum. The _____ _____ is responsible for docking the ribosome to the membrane.

Protein synthesis then continues with the newly synthesized proteins being deposited into the lumen of the endoplasmic reticulum. There, the N-terminal sequence is cleaved by _____ _____.

5. What are the roles of ubiquitin and the large 26S ATP-dependent protease complex in degrading proteins?

Answers

1. The burial of hydrophobic residues away from the aqueous solvent.

2. Hsp70s bind to exposed hydrophobic patches on proteins. Because the protein's structure would never tolerate the placement of a significant number of hydrophobic amino acids on the exposed surface, the fact that hydrophobic patches are exposed at all signals that the protein is not in its native conformation, and may be in need of a chaperone to assist in folding.

3. a. T; b. F; c. F; d. T; e. F.

4. Rough endoplasmic reticulum or RER; ribosomes; signal sequence; signal recognition particle; docking protein or SRP receptor; signal peptidase.

5. Proteins destined for degradation are covalently modified by conjugation to ubiquitin. Ubiquitinated proteins are degraded by the protease complex.

Additional Problems

1. The textbook tells us that Christian Anfinsen pointed out 40 years ago that all the information necessary for a protein to fold is contained within its primary structure. What made him say this?

2. Describe the mechanism of action of chaperonins in protein folding.

3. What does retrograde transport from the ER mean?

4. Describe the routes followed by proteins that reside in different mitochondrial compartments.

5. It is known from experiments that mature mitochondria and chloroplast will still actively import proteins. Speculate as to why this might be the case.

Abbreviated Answers

1. Anfinsen knew that the amino acid sequence contained the information required for proper folding because some proteins could be denatured and subsequently renatured all on their own. This generally required the protein to be in a very dilute solution, conditions never encountered in the living cell. Accordingly, many proteins fold with the assistance of molecular chaperones.

2. Chaperonins are members of the Hsp60 family. An unfolded protein with surface-exposed hydrophobic regions binds to hydrophobic patches present on the apical domain of the interior surface of the GroEL cavity. Upon binding ATP, GroES is recruited to cover the apical domain and conformational changes occur within GroEL that bury the hydrophobic patches. This causes the release of the unfolded or partially folded polypeptide, where it exists in the central cavity essentially free from other similarly partially folded polypeptides with which it could potentially form aggregates. After a short time, the bound ATP is hydrolyzed, causing release of GroES and repositioning of the GroEL apical domain hydrophobic patches. If the polypeptide has folded successfully, it will escape from the GroEL cavity. If not, it can be recaptured by GroEL for another round of ATP-induced folding reactions.

3. If a protein is translocated into the ER lumen, but fails to fold correctly or assemble as a subunit of a multimeric protein, it can be transported back out of the ER through the Sec61p translocon. Upon

reaching the cytoplasm, the offending protein can then be destroyed by the proteosome. The movement of a protein out of the ER through the Sec61p translocon is called retrograde transport.

4.   Mitochondrial precursors all start their journey into the organelle by interacting with the TOM complex, a series of receptors and translocons in the outer membrane. A protein destined to integrate into the outer membrane is transferred from the TOM complex to a SAM complex, also in the outer membrane, from which it is inserted across the hydrophobic core of the membrane. Proteins that will take up residence in the inner membrane pass through the TOM complex and engage the TIM22 complex. The TIM22 complex mediates the insert in of the protein into the membrane. Proteins residing in the mitochondria matrix pass from the TOM complex to a different inner membrane complex, TIM23. The TIM23 complex mediates the passage of the precursor protein across the inner mitochondria membrane into the matrix, where it is acted upon by the matrix processing protease to remove the targeting peptide.

5.   Although the organelles are mature, they must still import proteins to replace those lost to normal turnover. Many active proteolytic enzymes are present in these organelles, and proteins can have a short half-life here as well as in the cytoplasm.

Summary

A great variety of modifications are introduced post-translationally into proteins, proteolytic cleavage being a particularly prevalent change. Proteolytic cleavage can serve a number of ends: Generating diversity in the protein, activating its biological function, or facilitating the sorting and dispatching of proteins to their proper destinations in the cell. In the latter role, a leader peptide located at the N-terminus of the protein acts as a signal sequence, which tags the protein as belonging in a particular compartment or organelle. These signals are recognized by protein translocation systems.

Some of these systems identify the protein before its synthesis is complete. For example, the eukaryotic "signal recognition particle" (SRP) binds to the leader sequence of proteins destined for processing in the endoplasmic reticulum, just as this signal emerges from the ribosome. The SRP then chauffeurs the ribosome to the cytosolic face of the ER and docks it there so that the growing polypeptide chain is threaded through the ER membrane into the ER lumen. Within the lumen, the leader sequence is removed by signal peptidase. Additional modifications (such as glycosylation) may be introduced before the nascent polypeptide becomes a mature protein and gains its final destination.

Other protein translocation systems, such as those serving in mitochondrial protein import or prokaryotic protein export, employ molecular chaperones to keep the completed polypeptide in a partially unfolded state as it is shepherded through the cytoplasm from the ribosome to the membrane-embedded translocation apparatus. Once there, this apparatus catalyzes the energy-dependent translocation of the protein across the membrane. Typically, signal sequences are "cleavable presequences" clipped from the polypeptide once they have reached the other side of the membrane.

Proteins are in a dynamic state of turnover, with protein degradation serving an important role in determining the half-life of a protein in the cell. Protein degradation may be non-selective, as in lysosomal degradation, or selective, as in the ubiquitin-mediated pathway. The latter system targets proteins for degradation by a large multi-subunit catalytic ATP-dependent protease complex by labelling them with ubiquitin. Ubiquitin is a 76-residue polypeptide that becomes covalently attached to proteins via linking its C-terminal glycine a-carboxyl group to free —NH_2 groups in the protein. Ubiquitinylation of a protein is determined by the nature of the amino acid residue at the protein's N-terminus.

Chapter 33

Metabolic Integration and Organ Specialization

· ·

Chapter Outline

- ❖ Metabolism: Five functional blocks
    - ⅄ Catabolic activities
        - • Foods oxidized to carbon dioxide and water
        - • ATP and NADPH produced
    - ⅄ Anabolic activities
        - • Metabolic intermediates from catabolism converted to variety of molecules
        - • ATP and NADPH consumed
    - ⅄ Macromolecular synthesis
        - • Anabolic products used to synthesize biopolymers
        - • ATP principal source of energy
            - • GTP: Protein synthesis
            - • CTP: Phospholipid synthesis
            - • UTP: Polysaccharide synthesis
    - ⅄ Photochemical activities
        - • Light energy used to produce ATP and NADPH
    - ⅄ Carbon dioxide fixation
        - • ATP and NADPH used to fix carbon dioxide and convert to intermediate
- ❖ Ten key intermediates
    - ⅄ Carbohydrates
        - • Triose-P, tetrose-P, pentose-P, hexose-P
    - ⅄ α-keto acids
        - • Pyruvate, oxaloacetate, α-ketoglutarate
    - ⅄ CoA derivatives
        - • Acetyl-CoA, succinyl-CoA
    - ⅄ PEP
- ❖ ADP/ATP and NAD/NADPH couple catabolism to anabolism
- ❖ Stoichiometries of ATP utilization
    - ⅄ Reaction stoichiometry: Chemical stoichiometry: Reactants and products balanced
    - ⅄ Obligate coupling stoichiometry: Initial substrate of one pathway and final product of second pathway determine stoichiometry
    - ⅄ Evolved coupling stoichiometry: Stoichiometry of ATP coupled to pathway not fixed
- ❖ Metabolic roles of ATP
    - ⅄ Stoichiometry establishes large K_{eq}: Unidirectional process
    - ⅄ ATP (AMP and ADP) allosteric effectors
    - ⅄ Adenylate kinase interconverts ATP, ADP, and AMP
    - ⅄ Energy charge: E.C. varies from 0 to 1
        - • R response to E.C.
            - • Active when E.C. low: Activity decreases as E.C. approaches 1
            - • Enzymes in catabolic pathways show R response
        - • U response
            - • Active when E.C. close to 1: Activity decreases as E.C. decreases

- Enzymes in anabolic pathways show U response
- Phosphorylation potential: Ranges from 200 to 800 M^{-1}
- ❖ Energy balance in cells: AMP-activated protein kinase (AMPK) is cellular sensor
  - Inactive when ATP is high, active when ATP is low, AMP stimulates
  - Serine/threonine kinase
  - Regulated by hormone (e.g., leptin) and muscle activity
  - Activated by diabetes drug metformin
  - Key targets
    - Phosphofructokinase-2 (to stimulate glycolysis)
    - Glycogen synthase, acetyl-CoA carboxylase, HMG-CoA reductase (inhibited)
    - Glycogen: Liver and muscle
- ❖ Human metabolism
  - Fuel stores
    - Glycogen: Liver and muscle
    - Triacylglycerol: Adipose tissue
    - Protein: Muscle
  - Fuel utilization preferences: Glycogen > triacylglycerol > protein
  - Organ metabolism and interplay
    - Brain
      - High respiratory metabolism
      - No fuel reserves
      - Glucose preferred fuel: From diet or from liver via gluconeogenesis
      - β-hydroxybutyrate during starvation: From liver
    - Muscle
      - Fatty acid, glucose, and ketone body metabolism at rest
      - P-creatine and glycogen utilization during intense activity
      - Fatigue caused by decrease in pH, not by depletion of reserves
      - Fasting muscle utilizes amino acids from protein
    - Heart
      - Preferred fuel fatty acids
      - Minimal reserves: Fatty acids, glucose, and ketone bodies must be supplied
    - Adipose tissue
      - Glucose converted to acetyl-CoA and fatty acids
      - Fatty acids also supplied by liver
      - Triacylglycerol production relies on glycerol-3-P from glucose
      - Glucose plays pivotal role
        - Source of glycerol-3-P
        - Fuel for pentose phosphate pathway
    - Liver
      - Buffers blood glucose levels
      - Fatty acid metabolism and ketogenesis
      - Cori cycle
      - Glucose-6-P plays key role
        - Glycogen metabolism
        - Gluconeogenesis/glycolysis
        - Production of NADPH from pentose phosphate
        - Production of acetyl-CoA
- ❖ Regulation of eating
  - Neuroendocrine signals from stomach, small intestines, pancreas, adipose tissue and central nervous system (hypothalamus mainly)
  - Short-term and long-term responses
    - Ghrelin and cholecystokinin are short-term
      - Ghrelin from stomach stimulates appetite when stomach is empty
      - Cholecystokinin from GI track inhibits eating

- Insulin and leptin are long-term
  - Insulin from pancreas stimulates glucose uptake
  - Leptin from adipocytes (released in response to insulin)
- Leptin
  - Blocks release of NPY (see below): Suppresses appetite
- Neurons involved: Two subsets
  - NPY/AgRP-producing neurons release neuropeptide Y: Stimulates eating
    - PYY_{3-36} from small intestine, leptin block NPY release
  - Melanocortin-producing neurons release melanocyte-stimulating hormones: Inhibit eating: AgRP (agouti-related peptide) blocks these
- AMPK
  - Leptin inhibits AMPK via melanocortin-4 receptor
  - Ghrelin and NPY activate AMPK
  - Malonyl-CoA serves as indicator molecule
- Longevity
  - Caloric restriction diet leads to longevity
  - Genetic control of longevity via SIRT1
    - NAD^+-dependent protein deacetylase
    - Inactivates PPARγ (Active PPARγ stimulates genes involved in fat storage
    - Stimulates PGC-1 leading to stimulation of gluconeogenesis
    - Resveratrol: Component of red wines that stimulates SIRT1

Chapter Objectives

Metabolism

So far, we have developed a complicated picture of intermediary metabolism, and it is time to attempt to simplify and unify. There are a small number of intermediates that serve crucial roles in intermediary metabolism. These include sugar phosphates, pyruvate, oxaloacetate, α-ketoglutarate, acetyl-CoA, succinyl-CoA, and PEP. The sugar phosphates are found in glycolysis, gluconeogenesis, the pentose phosphate pathway, and the Calvin cycle. Pyruvate, oxaloacetate, and α-ketoglutarate are keto acids. Pyruvate derives from a number of sources including glycolysis and amino acids and is the port of entry into the citric acid cycle for glucose-derived carbons. Oxaloacetate and α-ketoglutarate are citric acid cycle intermediates and both can be produced from amino acids by deamination. Acetyl-CoA is consumed in the citric acid cycle and is a common denominator between fatty acids, sugars, and amino acid. Succinyl-CoA, a citric cycle intermediate, is the place of entry of propionate from dietary sources and odd-chain fatty acid catabolism, is a product of amino acid catabolism, and is used in heme biosynthesis.

ATP and NADPH serve critical roles in coupling catabolism and anabolism. Catabolism is largely oxidative in nature, leading to reduction of cofactors NAD^+ and FAD. Anabolic pathways are reductive with NADPH usually serving as the immediate source of electrons. This coenzyme is reduced in the pentose phosphate pathway. Additionally, cycles exist to move electrons from NADH to $NADP^+$. Catabolic pathways are exergonic and lead to synthesis of ATP. ATP is then consumed in anabolic, energy-requiring pathways. The coupling of ATP production to a complex metabolic pathway such as aerobic oxidation of glucose to CO_2 and H_2O has a stoichiometry that is not defined by simple chemical considerations. Rather, ATP coupling stoichiometry is an evolved quantity. Nevertheless, under physiological conditions, the complete oxidation of glucose gives high yields of ATP. Furthermore, the process is always far from equilibrium making regulation by kinetic controls possible.

ATP Equivalents

The metabolic unit of energy exchange is the ATP equivalent defined as the amount of energy released upon hydrolysis of ATP to ADP. The ATP equivalent of key metabolic reactions is given below.

ATP hydrolysis, 1.0
PP_i hydrolysis, 1.0
ATP to AMP and 2 P_i, 2.0
NADH oxidation, 3.0 ATP (2.5 in mitochondria)
$FADH_2$ oxidation, 2.0 ATP (1.5 in mitochondria)
NADPH oxidation, 3.5 to 4 ATP

Metabolic Integration

The major organs specialize in metabolism of particular fuels and there is an interplay among the liver, muscles, heart, adipose tissue, and brain to ensure that the energetic demands are met. For example, glucose can be supplied to other tissues by the liver by gluconeogenesis and glycogenolysis; muscle can produce lactic acid during times of intense energy demands; and this lactic acid is sent to the liver for reprocessing into glucose. Energy demands are ultimately met by diet ,and animals have evolved a complex system of hormonal regulation to regulate energy storage and appetite. Brain, stomach, small intestines, pancreas, and adipose tissue all play roles in stimulating or suppressing appetite.

Problems and Solutions

1. (Integrates with Chapters 3, 17, and 21) *The conversion of PEP to pyruvate by pyruvate dehydrogenase (glycolysis) and the reverse reaction to form PEP from pyruvate by pyruvate carboxylase and PEP carboxykinase (gluconeogenesis) represents a so-called substrate cycle. The direction of net conversion is determined by the relative concentrations of allosteric regulators that exert kinetic control over pyruvate kinase, pyruvate carboxylase, and PEP carboxykinase. Recall that the last step in glycolysis is catalyzed by pyruvate kinase:*

$$PEP + ADP \leftrightarrows pyruvate + ATP$$

The standard free energy change is –31.7 kJ/mol.
  a.   Calculate the equilibrium constant for this reaction.
  b.   If [ATP] = [ADP], by what factor must [pyruvate] exceed [PEP] for this reaction to proceed in the reverse direction?
The reversal of this reaction in eukaryotic cells is essential to gluconeogenesis and proceeds in two steps, each requiring an equivalent of nucleoside triphosphate energy:

Pyruvate carboxylase
$$Pyruvate + CO_2 + ATP \rightarrow oxaloacetate + ADP + P_i$$
PEP carboxykinase
$$Oxaloacetate + GTP \rightarrow PEP + CO_2 + GDP$$
$$Net: Pyruvate + ATP + GTP \rightarrow PEP + ADP + GDP + P_i$$

  c.   The ΔG°' for the overall reaction is +0.8 kJ/mol. What is the value of K_{eq}?
  d.   Assuming [ATP] = [ADP], [GTP] = [GDP], and P_i = 1 mM when this reaction reaches equilibrium, what is the ration of [PEP]/[pyruvate]?
  e.   Are both directions in the substrate cycle likely to be strongly favoured under physiological conditions?

Answer: a.   From $\Delta G° = -RT \ln K_{eq}$ we can write:

$$K_{eq} = e^{\frac{-\Delta G°'}{RT}}$$

The value of RT at room temperature is:

$$(8.314 \times 10^{-3})(298) = 2.48$$

$$K_{eq} = e^{\frac{-(-31.7)}{2.48}} = 360\ 000$$

b.   Given [ATP] = [ADP], and K_{eq} is 360 333, the reaction will proceed in reverse when $\Delta G > 0$. ΔG is given by:

$$\Delta G = \Delta G°' + RT \ln \frac{[ATP][pyruvate]}{[ADP][PEP]}$$

$$\text{But } \Delta G°' = -RT \ln K_{eq}$$

$$\text{Thus, } \Delta G = RT \ln \frac{[ATP][pyruvate]}{[ADP][PEP]K_{eq}}$$

$$K_{eq} = 360\ 333$$

For the reaction to go in reverse and $\Delta G > 0$, term in the ln must be >1. Thus:

$$[ATP][pyruvate] > [ADP][PEP]\ 360\ 333$$

When [ATP] = [ADP], [pyruvate] > 360 333[PEP].

c. The following formula is used to determine K_{eq}: $\Delta G^{o\prime} = -RT\ln K_{eq}$. Solving for K_{eq}, we find that

$$K_{eq} = e^{\frac{-\Delta G^{o\prime}}{RT}}$$

Given R = 8.3145 J/mol, T = 298 (i.e., 25°C)

$\Delta G^{o\prime}$ = 0.8 kJ/mol or 800 J/mol

$$K_{eq} = e^{-\frac{800}{8.3145 \times 298}} = 0.724$$

d. When the reaction reaches equilibrium, the ratio of [PEP] to [pyruvate] is:

$$K_{eq} = 0.724 = \frac{[PEP][ADP][GDP][P_i]}{[pyruvate][ATP][GTP]}$$

$$0.724 = \frac{[PEP] \times 1 \times 10^{-3}}{[pyruvate]} \text{ or}$$

$$\frac{[PEP]}{[pyruvate]} = 724$$

For the reaction: PEP + ADP → pyruvate + ATP, from (b) we calculated:

$$\frac{[pyruvate]}{[PEP]} = 360\ 333 \text{ at equilibrium}$$

Ratios of [pyruvate] to [PEP] smaller than this value will react in the direction of pyruvate production until the equilibrium value is reached. Thus,

$$\frac{[pyruvate]}{[PEP]} < 360\ 000 \text{ proceeds spontaneously, or}$$

$$\frac{[PEP]}{[pyruvate]} > \frac{1}{360\ 000} > 0.0000028 \text{ proceeds spontaneuosly}$$

From (d), we found that as long as the ratio of [PEP] to [pyruvate] does not exceed 724, the reaction will proceed as written. Thus, both reactions will be favorable as long as [PEP]/[pyruvate] is between 0.0000028 and 724.

3. Strenuous muscle exertion (as in the 100 metre dash) rapidly depletes ATP levels. How long will 8 mM ATP last if 1 gram of muscle consumes 300 μmol of ATP per minute? (Assume muscle is 70% water). Muscle contains phosphocreatine as a reserve of phosphorylation potential. Assuming [phosphocreatine] = 40 mM, [creatine] = 4 mM, and $\Delta G^{o\prime}$ (phosphocreatine + H_2O ⇌ creatine + P_i) = −43.3 kJ/mol, how low must [ATP] become before it can be replenished by the reaction phosphocreatine + ADP ⇌ ATP + creatine? [Remember, $\Delta G^{o\prime}$ (ATP hydrolysis) = −30.5 kJ/mol.]

Answer: One gram of muscle contains approximately 0.7 g of H_2O, or 0.7 mL. If the [ATP] = 8 mM, 0.7 mL contains

$$0.7 \times 10^{-3} L \times 8 \times 10^{-3} \frac{mol}{L} = 5.60 \times 10^{-6} mol \text{ or } 5.6 \ \mu mol \text{ ATP}$$

If ATP is consumed at the rate of 300 μmol per min, it will last

$$\frac{5.6 \ \mu mol}{300 \ \frac{\mu mol}{min}} = 0.019 \text{ min or } 1.12 \text{ sec}$$

Phosphocreatine and ATP are coupled by the following reaction:

$$\text{phosphocreatine} + ADP \rightarrow ATP + \text{creatine}$$

This is the sum of two reactions:

phosphocreatine + H_2O → creatine + P_i $\Delta G^{\circ\prime} = -43.3$ kJ/mol

and P_i + ADP → ATP + H_2O $\Delta G^{\circ\prime} = 30.5$ kJ/mol

Thus, the overall $\Delta G^{\circ\prime} = -12.8$ kJ/mol. For the reaction to be favourable, ΔG must be less than zero or

$$\Delta G = \Delta G^{\circ\prime} + RT \ln \frac{[\text{creatine}][\text{ATP}]}{[\text{phosphocreatine}][\text{ADP}]} < 0 \text{ or}$$

$$\Delta G^{\circ\prime} + RT \ln \frac{[\text{creatine}][\text{ATP}]}{[\text{phosphocreatine}][\text{ADP}]} < 0$$

$$RT \ln \frac{[\text{creatine}][\text{ATP}]}{[\text{phosphocreatine}][\text{ADP}]} < \Delta G^{\circ\prime}$$

$$\frac{[\text{ATP}]}{[\text{ADP}]} < \frac{[\text{phosphocreatine}]}{[\text{creatine}]} \times e^{\frac{-\Delta G^{\circ\prime}}{RT}}$$

$$\frac{[\text{ATP}]}{[\text{ADP}]} < \frac{40\ mM}{4\ mM} \times e^{\frac{-(-12.8)}{2.48}}$$

$$\frac{[\text{ATP}]}{[\text{ADP}]} < 1750$$

The reaction is favourable and ADP is phosphorylated at the expense of phosphocreatine when [ATP]< 1750 [ADP] and [Cr-P] = 40 mM and [Cr] = 4 mM.

5. *(Integrates with Chapter 3) Assume the total intracellular pool of adenylates (ATP + ADP + AMP) = 8 mM, 90% of which is ATP. What are [ADP] and [AMP] if the adenylate kinase reaction is at equilibrium? Suppose [ATP] drops suddenly by 10%. What are the concentrations now for ADP and AMP, assuming adenylate kinase reaction is at equilibrium? By what factor has the AMP concentration changed?*

Answer: Adenylate kinase catalyzes the following reaction: ATP + AMP → ADP + ADP

The equilibrium constant for the reaction $K_{eq} = 1.2$ (given in Figure 33.2).

$$K_{eq} = \frac{[\text{ADP}]^2}{[\text{ATP}][\text{AMP}]}$$

Let $T = [\text{ATP}] + [\text{ADP}] + [\text{AMP}]$, the total concentration of adenylates

If $[\text{ATP}] = 90\% \times T = 0.9 \times 8$ mM = 7.2 mM

$[\text{ADP}] + [\text{AMP}] = 8$ mM $- 7.2$ mM = 0.8 mM or

$[\text{AMP}] = 0.8$ mM $- [\text{ADP}]$

Substituting this expression and the value of 7.2 mM for [ATP] into the equilibrium equation, we find:

$$K_{eq} = \frac{[\text{ADP}]^2}{7.2 \text{ mM} \times (0.8 \text{ mM} - [\text{ADP}])} \text{ or}$$

$$[\text{ATP}]^2 + 7.2 \text{ mM} \times K_{eq} \times [\text{ADP}] - 7.2 \text{ mM} \times 0.8 \text{ mM} \times K_{eq} = 0$$

By substituting $K_{eq} = 1.2$, we find: $[\text{ATP}]^2 + 8.64 \times 10^{-3} \times [\text{ADP}] - 6.91 \times 10^{-6} = 0$
This is a quadratic equation whose solution is [ADP] = 7.2 mM

If the [ATP] suddenly falls by 10%, we have:

$$[ATP] = 7.2 \text{ mM} - 10\% \times 7.2 \text{ mM} = 6.48 \text{ mM}$$

$$[ADP] + [AMP] = 8 \text{ mM} - 6.48 \text{ mM} = 1.52 \text{ mM or}$$

$$[AMP] = 1.52 \text{ mM} - [ADP]$$

Substituting this expession and the value of 6.48 mM for [ATP]

into the equilibrium equation, we find:

$$K_{eq} = \frac{[ADP]^2}{6.48 \text{ mM} \times (1.52 \text{ mM} - [ADP])} \text{ or}$$

$$[ADP]^2 + 6.48 \text{ mM} \times K_{eq} \times [ADP] - 6.48 \text{ mM} \times 1.52 \text{ mM} \times K_{eq} = 0$$

By substituting $K_{eq} = 1.2$, we find:

$$[ADP]^2 + 7.78 \times 10^{-3} \times [ADP] - 1.18 \times 10^{-5} = 0$$

A quadratic equation whose solution is [ADP] = 1.30 mM

$$[AMP] = 1.52 \text{ mM} - [ADP] = 0.22 \text{ mM}, [ATP] = 6.48 \text{ mM}$$

This relatively modest change in [ATP], causes almost a doubling of [ADP] levels and a 3.5-fold increase in [AMP].

7. (Integrates with Chapters 9 and 22) Leptin not only induces synthesis of fatty acid oxidation enzymes and uncoupling protein 2 in adipocytes, but it also causes inhibition of acetyl-CoA carboxylase, resulting in a decline in fatty acid biosynthesis. This effect on acetyl-CoA carboxylase, as an additional consequence, enhances fatty acid oxidation. Explain how leptin-induced inhibition of acetyl-CoA carboxylase might promote fatty acid oxidation.

Answer: Acetyl-CoA carboxylase catalyzes the production of malonyl-CoA and inhibition of this enzyme will immediately inhibit fatty acid biosynthesis because malonyl-CoA is a substrate for fatty acid synthase. Malonyl has another regulatory role in fatty acid metabolism: it inhibits carnitine acyltransferase the enzyme responsible for fatty acid uptake by the mitochondria. As malonyl-CoA levels fall, carnitine acyltransferase will cause an increased uptake of fatty acids into the mitochondria where they are metabolized by β-oxidation.

9. (Integrates with Chapter 22) Assume each NADH is worth 3 ATP, each FADH₂ is worth 2 ATP, and each NADPH is worth 4 ATP. How many ATP equivalents are produced when 1 molecule of palmitoyl-CoA is oxidized to 8 molecules of acetyl-CoA by the fatty acid β-oxidation pathway? How many ATP equivalents are consumed when 8 molecules of acetyl-CoA are transformed into 1 molecule of palmitoyl-CoA by the fatty acid biosynthetic pathway? Can both of these metabolic sequences be metabolically favourable at the same time if ΔG for ATP synthesis is +50 kJ/mol?

Answer: To convert palmitoyl-CoA to 8 acetyl-CoAs we must run β-oxidation 7 times. This produces 7 NADH and 7 FADH₂, which accounts for ($7 \times 3 = 21 + 7 \times 2 = 14$) 35 ATP.

To synthesize palmitoyl-CoA starting with 8 acetyl-CoAs, we would have to convert 7 acetyl-CoA to malonyl-CoA, and then run 7 cycles of fatty acid biosynthesize, with each cycle consuming 2 NADPH. Production of 7 malonyl-CoA would consume 7 ATP. Consumption of 14 NADPH would account for 56 ATP. The total ATP cost for production is 63 ATP.

For the reactions to be favourable at the same time, each of their ΔGs would have to be negative. Since palmitoyl-CoA to 8 acetyl-CoA supports production if 35 ATP this "costs" ($35 \times 50 =$) 1750 kJ/mol. Provided ΔG for the reaction is more negative than this value, the reaction will be favourable. For the reaction going from acetyl-CoA to palmitoyl-CoA, it consumes 63 ATP at a cost of ($63 \times 50 =$) 3150 kJ/mol. (That is, hydrolysis of 63 ATP releases –3150 kJ/mol.)

11. (Integrates with Chapter 21) In type 2 diabetes, glucose production in the liver is not appropriately regulated, so glucose is over produced. One strategy to treat this disease focuses on the development of drugs targeted against regulated steps in glycogenolysis and gluconeogenesis, the pathways by which liver produces glucose for release into the blood. Which enzymes would you select for as potential targets for such drugs?

Answer: Type 2 diabetes is characterized by hyperglycemia. Since the liver is a source of blood glucose via gluconeogenesis or glycogenolysis, lowering hepatic glucose release might address the problem. It would make sense to stop glycogen breakdown and stimulate glycogen synthesis by targeting glycogen phosphorylase to inhibit it or glycogen synthase to stimulate it. Another target you could consider is glycogen phosphorylase kinase, the enzyme that regulates both glycogen phosphorylase and glycogen synthetase. For glucose to exit liver cells and enter the bloodstream, glucose-6-phosphatase must be active. This enzyme might also be a good target.

Finally, it might be useful to regulate glycolysis/gluconeogenesis at the interconversion between fructose-6-phosphate and fructose-1,6-bisphosphate. This interconversion is accomplished by phosphofructokinase I and fructose-1,6-bisphosphatase. Finally, fructose-2,6-bisphosphate plays a role in regulation of glycolysis and gluconeogenesis, so it might be useful to target phosphofructokinase II, a bifunctional enzyme that also has fructose-2,6-bisphosphatase activity.

13. *The existence of leptin was revealed when the ob/ob genetically obese strain of mice was discovered. These mice have a defect leptin gene. Predict the effects of daily leptin injections on ob/ob mice on food intake, fatty acid oxidation, and body weight. Similar clinical trials have been conducted on humans, with limited success. Suggest a reason why this therapy might not be a miracle cure for overweight individuals.*

Answer: Leptin, a 146-amino acid peptide is produced by adipocytes in response to insulin. High leptin levels in blood lead to appetite suppression. Fat metabolism is also regulated by leptin. Triacylglycerol production is inhibited and fat metabolism increased. Further, leptin induces synthesis of uncoupling protein 2, which leads to energy loss as heat. Uncoupling protein 2, in effect, short-circuits the proton gradient in the mitochondria. The energy of the gradient is dissipated as heat and thus not used for ATP production. Leptin also blocks NPY release by the hypothalamus. Since NYP is orexigenic, downregulation of it by leptin leads to loss of appetite. Given all this, we might expect the *ob/ob* mice to have lower body weight as a consequence of increase fat metabolism in adipocytes, inefficiency of electron transport in adipocytes, and decrease in food intake.

In obese individuals, leptin may not be the problem. Since leptin is produced by adipocytes, obese individuals may already have high blood levels of leptin, and so increasing levels by injection may not have big effects.

15. *The Human Biochemistry box The Metabolic Effects of Alcohol Consumption, points out that ethanol is metabolized to acetate in the liver by alcohol dehydrogenase and aldehyde dehydrogenase:*

$$CH_3CH_2OH + NAD^+ \leftrightarrows CH_3CHO + NADH + H^+$$
$$CH_3CHO + NAD^+ \leftrightarrows CH_3COO^- + NADH + H^+$$

These reactions alter the NAD$^+$/NADH ratio in liver cells. From your knowledge of glycolysis, gluconeogenesis, and fatty acid oxidation, what might be the effect of an altered NAD$^+$/NADH ratio on these pathways? What is the basis of this effect?

Answer: With these two reactions going rapidly, NAD$^+$ supplies might be expected to be limiting. This would turn down glycolysis at glyceraldehydes-3-phosphate dehydrogenase. Fatty acid oxidation would also suffer because NAD$^+$ is required in one step of β-oxidation. The citric acid cycle would also be affected because NADH is a negative regulator of several steps. Lastly, we might expect in increase in gluconeogenesis because the glyceraldehydes-3-phosphate step would be stimulated by excess NADH to run in the direction of gluconeogenesis.

17. a. *Some scientists support the "malonyl-CoA hypothesis," which suggests that malonyl-CoA is a key indicator of nutrient availability and the brain uses its abundance to assess whole-body energy homeostasis. Others have pointed out that malonyl-CoA is a significant inhibitor of carnitine acyltransferase-1 (see Figure 9.16). Thus, malonyl-CoA may be influencing the levels of another metabolite whose concentration is more important as a signal of energy status. What metabolite might that be?*
b. *Another test of the malonyl-CoA hypothesis was conducted through the creation of a transgenic strain of mice that lacked functional hypothalamic fatty acid synthase (see Chapter 9). Predict the effect of this genetic modification on cellular malonyl-CoA levels in the hypothalamus, the eating behaviour of these transgenic mice, their body fat content, and their physical activity levels. Defend your predictions.*

Answer: Malonyl-CoA derives from acetyl-CoA by carboxylation and it is the immediate source of 2-carbon acetyl units for fatty acid biosynthesis. High levels of malonyl-CoA would likely be an indicator of abundant metabolites that are converted to acetyl-CoA (like sugars or amino acids). Additionally, high malonyl-CoA levels would occur when fatty acids are abundant and there is little need for synthesis of fatty acids. In this case, fatty acids are activated by addition of coenzyme A. Thus, malonyl-CoA levels would also be expected to reflect fatty acyl-CoA levels.

b. Mice missing fatty acid synthase could not consume malonyl-CoA leading to elevated levels of this metabolic intermediate. This would be expected to lead to a decrease in eating behaviour and an increase in weight loss. In studies on mice using inhibitors of fatty acid synthase, food intake was suppressed and skeletal muscles increased oxidation of fatty acids leading to weight loss. (See Lane, M.D., et al., 2008, Regulation of food intake and energy expenditure by hypothalamic malonyl-CoA. *International Journal of Obesity* 32 (suppl.4) S49–S54.) All of these responses were reversed when a viral vector expressing malonyl-CoA decarboxylase was introduced into the hypothalamus (stereotactically), indicating that malonyl-CoA levels were driving the responses.

Questions for Self-Study

1. Describe the interplay between β-oxidation, a catabolic pathway, and fatty acid biosynthesis, an anabolic pathway. How are the two connected? Does degradation of a fatty acid provide sufficient resources to support resynthesis of a fatty acid of the same length?

2. What two important compounds couple anabolism and catabolism?

3. Metabolism in a typical aerobic heterotropic cell (a chemoheterotroph) can be described as an interaction of three functional blocks: catabolism, anabolism, and macromolecular synthesis and growth. How is this picture altered for a chemoautotroph? A photoheterotroph? A photoautotroph?

4. The balanced equation for oxidation of glucose via glycolysis, the citric acid cycle, and electron transport is $C_6H_{12}O_6 + 6\ O_2 + 38\ ADP + 38\ P_i \rightarrow 6\ CO_2 + 38\ ATP + 44\ H_2O$. Of the ATPs produced, how many derive from simple chemical stoichiometry and how many from evolved coupling stoichiometry?

5. Describe the reaction catalyzed by adenylate kinase. What important allosteric regulator is produced by this reaction?

6. Table 33.1 is reproduced below with the last three columns randomly ordered. Rearrange the entries in these columns to correct Table 33.1.

Organ	Energy Reservoir	Preferred Substrate	Energy Source Exported
Brain	Glycogen, triacylglycerol	Fatty acids	Fatty acids, glycerol
Skeletal muscle (resting)	Triacylglycerol	Glucose(ketone bodies during starvation)	Fatty acids, glucose, ketone bodies
Skeletal muscle (prolonged exercise)	Glycogen	Fatty acids	None
Heart muscle	None	Glucose	Lactate
Adipose tissue	Glycogen	Amino acids, glucose, fatty acids	None
Liver	None	Fatty acids	None

Answers

1. In β-oxidation, fatty acids are converted into acetyl-CoA units. During the process, coenzymes are reduced. Fatty acid biosynthesis involves joining of acetyl units and oxidation of reduced coenzymes. Per acetyl unit, the number of reduced coenzymes produced in β-oxidation balances the number of reduced coenzymes consumed during fatty acid synthesis. However, fatty acid synthesis is driven by hydrolysis of high-energy phosphate bonds, whereas β-oxidation, once primed, is thermodynamically spontaneous. To support anabolism of fatty acids from a catabolic series, some of the acetyl units of the catabolic series would have to be consumed in the citric acid cycle to provide energy for fatty acid biosynthesis.

2. ATP and NADPH.

3. For a photoautotroph, an additional block is added in which light energy is converted to ATP and reducing equivalents which are used, in turn, to fix carbon dioxide. A photoheterotroph can also harvest light but cannot fix carbon dioxide. Thus, its block lacks the ability to produce reducing equivalents using light energy and to fix carbon dioxide. The chemoautotroph can fix carbon dioxide with reducing equivalents derived from inorganic compounds.

4. The conversion of glucose to 2 pyruvates produce 2 ATP. Two additional ATP are generated by substrate-level phosphorylation in the citric acid cycle in which 2 pyruvates are metabolized to carbon dioxide and water. Thus, the simple chemical reaction stoichiometry is 4 ATP.

5. The reaction catalyzed by adenylate kinase is ATP + AMP → 2 ADP. In the reverse reaction, AMP, an important allosteric regulator, is produced from ADP.

6.   Table 23.1

Organ	Energy Reservoir	Preferred Substrate	Energy Source Exported
Brain	None	Glucose(ketone bodies during starvation)	None
Skeletal muscle (resting)	Glycogen	Fatty acids	None
Skeletal muscle (prolonged exercise)	None	Glucose	Lactate
Heart muscle	Glycogen	Fatty acids	None
Adipose tissue	Triacylglycerol	Fatty acids	Fatty acids, glycerol
Liver	Glycogen, triacylglycerol	Amino acids, glucose, fatty acids	Fatty acids, glucose, ketone bodies

Additional Problems

1. A plot of the rate of running versus distance for recent world records of several races is shown below. It appears that the data can be divided into three linear regions. For each region, describe the source of energy being utilized by muscle.

2. In brown fat, the protein thermogenin functions in a substrate cycle. Describe this cycle and state its purpose.

3. The energy of ATP hydrolysis is a highly exergonic process with a large negative free energy change. We have discussed in this chapter how coupling of ATP hydrolysis is used to drive pathways. Give an example of a reaction driven by ATP hydrolysis and describe how ATP hydrolysis is coupled to the reaction.

4. Explain why NADPH and NADH have different energy equivalents.

5. Why is there a difference in energy between cytosolic NADH and mitochondrial NADH?

6. Carl and Gerti Cori were the first to describe the metabolic interplay between muscle and liver involving lactic acid formation in muscle and glucose formation in liver. This metabolic couple is known as the Cori cycle. Describe it.

Abbreviated Answers

1. The first two points on the graph represent the winning performances for the 100- and 200-metre dash. These races are run almost completely on high-energy phosphate stores of ATP and phosphocreatine, which limit the muscle to about 20 seconds of intense activity. The group of races constituting the line of high slope is using a combination of aerobic and anaerobic respiration. At the end of these races, high-energy phosphate stores are exhausted, lactic acid levels have risen, and aerobic respiration is functioning maximally. The long-distance races rely completely on aerobic respiration. (It is of interest to note that the 2000-metre race, a gruelling contest, is at the break-point between the long-distance races and the anaerobic/aerobic-dependent races.)

2 Thermogenin functions as a proton channel in the inner mitochondrial membrane. The substrate cycle involves protons as substrates. Protons are pumped out of the mitochondria by electron transport but are allowed back in via thermogenin. Thus, protons move from one side of the membrane to the other. The purpose is to generate heat.

3. Any one of the biotin containing enzymes is a good example. Biotin is involved in metabolism of 1-carbon units at the oxidation level of a carboxylate. The reaction mechanism involves formation of a phosphorylated bicarbonate intermediate by nucleophilic attack of bicarbonate on the γ-phosphate of ATP, releasing ADP. This activated carboxylate is then transferred to enzyme-bound biotin, and from

there to substrate to produce the carboxylated product. Carboxylation of biotin thus depends on ATP hydrolysis.

4. The oxidized and reduced forms of these dinucleotides are maintained by the cell at very different levels. [NADPH] is used as a primary source of electrons for metabolic pathways and cells maintain [NADPH] > [NADP$^+$]. The situation for [NADH] is just the opposite.

5. The ratio [NADH] to [NAD$^+$] is likely to be different in the cytosol and the mitochondria. In addition, in order to use oxidation of NADH to NAD$^+$ to drive synthesis of ATP, cytosolic NADH will have to donate electrons to the electron transport chain against the high [NADH] gradient in mitochondria.

6. In the Cori cycle, muscle produces lactic acid as a consequence of intense activity. Lactic acid is sent via the blood to the liver where it is used in gluconeogenesis to produce glucose. Liver cells are capable of releasing glucose back to the blood because they have glucose-6-phosphatase.

Summary

The metabolism of a typical heterotrophic cell can be represented as three interconnected functional blocks composing the metabolic pathways of 1) catabolism, 2) anabolism, and 3) macromolecular synthesis and growth. An energy cycle exists whose agents are ATP and NADPH. Energy and reducing power is delivered from catabolism to anabolism in the form of ATP and NADPH, and ATP and NADPH are regenerated from ADP and NADP$^+$ via catabolic reactions. Phototrophic cells contain a fourth metabolic system consisting of the photochemical apparatus for transforming light into chemical energy. In autotrophic cells, a fifth system occurs, the carbon dioxide fixation pathway for carbohydrate synthesis.

Three levels of stoichiometry can be recognized in metabolism: 1) simple reaction stoichiometry, 2) obligate coupling stoichiometry, and 3) evolved coupling stoichiometry, particularly as represented in ATP coupling. The net yield of 38 ATP/glucose in cellular respiration is a biological adaptation, not the consequence of inviolable chemical laws. At 38 ATP/glucose, the K_{eq} for cellular respiration is 10^{170}. The ATP coupling coefficient is defined as the number of ATP phosphoric anhydride bonds formed or broken in a given metabolic sequence. The ATP equivalent is the metabolic unit of energy exchange. All substrates, metabolites, and coenzymes can be assigned an ATP value reflecting the net cost of their metabolic conversion in ATP equivalents. NADH has an ATP value of 3; FADH$_2$ of 2; and NADPH of 4. Considering the thermodynamics of a generally defined conversion, A→B, the nature and magnitude of the ATP equivalent can be illustrated. Coupling the A→B conversion to ATP hydrolysis raises the equilibrium ratio, [B]$_{eq}$/[A]$_{eq}$, by 1.4×10^8-fold. The energetics of ATP is crucial to the solvent capacity of the cell: the thermodynamic favorability of phosphoryl transfer by ATP makes it possible for the cell to carry out reactions with great efficiency, even though [reactants] are low.

If the ATP coupling coefficient for a particular metabolic sequence in one direction differs by 1 or more from the ATP coupling coefficient for the counterpart sequence running in the opposite direction, a substrate cycle is possible. In the absence of regulation, such substrate cycles could result in the net hydrolysis of ATP and wasteful dissipation of cellular energy. Phosphofructokinase (PFK) and fructose bisphosphatase (FBPase) constitute an example of a substrate cycle; both reactions are thermodynamically favourable under physiological conditions. It turns out that ATP coupling coefficients for opposing sequences always differ, and this difference allows both sequences to be thermodynamically favourable.

The concept of unidirectionality reveals an important feature of metabolic relationships: nearly all metabolic pathways are unidirectional and fulfill only one purpose, either synthesis or degradation. For this to be possible, both pathways in pairs of opposing sequences must be thermodynamically favourable at essentially the same time and under the same conditions. The ATP coupling coefficient for each metabolic sequence has evolved so that the overall equilibrium for the conversion is highly favourable. This function of ATP in metabolism can be represented as the stoichiometric role of ATP. The most vivid illustration of ATP and unidirectionality is given by the grandest pair of opposing metabolic sequences in the biosphere—cellular respiration and photosynthetic CO$_2$ fixation. Cellular respiration has a coupling coefficient of +38 ATP and proceeds with a K_{eq} of 10^{170}; carbon dioxide fixation has a coupling coefficient of −66 ATP and a K_{eq} of 10^{60}.

ATP also acts as an important allosteric effector in the kinetic regulation of metabolism, thereby serving a second distinctive role in metabolism. Energy charge is a concept that provides a measure of how fully charged the adenylate system is with high-energy phosphoryl groups. Enzymes can be classified as R or U in terms of their response to energy charge. R-type enzymes are members of ATP-regenerating metabolic pathways, while U enzymes are characteristically in biosynthetic, or ATP-utilizing sequences. Thus, R and U pathways are diametrically opposite with regard to ATP involvement. The reciprocal relationship between R and U systems means that energy charge reaches a point of metabolic steady-state at an E.C. value of 0.85–0.88. Phosphorylation potential is a better index of the cell's momentary capacity to drive phosphorylation reactions.

In multicellular organisms, organ systems have arisen to carry out specific physiological functions. Essentially all cells in these organisms have the same set of enzymes in the central pathways of intermediary metabolism, but the various organs do differ significantly in the metabolic fuels—glucose, glycogen, fatty acids, amino acids—that they prefer to use for energy production. Brain has a very high respiratory metabolism, essentially no fuel reserves, and is dependent on a supply of blood glucose as its principal fuel. Muscle is intermittently active as muscle contraction and relaxation takes place on demand. ATP is necessary to drive contraction in response to a increased $[Ca^{2+}]$ pulse as the metabolic signal. The Ca^{2+}-ATPase operating during muscle relaxation uses almost as much ATP as the acto-myosin contractile system. Muscle is a major storage site of glycogen. During strenuous exercise, the rate of glycolysis in muscle may increase 2000-fold. Muscle fatigue is the result of a drop in cytosolic pH due to the accumulation of H^+ released during glycolysis. Heart, a rhythmically active muscle system, has minimal reserves of fuel such as glycogen or triacylglycerols, and prefers free fatty acids as fuel. Adipose tissue is a metabolically active, amorphous tissue widely distributed throughout the body. A 70 kg person has enough triacylglycerols stored in adipose tissue to fuel 3 months' worth of modest activity. Glucose is the signal for release of fatty acids from adipocytes to the blood: when glucose levels are sufficient, adipocytes can form glycerol 3-phosphate allowing triacylglycerol synthesis from fatty acids generated by triacylglycerol turnover. Brown fat is a form of adipose tissue containing lots of mitochondria. In brown fat, oxidative phosphorylation is uncoupled by thermogenin and the energy of fatty acid oxidation is released as heat. The liver is a major metabolic processing organ. It serves an essential role in buffering [blood glucose]. It is also a centre for fatty acid turnover, ketone body formation, and conversion of amino acids into other metabolic fuels.

Glossary

• •

AAA+ ATPase family   A group of proteins with ATPase activity associated with a variety of cellular activities.

ABC transporters   Membrane transport proteins that move xenobiotics across biological membranes. Often problematic in cancer chemotherapy because they expel therapeutic drugs.

abzymes   Catalytic antibodies.

accessory pigments   Visible light-absorbing pigments in plants and photosynthetic bacteria that, along with chlorophylls, absorb sunlight.

acetylcholinesterase   An enzyme in the synaptic cleft that hydrolyzes acetylcholine, a neurotransmitter.

acetylcholine transport protein   A membrane protein used to restock synaptic vesicles with acetylcholine. Uses a proton gradient formed by ATP-driven proton pump to concentrate acetylcholine.

active site   The region of the enzyme that binds the substrate and catalytically transforms it.

active transport   Movement of molecules across a membrane that uses an energy source, typically hydrolysis of ATP, to produce a concentration gradient of the molecules across the membrane.

acyl carrier protein   A protein that binds activated intermediates of fatty acid synthesis through a thioester linkage.

acyl-CoA dehydrogenases   Enzymes involved in catabolism of fatty acids by β-oxidation including very long-chain (VLCAD), long-chain (LCAD), medium-chain (MDAC), and short-chain acyl-CoA dehydrogenases (SCAD)

ADAR   Adenosine deaminases that act on RNA in RNA editing to convert A to I.

adipocytes (adipose cells)   Animal cells where fats (triacylglycerols) are stored.

aerobes   Organisms that use oxygen as an electron acceptor in energy-producing pathways.

agarose and agaropectin   Agarose is a chain of alternating D-galactose and 3,6-anhydro-L-galactose with side chains of 6-methyl-galactose. Agaropectin is similar to agarose but with sulfate ester side chains and D-glucuronic acid. Agarose is the neutral component of agar, whereas agaropectin is the negatively charged component.

agouti-related peptide   Peptide hormone that blocks activity of melanocortin-producing neurons. Melanocortin blocks eating behaviour.

alcaptonuria   A genetic disease in which homogentisate collects in the urine because of a deficiency in homogentisate dioxygenase.

aldaric acid   A sugar acid with two carboxylic acid groups often at C-1 and C-6 (for hexoses).

aldonic acid   A sugar acid formed from by oxidation of the aldehyde carbon of an aldose sugar to a carboxyl group.

aldose   A monosaccharide containing an aldehyde group.

alginates   Polysaccharides that bind metal ions, particularly calcium.

alleles   Alternative forms of a gene at a particular location or locus.

allosteric regulation   The activation or inhibition of enzymatic activity through non-covalent interaction of the enzyme with small molecules other than the substrate.

α-amanitin   A mushroom poison that differentially inhibits eukaryotic RNA polymerases. RNA polymerase I is resistant, II is highly sensitive, and III intermediate.

α-helix   A common secondary structure in proteins, which is almost always right handed.

amino acids   Building blocks of proteins with a tetrahedral α-carbon covalently linked to an amino group and a carboxyl group.

aminoacyl-tRNA synthetases   Enzymes that attach amino acids to appropriate tRNAs in aminoacyl linkage.

aminotransferases   Pyridoxal phosphate containing enzymes that exchange nitrogen between amino acids and α-keto acids.

ammonotelic organisms   Aquatic animals that excrete excess nitrogen as ammonia.

amphibolic pathway   A metabolic pathway that can be both catabolic and anabolic.

amphipathic   Possessing both polar and non-polar groups.

amphiphilic   Having both strongly polar and strongly non-polar groups on a single molecule. Also known as *amphipathic*.

anabolism   Metabolism in which complex biomolecules, such as carbohydrates, lipids, and proteins, are generated from simpler precursors.

anaerobes   Organisms that can subsist without O_2.

anaplerotic reaction   A reaction that replenishes metabolites that are removed from a central metabolic pathway like the citric acid cycle.

androgens   Male sex hormone steroids.

annexins   Family of calcium-binding proteins that interact with membranes and phospholipids in a calcium-dependent manner.

antibody   An immune system protein capable of recognizing and binding a "foreign substance" known as an antigen.

anticodon The three-nucleotide unit in tRNA that recognizes and base pairs with a particular mRNA codon.

antigen A molecule specifically recognized and bound by an antibody.

antiparallel α-helix proteins Proteins whose structures are heavily dominated by α-helices.

antiparallel β-sheet A secondary protein conformation in which the adjacent strands of a β-strand run in opposite directions.

apoenzyme The protein portion of an enzyme devoid of its cofactors or prosthetic groups.

apoptosis Programmed cell death.

archaea Prokaryotes that are capable of living in extreme conditions like temperature, pH, or osmotic pressure.

aspartic proteases A family of proteolytic enzymes that are active at acidic pH and possess two aspartic acid residues at the active (catalytic) site.

ATP equivalent A metabolic unit of exchange; the conversion of ATP to ADP.

autogenous regulation of a gene (autoregulation of a gene) The regulation of expression of a gene by the product of the gene.

autophosphorylation The ability of a kinase to phosphorylate residues in its own amino acid sequence.

autotroph An organism that uses carbon dioxide as its sole source of carbon.

• •

Baa helix Basic amphiphilic alpha helix to which calmodulin binds.

bacteriophage Viruses that infect bacteria.

ballistic method A technique of transformation in which microprojectiles coated with DNA are fired into recipient cells by a gas-powered gun.

base pair Two nucleotides in nucleic acid chains that are paired because of hydrogen bonding between their bases, such as A with T and C with G.

β-bulge A structure in which one residue of a β-strand is not H-bonded but residues on either side of it are H-bonded to contiguous residues in the adjacent strand.

β-oxidation The oxidative degradation of a fatty acid into acetyl-CoA by repeated oxidations and cleavages at the β-carbon of a fatty acid.

β-pleated sheet A common secondary structure in proteins in which the polypeptide chain is arranged in an extended, pleated fashion. Several such strands side-by-side are typically joined by H-bonds to form a sheet. Adjacent strands may be either parallel or antiparallel.

β-turn   A simple structure observed in many proteins in which the peptide chain forms a tight loop with the carbonyl oxygen of one residue hydrogen-bonded with the amide proton of the residue three positions down the chain.

bifunctional enzyme (tandem enzyme)   A protein possessing two distinct enzymatic functions.

bile acids   Polar carboxylic acid derivatives of cholesterol that are important in the digestion of food, especially the solubilization of ingested fats.

binuclear centre   A closely associated pair of metal ions.

BLOSUM   A scoring matrix used in protein sequence comparisons to quantitate the degree of sequence similarity between two proteins.

Bohr effect   When the oxygen affinity of hemoglobin in red blood cells decreases due to a lowering of the pH.

branch migration   The procession of base-pairing between an invading DNA strand and one strand of a DNA duplex during recombination.

branching and debranching enzymes   Enzymes involved in metabolism of glucose polymers by adding or removing branches.

bromodomains   Protein domains that bind acetylated lysine.

brown fat   A specialized type of adipose tissue found in newborns and animals involved in heat production.

buffer   A solution component that tends to resist changes in pH as acid or base is added. Typically, a buffer is composed of a weak acid and its conjugate base.

bZIP   A-DNA binding motif characterized by an α-helical structure with basic amino acids on one end and a leucine zipper at the other. Leucine zipper have leucines spaced every seven residues along the helix.

• •

Calmodulin   Calcium-binding protein with EF hand calcium-binding motif that imparts calcium regulation to a number of proteins.

caloric homeostasis   The constant availability of fuels in the blood.

Calvin–Benson cycle (Calvin cycle)   The set of reactions that transform 3-phospho-glycerate into hexose during photosynthesis.

CAP   Catabolite activator protein—a positive regulator of transcription that binds cAMP and sometimes called CRP (cAMP receptor protein). The term "cap" also refers to modification of the 5′-end of mRNAs in eukaryotes by 7-methylG.

carbamoyl-phosphate synthetase   Enzymatic activity that produces carbamoyl phosphate from ammonia and bicarbonate using ATP hydrolysis.

carbohydrate   A class of molecules with molecular formula $(CH_2O)_n$, where n is three or more.

carbon dioxide fixation   The synthesis of carbohydrates from carbon dioxide and water.

cardiac glycosides   Potent inhibitors of the Na^+–K^+ pump. Inhibition of the pump results in increases in sodium that is exchanged for calcium, which increases the strength of contraction of cardiac muscle.

carnitine acyltransferase   Enzyme that moves an acyl group from acyl-CoA to carnitine. Acyl carnitine is carried across the inner mitochondrial membrane.

caspases   Proteases that are activated by apoptosome during apoptosis.

catabolism   Energy-yielding metabolism involving the oxidative degradation of complex nutrient molecules such as carbohydrates, lipids, and proteins.

catalytic power   The ability of enzymes to accelerate reaction rates.

CCT   The eukaryotic analog of GroEL, a chaperonin that functions in protein folding.

cDNA library   A DNA library constructed by synthesizing cDNA from purified cellular mRNA.

cellulose   A structural polysaccharide and linear homopolymer of D-glucose units linked by $\beta(1 \rightarrow 4)$ glycosidic bonds.

cerebroside   A sphingolipid containing one sugar residue as the head group.

chaperones   Proteins or protein complexes that aid in protein folding by preventing inappropriate hydrophobic interactions.

chemical mutagens   Agents that chemically modify bases so that their base-pairing characteristics are altered.

chemotrophic organism   An organism that obtains energy by metabolizing organic compounds.

chiral compound   A compound with one or more atoms that have four different groups attached. Variations in the arrangement of groups form stereoisomers.

chitin   A structural polysaccharide with repeating units of N-acetyl-D-glucosamine in $\beta(1 \rightarrow 4)$ linkage.

chloroplasts   Chlorophyll-containing photosynthetic organelles that harvest light and transform it into metabolically useful chemical forms. Found in plants and algae.

cholecystokinin   A peptide hormone released by the GI tract during eating. Signals satiety and curtails eating.

chromatin   A complex of DNA and protein in a eukaryotic cell nucleus.

chromatography   Experimental techniques for the separation of mixtures. Methods include ion exchange chromatography, high-performance liquid chromatography, and gas chromatography.

chromodomains   Protein domains that bind methylated lysine.

chromosome A single, large DNA molecule and its associated proteins, containing many genes.

chromosome walking A technique for ordering DNA fragments in a genomic library. It involves hybridization, restriction mapping, and isolation of overlapping DNA molecules.

clamp loader A protein complex that loads a β-subunit dimer around DNA. The β-subunit dimer is a protein ring that tethers a polymerase to DNA.

cloning The amplification of identical DNA molecules or cells from a single parental DNA molecule or cell.

cloning vector A plasmid used to carry a segment of a foreign DNA and to introduce it into a cell where it can be replicated.

codon A sequence of three adjacent nucleotides in mRNA that codes for a specific amino acid.

coenzyme An organic molecule that helps an enzyme to carry out its catalytic function.

coenzyme Q Ubiquinone—a compound that participates in one- and two-electron transfer reactions. A mobile lipid-soluble carrier of electrons.

cofactor An inorganic ion or organic molecule required by an enzyme for catalytic activity.

collagen A fibrous protein that is a principal constituent of connective tissue in animals.

colligative properties Properties of solutions that depend only on the concentration of solute species and not on their nature.

competitive inhibitor A reversible inhibitor of an enzyme that competes with the substrate for binding at the active site of the enzyme.

complementarity-determining region (CDR) In an immunoglobulin, regions that form the structural site that is complementary to some part of an antigen's structure, providing the basis for the antibody:antigen recognition.

complementary DNA (cDNA) A DNA copy of a mRNA molecule.

configuration A spatial arrangement of covalently bonded atoms, which cannot be altered without breaking and reforming covalent bonds.

conformation A three-dimensional structure or spatial arrangement of a molecule that results from free rotation of substituent groups around single bonds.

constitutive expression The continuous expression of genes independently of regulation.

constitutive splicing A type of splicing in which every intron is removed and every exon is incorporated into the mature RNA without exception.

converter enzyme (modifying enzyme) An enzyme that catalyzes the covalent modification of another enzyme, thereby changing its catalytic activity.

cooperativity A behaviour in which the binding of one ligand to a protein influences the affinity of the protein for additional molecules of the same ligand. Cooperativity can be positive or negative.

corepressors   A metabolite that binds to and activates a protein that functions to repress gene expression.

corticosteroids   Steroid hormones formed by the adrenal cortex.

coupled reactions   Two chemical reactions that have a common intermediate to transfer energy to one another.

covalent modification   The reversible covalent attachment of a chemical group to an enzyme in order to regulate the activity of the enzyme.

cristae   The folds of the inner mitochondrial membrane, which provide the inner membrane with a large surface area in a small volume.

critical micelle concentration (CMC)   Concentration of an amphipathic molecule that form micelles. Below this value, molecules do not aggregate into micelles.

cruciform   A cross-shaped tertiary structure of DNA that arises when inverted repeats form a structure that involves intrastrand base pairing.

cyclic photophosphorylation   Phosphorylation of ADP as a consequence of light-driven movement of electrons in a cyclic pathway leading to proton gradient formation.

cytochrome P-450   A cytochrome found in liver and involved in hydroxylation of xenobiotics to detoxify them by making them more water soluble.

cytochromes   Proteins containing heme prosthetic groups; they serve as electron carriers in oxidation–reduction reactions such as respiration and photosynthesis.

• •

Dark reactions of photosynthesis   The reactions of photosynthesis that do not require light, notably carbon dioxide fixation.

debranching enzyme   An enzyme that can degrade a branched polymer, such as a limit dextrin, by repositioning or removing branches.

degenerate codons (synonymous codons)   Codons that specify the same amino acid.

denaturation   The loss of structural order in a macromolecule; it is accompanied by loss of function.

denitrifying bacteria   Bacteria capable of using NO_3^- and similar forms of oxidized inorganic nitrogen as electron acceptors in place of oxygen in energy-producing pathways.

density gradient ultracentrifugation   A centrifugation technique for separating macromolecules based on their densities.

deoxyribonucleotide   Nucleotides containing 2-deoxy-D-ribose as the pentose.

designer enzymes   Synthetic enzymes tailored to carry out specific catalytic processes.

dextrorotatory isomer A stereoisomer that rotates the plane of plane-polarized light clockwise.

diabetes mellitus A common endocrine disease characterized by an abnormally high level of glucose in the blood.

dialysis Removal of small molecules and ions from macromolecules in solution by allowing them to pass through a semipermeable membrane.

diastereomer For molecules with more than one asymmetric centre, one of a pair of non-mirror image stereoisomers that differ in configuration at only one of the asymmetric centres.

diploid cells Cells containing two sets of chromosomes.

direct reversal repair DNA repair process that directly corrects the DNA defect.

discriminator base The N of NCCA the last four bases in a tRNA. This base is invariant in the tRNAs for a particular amino acid.

DNA polymerase An enzymatic activity that uses dNTPs to elongate the 3'-end of a DNA or RNA using a complementary ssDNA template. DNA polymerase I, II, III, IV, and V are bacterial enzymes, DNA polymerase α, ε, ϕ, τ, β, γ, δ are eukaryotic polymerases.

docking protein (SRP receptor) A heterodimeric transmembrane protein that binds to the SRP-ribosome complex to stimulate the ribosome to resume polypeptide synthesis.

domains Compact structures found in proteins as distinct regions that are often stable by themselves. Also referred to as modules.

double-reciprocal plot (Lineweaver–Burk plot) A graph of the reciprocal of the initial velocity versus the reciprocal of the substrate concentration for an enzyme-catalyzed reaction. It allows an accurate graphical determination of the K_m and the $V_{\max}$.

• •

EC **numbers** Systematic classification of enzymes into one of six major classes. Major classes are further divided into subclasses, sub-subclasses, and sub-sub-subclasses. For example, EC 1.1.1.1 is alcohol dehydrogenase that uses NAD^+.

Edman degradation N-terminal chemistry used to sequence proteins. The chemistry modifies and cleaves only the N-terminal residue, creating a new N-terminus that is subjected to another round of Edman degradation.

EF-Tu and EF-Ts Proteins involved in elongation of protein synthesis in bacteria. EF-Tu is a thermal unstable protein; EF-Ts is a thermal stable protein.

eicosanoids (prostaglandins, thromboxanes, and leukotrienes) Breakdown products of phospholipids. Compounds with hormone-like activities that are derived from 20-carbon polyunsaturated fatty acid arachidonic acid used to synthesize prostaglandins, thromboxanes, and leukotrienes.

electrolytes Substances capable of generating ions in solution, thereby causing an increase in the electrical conductivity of the solution.

electron-transport pathway A metabolic pathway in which electrons from the tricarboxylic acid cycle are passed through membrane-associated proteins to reduce O_2 to H_2O.

electroporation A transformation procedure in which the membranes of cells exposed to pulses of high voltage are rendered momentarily permeable to DNA molecules.

elongation In protein synthesis, the successive addition of amino acids to a polypeptide chain by ribosomes.

elongation factors Proteins required for the ribosome-catalyzed growth of a polypeptide chain. Examples include EF-Tu, EF-Ts, and EF-G. EF-G catalyzes translocation during protein synthesis during which the peptidyl-tRNA is moved from the A site to the P site.

Embden–Meyerhof pathway Glycolysis—conversion of glucose into two pyruvate.

enantiomer Mirror image, non-superimposable stereoisomers.

endergonic A process that has a positive ΔG value (energy absorbing).

energy charge An index of the capacity of the adenylate system (ATP/ADP/AMP system) to provide high-energy phosphoryl groups in order to drive thermodynamically unfavourable reactions.

energy transduction The transformation of energy from one form to another.

enhancer (upstream activation sequence; UAS) Nucleotide sequence involved in regulating the transcription of a gene.

enthalpy (H) A thermodynamic quantity, defined as the heat of a reaction at constant pressure.

entropy A measure of disorder and randomness in a system or its surroundings.

enzyme A protein that catalyzes a specific chemical reaction. Catalytic RNAs are ribozymes.

enzyme kinetics The study of rates of enzyme-catalyzed reactions.

enzyme substrate complex (ES) A complex formed when substrate molecule(s) bind non-covalently to the active site of an enzyme.

episomes Plasmids capable of chromosomal integration.

essential amino acids Amino acids that cannot be synthesized by the body and must be obtained from dietary sources.

estrogens Female sex hormone steroids.

eukaryote A single-celled or multicelled organism whose cells have a membrane-bound nucleus, organelles, and many chromosomes.

excision repair The replacement of damaged or modified bases in DNA by endonucleolytic cleavage.

exergonic A process with a negative ΔG value (energy releasing).

exon The region of a eukaryotic gene that codes for sequences joined during the process of splicing.

exon insertion The process whereby exons encoding particular functional or structural domains of proteins from one gene are inserted into another.

exon shuffling The exchange of exons between genes via recombination events.

exosome A protein complex involved in degradation of RNA.

expressed sequence tags (ESTs) Relatively short (< 200 bases) sequences obtained by determining the nucleotide sequence of randomly selected cDNAs.

expression vector A cloning vector that allows a cloned inserted DNA to be transcribed into RNA and often translated into protein.

• •

Facultative anaerobes Organisms that can adapt to anaerobic conditions by substituting other electron acceptors for O_2 in their energy-producing pathways.

familial hypercholesterolemia A variety of inherited metabolic defects that lead to greatly elevated levels of serum cholesterol, much of it in the form of LDL particles.

fasting state A situation in which food intake by an organism is zero.

fatty acid synthase A single polypeptide chain that contains all the enzymatic activities necessary to synthesize fatty acids. Found in animals.

fermentation The anaerobic catabolism of organic molecules for the production of energy. In alcoholic fermentation, pyruvate is converted to ethanol and carbon dioxide.

fibrous proteins Proteins that have relatively simple, regular linear structures that often serve structural roles in biological systems.

filamentous phage Single-stranded DNA-containing bacterial viruses that package their genome into long, thin tubes constructed from thousands of protein monomers.

first law of thermodynamics A principle stating that the total energy of an isolated system is conserved.

fitness The ability of an organism to survive and reproduce.

flagellum A bacterial filament made out of the protein flagellin. Also, long projection of the plasma membrane of a eukaryotic cell filled with microtubules and involved in motility. Cilium is a short version of a flagellum. Cells might have one or two flagella but many cilia.

flavoprotein Protein conjugated with a flavin coenzyme.

flippase ATP-dependent enzyme that transports phosphatidyl serine (and to a lesser extend PE) from the outer leaflet to the inner leaflet of a plasma membrane.

floppase ATP-dependent enzyme that transports cholesterol, phosphatidyl choline, and sphingomyelin from the outer leaflet to the inner leaflet of a plasma membrane.

fluid mosaic model A model proposed for the structure of biological membranes. In this model, membranes are dynamic structures composed of protein and phospholipid molecules that move laterally.

freeze fracture electron microscopy A technique used to visualize the structure of biological membranes.

furanose A five-membered ring monosaccharide formed by intramolecular hemiacetal formation.

• •

G **protein** Protein capable of binding and hydrolyzing GTP. Found in signal transduction pathways and protein translation.

G-protein–coupled receptors Integral membrane proteins with several membrane-spanning regions and an intracellular domain that binds G protein.

gaba Gamma amino butyric acid, an inhibitory neurotransmitter that regulates chloride channels.

galactosemia A disease in which toxic levels of galactose accumulate in the body, causing cataracts and permanent neurological disorders.

gene The element or unit carrying and transferring inherited characteristics from parent to offspring. Genes are contained in chromosomes.

gene conversion A recombination process whereby two different sequences in a genome interact in such a way that one is converted to the other.

gene pool The sum of all the alleles of a particular gene found in a population.

gene replacement therapy A technique in which cells are removed from a patient, genetically manipulated, and returned to the patient in order to correct a human genetic disorder.

gene sharing When the product of a single gene gains a second function without losing its primary function.

gene therapy The repair of a genetic deficiency by introduction of a functional version of the gene.

general genetic recombination The process whereby DNA sequences are exchanged between homologous chromosomes, resulting in the arrangement of genes into new combinations.

general transcription factors Proteins required for transcription by RNA polymerase II that bind to elements near the site of initiation of transcription.

genetic recombination The formation of chromosomes with combinations of gene types different from those found in the parental chromosomes.

genomic library A DNA library prepared by isolating the total DNA from an organism, digesting it into fragments, and cloning the fragments into an appropriate vector.

genomics The study of the whole genome of organisms.

genotype The genetic make-up of an organism, as opposed to its phenotype or outward characteristics.

germ cells The sperm and the eggs of multicellular organisms.

ghrelin An appetite-stimulating peptide hormone produced in the stomach.

Gibbs free energy (*G*) A thermodynamic state function relating enthalpy, entropy, and temperature; $G = H - TS$.

globular protein A water-soluble protein that is roughly spherical in shape. It consists of one or more compactly folded polypeptide chains.

glucogenic compound A compound that can be used for gluconeogenesis in animals. Most amino acids are glucogenic.

gluconeogenesis An anabolic pathway for the production of glucose from noncarbohydrate precursors.

glutamate (glutamic acid) An acidic amino acid with a side chain containing a carboxyl group. Also used as an excitatory neurotransmitter amino acid.

glutamate dehydrogenase An enzyme that catalyzes the reductive amination of α-ketoglutarate to produce glutamate.

glutamine synthetase An enzyme that catalyzes the ATP-dependent amidation of the γ-carboxyl group of glutamate to form glutamine.

glycerophosphate shuttle A process whereby two different glycerophosphate dehydrogenases, one in the cytoplasm and one in the outer face of the mitochondrial inner membrane, work together to deliver electrons to the mitochondrial electron-transport system.

glycoconjugate A carbohydrate in which one or more sugar residues is covalently linked to a peptide chain, lipid, or protein.

glycogen The major form of storage polysaccharide in animals.

glycogen phosphorylase Enzyme that releases glucose from glycogen as glucose-1-phosphate. Activated by glycogen phosphorylase kinase.

glycogen synthase Enzyme that uses UDP–glucose to synthesize glycogen.
glycolipid A carbohydrate covalently linked to a lipid molecule.

glycolysis The metabolic pathway responsible for the stepwise degradation of glucose and other simple sugars to pyruvate, during which energy is released from the sugar and captured in the form of ATP under anaerobic conditions.

glycoprotein A protein containing a covalently linked carbohydrate.

glycosaminoglycans A class of polysaccharides consisting of linear chains of repeating disaccharides in which one of the monosaccharide units is an amino sugar and one (or both) of the monosaccharides contains at least one negatively charged sulfate or carboxylate group.

glycosidic bond A bond between the anomeric carbon of a sugar and the oxygen atom of an alcohol.

glyoxylate cycle A modification of the tricarboxylic acid cycle, used by plants and bacteria to produce 4-carbon dicarboxylic acids (and eventually sugars) from 2-carbon acetate units.

glyoxysomes A plant peroxisome that contains the enzymes for the glyoxylate cycle.

grana Stacks of flattened vesicles formed from the thylakoid membrane in chloroplasts.

gratuitous inducers Non-metabolizable substrate analogs capable of activating the transcription of catabolic enzymes.

GroES–GroEL complex A bacterial protein complex that functions as a chaperonin to help proteins fold.

group transfer potential The measure of the ability of a compound to donate a functional group to a specific receptor molecule or to water.

growth medium The nutrients needed for a microorganism to grow in a laboratory.

GTPase-activating protein (GAP) Protein capable of increasing GTPase activity of a G protein.

gyrase A type II topoisomerase that acts to overcome torsional stress imposed upon DNA unwinding by adding negative supercoils to DNA using ATP hydrolysis.

• •

Halophiles Prokaryotes that can live in water with high salt levels.

Hanes–Woolf plot Plots of [S]/v versus [S] for enzyme kinetic data.

haploid cells Cells containing only one set of chromosomes.

HAT Histone acetyltransferase—an enzyme that acetylates lysines on histone proteins using acetyl-CoA.

Hatch–Slack pathway A reaction pathway in plants to attach carbon dioxide to form a 4-carbon compound that serves as a CO_2 delivery system.

HDACs Histone deacetylase complexes—enzyme activity that removes acetyl groups from histones.

heat shock proteins Proteins synthesized by cells in response to a sudden increase in temperature. Many heat shock proteins are chaperonins.

helix-turn-helix A description of a structural motif found in DNA-binding proteins.

heme   The iron–porphyrin prosthetic group of heme proteins.

hemiacetal   The product formed when an alcohol reacts with an aldehyde.

hemiketal   The product formed when an alcohol reacts with a ketone.

hemoproteins   Heme-containing proteins.

Henderson–Hasselbach equation   An equation relating the pH, pKa, and concentrations of the proton-acceptor [A⁻] and proton-donor species [HA] in a solution.

heredity   Loosely defined as the tendency of an organism to possess the characteristics of its parent(s).

heterogeneous nuclear RNA (hnRNA)   A large mRNA precursor with stretches of nucleotide sequence that have no protein-coding capacity.

heterotroph   An organism that requires an organic form of carbon, such as glucose, in order to generate metabolic energy and to synthesize other essential carbon compounds.

HGPRT (hypoxanthine-guanine phosphoribosyltransferase)   An enzyme in the purine salvage pathway that produces IMP. Defects in this enzyme cause Lesch–Nyhan syndrome.

high-density lipoprotein (HDL)   A plasma lipoprotein that contains a significant amount of protein and that transports cholesterol and cholesterol esters from tissues to the liver.

high-performance liquid chromatography (HPLC)   A chromatographic technique for separating components of a mixture by forcing the liquid mixture though a column under high pressure.

histones   A class of arginine- and lysine-rich basic proteins that interact ionically with anionic phosphate groups in the DNA backbone to form nucleosomes.

HIV-1   Human immunodeficiency retrovirus that causes AIDS.

HMG-CoA reductase   Hydroxymethylglutaryl-CoA reductase catalyzes production of 3R-mevalonate from HMG CoA. This is the rate-limiting step in cholesterol synthesis and the site of action of statin drugs.

Holliday junction   A cross-strand intermediate in genetic recombination in which two double-stranded DNA molecules are joined by the reciprocal crossover involving one strand of each molecule.

holoenzyme   A catalytically active complex of protein and cofactor.

homeobox domain   A DNA motif that encodes a related 60-amino acid sequence found in a number of proteins that act as a sequence-specific transcriptional factor.

homeostasis   Maintaining a constant internal environment with respect to parameters like temperature, osmotic pressure, and pH.

homologous genetic recombination   The recombination of two DNA molecules of similar sequences.

homologous proteins Homologous proteins are proteins that share a common evolutionary ancestor, which is often evidenced by a significant degree of sequence or structural similarity.

HTH motif A DNA binding motif characterized by two successive α-helices separated by a β-turn. Proteins with HTH motifs function as dimers.

hydration A state in which a molecule or ion is surrounded by water molecules.

hydrogen bonds Weak chemical forces between a hydrogen atom covalently bonded to an electronegative atom such as oxygen or nitrogen and a second electronegative atom that serves as the hydrogen-bond acceptor.

hydropathy plot A technique to detect hydrophobic and hydrophilic regions within a polypeptide chain by plotting the average hydrophobicity of a window of amino acids versus location as the window is moved across the amino acid sequence.

hydrophobic interactions The association of non-polar groups or molecules with each other in aqueous environments.

hydroxyapatite Calcium–phosphate complex found in microcrystals in bone tissue.

hydroxyurea A free-radical quenching agent and inhibitor of ribonucleotide reductase.

hyperuricemia Chronic elevation of blood uric acid levels, which occurs in about 3% of the population as a consequence of impaired excretion of uric acid or overproduction of purines.

• •

Illegitimate recombination A rare recombination that occurs between non-homologous DNA independently of any unique sequence element.

immunoglobulin A major class of antibody molecules found circulating in the bloodstream.

immunoglobulin fold A collapsed β-barrel domain consisting of two layers of a total of seven β-strands.

indirect readout The ability of a protein to indirectly recognize a particular nucleotide sequence by recognizing local conformational variations in double-helical DNA resulting from the effects that base sequences have on DNA structure.

inducers Substrates capable of activating the synthesis of enzymes that metabolize them.

induction of enzyme synthesis An increase in enzyme synthesis by the activation of transcription of the gene encoding the enzyme.

inhibitor A compound that decreases the velocity of an enzymatic reaction.

initiation In protein synthesis, the first phase that primes the ribosome for polypeptide formation.

initiation complex A complex consisting of 70S ribosome with GTP, N-formyl-Met-tRNA$_f^{Met}$, and mRNA ready for the elongation steps in protein synthesis.

initiation factors (IFs)   Proteins necessary for the initiation of protein synthesis.

initiator tRNA   A special tRNA charged with methionine and used to start protein synthesis.

insulin   Polypeptide hormone of the β-cells of the islets of Langerhans in the pancreas of all vertebrates that regulates carbohydrate metabolism.

integral membrane protein (intrinsic membrane protein)   A membrane protein with hydrophobic surfaces that penetrate or extend all the way across the lipid bilayer.

intercalation   The insertion of a molecule between stacked structural elements such as the insertion of a planar molecule between two successive bases in a nucleic acid.

intermembrane space   The space between an inner and outer membrane.

international unit (IU)   One IU is the amount of enzyme that catalyzes the formation of 1 micromole of product in one minute at a specified pH, temperature, and ionic strength.

intrinsic termination   Transcription termination in bacteria that occurs because the transcript forms a RNA hairpin with a GC rich stem, followed by a run of Us that cause the RNA polymerase to pause and terminate transcription.

intron (intervening sequence)   A sequence of nucleotides in a gene that is transcribed but is not found in the mature mRNA.

invertase   An enzyme that hydrolyzes sucrose to fructose and glucose. The optical rotation changes sign during digestion.

ion channels   Membrane proteins through which ions can pass. Channels can be gated (regulated to open and close) by ligands (ligand-gated) or membrane voltage (voltage-gated).

ion exchange chromatography   A method for separating substances on the basis on their charge.

ionic bonds   Weak bonds that are the result of attractive forces between oppositely charged polar functions, such as negative carboxyl groups and positive amino groups.

islets of Langerhans   Cells in the pancreas that secrete insulin.

isoacceptor tRNAs   The set of tRNAs specific for a particular amino acid.

isoelectric focusing   An electrophoretic technique for separating proteins according to their isoelectric point or pI.

isoelectric point   The pH at which a compound is electrically neutral.

isomerases   A group of enzymes that interconvert isomers.

• •

Katal   One katal is the amount of enzyme catalyzing the conversion of one mole of substrate to product per second. One katal equals 6×10^7 international units.

keratins Insoluble structural proteins with parallel polypeptide chains in the α-helical or β-sheet conformations.

ketogenesis The synthesis of acetone, acetoacetate, and β-hydroxybutyrate generated from acetyl-CoA.

ketogenic compounds A compound such as an amino acid that can be degraded to yield acetyl-CoA, thereby contributing to the synthesis of fatty acids or ketone bodies.

ketone bodies Fuel molecules (acetone, acetoacetate, and β-hydroxybutyrate), synthesized in the liver from acetyl-CoA. During starvation and in untreated diabetes mellitus, ketone bodies become a major source of fuel.

ketose A monosaccharide containing a ketone group.

kinases Enzymes that transfer the terminal (gamma) phosphate of ATP to some target molecule, usually on a hydroxyl group.

Klenow fragment The larger fragment of DNA polymerase I that contains the polymerase and 3'-exonuclease activity.

Krebs cycle The tricarboxylic acid cycle.

• •

Lactose intolerance A metabolic disorder caused by the inability to digest lactose due to the absence of the enzyme lactase in the intestine.

lamellae The paired folds of the thylakoid membrane of chloroplasts.

lariat A branched, covalently closed loop of RNA formed as an intermediate during RNA splicing.

leader peptide An N-terminal sequence of amino acids in a protein that is synthesized on the RER and is destined to be a membrane protein or to be secreted.

leading strand/lagging strand During DNA replication, the leading strand is the newly synthesized strand that is elongated in a continuous manner in the direction of movement of a replication fork. The lagging strand is synthesized as Okazaki fragments because it is on the opposite strand from the leading strand.

Leloir pathway The catabolism of galactose.

lethal synthesis The metabolic transformation of an otherwise innocuous compound into a poisonous derivative.

leucine zipper A dimerization structural motif consisting of 7-residue repeats of leucine in an alpha helix and found in DNA-binding proteins.

leukotrienes A class of molecules derived from arachidonic acid; they stimulate contractions in vascular, respiratory, and intestinal smooth muscle.

levorotatory isomer A stereoisomer that rotates the plane of plane-polarized light counterclockwise.

ligand A molecule that is bound to another, usually larger molecule.

light reactions of photosynthesis The reactions of photosynthesis that require light and cannot occur in the dark.

limit dextrins Highly branched oligosaccharides that are left over after extensive removal of glucose units from starch or glycogen by α-amylase, glycogen phosphorylase, or starch phosphorylase.

Lineweaver–Burk double reciprocal plot Plot of 1/v versus 1/[S] for enzyme kinetic data.

linking number (L) The basic parameter characterizing supercoiled DNA. The number of times the two strands of DNA are intertwined.

lipid A class of biological molecules defined by low solubility in water and high solubility in non-polar solvents.

lipid anchored protein Protein to which lipid is covalently attached causing the protein to localize in a biological membrane.

lipid bilayer A back-to-back arrangement of lipid monolayers in which the hydrophobic tails aggregate in the interior of the bilayer and the polar head groups face outward into the aqueous environment.

lipidomics Global analysis of lipids and their interacting protein partners in organs, cells, and organelles.

lipopolysaccharide A lipid group joined to a polysaccharide made up of long chains with many different sugars.

lipoproteins Proteins conjugated with lipids including high-density (HDL), low-density (LDL), intermediate-density (IDL), very-low-density lipoproteins (VLDL), and chylomicrons.

liposome A closed, spherical structure formed from a single phospholipid bilayer, which can be used as a drug and enzyme delivery system in therapeutic applications.

locus The chromosomal location of a gene.

low-density lipoproteins (LDLs) Plasma lipoproteins with a low protein-to-lipid ratio.

lymphocytes White blood cells involved in the immune response. B lymphocytes, from bone marrow, synthesize and secrete antibodies. T lymphocytes, from the thymus gland, play a regulatory role in the immune response or act as a killer of foreign and virus-infected cells.

• •

Macromolecules Proteins, polysaccharides, and polynucleotides (DNA and RNA).

major groove The larger of the two grooves created on the surface when DNA forms a double helix.

malate–aspartate shuttle An electron-transport shuttle system in which malate and aspartate are carried across the inner mitochondrial membrane.

MAPKs Mitogen-activated protein kinases are protein kinases activated by mitogens, agents that induce cell division.

maple syrup urine disease A heredity defect in the oxidative decarboxylation of branched chain α-keto acids leading to elevated levels of valine, leucine, and isoleucine in blood and urine. The urine of these individuals smells like maple syrup; the disease is fatal unless dietary intake of these amino acids is restricted in early life.

matrix The space enclosed by the inner mitochondrial membrane.

mediator A protein complex active in eukaryotic transcription that links specific transcription activators bound to enhancers and general transcription factors/RNA polymerase II located at promoters.

melanocortin Peptide hormones that inhibit neurons that initiate eating behaviour.

membrane rafts Microdomains within biological membranes that are aggregates of cholesterol and glycosphingolipids.

messenger RNA (mRNA) A ribonucleic acid, which serves to carry the information or "message" that is encoded in genes to the sites of protein synthesis in the cell where this information is translated into a polypeptide.

met aminopeptidase A protein that removes the invariant Met initiating all polypeptide chains.

metabolic channelling A process whereby the product of an enzymatic reaction in a pathway is delivered directly to the next enzyme in the pathway for which it serves as the substrate.

metabolism The sum of the chemical changes that convert nutrients into energy and finished products in an organism.

metabolites Simple organic compounds that are substrates, intermediates, or products in cellular energy transformation and in the biosynthesis or degradation of biological molecules, such as amino acids, sugars, fatty acids, and nucleotides.

metabolomics The study of small molecule profile of a biological system under a particular condition.

metalloenzyme An enzyme that binds a metal tightly or that requires a metal ion to maintain activity or stability.

metalloproteins Proteins conjugated with metals.

methanogens Archaea that are obligate anaerobes and that generate methane from CO_2 and H_2 or from organic compounds.

methylmalonyl-CoA mutase A vitamin B_{12}–dependent enzyme used in catabolism of odd chain fatty acids.

micelle A structure formed by amphipathic molecules in aqueous solution in which the hydrophobic portions aggregate in the interior of the structure and the hydrophilic portions of the molecules project into the aqueous environment.

Michaelis constant (K_m) The concentration of substrate at which an enzyme-catalyzed reaction proceeds at one-half its maximum velocity.

Michaelis–Menten equation A rate equation relating the initial velocity (v_o) of an enzymatic reaction to the substrate concentration [S]. $v_o = V_{max} [S]/ (K_m + [S])$ where V_{max} is the maximum velocity and K_m is the Michaelis constant.

microtubules Hollow, cylindrical structures, approximately 30 nm in diameter, formed from tubulin, a heterodimeric protein.

mineralocorticoids Steroid hormones, such as aldosterone, that regulate water and salt balance.

minor groove The smaller of the two grooves created on the surface when DNA forms a double helix.

mismatch repair DNA repair that corrects base-pair errors introduced during DNA replication.

Mitchell's chemiosmotic hypothesis A proposal stating that the energy stored in a proton gradient across a membrane by electron transport drives the synthesis of ATP in cells.

mitochondria The power plants of cells, which carry out the energy-releasing aerobic metabolism of carbohydrates and fatty acids with the concomitant capture of energy in metabolically useful forms such as ATP.

modulator proteins Proteins that bind to enzymes, and, by binding, influence the activity of the enzyme.

monosaccharide A simple sugar of three or more carbon atoms with the formula $(CH_2O)_n$ where n is 3 or larger.

mosaic proteins Proteins composed of several different structural motifs.

motor proteins Proteins that function as molecular motors to produce movement by transferring chemical energy (ATP hydrolysis or ion gradients) into mechanical energy of motion, examples include dyneins, kinesins, myosins, and DNA helicase.

multifunctional polypeptides Single polypeptide chains having two or more enzymatic centres.

mutant An organism with a change in its genetic information.

mutase An enzyme that moves the location of some functional group on a molecule.

myofibrils Actin/myosin fibres that are found in striated muscle cells known as muscle fibres (long multinucleated skeletal muscle cells).

• •

Natriuretic hormones   Atrial (ANP) or brain (BNP) peptide hormones that regulate sodium levels.

natural selection   The differential reproduction of genetically distinct individuals within a population.

neo-Darwinian theory of evolution   The view that natural selection determines the frequency of alleles in a population, and ultimately, the genetic makeup of populations.

neutral theory of molecular evolution   A postulate stating that the majority of molecular changes in evolution are due to the random fixation of neutral mutations within the population.

neuropeptide Y   A protein that stimulates neurons that initiate eating behaviour.

neurotransmitter   Chemical substance used to transmit a signal across a synaptic cleft.

nitrate assimilation   A two-step metabolic pathway, where NO_3^- is reduced to NH_4^+ in green plants, various fungi, and certain bacteria.

nitrate reductase   The enzyme that catalyzes the first step in nitrate assimilation: reduction of nitrate to nitrite.

nitrifying bacteria   A group of chemoautotrophs that oxidize NH_4^+ to NO_3^-.

nitrite reductase   The enzyme that catalyzes the second step in nitrate assimilation: reduction of nitrite to ammonium.

nitrogen fixation   The formation of NH_4^+ from N_2 gas; this reduction occurs only in certain prokaryotic cells.

nitrogenase   The enzyme that catalyzes nitrogen fixation, an 8 electron reduction of dinitrogen to ammonium.

non-cyclic photophosphorylation   Phosphorylation of ADP as a consequence of movement of electrons in a photosystem from water to $NADP^+$ resulting in a proton gradient.

non-essential amino acids   Amino acids that can be synthesized by an organism and thus are not required in the diet.

nonsense codons   Codons UAA, UAG, and UGA that do not specify any amino acids but serve as termination codons.

nonsense suppressors   Mutations in tRNA genes that alter the tRNA so that the mutant tRNA can now read a stop codon and insert an amino acid.

nuclear magnetic resonance (NMR)   A spectroscopic technique used to study the structures of molecules in solution. In NMR, the absorption of electromagnetic energy by molecules in magnetic fields provides information about molecular structure and dynamics.

nucleases   Enzymes that hydrolyze nucleic acids.

nucleic acid   Linear polymers of nucleotides linked in a 3' to 5' fashion by phosphodiester bridges (DNA and RNA).

nucleolus   A specialized region of the nucleus at which ribosome subunits are assembled. The nucleolus is centred on a chromosome in a region at which ribosomal RNA genes are in a tandem cluster.

nucleoproteins   Proteins conjugated with nucleic acids.

nucleoside   A compound formed by the linkage of pentose sugar to a purine or pyrimidine base.

nucleoside diphosphate kinase   An enzyme that phosphorylates NDPs using ATP, thus producing GTP, CTP, and UTP.

nucleosomes   Structures in which the DNA double helix is wound around a protein core composed of pairs of four different histone proteins.

nucleotide   A nucleoside with a phosphoric acid esterified to a sugar hydroxyl group.

nucleus   The organelle that is the repository of genetic information in the form of linear sequences of nucleotides in the DNA of eukaryotes.

• •

O**bligate aerobes**   Organisms, like humans, for which O_2 is essential to sustain life.

obligate anaerobes Organisms that cannot use O_2 at all and are even poisoned by it.

Okazaki fragments   Short ssDNA chains of about 1000 residues in length, which are formed during the discontinuous synthesis of the lagging strand of DNA.

oligopeptides   Peptide chains of more than 12 and less than 20 amino acid residues.

oligosaccharide   A polymer of approximately 2 to 10 monosaccharide units linked by glycosidic bonds.

operon   A cluster of genes encoding the enzymes of a particular metabolic pathway, along with the regulatory sequences that control their transcription. Inducible operons are expressed only in the absence of their corepressors or only in the presence of small molecule inducers.

operon hypothesis   A theory that accounts for the coordinate regulation of related metabolic enzymes.

optical activity   The ability of a substance to rotate the plane of plane-polarized light.

ORC   Origin recognition complex—a protein complex that binds to replication origins.

organelles   Membrane-bound structures found in eukaryotic cells; they perform specialized cell functions. Examples include nucleus, mitochondria, chloroplasts, endoplasmic reticulum, Golgi apparatus, vacuoles, peroxisomes, lysosomes, and chromoplasts.

ORI origin of replication   A DNA sequence site for the beginning of DNA replication.

orthologous proteins   Proteins from different species that have an evolutionary ancestor that existed before the species split. Orthologous proteins often have similar functions in different species.

ouabain   A highly toxic cardiac glycoside used to inhibit the sodium pump.

oxidative phosphorylation   The enzymatic phosphorylation of ADP to ATP coupled to the transfer of electrons from a substrate to O_2.

oxygen-evolving complex   The PSII complex of photosynthesis that is responsible for the photolysis of water.

• •

Palindromes (inverted repeats)   A segment of duplex DNA in which the base sequences of the two strands exhibit two-fold rotational symmetry.

paralogous proteins   Homologous proteins that evolved from an ancestral gene by gene duplication.

parvalbumin   Calcium-binding protein in neurons with high firing rate. First calcium-binding protein discovered to have calcium-binding EF hand.

patch recombinants   Recombinant heteroduplexes that are formed by (-) strand cleavage at a Holliday junction.

PCR (polymerase chain reaction)   An *in vitro* technique for amplifying a specific region of DNA using a thermostabile DNA polymerase and primers that flank the sequence to be amplified.

pentose phosphate pathway (hexose monophosphate shunt; phosphogluconate pathway)   A metabolic pathway that interconverts pentoses and hexoses and is a source of NADPH.

peptide bond   An amide bond between amino acids.

peptidyl transferase   The catalytic activity of the large RNA of the large subunit of a ribosome that produces peptide bonds.

peripheral membrane protein (extrinsic membrane protein)   A membrane protein that does not penetrate the bilayer to any significant extent but is associated with the membrane by ionic interactions and hydrogen bonds.

peroxisomes   Eukaryotic, cytoplasmic, membrane-bound organelles which carry out a variety of flavin-dependent oxidation reactions, regenerating oxidized flavins by reaction with oxygen to produce hydrogen peroxide, H_2O_2.

phenotype   The observable characteristics of an organism.

phenylketonuria   A genetic disease in which phenylpyruvate collects in the urine, causing severe mental retardation unless a newborn is placed on a diet low in phenylalanine.

phosphatase   An enzyme that removes phosphates from substrates by hydrolysis.

phosphofructokinase-2   Along with fructose-2,6-bisphosphatase, regulates levels of fructose-2,6-bisphosphate, a regulator of glycolysis and gluconeogenesis.

phospholipids   A class of lipids, each member of which contains a phosphate moiety.

phosphoprotein phosphatase   A protein that hydrolyzes phosphate from phosphorylated proteins.

phosphoproteins   Proteins that have phosphate groups typically esterified to the hydroxyls of serine, threonine, or tyrosine residues.

photophosphorylation   Light-driven ATP synthesis from ADP and P_i catalyzed by ATP synthase.

photorespiration   The light-dependent uptake of O_2 accompanied by the release of CO_2 and metabolism of phosphoglycolate.

photosynthesis   The use of light energy to produce ATP and NADPH. These energy-rich substances can drive carbohydrate synthesis from carbon dioxide and water.

photosystem (photosynthetic unit)   In photosynthetic cells, a membrane-bound reaction centre with an antenna of several hundred light-harvesting chlorophyll molecules.

phototrophic organisms   Organisms that grow by transforming light energy into chemical energy.

phylogeny   The origin and evolution of the many types and species of organisms.

phytol   A breakdown product of chlorophyll that occurs in the fat of ruminant animals.

PIDs (protein interaction domains)   Protein domains that mediate protein–protein interactions.

pitch   The axial distance required to complete one turn of a helix.

plasmalogens   Ether glycerophospholipids in which the alkyl moiety is *cis-α,β*-unsaturated.

plasmids   Circular, extrachromosomal DNA.

plastids   Self-replicating organelles in plants.

platelet activating factor   The compound 1-alkyl-2-acetylglycerophosphocholine, which has the ability to dilate blood vessels in order to reduce blood pressure in hypertensive animals and to aggregate platelets.

P/O ratio   The ratio of the number of molecules of ATP synthesized to the number of atoms of oxygen reduced in oxidative phosphorylation.

point mutations   A class of mutations in which one base pair is substituted for another. Two possible types are transitions (a purine–purine or pyrimidine–pyrimidine replacement) and transversions (a purine–pyrimidine or pyrimidine–purine replacement).

poly(A) tail The 3′-end of eukaryotic mRNAs with from 100 to 200 As. Polyadenylation signal (AAUAAA) is a sequence on a RNA transcript that directs cleavage of the RNA downstream of the signal. The new 3′-end is then polyadenylated by poly(A) polymerase.

polycistronic mRNA An mRNA containing more than one open reading frame each coding for a protein.

polylinker A short region of DNA sequence bearing numerous restriction sites.

polymerase chain reaction (PCR) A repetitive polymerization technique for dramatically amplifying the amount of a specific DNA segment.

polypeptide A long chain of amino acids linked by amide bonds.

polyribosomes (polysomes) Multiple ribosomes attached to mRNA.

polysaccharide A polymer of many monosaccharide units linked by glycosidic bonds. These polymers can be either linear or branched.

porins Proteins found in the outer membranes of Gram-negative bacteria that span the membranes forming a β-barrel.

post-translational modification Enzymatic processing of a polypeptide chain after genetic information from DNA has been translated into newly formed protein.

preprohormones Peptide hormones that must be processed by proteolysis to become active.

Pribnow box A nucleotide sequence involved in the initiation of transcription of prokaryotic genes.

primary structure The amino acid sequence of a protein.

primer A short nucleotide oligomer to which a polymerase adds monomers.

processing Alterations that convert a newly synthesized RNA into mature messenger RNA.

processivity In DNA synthesis, the degree to which an enzyme remains associated with the template during nucleotide addition.

prochiral An achiral centre that can be made chiral by replacement of a single group about the achiral centre.

prokaryotes Single-celled organisms that lack nuclei and other organelles.

promoter A nucleotide sequence at which transcription initiation is regulated and initiated.

proproteins Larger inactive protein precursors that are activated through proteolysis.

prostaglandins Compounds that have hormone-like properties and are derived from arachidonic acid.

prosthetic group A molecule that is tightly bound to an enzyme.

proteasome A protein complex involved in degradation of intracellular proteins.

protein   A molecule composed of one or more polypeptide chains, each with a characteristic sequence of amino acids linked by peptide bonds.

protein isoforms   A set of related polypeptides derived from a common gene by differential RNA splicing.

protein kinase A   Cyclic AMP–dependent protein kinase that phosphorylates Ser or Thr on a number of target proteins.

protein module   A tertiary structural motif or domain that may exist in several different proteins or that may occur two or more times in the same protein.

protein translocation   The targeting of proteins to their proper destinations in cells.

proteoglycans   A family of glycoproteins whose carbohydrate moieties are predominately glycosaminoglycans.

proteomics   The study of the totality of proteins expressed by an organism under a particular condition.

pseudosubstrate sequence   A sequence used to regulate protein kinases by intrasteric control. Pseudosubstrate sequences mimic the target sequence but lack the OH-bearing side chain.

purines   A structure containing a pyrimidine ring fused to a five-membered imidazole ring.

pyranose   A six-membered ring monosaccharide formed by intramolecular hemiacetal formation.

pyrimidine   A six-membered heterocyclic aromatic ring containing two nitrogen atoms.

pyruvate dehydrogenase complex   Enzyme complex that metabolizes pyruvate to acetyl-CoA and CO_2. Catalysis is a multistep process involving water-soluble vitamins niacin, riboflavin, thiamine, lipoic acid, and pantothenic acid.

PYY$_{3-36}$ Peptide hormone produced in small intestines. Inhibits eating by acting on NPY/AgRP-producing neurons in the brain.

• •

Q cycle   Movement of electrons from coenzyme QH_2 to cytochrome c during electron transport in complex III.

quaternary structure   The three-dimensional organization of two or more polypeptide chains in a multisubunit protein.

• •

R **state**   The active conformation of an allosteric enzyme.

Ramachandran plot   Plots of the two dihedral angles about the alpha carbon of amino acid residues within a protein chain.

random genetic drift   A random change in allelic frequency.

rate limiting step   The slowest step in a chemical reaction. This step has the highest activation energy among the steps leading to the formation of a product from a reactant.

rate of nucleotide substitution   The number of nucleotide substitutions per site per year.

rate of product formation   In an enzyme-catalyzed reaction, the rate of the formation of product with time: $v = d[P]/dt$.

reaction centre   A complex of a pair of photochemically reactive chlorophyll a molecules that forms the core of a photosystem. The reaction centre is the site of conversion of photochemical energy into electrochemical energy during photosynthesis.

receptor guanylyl cyclase   Single transmembrane segment protein with guanylyl cyclase activity on intracellular domain.

receptor tyrosine kinase   Single transmembrane segment protein with tyrosine kinase activity on intracellular domain.

recombinant DNA   A DNA molecule that includes DNA from different sources.

recombinant DNA technology (genetic engineering)   The process of isolating, manipulating, and cloning a sequence of DNA.

recombinant plasmids   Hybrid DNA molecules consisting of plasmid DNA sequences plus inserted DNA elements (called inserts). Also known as chimeric plasmids.

reducing sugar   A carbohydrate whose free anomeric OH group can reduce oxidizing agents.

Refsum's disease   An inherited metabolic disorder that results in defective night vision, tremors, and other neurological abnormalities, caused by an accumulation of phytanic acid in the body.

regulatory proteins   Proteins that do not perform any obvious chemical transformation but can regulate the ability of other proteins to carry out their physiological functions.

release factors   Proteins that promote polypeptide release from the ribosome.

replication   *In vivo* DNA synthesis. Replication is always semiconservative, meaning the new dsDNA is composed of one strand from the original DNA and one newly synthesized complementary strand.

replication forks   During DNA replication, it is the Y-shaped junction where the double-stranded DNA template is unwound and the new DNA strands are synthesized.

replicons   The units of DNA replication.

repression   A decrease in protein synthesis arising from cessation of transcription of the gene encoding the protein.

response elements   Promoter modules in genes that serve as binding sites for proteins that activate transcription.

restriction endonucleases   Enzymes, isolated chiefly from bacteria, that have the ability to cleave double-stranded DNA, typically at short, defined sequences.

resveratrol   A phytoalexin found in red wines that is a potent activator of sirtuin, an enzyme involved in longevity.

retroviruses   A class of eukaryotic RNA viruses that has single-stranded RNA genomes that replicate through a double-stranded DNA intermediate using reverse transcriptase.

rho termination factor   A bacterial protein that functions during termination of transcription.

ribonucleotide   A nucleotide containing D-ribose as its pentose.

ribosomal RNA (rRNA)   Ribonucleic acid, which serves as a component of ribosomes.

ribosomes   Compact ribonucleoprotein particles responsible for protein synthesis and found in the cytosol of all cells, as well as in the matrix of mitochondria and the stroma of chloroplasts.

ribozymes   Catalytic RNAs.

RNA polymerase   An enzyme that uses NTPs to produce RNA. RNA polymerase holoenzyme refers to a protein complex in bacteria capable of initiating transcription as specific locations termed promoters. The core complex cannot initiate but does elongate. RNA polymerases I, II, and III are eukaryotic enzymes.

rubisco   Ribulose bisphosphate carboxylase/oxygenase, an enzyme in photosynthesis that attaches carbon dioxide to an organic compound.

• •

Saponification   The process of hydrolysis of acylglycerols with alkali to yield glycerol and salts of free fatty acids.

sarcomeres, sarcoplasmic reticulum, sarcolemma   Sarcomeres are the functional structural units of muscle contraction. Linear arrays of sarcomeres are myofibrils. Sarcoplasmic reticulum is a specialized endoplasmic reticulum surrounding sarcomeres. Sarcolemma is a specialized plasma membrane of a muscle fibre.

saturated fatty acid   A fatty acid that does not contain a carbon–carbon double bond.

scaffolding proteins   Proteins that bind on either side of a plasma membrane and influence membrane curvature.

scramblase Calcium-activated enzyme that catalyze bidirectional movement of lipids between inner and outer leaflets of the plasma membrane.

second law of thermodynamics A law stating in part that the total entropy of the universe always increases in a spontaneous process.

second messenger An intracellular agent synthesized in response to an external signal or first messenger, such as a hormone.

secondary structure The arrangement in space of atoms in the backbone of a polypeptide chain or a nucleic acid stabilized by hydrogen bonds.

selenocysteine An amino acid coded by special UGA stop codons and derived from serine by replacement of serine's hydroxyl group with selenium. One-letter and three-letter codes: U and Sec.

semiconservative model for DNA replication The process for duplicating DNA in which the nucleotide sequence in one strand dictates the sequence in the other, complementary strand, resulting in two daughter molecules of double-stranded DNA, each of which contains one of the parent strands.

sequence alignments A comparison of two sequences by juxtaposing two nucleotide or amino acid sequences and analyzing their similarities.

sequential model for allosteric behaviour A model for the cooperative binding of identical ligands to an oligomeric protein.

serine proteases A family of proteolytic enzymes that have serine at their active site. Serine is a member of a catalytic triad that includes histidine and aspartic acid.

severe combined immunodeficiency syndrome (SCID) A group of related inherited disorders characterized by the lack of an immune response to infectious disease.

Shine–Dalgarno sequence A mRNA sequence, rich in purine, which is required for mRNA binding to prokaryotic ribosomes.

shuttle vectors Plasmids capable of propagating and transferring genes between two different organisms, one of which is typically a prokaryote and the other an eukaryote.

sickle-cell anemia A human disease characterized by crescent-shaped red blood cells.

signal recognition particle (SRP) A nucleoprotein assembly that binds to the signal sequence to halt further protein synthesis by the ribosome.

signal sequence (signal peptide) The N-terminal sequence of residues in a newly synthesized polypeptide that targets the protein for translocation across a membrane.

signalsome Complex formed by a protein with several protein interaction domains during signal transduction.

single-stranded assimilation (single-stranded uptake) A process driven by branch migration, which displaces the homologous DNA strand from the DNA duplex and replaces it with the invading ssDNA strand.

siRNA Small interfering RNAs 20 to 25 nucleotides long that are involved in RNA interference, a process by which RNA blocks gene expression.

siroheme A novel heme prosthetic group found in photosynthetic nitrite reductases.

sirtuin 1 NAD^+-dependent protein deacetylases involved in longevity.

site-specific genetic recombination Genetic recombination occurring only at specific sequences.

small nuclear RNA (snRNA) A class of RNA molecules found only in the nucleus of eukaryotic cells.

SNAREs A family of proteins that "snare" vesicles to initiate fusion of a vesicle with the plasma membrane.

snRNPs ("snurps") Small nuclear ribonucleoprotein particles.

solid phase synthesis Synthesis during which the product is produced while attached to a solid support matrix. Used in chemical synthesis of proteins and nucleic acids.

solvent capacity The capacity of the cell to keep all of its essential metabolites and macromolecules in an appropriate state of solvation.

somatic cells All body cells except for the germ cells (sperm and eggs).

SOS response A repair system that allows DNA replication to continue at lesion in DNA.

specific activity The number of micromoles of a substrate transformed by an enzyme per minute per milligram of protein at 25°C; it is a measure of enzyme activity and purity.

specificity The ability of an enzyme to discriminate among competing substrates.

spectroscopic methods Techniques that measure the absorption and emission of energy of different frequencies by molecules and atoms.

sphingolipids A class of lipids that contains an 18-carbon amino alcohol backbone, called a sphingosine, joined to a fatty acid.

splice recombinants Recombinant heteroduplexes that are formed by (+) strand cleavage at a Holliday junction.

spliceosome A multicomponent complex formed from the association of various snRNPs with pre-RNA.

standard reduction potential A quantity (voltage) that indicates the tendency of a chemical species to donate or accept electrons.

starch A storage polysaccharide in plants.

steady state A state in which the rate of disappearance of a compound is equal to its rate of synthesis. That is, the change in concentration of the compound with time is equal to zero.

steady state (cellular) A state of apparent constancy, which is actually very dynamic. In this state, energy and material are consumed by the cell and used to maintain the harmonious stability and order of the cell.

steroid A lipid containing 18 or more carbon atoms and a fused four-ring polyprenyl structure.

steroid hormones Hormones that derive from cholesterol.

stoichiometry The measurement of the amounts of chemical elements involved in chemical reactions.

stomata Microscopic pores on a leaf through which carbon dioxide diffuses directly into photosynthetic cells.

stop-transfer sequence A hydrophobic 20-residue peptide that stops the passage of a growing polypeptide chain through the ER membrane.

storage proteins A class of proteins whose biological function is to provide a reservoir of amino acids.

stroma The soluble portion of a chloroplast.

structural complementarity Having a molecular surface with chemical groups arranged to interact specifically with complementary chemical groups on another molecule.

structural polarity Arrangement of monomers in a polymer such that the polymer ends are distinct.

substrate The substance upon which an enzyme acts.

substrate-level phosphorylation Phosphorylation of a nucleoside diphosphate to a nucleoside triphosphate by transfer of a phosphoryl group from a non-nucleoside substrate.

suicide substrate A substrate analog that is transformed by an enzyme into a substance that irreversibly inactivates the enzyme.

sumoylation Post translational modification of a protein by a small ubiquitin-like modifer (sumo).

supercoil Underwound (negative supercoil) or overwound (positive supercoil) double-stranded DNA.

supramolecular complexes The combination of various members of one or more classes of macromolecules. Examples include multifunctional enzyme complexes, ribosomes, chromosomes, and cytoskeletal elements.

synapsis A process of chromosome pairing in which two homologous DNA duplexes are juxtaposed so that their sequences are aligned.

synaptic cleft Space between two neurons across which a signal must be transmitted to pass a signal from one neuron to the next.

synonymous codons Different codons that specify the same amino acid.

system   That portion of the universe with which we are concerned; the rest of the universe is called the surroundings. Systems may be closed, isolated, or open to the surroundings.

• •

T **state**   The less active conformation of an allosteric enzyme.

telomeres   Special tandem repetitive DNA 5 to 8 bp long on the ends of eukaryotic chromosomes. Telomeres are formed by telomerase, an RNA-dependent DNA polymerase that extends the 3′-end of chromosomes using an RNA template that is part of the telomerase complex.

template   A strand of DNA or RNA whose sequence of nucleotide residues acts as a pattern for the synthesis of a complementary strand.

termination   The final step in a process such as protein synthesis.

terpenes   A class of lipids formed from combinations of two or more molecules of 2-methyl-1,3-butadiene, also known as isoprene.

tertiary structure   The compact three-dimensional folded shape of a polymer.

thermodynamics   A collection of laws and principles describing the flows and interchanges of heat, energy, and matter in systems of interest.

thermogenin   An inner mitochondrial protein that short circuits the proton gradient converting the energy to heat.

third base degeneracy   The irrelevance of the third base in a codon.

third law of thermodynamics   A law that states that entropy of any crystalline, perfectly ordered substance must approach zero as the temperature approaches 0 K, and at $T = 0$ K, entropy is exactly zero.

thromboxanes   Molecules derived from arachidonic acid that are involved in platelet aggregation during blood clotting.

thylakoid membrane   The inner-membrane system of chloroplasts, which is organized into paired folds that extend throughout the organelle. It is the site of light-dependent reactions of photosynthesis, leading to the formation of NADPH and ATP.

thylakoid space (thylakoid lumen)   The interior of the thylakoid vesicles.

thylakoid vesicles   Flattened sacs or disks arising from the paired folds (lamellae) in chloroplasts.

titration curve   A graph of the pH versus the equivalents of base added during the titration of an acid.

tobacco mosaic virus   An RNA virus infecting plants.

topoisomerase   An enzyme capable of changing the linking number of a DNA molecule by breaking one or both strands of DNA, and rejoining the ends.

transcription An enzymatic process in which an RNA copy is made of the sequence of bases along one strand of DNA.

transcription attenuation A regulatory mechanism that manipulates transcription termination or transcription pausing to regulate gene transcription downstream.

transcriptomics The study of global messenger RNA expression of an organism.

transduction The transfer of genetic information from one cell to another by means of a viral vector.

transfection The uptake of viral DNA by competent cells.

transfer RNA (tRNA) Ribonucleic acids that serve as carriers of amino acid residues for protein synthesis.

transformation The uptake, integration, and expression of naked DNA by competent cells.

transgenic animals Animals that have acquired new genetic information as a consequence of the introduction of foreign genes.

transition state A high-energy, unstable arrangement of atoms, in which bonds are being broken and formed. It represents the transition between reactants and products in a chemical reaction.

transition state analogs Stable molecules that are chemically and structurally similar to the transition state and that bind more strongly than a substrate or a product to the active site of an enzyme.

transitions DNA mutations that change one purine for another or one pyrimidine for another (c.f. **transversions**).

translation The process that converts genetic information embodied in the base sequence of a messenger RNA molecule into the amino acid sequence of a polypeptide chain.

translocons A selective permeable protein-conducting channel that catalyzes movement of proteins across membranes.

transpeptidation The peptide bond-forming reaction in protein synthesis.

transport proteins A class of proteins whose job is to transport specific substances from one place to another.

transposons Segments of DNA that are moved enzymatically from place to place in the genome, the smallest of which is called an insertion sequence or IS.

transversions DNA mutations that replace a purine for a pyrimidine or vice versa.

triacylglycerols (triglycerides) Molecules consisting of glycerol esterified with three fatty acids.

tricarboxylic acid cycle (TCA cycle; citric acid cycle; Krebs cycle) A metabolic pathway in which an acetyl group is oxidized to CO_2, and the energy released is captured as ATP, NADH, and $FADH_2$.

troponin-C   Calcium-binding protein found in skeletal muscle.

turnover number (k_cat)   The measure of an enzyme's maximal catalytic activity, or the number of substrate molecules converted into product per unit of time when the enzyme is saturated with substrate.

tyrosine kinases   A group of enzymes that phosphorylate targets on tyrosine residues using ATP.

• •

Ubiquitin   A small 76-amino acid protein often attached to lysines on proteins destined to be degraded. Ubiquitination is involved in a large number of cellular processes in addition to protein degradation.

UDP–glucose   An activated form of glucose used during glycogen synthesis.

ultrafiltration   A technique for removing small molecules from solutions of macromolecules and/or for concentrating dilute solutions of macromolecules.

uncoupler   A compound that disrupts the normally tight coupling between electron transport and the phosphorylation of ADP.

unsaturated fatty acid   A fatty acid that contains one or more carbon–carbon double bonds.

upstream/downstream   Refers to directions along a DNA. Upstream is in the 5'-direction and downstream is in the 3'-direction. Upstream locations are indicated by negative numbers, whereas downstream locations are positive numbers. In transcription, +1 is defined as the start of transcript.

ureotelic organisms   Organisms, such as terrestrial vertebrates, which excrete excess nitrogen as urea.

uricotelic organisms   Organisms, such as birds and reptiles, that excrete nitrogen as uric acid.

uronic acid   A acid sugar formed by oxidation of a hydroxyl group to a carboxyl group. Uronic acid sugars contain both a carbonyl carbon (ketose or aldose) and a carboxyl group.

• •

Van der Waals forces   Weak, chemical forces induced by electrical interactions between approaching atoms or molecules as their electron clouds fluctuate instantaneously in time.

viruses   Supramolecular complexes of nucleic acid (DNA or RNA), encapsulated in a protein coat and in some instances, surrounded by a membrane envelope. Within a host cell, they become self-replicating.

• •

Waxes   Esters of long-chain alcohols with long-chain fatty acids.

weak chemical forces   Forces ranging from 4 to 30 kJ/mol, including hydrogen bonds, van der Waals forces, ionic bonds, and hydrophobic interactions.

wild-type   The reference phenotype.

wobble position   The first base of the anticodon. It pairs with the third base of a codon.

• •

YACs   Yeast artificial chromosomes—cloning vectors that are used to clone megabase pairs of DNA.

• •

Zinc finger   A description of a structural motif found in DNA-binding proteins.

zwitterion   A neutral molecule with both a positive and a negative charge.

zymogen (proenzyme)   An enzyme that exists as an inactive precursor until one or several of its peptide bonds are cleaved. At that point, the enzyme acquires full enzymatic activity.